Colchicine —

in Agriculture, Medicine,
Biology, and Chemistry

Colchicine—

in *Agriculture*
Medicine
Biology
and *Chemistry*

O. J. EIGSTI, Ph.D.

Colchicine Research Foundation, Inc.
Normal, Illinois, U. S. A.

Pierre DUSTIN, Jr., M.D.

Department of Pathology
University of Brussels, Belgium

 The Iowa State College Press, Ames, Iowa, U.S.A.

*All rights reserved. Composed and printed by
The Iowa State College Press, Ames, Iowa, U.S.A.
Copyright, 1955, by The Iowa State College Press.*

Reprinted, 1957

Library of Congress Catalog Card Number: 54–7657

To the memory of Albert Pierre Dustin, 1884–1942, whose concepts concerning the regulation of mitotic activity prepared a foundation for the broad scope of biological research that followed the rediscovery in 1934 of the effects of colchicine upon mitosis.

Preface

When an American botanist and a Belgian pathologist collaborate in writing a book, the obstacles to be encountered are necessarily numerous, and this is true of the present work even though the subject is limited to the single substance, *colchicine*. Our collaboration has required intercontinental travel, hours spent together in discussing factual materials from plant and animal sciences, countless days assembling a vast bibliography.

Finally, our cooperative project made it necessary to overcome barriers inherent in our widely different research fields, to resolve problems arising from the use of different languages, and to recognize the dissimilar perspectives of the American and European educational systems. But a common ground of interest was maintained, irrespective of personal interests, through a constant realization of the remarkable and singular properties of colchicine as a mitotic poison and as a tool for experimental work. Moreover, research programs in mitotic problems which each of us had developed prior to the work with colchicine provided a basis of mutual interest.

This work actually had two beginnings when in 1942, almost simultaneously, two scientists commenced manuscripts, each without knowledge of the other. One of them was A. P. Dustin, Sr., of Brussels, whose untimely death occurred in the year his review was started. The task of completing this study fortunately passed to Dr. Dustin's son, and in 1947 the botanical writing done in America by the senior author and the medical studies under way in Europe were brought together into one joint project. It was decided to integrate the many lines of research with colchicine into one study. This book is the result of that cooperative effort.

A survey of the chapters comprising this study will indicate the many lines of research that have been included. The modern literature on colchicine is vast. The references to *gout* alone would require pages. Rather than catalog titles, we have brought together significant contributions and have attempted to correlate the various lines of research. Whenever possible, we summarize the basic contribution, point out differences of opinion, and, most important, call attention to work that needs to be accomplished. Finally, in retrospect over the modern period of studies of colchicine, one of our purposes has been to point out the progress made, rather than to predict what is to come.

For the shortcomings, the errors of interpretation, statements of viewpoints not pleasing to all specialists, which may be found in any portion of this book, the authors assume full responsibility. We who have assembled as many as possible of the important facts about colchicine welcome corrections and comments concerning the conclusions which we have reached.

The modern period of research with colchicine began in 1889, when Pernice described metaphasic arrest produced by this drug. Until Pernice's report was rediscovered, Dixon and Malden were cited as the pioneers. Thus, our search for *all* references to colchicine was rewarded. Special recognition is due to Nancy Gay-Winn, whose diligent quest led to this classic work by Pernice.

Colchicine in its present role as a mitotic poison and as a tool for biological research was discovered in 1934 at Brussels, Belgium, in the laboratory of Professor A. P. Dustin, Sr., who for a long time had been investigating means of altering mitosis. When colchicine was suggested by a Brussels medical student, F. Lits, the characteristics of colchicine were quickly measured. Our review covers the period from 1934 to the middle 1950's.

In 1937 botanical research began in several countries, generally following descriptions or reports of unusual observations from animal cells. In this same year, the scientists at Brussels included *Allium* root tips for their tests. Other botanists chose *Allium* root tips or plant materials to illustrate the action of colchicine. In this year the role of colchicine as an agent for the induction of polyploidy was conclusively demonstrated.

The horizons of colchicine research widened quickly when botanists learned how effectively the drug could be used in their work. Laymen became interested in the drug as references to cancer entered the discussions and as the creation of new varieties of plants stimulated new programs in agriculture. A broad scope of research was opened up by this single substance.

Organic chemists realized that Windaus' concept of the structural formula for colchicine needed revision. In 1940 definite evidence was at hand. There followed an unusually large volume of research on the chemistry of colchicine. In 1947 we realized the need for specialized help. Fortunately, Dr. James D. Loudon of Glasgow University, Scotland, who worked with the group that began the revision of colchicine structure, generously contributed to this aspect of the study. We express our gratitude to him for the writing of Chapter 6.

Colchicum, which is a drug plant of antiquity, has a long history in the annals of pharmacy. Professor F. Santavy of the Medical Institute of Olomouc, Czechoslovakia, provided special materials for Chapter 5. Many facts about the pharmacognosy of *Colchicum* were compiled by Mr. Ikram Hassan of the University of Panjab, Lahore, Pakistan. We appreciate their special aid in the preparation of Chapter 5.

However, the authors, and not the contributors mentioned, assume full responsibility for the material published. We are grateful for help from our publishers, the Iowa State College Press, and particularly its Chief Editor, Mr. William H. Van Horn.

Financial aid is necessary for a project of this proportion not designed specifically for return of investment. We have received support from organizations whose contributions were made without consideration of a future financial return.

Some grants-in-aid were made to each author and some jointly to this project. Without citing specific contributions it is our pleasure to acknowledge with thanks the following organizations, foundations, and agencies providing funds. But quite as important as the financial aid, have been the approval and encouragement given to us in our efforts.

These contributors are listed herewith: Carnegie Corporation of New York, Century Fund, Northwestern University, Colchicine Research Foundation, Fonds National de la Recherche Scientifique (Brussels), Funk Brothers Seed Company, Genetics Society of America, General Biological Supply House, Graduate Committees on Research of the University of Oklahoma and Northwestern University, John Crerar Library, Lady Tata Memorial Fund, National Cancer Institute of the National Institute of Health, U. S. A., Rosenheim Foundation, Pakistan, United States Educational Foundation, Pakistan, United States Educational Foundation, India, United Nations Educational and Scientific Organization, University of Oklahoma Research Institute, University of Oklahoma, Department of Plant Sciences, Université libre de Bruxelles, Faculté de Médecine, Belgium.

Contributions in preparing the manuscript were made during the course of our work. For illustrations, photographs, typing, photomicrography, bibliography, and reference work we express our thanks.

C. A. Berger, A. M. Brues, Joseph Carlson, George L. Cross, Agnes W. Eigsti, M. Fauconnier, M. E. Gaulden, Tilman Johnson, H. Kihara, Carol S. Lems, A. Lonert, E. Lotens, Marjorie Lindholm, Elizabeth McKee, Portia M. Mercier, Leona Schnell, Barbara Tenney Sherman, Marselda Scarff, Harvey Smith, Herbert Taylor, Atlee S. Tracy, Ruth Witkus, Vera Williamson, Nancy Gay-Winn.

Scientists around the world gave us unpublished materials, references, and specific aid toward the manuscript. We acknowledge the help of the following: John Beal, C. A. Berger, P. Bhaduri, Muriel Bradley, James Brewbaker, Max E. Britton, Meta S. Brown, A. M. Brues, Otto Bucher, Joseph Carlson, Belayet H. Choudhury, Jens Clausen, J. W. Cook, Geo. H. Conant, Alan Conger, Geo. L. Cross, George Darrow, Haig Dermen, Sam Emsweller, Rob't. K. Enders, K. Frandsen, D. U. Gardner, Mary E. Gaulden, Pierre Gavaudan, C. J. Gorter, Ake Gustafson, A. Hecht, E. K. Ammal Janaki, Tilman Johnson, A. Josefson, Theo Just, H. Kihara, Peo Koller, Ernest Lahr, Hans Lettre, Albert Levan, S. Lodhi, James Loudon, P. Maheswari, G. P. Majumdar, Ralph G. Meader, Arne Muntzing, A. Mohajir, B. R. Nebel, Fredrich Nilsson, I. Nishiyama, Gosta Olsson, Joseph O'Mara, Gunar Ostergren, B. Pal, Barbara Palser, Joseph Peters, S. Ramanujam, F. Ramirez, M. L. Ruttle, Leona Schnell, E. R. Sears, Paul Sentein, Barbara Tenney Sherman, H. Shimamura, H. Slizynska, B. Slizynski, Harold H. Smith, Paul F. Smith, Leon Snyder, Leon Steele, G. Ledyard Stebbins, Jr., S. G. Stephens, Robert N. Stewart, R. R. Stewart, Betty Thomson, Geo. Tischler, Paul Voth, B. Wada, Hanford Tiffany, I. E. Jeffs, S. J. Wellensiek, M. Westergaard.

O. J. EIGSTI
PIERRE DUSTIN, JR.

October, 1954

Table of Contents

CHAPTER 1

The Parent Plant

1.1: The Knowledge of *Colchicum* in Ancient Civilizations

The history of *Colchicum,* the drug of ancient and modern materia medica, is rooted in the myths and the written records of ancient Egypt, India, and Greece, and runs its course through the ages into the world of today. Not only do modern formularies admit *Colchicum,* the producer of the pure substance *colchicine,* but this plant is probably one of those mentioned in the Ebers Papyrus. This Egyptian document was prepared about 1550 B.C., and is our oldest medical text. *Colchicum* could be one of the saffron plants of the Papyrus. From this early age through thirty-five centuries of medical history to the compilation of the modern pharmacopeias, very few drug plants have survived. In fact, only eighteen, among seven hundred plants[44] originally listed as material for ancient Egyptian practitioners, achieved such historical fame.

The Egyptian civilization developed a code for practicing medicine in which plant products played an important role, and the Ebers Papyrus summarized this accumulation of knowledge. Egyptian doctors were advised in the Papyrus to give various seeds to their patients for relief from aches and pains. The seeds were administered on bread.[5] While *pure* colchicine was not given in these doses, we can assume that the drug was used in treating rheumatism and gout, ailments which then and even yet afflict the human race. It is probable also that, if seeds were used, a large quantity would have been administered to the patient.

A danger associated with using colchicine in the crude form is the poisonous property of the drug. Enough active substance can be given to cause death in warm-blooded animals. Dry seeds may have as much as four parts of the drug per thousand of dry raw material. Perhaps some patients died from the colchicine prescription, for severe punishments were said to be meted out to ancient doctors when a patient succumbed. In some instances the physician even paid with his life.[29] Since gout and rheumatism were common ailments among the noble and the wealthy, the attending physicians, who were often servants of the court, must have held a rather precarious position. Yet, in spite of its poisonous nature, *Colchicum* in correct dosage was capable of relieving pain if administered as seed, powdered corm, or even dried flowers. It is probable that substitutes for *Colchicum,* as well as similar plants containing very small amounts of colchicine, were employed.

Plants were frequently used in ancient days without sound basis, and more magic than medicine was practiced; in fact, magic and the medicine man have been associated through the ages. Our modern word *pharmacy* originates[24] from an Egyptian term *pharmaki* and the Greek *pharmakon.* These terms are in turn related to another Egyptian word *pharmagia,* which means the art of making magic.

Another civilization, the Hindu, developed a medical system independent of the Egyptian and the Babylonian. This period is known as the Vedic,[29] and extends from 2000 B.C. to 800 B.C. Much information about treating diseases with plants is transmitted in the Vedic text.[29] Although in this book specific plants are mentioned and certain diseases noted, and while *Colchicum luteum,* a producer of pure colchicine, is common in the Indus River area of the Himalayas, the present Indian *Colchicum* cannot be deciphered from this book.

At some time during the Vedic period a traffic in drugs was established between the Orient and Arabia. Good evidence is at hand to show that Hindu medicine had an influence upon Arabian medical knowledge. There was a serious decline in Hindu medicine, but the traffic in drugs continued. This exchange reached such proportions that Pliny the Elder complained about his money being drained to the Orient for drugs. Two species, known as the Kashmir hermodactyls,[7] could have been among these drugs. They are identified as *Colchicum luteum* and *Merendera persica.* Although both contain colchicine, the respective quantities differ markedly, as will be described later.

Botanical historians[21] tell of an ancient class in Greece known as the Rhizotomi, or root gatherers. They were pharmacobotanists practicing their art in the pre-Hippocratic era; their powers resembled those of magicians, associating all manner of ritual with the collection, preparation, and dispensing of roots. Such details as the wind direction, time, season, as well as astronomical signs were observed.

Since foods were primarily grain and leaves, the roots must have served other purposes such as medicine. Driving away evil spirits that caused disease may have been helped by using underground plant parts, and the trade in roots by the Rhizotomi flourished.[21]

More than fifty species containing colchicine are native to the region where the Rhizotomi practiced.[41] The most notable species is

Colchicum autumnale,[41] that produces flowers in autumn followed by leaves, fruits, and seeds the next spring. Such an unusual habit must have attracted these pharmacobotanists.[21]

Perhaps the best link between ancient and modern medicine is seen in the two drugs found in Oriental bazaars: the Surinjan-i-talkh and the Surinjan-i-chirrin.[7] These corms are distinguished as bitter and sweet surinjan and are obtained from the Kashmir hermodactyls growing in the northwest Himalayan foothills.[7] Botanically the drugs are identified as (1) *Colchicum luteum,* the bitter, and (2) *Merendera persica,* the sweet; both contain colchicine, 0.2 per cent and 0.02 per cent, respectively.[30] Pharmacists advise their use for rheumatism as well as for aching joints.

If these same hermodactyls entered the drug trade from the Orient to Arabia, then early Arabian physicians may have borrowed their ideas for treating gout from this source. It is difficult to determine how many centuries have passed since the Hindu specialists began collecting the hermodactyls and other plants useful in medical practice. But their knowledge of herbs has been handed down for countless generations to their successors of the present day.

The ancient usage of *Colchicum,* along with an antiquity in medicine, can be established through several sources: the Ebers Papyrus, a drug traffic from the Orient, and the evidence about a pharmacobotanical trade practiced by the Rhizotomi. Present-day surinjan may link the past to modern medicine.

Our discussion of the knowledge of *Colchicum* in the ancient world turns for a moment to Greek history and mythology, and it is in Greece that the period we are examining will close with the organization of medical knowledge around the system of Hippocrates.

Colchicum is named for the land of Colchis at the eastern tip of the Black Sea.[47, 22] In this area the plants are most abundant. When Colchis was mentioned to the Greek, visions of sorcery immediately arose. This was the land where Jason secured the Golden Fleece. Here he met the sorceress Medea, famous for her powerful life-giving brews. She was said to have rejuvenated Jason's aging father by substituting a special potent mixture for his blood. Many of her directions for poisonous mixtures required underground roots. Magic powers were associated with these ingredients that figured in Medea's sorcery.[6]

Among the instructions for making a certain mixture were specific details for collecting the poisonous plants.[6] In one instance, only during a hoarfrost could roots be dug. While boiling the juices in a pot, it was said olive branches touching the brew would immediately bring forth flowers and fruits.

The ancient Colchian kings had gardens containing poisonous species. Undoubtedly the knowledge of the toxic properties of plants was at their disposal. Such plants might have served their intrigues and provided means for the elimination of competitors or persons convicted of crime.

1.2: Botanical Studies of *Colchicum* From Dioscorides to Twentieth-Century Investigators

In the land of Colchis, along the Black Sea, an autumn-flowering crocus-like plant occurs in abundance (Fig. 1.1). Dioscorides, first century botanist-physician, knew about this particular species from either personal observations in the area or through reports by travelers to this region. This fall-blooming meadow saffron was named the

Fig. 1.1—Flowers of **Colchicum autumnale** showing only the floral parts above ground. (Photograph, courtesy of General Biological Supply House, Chicago, Ill.)

Colchicon,[22] a name which has been continued in its Latinized form to the present time.

Dioscorides made very careful descriptions dealing with such phases as growth, development, and morphology of the plant. His drawings involving two plants (Fig. 1.2), one with fruits, seeds, and leaves, the other with flowers only, clearly show that he associated

292   Pedacii Dioſcoridis **Viertes Buch/**

Herbſtblumen.   Herbſtblumen.

Fig. 1.2—Diagrams showing the seed-producing portion of **Colchicum autumnale,** and the flower stalk appearing in autumn. **A,** fruiting; **B,** flowering. (After drawings by Dioscorides)

autumnal flowering with spring fruiting, both having the same underground portion. This was a careful scientific observation for his day. Such great detail was given to the corm, bud, leaf, flower, and seed that writers copied his observations and drawings for the next fifteen centuries.

Since the botanical and medical professions were closely allied in the times of Dioscorides, it was natural that the objective of his study should extend beyond strictly botanical descriptions and that his primary interest should be in the medical application of plants. He warned that *Colchicon* was a dangerous poison and compared it with the mushroom that causes death (Fig. 1.3). He was concerned that this plant might be used by practitioners unaware of its poisonous nature, and the effect of his careful descriptions and stern warnings was so profound that many followers avoided the use of *Colchicon*.

Herbſtblumen / Spinnblumen / Colchicon, Bulbus Agreſtis. Cap. lrrr.

Pinnblumen / Nachtblumen / Herbſtblumen / Griechiſch Colchicon, zu Latein Bulbus Agreſtis, ſindt weißlechte Blumen / den Saffran Blättern ehnlich / vnnd wachſen im außgang deß Herbſts / nach den Blumen gewinnen ſie Blätter wie die Blätter der Wurtzeln / die man Griechiſch vnd zu Latein engentlich Bulbos nennt / außge-nommen daß ſie feyſter ſindt: Sie haben Stengel einer Spannen hoch / mit rohtem Sa-men / rohtlechte Wurtzeln / die bekleidet ſindt mit braunrohte / etwas ſchwartzfärbigen Rin-den / wenn man die Rinde abthut / ſo ſindt die Wurtzen weiß / zart / ſüß / voller Safft / jhre Wurtzel hat in der mitte an einer Seitten von vnden auff ein Kerff oder Ritz / dardurch die Blume wächſt vnd außbricht. Der Herbſtblumen wachſen viel in Meſſenia vnd Colchis. Die Wurtzeln geſſen / tödten wie die gifftige Schwämm / mit würgen vnd erſtecken. Dieſes Kraut haben wir auch allein darumb beſchrieben / damit niemandt daſſelbige / oder ſeine Wurtzeln vnwiſſentlich an ſtatt der Bulbenwurtzeln eſſe / denn etliche durch jhre ſüſſigkeit darzu werden gereitzt. Wider dieſes Gifft braucht man bequemlich die Artzney / die droben wider die gifftige Schwämm beſchrieben worden ſindt / Kühmilch iſt auch gut darwider getruncken / alſo daß man keiner andern Artzney bedarff / wo Kühmilch vorhanden iſt.

Bb ij   Men-

Fig. 1.3—Dioscorides' description of **Colchicum** taken from the **Krauterbuch** of Pedanius Dioscorides, printed by J. Bringern, Frankfurt, 1610. Reproductions obtained thrcugh court-esy of John Crerar Library, Chicago, Ill.

In spite of such warnings, Dioscorides believed plants were very useful in the medical practice. Accordingly, other less poisonous species were recommended. In one case he suggested the *Ephemeron* instead of the *Colchicon,* particularly for those tumors that had not yet spread into the body. The *Ephemeron* is now identified as *Colchicum lingulatum,* [41] which contains less colchicine than *C. autumnale,* the autumn-flowering plant, his *Colchicon.*[47] There can be no doubt that his careful attention to species difference distinguished him as a great botanist.

The Greek physicians at the beginning of the Christian era de-veloped a distrust for Oriental medicine, notably the plants that were used in drug traffic.[22] This suspicion had been aroused as early as the time of Hippocrates. Perhaps there was some basis for their doubt. If our assumption was correct that Kashmir hermodactyls were introduced into this drug traffic from the Orient to the West, then two very similar drugs would have appeared. These are *Colchicum luteum* and *Merendera persica,* which were described in the last section. While the alkaloid contents of these two plants differ considerably, it is probable that then as now they were sold under the name *surinjan.* A careful worker like Dioscorides would not have been misled by these substitutions, but not all Greek physicians were skilled in distinguishing botanical specimens, and they undoubtedly appreciated the excellent services rendered by Dioscorides through his botanical investigations.

In the following fifteen centuries, down through the period of the Herbalists, nothing different was added to the description of *Colchicon.* In fact, the Herbalists merely copied and repeated what Dioscorides and several other botanists of his period had written.[47] The great contributions made during the fifteenth to seventeenth centuries, of course, were the translation, copying, and printing which made book production easier than at any previous period in history.

The Herbalists[22] collected interesting names that became associated with *Colchicon.*[47] These usually refer to the poisonous features or to some unusual habit such as fall flowering and spring fruiting. The plants were called *"mort au chien,"* or "death to dogs."[47] The name *"bulbus agrestis,"* or "wild bulb," was commonly used.[47] Since the flowers appeared in clusters out of the ground without leaves associated, a descriptive name "naked ladies" was given. Probably the most involved name was the Latin *"Filius ante patrem,"* translated "son before the father," meaning a deviation from established biological laws.[47] This is understandable, for when they associated the spring seeds and fruiting with the flowers that came up the same year in autumn, several months later, it was an instance of the offspring preceding the parents. However, Dioscorides had made the correct interpretation because his diagrams (Fig. 1.2) clearly associated buds, flowers, leaves, and fruits at the correct season and he realized that the flowering plants of autumn put forth fruits the next spring. Some Herbalists devoted much discussion to the growth habits involving flowering and fruiting. Finally, the common name *Hermodactyl* caused confusion for a long time until it was clearly shown that the *Colchicon* and *Hermodactyl* were the same plant.[39]

Linnaeus kept the original name given by Dioscorides, changing it from the Greek *Colchicon* to Latin *Colchicum,* when he devised his extensive system of nomenclature. A binomial affixed to the autumn crocus was published in *Species Plantarum,* 1753: *Colchicum autumnale* L. The species describes the fall-flowering character, and the genus retains the original reference to the land of Colchis. Very few changes were made in descriptions as originally given by the Greek botanist. Linnaeus made an important contribution in showing relationships between the *Colchicum* group and other families of plants.[41]

The genus *Colchicum* L. belongs to the tribe Colchiceae, which also includes *Merendera* Ram., *Bulbocodium* L., and *Synsiphon* Regel. This tribe is a part of the subfamily Melanthoideae. The family Liliaceae shows many relationships to the species *Colchicum*; hence their correct position is within the lily family. At one time the family Colchicaceae was on the same level of importance that was given the Liliaceae, but this became changed to the system listed above.

An excellent monograph[41] dealing with *Colchicum* was published by Stefanoff in 1926. Considerable revision has been made and ten new species have been added. The text is in Bulgarian, but the descriptions and keys are printed in Latin, thus making this information available to specialists of any nationality. Useful distribution maps are attached to the monograph.[41]

The genus is divided into two subgenera:[41] (1) *Archicolchicum* including seven sections, and (2) *Eucolchicum* with a single section. An Indian species, *C. luteum* Baker, official in the *Indian Pharmacopoeia* belongs to the first subgenus, whereas the most notable drug species, *C. autumnale* L. is placed in the subgenus *Eucolchicum*. All species belonging to the latter subgenus flower in the autumn, while the members of the first subgenus have many members that bloom in the spring.

A total of 64 species are described and extensively reviewed for their geographical distribution. All belong to the Northern Hemisphere and are primarily indigenous to the Mediterranean region, although many species range over Europe and North Africa and extend eastward into India along the northwestern Himalayan ranges.

Thirty-six species flower in the months of September to November. Except for several unknown, the remaining twenty-five species bloom during the spring, early in January, or late in June. These characteristics are noted in the list of species given in Table 1.1.

Cytological investigations include eleven species for which exact chromosomal determinations have been made.[26, 30] There is no evidence that speciation has proceeded along a polyploidy series with or without hybridization. In fact, the number for these at hand is entirely heteroploid. No correlation exists between taxonomic position and chromosome number. Certainly the diploid numbers ranging from 36 to 54 are not exceptionally high. In light of the polyploidizing effect of colchicine on many plant cells, the suggestion has been made that perhaps within this group high numbers may be found. Chapters 4 and 17 deal with this problem and show by resistance to the drug how polyploidy could not be developed. Furthermore, there is no indication that other species of plants found in the

TABLE 1.1
THE GENUS COLCHICUM LINNAEUS
(After Stefanoff)

Family: Liliaceae
    Subfamily: Melanthoideae
       Tribe: Colchiceae

Species Name	Authority	Flowering Date	Chromosome Number
Subgenus 1. *Archicolchicum:*			
Section 1. Luteae			
C. luteum	Baker	Feb.–May	$2n = 38$
C. regelii	Stef.	Feb.–March	
C. hissaricum	Stef.	July	
C. robustum	Stef.	Feb.–May	
Section 2. Bulbocodiae			
C. szovitsii	F. M.	Jan.–April	
C. crocifolium	Boiss.	Feb.–March	
C. fasciculare	Boiss.	Jan.–Feb.	
C. libanoticum	Ehrenb.	June	
C. ritchii	R. Br.	Nov.–Jan.	
C. schimperi	Janka	Dec.	
C. tauri	Siehe	Feb	
C. serpentinum	Woronow ap. Mischenko	not given	
C. hydrophilum	Siehe	May–June	
C. hirsutum	Stef.	April–May	
C. nivale	Boiss. et Huet	April–June	
C. biebersteinii	Rouy	Feb.–March	
C. davidovi	Stef.	Feb.–April	
C. catacuzenium	Heldr	March–May	
C. hungaricum	Janka	Dec.–April	
C. doerfleri	Hal	Feb.–April	
C. macedonicum	Kosanin	June	
C. triphyllum	Kze	March	
C. kurdicum	Stef.	June	
C. caucasicum	Spreng.	March–May	
C. soboliferum	Stef.	Feb.–April	
C. atticum	Sprun.	Nov.–March	
C. jordanicolum	Stef.	not given	
C. sieheanum	Hausskn.	Sept.	
C. procurrens	Baker	Oct.	
Section 3. Vernae			
C. vernum	Ker-Gawl.	March–May	
Section 4. Montanae			
C. montanum	L.	Sept.–Oct.	$2n = 54$
Section 5. Cupaniae			
C. cupani	Guss.	Sept.–Dec.	
C. psaridis	Heldr.	Sept.–Dec.	
C. boissieri	Orph.	Sept.–Dec.	

(continued on next page)

Table 1.1 (*continued*)

Species Name	Authority	Flowering Date	Chromosome Number
	Section 5. Cupaniae (*continued*)		
C. pusillum	Sieb.	Oct.–Nov.	
C. hiemale	Freyn	Dec.–Jan.	
C. troodi	Kotschy	Oct.	
C. steveni	Kunth.	Sept.–Jan.	
C. parlatoris	Orph.	Aug.–Nov.	
	Section 6. Filifoliae		
C. filifolium	Stef.	Oct.–Nov.	
	Section 7. Arenariae		
C. arenarium	W. K.	Sept.–Oct.	
C. alpinum	Lam. et DC.	Aug.–Sept.	

Subgenus 2. *Eucolchicum*:

Species Name	Authority	Flowering Date	Chromosome Number
	Section 8. Autumnales		
C. corsicum	Baker	Sept.	
C. micranthum	Boiss.	Sept.	
C. borisii	Stef.	Aug.	
C. umbrosum	Stev.	Aug.–Sept.	
C. laetum	Stev.	Sept.	
C. kotschyi	Boiss.	Aug.–Nov.	
C. decaisnei	Boiss.	Oct.	
C. neapolitanum	Ten.	Aug.–Sept.	$2n = 38$
C. longifolium	Cast.	Aug.–Oct.	
C. kochii	Parl.	Aug.–Sept.	
C. lingulatum	Boiss. et Sprun	Sept.–Oct.	
C. haynaldii	Heuff.	Sept.–Oct.	
C. autumnale	L.	Aug.–Oct.	$2n = 38$
C. lusitanum	Brot.	Sept.–Nov.	
C. tenorii	Parl.	Sept.	$2n = 40$
(C. byzantium Ten.)			
C. levieri	Janka	Sept.	
C. visianii	Parl.	Sept.	
C. turicum	Jka	Aug.–Oct.	
C. variegatum	L.	Sept.–Oct.	$2n = 44$
C. latifolium	S. S.	Aug.–Oct.	$2n = 54$
C. speciosum	Stev.	Aug.–Oct.	$2n = 38$
C. bivonae	Guss.	Sept.–Oct.	$2n = 36$

regions where *Colchicum* is abundant are unusually high in chromosome numbers. This question was raised after the cytological work revealed an action on mitotic processes in plants.

Additional references and details concerning the botanical features of the official drug-producing species are given in Chapter 5.

1.3: Medical Applications of Colchicine

Hippocrates founded modern medicine; he swept away many mystical concepts, introduced new explanations for disease, and left a profound influence upon the medical profession. About three or four hundred drugs were kept in his materia medica, some of them introduced from the East where he was a visitor. The ritual of magic and charm was eliminated as much as possible, but his direct contacts with Hindu medicine did leave impressions. He made no reference to a specific treatment for gout, although he was familiar with the ailment called *podagra*[19] in various aspects. It is possible that the bitter hermodactyls were a part of his materia medica.

A *History of Plants* prepared by Theophrastus (372?–285 B.C.) described five hundred plants[19] for medicinal use. This study marks a new age, which continued the advancement of medicine started by Hippocrates. Gout was a familiar disease in Theophrastus' day, but he does not record specifically the form of drug for treating the difficulty. However, Theophrastus gave stern warning that the bitter hermodactyls were powerful poisons. There can be no doubt that the practice of medicine was enlarged by the work of Theophrastus.

The first materia medica with accurate descriptions was firmly established by Dioscorides in the first century A.D. He showed an acquaintance with the studies of Theophrastus and gave many new details from his private observations that became useful to practicing doctors. *Colchicon* was very poisonous and in its place the *Ephemeron* was recommended for those "tumors" that had not yet "spread into the body." This same plant, the *Ephemeron,* was advocated by Galen in the second century A.D. The *Colchicum* treatment for gout may have been advocated by Galen because the bitter hermodactyls were listed in his materia medica and he was well acquainted with gout. The hermodactyls and *Ephemeron* are both members of the *Colchicum* genus.

Aretaeus, the Cappadocian, contemporary with Galen, clearly recognized podagra and noticed that many remedies were advocated. He observed innumerable remedies were suggested for gout; in fact, this calamity usually made the patient "an expert druggist." [19] Many plants were dispensed from the pharmacist. In light of the widespread distribution of colchicine-producing species, a large selection might have been in the hands of the druggists.

About this same time, the "Doctrine of Signatures" was promoted by Pliny,[46] who also made his mark upon medical thought. Plants were chosen for a specific disease by means of suggestive associations. For instance, saxifrages grew among rocks; therefore kidney stones could be dissolved by juices from this plant. Solomon's seal in cross section of the root looked like the King's seal; hence the plant should be used to seal wounds. Perhaps gout, frequently attacking the fingers, was treated by the hermodactyls since these flowers came up like the fingers of a hand. Recalling that a translation of *hermodactyl* means "fingers of Hermes," the doctrine would have provided good basis for treating these ills and aches.

Emperors, rulers, and the wealthy were most frequently afflicted with gout and arthritic rheumatism. One medical councilor, J. Psychriste, who was attached to the court of the Byzantine ruler Leon the Great (457–475 A.D.), used one single dose of bitter hermodactyl to cure gout.[19] Doctors attached to ruling classes found gout a prevalent disease among these personages, though specific directions for curing gout have not been recognized in most historical records. *Colchicum,* or the bitter hermodactyls are usually mentioned as first used in the sixth century.

Alexander of Tralles (*ca.* 560 A.D.) has been credited as the first to advocate bitter hermodactyl[19] to alleviate the pains from gout. He used a drastic purgative combining scammony, colcynth, aloes, hermodactyls with anise, myrrh, peppers, cinnamon, and ginger. His twelve books on medicine include many references to drug plants.

The seventh century physician,[39] Paul of Aeginata, recommended the hermodactyls when treating gout or other arthritic complaints. His record is likewise well established by the medical historians. Following him, two Arabian doctors, Rhazes and Avicenna, specifically proposed hermodactyls in cases of gout. The latter wrote from traditional belief and personal experience about the "Souradjan" from Arabia. Undoubtedly this is the same as the surinjan, or bitter hermodactyl, *Colchicum luteum* of the Indus River area. The combined periods of Paul of Aeginata, Rhazes, and Avicenna extend from the seventh century to 1037 A.D. The translations made by these physicians included many documents dealing with science and medicine,[39] and they exerted a profound influence upon medicine generally as well as upon the specific knowledge passed on about gout.

An extensive treatise on gout dedicated to the Emperor Michael Paleologus was prepared by a famous thirteenth century Greek physician, Demetrius Pepagomeus.[39] In this account, specific directions were stated for making a pill of hermodactyl, aloes, and cinnamon, to be used in treating podagra.

From the thirteenth to the sixteenth century, records about gout and drugs are scarce. Confusion embroiled the Greek doctors because of the widespread distrust for Arabian medicine and advice from the East. Others suggest that the stern warnings noted about the toxic property of *Colchicon,* beginning with Theophrastus and

Dioscorides, discouraged its uses. While relief was obtained quickly, the dangers associated with treatment were always present. As some writers believe, the chance of death was so great the gamble wasn't "worth the candle."

A German writer, Wirtzung (1500–1571), revived interest in bitter hermodactyl by his discussions on treating gout, and about this time joined in the call for return to *Colchicum* as a treatment for gout.[39] Later John Quincy published a *Complete English Dispensatory* and called attention to hermodactyls, identifying these drugs with *Colchicum*. Accordingly, the British formularies carried both *Hermodactyl* and *Colchicum* in the 1618 edition.[39] This practice was continued in subsequent editions of the *London Pharmacopoeia*: 1627, 1632, 1639; but both plants were dropped in 1650. The omissions continued for 149 years — until 1788, when *Colchicum* was admitted as official. *Hermodactyl* was dropped, never to be heard from again in materia medica.[39] This revival, after such a long period without recognition, requires some explanation.

Without doubt the renewal in the eighteenth century was largely due to the thorough studies by Baron Anton von Storck[39] (1731–1803), who experimented with *Colchicum* in a Vienna hospital. His own body was used for testing sensations as well as bodily changes induced by *Colchicum*. Students joined him in experiments that involved rubbing the tongue with some of the drug to experience the numbness, then recording the time necessary to render the tongue "void of sensation."

Dr. von Storck determined lethal doses for dogs, observing that "two drams killed the animal in 13 hours." Post-mortem studies established the changes induced by the drug, particularly among the internal organs. These tests aided in formulating correct dosages such as the oxymel colchici, used by many practitioners throughout Britain, France, and Germany. Undoubtedly the place gained for *Colchicum* in materia medica by the middle eighteenth century was a direct result of von Storck's effort.

While debates were going on as to the efficacy of *Colchicum*, Husson,[39] a military officer in the pay of the French king, gave out a vinous preparation called "Eau Médicinale," especially useful for gout. The identity of the effective ingredient was kept secret, known only to Husson. There arose quack preparations, i.e., Wilsons Tincture, Reynolds Specific, and others. Their true nature was always kept secret, but an English pharmacist discovered in 1814 that the active ingredient in Husson's preparation was *Colchicum*.

The combined research by Dr. von Storck and the popular success achieved by the "Eau Médicinale" preparations established *Colchicum* in modern materia medica as a specific for gout.

During the latter eighteenth and beginning nineteenth centuries, many English and French physicians wrote extensively about gout, recommending *Colchicum* for relief. The great nineteenth century doctor, Thomas Sydenham, who styled himself as the English Hippocrates,[19] was a martyr to gout. He offered theories for its nature and cause, and advocated treatment with *Colchicum*. Another successful student and physician was Alfred Baring Garrod, whose books[19] and papers contained valuable data about the changes induced by gout. In the nineteenth century almost every prominent doctor with a knowledge of gout had a particular theory as to its origin and nature. The forty-seven cases studied by Garrod are classic examples of sound scientific investigation. Like others, he stood behind the *Colchicum* treatment even though the poisonous nature of this crude drug was well known.

An application of colchicine reported in modern medical practice is the treatment of Hodgkin's disease in which instance remissions were obtained.[3]

1.4: Chemical Studies of the Pure Substance Colchicine

Accuracy in treating gout and in performing critical experiments demanded pure substances. Until the chemists' analysis and extraction of crystalline compounds from corm and seed, only the crude material was available to provide the active principles in the drug. A toxic principle involving pure colchicine was detected in substance from *Colchicum* seed in 1820,[38] but the compound was confused with veratrine. Later the name *colchicine*[16] was proposed for a crystalline material extracted by chemical procedures developed for this purpose. Thus, the first steps were taken toward solving the problems in the chemistry of colchicine. Chapter 6, devoted to the chemistry of this substance, illustrates the exceedingly complicated analytical work necessary to understand colchicine chemistry, much less to contribute to its development. But the rewards in a broad field of biology appear promising for experimenters who can obtain derivatives of known chemical organization and apply the same to critical biological test organisms.

Thorough descriptions characterizing crystalline colchicine were prepared by Zeisel in 1883, and by Houdé in 1884.[8] The formula $C_{22}H_{26}O_6N$ was proposed.[38] These analytical developments formed the groundwork for later work. Pharmacological studies using colchicine and its derivatives could then proceed on a sounder basis, as shown by the work done during the next several decades from the laboratories of Jacobj and Fuhner.[8]

One of the first derivatives studied was colchiceine, obviously demonstrating different biological[42] activity from that of colchicine.

This information has been linked with modern concepts of specific biological activity associated with certain chemical structures.[1] The Symposium on the Chemistry of Colchicine at the 1951–52 meeting of the American Association for the Advancement of Science at Philadelphia, Pennsylvania, dealt with this problem.

Advancement was made in colchicine chemistry when Adolph Windaus, after a long series of investigations, set forth the concept of a three-ring structure.[38] Upon analysis of oxidation products, his case was developed for three rings, A, B, and C, each constructed of 6 carbons, respectively. The first ring A is aromatic, 6 carbon with three associated methoxyl groups. This much of the Windaus formula has been confirmed and remains as earlier constructed.[9] Other parts required modification as will be shown below and in more detail in Chapter 6.

Unusually high water solubility characterizes colchicine in spite of a deficiency of the groups generally associated with this capacity.[9] To account for this feature and others, Dewar speculated that the structural concept should include a "tropolone" system and proposed that ring C was a 7-membered structure.[11]

Earlier than this proposal, doubts were raised by Cohen, Cook, and Roe in 1940[8] that led to changes in the central part of the structure, ring B. Changing ring B, as well as C, from a 6- to 7-membered ring appeared necessary. This first evidence for the need to modify Windaus' structure, which came from the Glasgow Laboratories,[9] has since led to extensive studies dealing with the structure of colchicine. Dr. James Loudon, a member of this team, has generously contributed the chapter on chemistry. Degradative work provided thorough evidence that ring B is 7-membered instead of 6 as originally proposed. Further confirmation came through synthesis work[34] upon dl colchinol methyl ether, also establishing the position of the amino group on ring B.

A compound described as octahydrodemethoxydesoxydesacetamido-colchicine,[33] has been obtained by degradation. Such a product derived from colchicine that is more or less a carbon skeleton for rings B and C presents opportunities for making some definitive proof of the structure of colchicine through synthesis.

Tropolone, as originally suggested by Dewar has been synthesized;[11] therefore, ring C of colchicine is essentially as predicted in earlier speculations. Much might be expected here for biological experimental procedures. Interesting tests with tropolonoid compounds have been tried. The "radiomimetic" action of a tropolonoid compound is of considerable interest.[43]

Polarographic evidence supports the work with colchicine and derivatives in several aspects.[36] Santavy and associates beginning in

1942 have been contributors.[35] Other similar results comparing in particular the infrared spectra of colchicine and its derivatives with the tropolone structure, also offer supporting evidence for the correctness of the structure of colchicine.[36]

Tools for deeper insight to biological problems arise from the many derivatives obtained with chemical studies.[25] There are also natural compounds accompanying the crude product from *Colchicum* which can be of value for experimental work. Numerous areas where such may be introduced shall be considered in chapters throughout this work.

When *iso*colchicine was prepared, additional c-mitotic* analysis could be made. Significant changes in the biological activity accompanied changes in chemical structure. The new compound has a c-mitotic activity 100 times lower than colchicine.[42] In this instance, ring C appears to be decisive through the interchanges of keto and methoxyl groups. Another well-known derivative, colchiceine, demonstrates little or no c-mitotic action in any concentrations tested.[42] These and other cases call for cooperative work between two highly complex laboratory operations, chemistry on one hand and experimental biology on the other. These areas are exceedingly difficult; the lack of control in biology often becomes frustrating to the physical scientist. Control or direction over life processes such as mitosis by designing chemical structures are intriguing fields for investigation.

1.5: New Biological Uses for Colchicine

Colchicine causes a "veritable explosion"[27] of mitoses when in contact with mitotically active tissues. The sudden increase in published reports dealing with colchicine was also described as a "veritable explosion" of publications,[16] particularly from 1938 to 1942. For this reason, Wellensiek proclaimed a new "fad" in biological research,[45] the "colchicine fad." An immense bibliography[16] has accumulated, chiefly since 1934.

Accurate historical records have established the way in which colchicine research began in new fields[45] and chronologies[23] have been written; no attempt shall be made to review this aspect.[10] Such sudden increase in research with a drug known to man for thirty-five centuries does arouse interesting speculations as to the causes for an immediate switch to this particular line of work. After research in several fields had shown unusual results, much work was soon under way. Here we touch upon the initiation of research with colchicine; extensive details are found in subsequent chapters.

---

* The adjective *c-mitotic* is derived from *c-mitosis,* which designates a mitosis occurring under the influence of colchicine.

An early experimenter with plants and colchicine was Charles Darwin who applied the drug to "insectivorous" and "sensitive" plants. The reactions in leaf movements were tested, but no conclusive results were obtained for colchicine, nicotine, or morphine. This work was done about 1875 and is of historical interest only. No modern colchicine papers cite Darwin's study.

Another report, untouched for sixty years, was obviously closer to the central theme: Pernice in 1889 clearly described the action of colchicine on mitosis.[17] His figures (Fig. 1.4) showing arrested metaphase are remarkable even though their significance was not entirely realized. Pernice conducted research far ahead of the knowledge at hand in his day.

Many references credit Malden with the first observation on mitotic effects of colchicine because he said the drug appeared to "excite karyokinesis" [9] in white blood cells. The full significance was not realized at this date, but Dixon and Malden[28] prepared an excellent report on the effects of colchicine on the blood picture.

This relationship between colchicine and leukocytosis was reexamined by Lits,[27] a student in the Pathology Laboratory, University of Brussels, Belgium, under the direction of the late Professor A. P. Dustin, Sr., in 1934. Since the mitotic effects induced by colchicine were so similar to those previously reported by Dustin and Grégoire[13] with sodium cacodylate, more than passing attention was paid to the results by Lits. The situation was ideal for striking at the basic biological issues since Professor Dustin had already devoted much time to the study of the action of chemicals upon mitosis.[12] Colchicine was effective in much less concentration and the volume of arrested metaphases in a given treated tissue was an impressive sight.

The Dustin school immediately established that colchicine acts upon mitosis whether using animal or plant tissues.[14] Their contribution was important and significant. With regard to polyploidy in *Allium* root tips they did not grasp its significance even though the preserved slides today show restitution nuclei that have multiples of chromosome sets.[14]

Independently, a penetrating analysis of colchicine acting upon mitosis was made by Ludford[28, 28a] with tissue culture methods using normal and malignant cells *in vivo* and *in vitro*. His results showed that metaphases were arrested. Amoroso urged using colchicine.

Attention was called to the possibilities of colchicine as a tool for cancer chemotherapy.[12] Two other projects specifically mention the use of colchicine as a means of attacking problems of cancer. One was done by Amoroso in 1935 when colchicine was given to mice bearing specific tumors.[9] The other reported regression of a spindle-

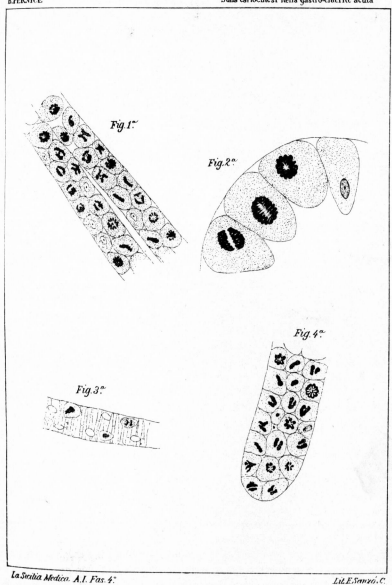

Fig. 1.4—Pernice's first description of colchicine-mitoses (in dog). 1. Gastric gland. 2. Arrested metaphases at the tip of a villosity of gastric mucosa. 3. Endothelial mitoses in the vessels of the mucosa. 4. Lieberkühn's gland crowded with abnormal mitoses. Note absence of anaphases and telophases. (After O. Eigsti, P. Dustin, et al.)

celled sarcoma of a mare that received colchicine by intramuscular injections.[9]

Reference to Dominici,[27] a pioneering investigator with irradiations and treatment of cancer, is frequently made, but his original studies have not been found except for a sentence carried in a textbook. Dominici died in 1919, so the relation between his work and modern studies is not as direct as many have been led to believe.

While the late Professor G. M. Smith of Yale attended the Second International Cancer Congress in Brussels in September, 1936, the work by the Dustin school came to his attention. Here an elaborate demonstration of research with colchicine was made. Before leaving Europe, Professor Smith purchased colchicine with the hope that specific research could be done in his laboratory in the United States.[18] Along with Professor D. U. Gardner and the late Professor E. Allen, he developed assay methods to test estrogenic hormones. Their preliminary paper was published in 1936.

In another laboratory Dr. A. M. Brues[4] and associates reported important observations on the effect of colchicine upon mitosis in regenerating liver. These studies struck at the basic mitotic problem.

At Cold Spring Harbor, Long Island, New York, Mr. E. L. Lahr initiated research similar to that reported by the Yale group. An Atlantic City A.A.A.S. sectional meeting, 1936–37, presented the work by Allen, Gardner, and Smith, which paper was heard by Carnegie staff scientists. Mr. Lahr performed two valuable services: first, he informed the geneticists at the Carnegie Institution about research with colchicine at the regular seminar attended by all the *Datura* workers; and secondly, his excellent slides showed metaphasic stages in tremendous numbers when colchicine was present. These results were freely demonstrated and thoroughly discussed with all who visited Mr. Lahr's laboratory.[15]

One day in February, 1937, the slides were shown to the senior author. The demonstration was so impressive that he obtained colchicine for *Allium* root tip tests before leaving the laboratory. Appropriate concentrations were determined for the experiment with plant materials. Within 72 hours, large bulbous tips appeared on onion roots immersed in colchicine; the cells showed polyploid restitution nuclei by acetocarmine methods. Since the senior author had been privileged to attend seminars in cytophysiology by Professor C. F. Hottes, University of Illinois, the polyploid cells found in treated root tips at the Carnegie Laboratories received more than average passing attention.[15]

The *Allium* root tip tests at the Carnegie Institution Laboratories were followed by seedling treatments. Each test pointed toward a potential use for inducing polyploidy. These preliminary results aroused discussion at Cold Spring Harbor which continued up to April 30, 1937.[15]

On this date, the senior author severed connections with the Carnegie Laboratories. Working conditions for continuing colchicine research with plant materials were obtained for him May 1, 1937, through the generosity of Dr. Geo. H. Conant in his Triarch Laboratories, Ripon, Wisconsin. Here the *Allium* test was repeated. *Datura stramonium* seedlings were treated with colchicine, and the drug was applied to the generative cell in pollen tube cultures. Remarkable results at Wisconsin confirmed the previous opinion that colchicine was an unusually effective substance. From these experiments the senior author developed a deep interest in colchicine research, and he has maintained a continued contact with various phases of it through the years.

Following the departure of the senior author from the Carnegie Laboratories, research workers investigating cytogenetic problems of *Datura* began treatments of seeds of this species with recommended dosages of colchicine.[40] Announcement of these results was made in a publication[2] by the French Academy of Science in September, 1937. By December, 1937,[2a] the evidence from *Datura* and other species clearly established the fact that colchicine was a new and effective tool for making polyploids experimentally. Since there are sufficient historical notes[45] and colchicine chronologies,[23, 40] an elaborate discussion does not seem needed here, except to recommend an article from the Botanical Review,[10] published in 1940, for important details of historical significance concerning the pioneering work with colchicine pursued at Cold Spring Harbor from January to December, 1937.

Independently, Doctors B. R. Nebel and M. L. Ruttle began research in April, 1937, and concluded important experiments that year, clearly demonstrating that colchicine acted upon mitosis.[32] Furthermore, this drug was an important tool for inducing polyploidy in plants.[32] Dr. D. F. Jones of Connecticut is credited with calling their attention to colchicine; however, they also acknowledged a bibliography in their early publications, mentioning the work by Dustin,[12] Ludford,[28] and Brues.[4]

In France, Dr. P. Gavaudan and associates published the first account[20] that called attention to polyploidy induced by colchicine. This paper was presented in June, 1937, but little notice was given to the contribution. The text clearly described doubling of the chromosomes along with specific figures. While Havas claims an earlier date in publication,[23] his paper completely disregarded polyploidy as a consequence of the colchicine treatment. In this regard

Gavaudan was more closely associated with cytogenetic aspects than Havas.

During the summer of 1937, a Swedish geneticist, Dr. A. Levan, visited genetics laboratories in eastern United States and was shown by Dr. Nebel data obtained from his colchicine studies. When Dr. Levan returned to Sweden, he began experiments with colchicine and made basic contributions to the concepts of polyploidy and colchicine mitosis.[26]

The Cold Spring Harbor studies exerted an influence that spread around the world. These activities plus the other biological work created an intense and wide interest that led to the "colchicine fad."[45] Many scientists went to work establishing facts about colchicine.[16] Generally, the cooperation was genuine, ideas were exchanged freely, mutual problems were discussed, and knowledge advanced rapidly. Significant contributions were made within a short time.

By 1938 colchicine was applied to many kinds of living cells, plant and animal, with outstanding specific reactions obtained by the treatment. Cancer control continued to be injected into the discussions. Geneticists discovered a very useful tool at their disposal for theoretical and practical work. These data were linked to publicity that developed a common language for layman and scientist.

In spite of volumes published, there remain unexplored problems which appear to have promise for more discoveries. Excellent research has been accomplished; future progress in agriculture, medicine, pharmacy, biology, and chemistry will be facilitated by the possession of such a tool as colchicine.[31]

REFERENCES

1. BERGNER, A. Studies on colchicine derivatives. Cancer. 3:134–41. 1950.
2. BLAKESLEE, A. Dédoublement du nombre de chromosomes chez les plantes par-traitement chimique. C. R. Acad. Sci. Paris. 205:476–79. 1937.
2a. ————, AND AVERY, A. Methods of inducing doubling of chromosomes in plants. Jour. Hered. 28:393–411. 1937.
3. BROUN, G., HAGER, V., GOEHAUSEN, M., GREBEL, C., SWEENEY, W., AND HELLMAN, R. Remission in Hodgkin's disease following colchicine, desoxycorticosterone and ascorbic acid. Jour. Lab. and Clin. Med. 36:803–4. 1950.
4. BRUES, A. The effect of colchicine on regenerating liver. Jour. Physiol. 86:63–64. 1936.
5. BRYAN, C. The Papyrus Ebers. Appleton & Co., New York. 1931.
6. BULFINCH, T. The age of fables. Thomas Crowell, New York. 1905.
7. CHOPRA, R. Indigenous drugs of India. Arts Press, Calcutta, India. 1933.
8. COHEN, A., COOK, J., AND ROE, E. Colchicine and related compounds. Chem. Soc. London Jour. 1940:194–97. 1940.
9. COOK, J., AND LOUDON, J. Alkaloids: colchicine. Ed. Holmes & Mankse. Academic Press, New York. 2:261–325. 1951.
10. DERMEN, H. Colchicine, polyploidy and technique. Bot. Rev. 6:599–635. 1940.
11. DOERING, W., AND KNOX, L. Synthesis of tropolone. Jour. Amer. Chem. Soc. 72:205. 1950.

12. Dustin, A. Contribution à l'étude des poisons caryoclasiques sur les tumeurs animales. Bull. Acad. Roy. Méd. Belg. 14:487–502. 1934.
13. ————, and Grègorie, C. Contribution à l'étude de l'action des poisons caryoclasiques sur les tumeurs animales. Bull. Acad. Roy. Méd. Belg. 13:585–92. 1933.
14. ————, Havas, L., and Lits, F. Action de la colchicine sur les divisions cellulaires chez les végétaux, C. R. Assoc. des Anat. 32:170–76. 1937.
15. Eigsti, O. A cytological study of colchicine effects in the induction of polyploidy in plants. Proc. Nat. Acad. Sci. 24:56–63. 1938.
16. ————, and Dustin, P. Colchicine bibliography. Lloydia. 10:65–114. 1947. Colchicine bibliography III. Lloydia. 12:185–207. 1949.
17. ————, ————, and Gay-Winn, N. On the discovery of the action of colchicine on mitosis in 1889. Science. 110:692. 1949.
18. Gardner, D. U. Personal communication. Yale University Medical School, New Haven, Conn. 1949.
19. Garrod, A. Gout and rheumatic gout. Longmans, London. 1876.
20. Gavaudan, P., and Pomriaskinsky-kobozieff, N. Sur l'influence de la colchicine sur la caryocinèse dans les méristèmes radiculares de l'*Allium cepa*. C. R. Soc. Biol. Paris. 125:705–7. 1937.
21. Greene, E. Landmarks of botanical history. Smithsonian Institution, Washington, D. C. No. 1870. 1909.
22. Gunther, R. Greek herbal Dioscorides. Oxford Univ. Press, London. 1934.
23. Havas, L. Colchicine chronology. Jour. Hered. 31:115–17. 1940.
24. Kremers, E., and Urdang, G. History of pharmacy. J. B. Lippincott Co., Philadelphia. 1940.
25. Lettré, H. Zur Konstitution des Colchicins. Angew. Chem. A/59:218–24. 1947. Zur Chemie und Biologie der Mitosegifte. Angew. Chem. 63:421–30. 1951.
26. Levan, A. Effect of colchicine on root mitosis in *Allium*. Hereditas. 24:471–86. 1938. Note on the somatic chromosomes of some *Colchicum* species. Hereditas. 26:317–20. 1940.
27. Lits, F. Contribution à l'étude des réactions cellulaires provoquées par la colchicine. C. R. Soc. Biol. Paris. 115:1421–23. 1933.
28. Ludford, R. J. The action of toxic substances upon the division of normal and malignant cells *in vitro* and *in vivo*. Arch. Exp. Zellforsch. und Mikr. Anat. 18:411–41. 1936.
28a. ————. Chemically induced derangements of cell division. Jour. Royal Microscopical Soc. 73:1–23. 1953.
29. Majumdar, G. The history of botany and allied sciences in ancient India. Arch. Internat. Hist. Sci. 14:100–133. 1951.
30. Mehra, P., and Khoshoo, T. Chromosome number and effect of colchicine on chromosomes of *Colchicum luteum* Baker. Curr. Sci. Bangalore. 17:242–43. 1948. Observations on some colchicine-containing plants. Jour. Pharm. and Pharmacol. 3:486–96. 1951.
31. Moreau, F. Alcaloïdes et plantes alcaloïfères. Presses Univ., Paris. 1946.
32. Nebel, B., and Ruttle, M. The cytological and genetical significance of colchicine. Jour. Hered. 29:3–9. 1938.
33. Rapoport, H., and Williams, A. The degradation of colchicine to octahydrodemethoxydesoxydesacetamido-colchicine. Jour. Amer. Chem. Soc. 73:1896. 1951.
34. ————, ————, and Cisney, M. The synthesis dl-colchinol methyl ether. Jour. Amer. Chem. Soc. 72:3324. 1950.
35. Santavy, F. Polarography and spectrography of colchicine and its derivatives. Publ. Fac. Med. Brno, Republ. Tchecosl. 19:1–24. 1946.
36. Scott, G., and Tarbell, D. Studies in the structure of colchicine. Jour. Amer. Chem. Soc. 72:240–43. 1950.
37. Sentein, P. Personal communication. Montpelier, France. 1952.
38. Séris, L. A propos de la formule de la colchicine. La Rev. Sci. Fas. 88:489–93. 1947.

39. SHARP, G. Colchicum studied historically. Pharm. Jour. and Pharmacist, London. 83:5–6. 1909.
40. SKOOG, F. Plant growth substances. Univ. Wisconsin Press, Madison. 1951.
41. STEFANOFF, B. Monographie der Gattung *Colchicum* L. Proc. Bulgarian Acad. Sci. 22:1–99. 1926.
42. STEINEGGER, E., AND LEVAN, A. Constitution and c-mitotic activity of iso-colchicine. Hereditas. 33:385–96. 1947. The c-mitotic qualities of colchiceine, trimethyl colchicinic acid and two phenanthrene derivatives. Hereditas. 34:193–203. 1948.
43. WADA, B. The effect of chemicals on mitosis studied in *Tradescantia* cells *in vivo* 1. p-acetylaminotropolone. Cytologia. 17:14–34. 1952.
44. WARREN, L. Pharmacy and medicine in ancient Egypt. Jour. Amer. Pharm. Assoc. 20:1065–76. 1931.
45. WELLENSIEK, S. The newest fad, colchicine, and its origin. Chron. Bot. 5:15–17. 1939.
46. WILLIAMS, T. Drugs from plants. Sigma Books Ltd., London. 1947.
47. WOODWARD, M. Gerard's herball. Houghton Mifflin Co., Boston. 1931.

CHAPTER 2

Nucleus and Chromosomes

2.1: Original Concepts

A basic and far-reaching discovery in biology emerged from the activities[29, 33] of the Laboratories of Pathological Anatomy, Faculty of Medicine, University of Brussels, under the direction of Professor Albert-Pierre Dustin: *Colchicine induced metaphasic arrest (stathmokinesis)*. Nuclear mitoses were studied experimentally at Brussels for more than a decade, 1924–1934, chemicals being applied by several methods. After colchicine was suggested,[61] evaluation of its mitotic activity came quickly, and showed that a powerful agent had been discovered. Comparative tests for mitotic poisons proved that colchicine was one thousand times more potent than sodium cacodylate, which they had studied previously.[30] Pure substance, in minute quantity, caused metaphasic stages to accumulate in a treated tissue far beyond the percentages found in untreated sarcomas. These original tests with colchicine, coupled with previous experience with other mitotic poisons, helped to frame the idea of metaphasic arrest by colchicine.[29]

The original slides preserving the tissues treated with colchicine were re-examined by the authors when they worked together in 1949.[35] From these impressive sections, new photomicrographs were made for this book (animal cells, cf. Chapter 10, Fig. 10.1; plant tissues, Fig. 2.1C). The total effectiveness displayed by the drug acting upon mitosis is re-emphasized by these pictures. Microscopic inspection reveals an unusual sight. Similar impressions of this totally different mitotic picture had been formed earlier when the senior author,[34] in 1937, saw animal cells treated with colchicine and placed beneath the microscope (cf. Chapter 1). The power to stop mitosis in metaphase was clear to us, and this property has been confirmed by many experimenters.[35] Everyone agrees that the reaction upon nuclear mitosis is specific, selective, and total, under prescribed conditions.[56, 58]

A large bibliography[35] has accumulated since 1934, but one of the original conclusions, metaphasic arrest, conceived by Professor A. P.

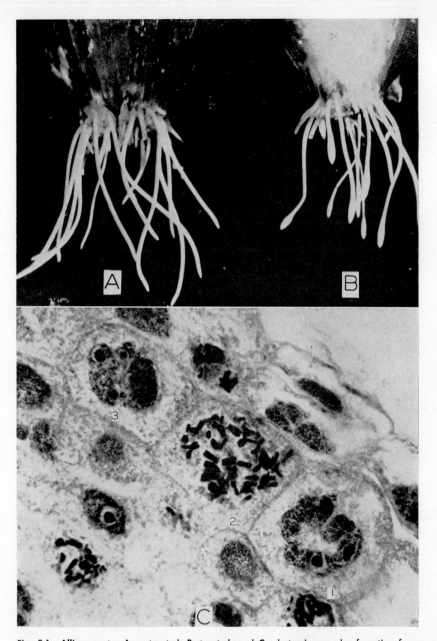

Fig. 2.1—**Allium** roots. A, untreated; B, treated; and C, photomicrograph of section from treated root. A. Roots grown in tap water do not show enlargement. B. Colchicine solution of 0.01 per cent causes spears, or colchicine-tumors. This group was one of the original tests run in 1937 at Cold Spring Harbor, Long Island, N. Y., by Eigsti. C. A photomicrograph prepared specifically for this monograph, from a slide of sectioned root tip made in the Brussels' laboratory, 1934 to 1937, and presently with the A. P. Dustin Collection, University of Brussels. The polyploid numbers can be seen, as well as large multinucleate cells, amoeboid nucleate cells, and pseudospindle. Similar views were illustrated by Havas, Dustin, and Lits in 1937.

Dustin, Sr., stands correct.[29] Almost universally, living cells respond to colchicine after one basic pattern, and new tests extend knowledge into other areas of science. The "colchicine-mitosis"[56] (abbreviated, c-mitosis) is built upon the principle of an arrested metaphase. A c-mitosis was conceived from experiments with plants after the idea had been developed from animal cells.[12, 15, 61, 62] Undoubtedly, the interest in colchicine by the biologist has stimulated an extensive research in the chemistry of this substance.[21]

Metaphasic arrest implies control over dividing cells; seemingly then, control over cancer might be obtained from the use of this chemical or others. This discovery raised hopes and new questions about the problem. However, biological problems being as complex as they are — and cancer is a major one — the answers have not come to us as definitely as might have been hoped or expected. Nevertheless, basic contributions to knowledge such as the idea of metaphasic arrest opened new frontiers in research,[59] even though magic cures have not been produced.

Chromosomal numbers in plant cells are frequently doubled after treatment with colchicine; polyploidy is a consequence of contact with the drug.[25] Since many species, including those important economically, i.e., wheat, cotton, oats, and tobacco, are natural polyploids, the suggestion was frequently made that this tool would help create new "synthetic" plants according to man's desires.[52] A revolution in agriculture was predicted when colchicine became known for its capacity to induce polyploidy. But many were disappointed as the heralded magic did not appear with each newly created tetraploid plant.[37] Informed geneticists, acquainted with polyploidy as a plant-breeding method,[82] did not underestimate the difficulties, nor did they fail to appreciate the opportunities provided by this new tool. Unfortunately, some practical agronomists[64] have condemned the use of colchicine for its failure to produce practical results within a short time; therefore, such research using induced polyploidy has been discouraged. Nevertheless, the technique is valuable for those able to direct such plant breeding, harmonizing theoretical and practical knowledge. For by these methods, mankind's food and fiber supply can be increased (cf. Chapters 12 and 13).

2.2: The Original Statements

When nuclear mitoses in the grafted sarcoma of the mouse were treated with colchicine,[29] deviations from normal division gave the observer a picture of an arrested mitosis. In 1934, Professor A. P. Dustin made the following description:

. . . after a very short prophase, the nuclear membrane disappears, the cytoplasm swells, and the chromosomes clump together in a strongly basophilic mass. The mitoses remain arrested in that state for about twenty-four hours.

During that period, a certain number of nuclei undergo degeneration. . . . After that period . . . cells . . . complete their division. . . . The achromatic figure becomes visible. . . . Chromosomes move toward the poles. . . . Cytoplasmic division is completed. . . . Some mitotic figures of too great size . . . and some pluricentric divisions remain as a testimony of the nucleotoxic effect. . . .*

These basic statements require no change today even though knowledge has expanded in many directions. Admittedly, as the basic idea becomes extended and broadened, additional points are added. For example, the c-mitosis illustrates enlargement of the original explanation, but no radical changes in concept are necessary.[56]

The Dustin school did not limit their work to animal cells. A Hungarian scientist, the late Dr. L. Havas, treated *Allium* root tips with colchicine.[31] His slides were a part of the Dustin collection available to the authors in 1949. Since the arrested metaphase or c-mitosis was so clearly preserved, new photomicrographs were made (Fig. 2.1C), showing the increase in numbers of chromosomes, large restitution nuclei, and "achromatic spheres." [86, 7] But the original text by the Brussels investigators did not mention the polyploid conditions of these cells.[31]

Independently, in 1937, the senior author tested cells from treated root tips (Fig. 2.1A and B) with acetocarmine methods; the tests showed that polyploidy was created in many different areas of the *Allium* root. The Brussels material and that used at Cold Spring Harbor (cf. Chapter 1) were, in every respect, similar.[34]

A third and independently conducted test with *Allium* roots and colchicine was reported by Dr. Pierre Gavaudan and associates. They published the first account of polyploidy induced by colchicine in June, 1937. Their report stated:[41]

It is evident that in these cases there is a separation of pairs of chromosomes, the number of chromosomes of a restitution nucleus is *double* the normal number. The chromosome list of Gaiser indicates that 2n-16 occurs in *Allium cepa*. Our results show "pseudomitoses" with more than thirty pairs.†

This original report and its significance were not mentioned in reviews[25, 52] or papers[56] in the period immediately following its publication. The more dramatic demonstrations that dealt with induction of polyploidy in plants overshadowed the original and what is now realized as a classic publication by the Gavaudan school.

As soon as Dr. Albert Levan returned to Sweden from America in the autumn of 1937,[56] experiments with *Allium* roots and colchicine were started. This material formed the basis for his concept of an arrested metaphase, as a colchicine-mitosis.[56] Remarkable simi-

---

* A translation of pertinent comments from the article cited in Reference No. 12, Chap. 1.

† Translated from paper written in French by authors cited in Reference No. 20, Chap. 1, and Reference No. 41 of this chapter.

larity exists between the separate descriptions with animal cells[29] by Professor Dustin and the plant work by Professor Levan. A colchicine-mitosis was described by him as follows:[56]

The effect of colchicine on the course of mitosis is entirely specific. . . . Modification in mitotic behavior . . . will be abbreviated "c-mitosis." . . . Prophase stages take place normally: the chromosomes divide, condense, and assume metaphase appearance. . . . They are scattered over the cell. . . . This condition (c-metaphase) lasts . . . long . . . after the disappearance of the nuclear membrane. . . . Formation of "c-pairs" is peculiar to material treated with colchicine. . . . Their origin is evidently due to a delay of the division of the centromere. . . . After a few hours . . . the two daughter chromosomes are straightened out . . . like "pairs of skis." . . . Centromeres are placed opposite one another in each pair. . . . During the c-anaphase . . . division of the centromeres does not take place quite simultaneously within one cell. . . . Inactivation of the spindle . . . is reversible. . . . After a period of 12–24 hours in pure water the spindle begins to regenerate. . . . In the course of the transition to normal spindle all kinds of abnormalities are seen. . . . After 36 hours the mitoses run their normal course. At a certain moment after transfer from colchicine . . . frequent diploid mitoses are seen. . . . Highly polyploid giant nuclei still linger in the prophase stages. . . . Numbers as high as five hundred were not rare.*

Summarily, these are the interesting points covered thus far. An unusual sight appears in a microscopic field focused upon tissues treated with colchicine; the nuclear mitoses are halted at metaphase, and converted into c-mitoses.[36, 78, 2] This power to induce c-mitosis belongs to select chemical and physical agents,[58, 33] of which the most potent, in this respect, is colchicine. It acts upon mitosis with great efficiency,[77] high specificity, and total selectivity. The obvious difference between normal nuclear mitosis and c-mitosis is the tremendous accumulation of chromosomes within a given area (Fig. 2.2) where numerous cells adjacent to each other are arrested in metaphase, a primary feature of c-mitosis activity.

Now the total or partial reaction from this drug depends upon the interaction of (1) a specific concentration, (2) given exposure period, (3) particular mitotic stage when chemical contacts nucleus, (4) cellular type, and (5) environment favorable to mitosis. Under these conditions metaphases are arrested. Consequently metaphasic

---

* A condensation of the concept of a c-mitosis taken from Levan, 1938, Reference No. 26, Chap. 1.

Fig. 2.2—Accumulation of arrested mitoses in animals injected with colchicine and sodium cacodylate, both spindle poisons. **A.** Spleen of **Siredon** five days after a single injection of colchicine. The organ has increased in size, and many arrested prophase-metaphases can be observed. These belong mainly to young red blood cells. The longitudinal splitting of chromosomes can be noticed at some places. (From an unpublished photomicrograph by Delcourt) **B.** Accumulation of arrested metaphases of the "ball" type in the intestinal crypts of the small intestine of a mouse. This condition follows injection of sodium cacodylate and is identical to that observed 6 hours after injection of colchicine. Cf. Chapter 17. (From an unpublished photomicrograph from the work of Piton and A. P. Dustin)

62831

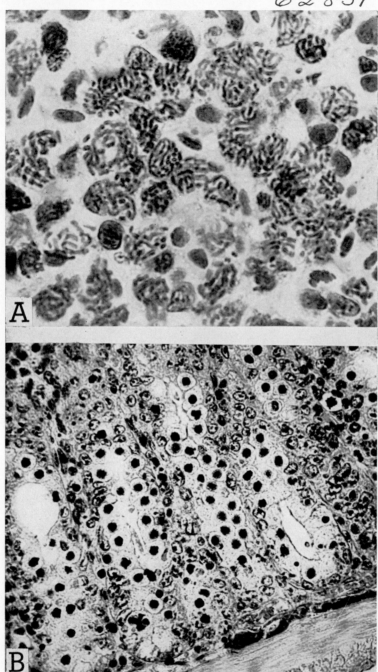

chromosomes accumulate in pairs, "colchicine-pairs," [56] in cytoplasm. Their distribution then is not the usual equatorial plate arrangement. Furthermore, an arrest at metaphase reduces the number of anaphases or telophases (Fig. 2.3) thus adding to the apparent increases in this one particular stage, the c-metaphase. That is why the observer is struck by a totally different mitotic pattern as he looks at treated tissues through the microscope. Usually tissues have a few metaphases, some anaphases, some telophases, but mostly non-dividing cells. Even a meristematic tissue in plants or a sarcoma of animals,[13]

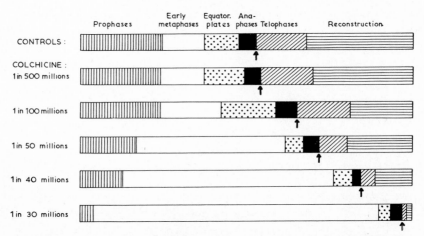

Fig. 2.3—Graphic representation of the percentages of mitotic stages in fibroblast cultures exposed for ten hours to solutions of colchicine. With increasing concentration, the percentage of metaphases with unoriented chromosomes increases. The displacement to the right of the arrow, indicating the end of anaphase, demonstrates that in the most concentrated solutions, nearly all mitoses remain arrested and do not proceed to telophase. This effect is clearly related to concentration. (After Bucher, 1947)

each noted for cell division, has only a limited number of cells showing chromosomes at a particular moment. It is not surprising that the accumulation of metaphases impressed one pioneering investigator who described this reaction by colchicine as "an explosion of mitoses."[61]

Ultimately, exclusive of recovery, the restitution nucleus is formed when the chromosomes transform[22] to interphase without forming the daughter nuclei. This transformation may start from an arrested metaphase, thus by-passing the c-anaphase. Or, the changes[22] may begin after the chromosomes of each c-pair have fallen apart in the c-anaphase[56] — a transition involving separate chromosomes. Sometimes the uncoiling begins as early as prophase.[93] These different points of origin mark three routes taken when the chromosomes "unravel" and undergo transformations to interphase. If the number of centromeres has doubled, a feature clearly seen at c-anaphase, then the chromosomal number in the restitution nucleus will be twice that of the nucleus before a c-mitosis began. One important consequence of the c-mitosis in contrast to the normal nuclear mitosis is the induction of polyploidy.[41, 56] But not all restitution nuclei become polyploid, since the changes[22] may start from a prophase or metaphase.[84] In fact, many animal cells treated with colchicine are arrested at metaphase. The transformation from this stage does not lead to a restitutional polyploid nucleus, for in these instances other changes occur.[29, 61]

Finally, the most significant biological feature basic to all these changes is *reversibility*.[56] After the colchicine in concentrations creating arrest becomes dissipated, the cell may recover; that is, a bipolar nuclear mitosis again proceeds in the same manner as before an arrest was induced. Such recovered cells will continue to divide thus as long as the cell lineage retains that power. No permanent damage, with few exceptions,[91] to spindle mechanisms or chromosomes is acquired from the arrested metaphase. Of course, the arrest may have been so severe that changes in metabolism cause the cell to degenerate and ultimately die, but our concepts of reversibility now refer to those cases where there is complete recovery, a reversibility to the bipolar mitosis. These can take place among plant and animal cells. The recovery pattern like the whole c-mitotic sequence is unique and notably uniform for many subjects.

Since there is the reversibility potential, a restitution nucleus with twice the number of chromosomes may regenerate its new spindle mechanism. From a genetic view this is a most significant aspect of reversibility, since the restitution nucleus with twice the number of chromosomes gives rise thereafter to daughter cells, each with a polyploid condition.

By this procedure of metaphasic arrest — c-anaphase, restitutional polyploid nucleus, and recovery — the induced polyploidy is transmitted to succeeding generations. This discovery has had important ramifications in agricultural research. Whereas control over cell division would appear to be desirable for treating certain diseases, this same control over cell division has entirely different, broad applications in agriculture. That is why a basic discovery in science can be so widely used in other fields.

2.3: Prophase

First reports said that colchicine had no influence upon prophase.[56, 29] Later by cinematographic record, no modification at prophase was noticed.[15] A general belief developed that this portion of nuclear mitosis was not changed by the drug, for data obtained by new methods from fixed and stained cells appeared the same for treated and untreated cases.

In animal cells the prophase stages were thought to be non-susceptible to colchicine because the drug did not penetrate the nuclear membrane.[62] Therefore chromosomes remained as usual until the membrane disappeared. Then the chromosomes came in contact with the drug present in the cytoplasm. After this period, contraction might take place.[71, 7, 77, 63, 83]

From plant tissues, fixed and stained, three important changes were compared at prophase.[65] First, chromatin threads developed the minor spiral in both instances. Second, the major spiralization proceeded along usual patterns. Third, chromosomes condensed into proportioned prophasic structures as this stage ended. The two distinct chromatids were strongly cleaved, appearing as longitudinal pairs twisted about each other in a relational coil (Fig. 2.10*A*). On these three points no noticeable differences among fixed and stained cells, treated and untreated, were observed.[65] But such opinions about the action of colchicine at prophase required modification as new techniques[93, 34, 39] replaced traditional cytological methods, and a wide range of concentrations was included.

Living cells were observed continuously from prophase through all mitotic stages in *Tradescantia* staminal hair cells.[93] By this method colchicine could be applied at any stage chosen by the investigator, who then followed the effects from that particular stage on through subsequent ones.

Strong concentrations (2 per cent) admitted during mid-prophase at the stage when chromosomes were condensing, caused the process to revert back to an interphasic dispersion of chromatin.[93] The time schedule for this reversion showed that a metaphasic arrest had not been reached, but the restitution nucleus was formed from a mid-prophase stage. In some cases the restitution nucleus appeared to be doubled for chromosomal number. Similar cases were reported for *Siredon* (Fig. 2.9A–D).[24, 84] This is one type of transformation from prophase to interphase.

Time schedules for the formation of chromosomes in prophase have been made with *Tradescantia*. This phase is called the *anachromasis*[93] period of chromosomes. Untreated cells require 97 minutes from early prophase to the polar cap stage. Longer time is taken in the presence of 0.05 per cent (121 min.), but a minimum time in 0.1 per cent (84 min.) is less than control. These concentrations permit the chromosomes to move into the arrested metaphase, whereas a stronger solution induces interphase. Colchicine slows down the process of anachromasis as it occurs in prophase. To contrast these developmental processes, new methods had to be developed.

The neuroblastic cells of grasshopper are used in another technique[39] with unusual possibilities for a different inspection of c-mitosis, particularly at prophase. Like the *Tradescantia* staminal hair cell method, the drug can be administered when mitosis reaches a certain stage; thus a new approach is made with animal cells. Time, gross changes, and unusual developmental sequences can be charted.

By this critical method the action of colchicine upon prophase was manifested in three distinct ways.[39] First, strong concentrations (50 and 25 $\times$ 10^{-6} *M* col.), applied at late and very late prophase, caused the chromosomes already partially formed to revert to an earlier dispersed phase. Second, lowering the concentration (2.5 $\times$ 10^{-6} *M*) induced precocious reduction in the relational coiling and an unusual contraction of the chromosomes before the nuclear membrane disappeared. At this concentration, prophase chromosomes, normally fixed with centromeres at the polar side of the nucleus, were disoriented. By microdissection methods, the polar fixation at prophase was tested.[39] Colchicine, in proper concentration, destroys some factor associated with this fixed position. Third, additional decrease in concentration (1.9 $\times$ 10^{-6} *M*) applied at prophase disposes the chromosomes into the "star" formation as soon as the nuclear membrane disappears. These stages may develop into a multiple-star phase, and from this formation chromosomes settle out to the bottom of the cell. These three conditions show that colchicine induces changes at prophase when certain concentrations are used. These changes are revealed when continuous records can be made.[39]

Thus colchicine may act upon chromosomes at prophase, causing interphase loss in relational coiling, contraction, destruction of intranuclear orientation, and predisposing the chromosomes to a star formation. These comparisons required a special technique able to focus attention upon specific stages, using a wide range of concentrations, and then following the successive development from one stage to the next. [39]

Pollen grains planted in colchicine sucrose-agar[34, 89] provide a special method for observing the effects of strong concentrations (1 per cent) upon prophasic stages. Each grain at the time a culture starts, begins with a nucleus in prophase. Pollen tubes grow and the cell lives for a time, but the prophase goes into interphase and does not move into an arrested metaphase. These unpublished data were collected from treated and untreated cells fixed and stained at given intervals.

Analyzing percentages of prophases, treated and untreated, there is noted a proportional decrease in the relative percentage of prophase as the experiments continue.[65] Inhibition of prophase is indicated with concentrations that cause arrest at metaphase (0.01 per cent). This decrease for *Allium* begins after twenty-four hours[60] (Table 2.1). At this period the c-metaphases have reached a peak.[60]

TABLE 2.1
PERCENTAGE OF C-MITOSES FOR ONE HUNDRED FIGURES
(After Mangenot, 1942)

Root Tips of Germinating Onion Seedlings—Colchicine 0.05%

	Control	24 hrs.	48 hrs.	72 hrs.	96 hrs.
Resting stage..........	85.0	85.0	86.2	90.0	96.6
Prophase.............	6.6	3.2	2.8	1.6	0.6
Meta-anaphase........	4.2	9.6	7.2	6.4	2.0
Telophase............	3.4	2.2	3.8	2.0	0.8

Onion Bulb Root Tips—Colchicine 0.05%

	Control	18 hrs.	40 hrs.	93 hrs.	184 hrs.
Resting stage..........	88.42	77.22	77.30	88.61	95.76
Prophase.............	8.21	7.18	7.53	1.84	0.69
Meta-anaphase........	1.57	14.30	13.84	8.46	3.00
Telophase............	1.78	1.30	1.30	1.07	0.53

Onion Bulb Root Tips—Combined Test—Heteroauxin 0.0001%—Colchicine 0.05%

	Control	24 hrs.	40 hrs.	67 hrs.	91 hrs.	139 hrs.
Resting stage......	88.42	80.5	84.50	89.20	90.70	97.30
Prophase.........	8.21	4.6	4.50	2.60	1.50	0.4
Meta-anaphase....	1.58	13.10	8.00	5.30	4.80	1.40
Telophase........	1.78	1.80	3.00	1.90	3.00	0.90

A similar inhibition was seen in neuroblastic cells[39] but expressed in somewhat different manner. Cells subjected to colchicine in late prophase remained arrested in prophase for 150 minutes before developing a metaphase stage.[39] This process at late prophase, a transition from prophase to metaphase, requires 32 minutes.[39]

Critical time-dose relationships must be observed to produce maximum arrested metaphases in regenerating liver of rat.[11, 12, 13] This dose is one microgram per gram of body weight. Above this concentration, colchicine causes reduction in the mitotic stages in metaphase. Even before any supralethal dose kills the animal, the inhibiting action upon mitosis is observed. That is, the prophases do not seem to move into the arrested metaphase. This would seem to be an inhibition at prophase. Under optimum conditions for dose-time relations, the maximum metaphasic arrest is obtained in mammals at 8 to 10 hours following the injection of colchicine.[61]

Amoeba sphaeronucleus may grow in colchicine without noticeable changes. When colchicine is injected into the cytoplasm by micropipette, action upon mitosis occurs. Amounts injected when the nucleus is in prophase cause return to interphase. Continuous photographic records verified this process. About 1 per cent strengths are needed to induce such chromosomal changes.[20]

Different cells in *Allium* root tips show variation in degree of polyploidy. Pericycle cells may contain several hundred chromosomes, yet the cells at the tip, a meristematic area, will have the diploid number. Seventy-two hours of treatment with adequate concentrations do not induce polyploidy among restricted groups of cells.[65, 67] This has been called a prophase "resistance," characteristic of younger cells.[86] Practical significance becomes attached to this feature if polyploids are to be induced without any diploid cells accompanying the new tissues. Prophase stages are more involved than was formerly accepted.

Two terms might be useful in discussing prophase influences by colchicine and other chemicals: (1) the pre-prophase poison which prevents resting cells from entering the prophase, and (2) the prophase poison, as described above, that inhibits the normal prophase development and in exceptional cases causes a change to interphase. Plants and animals differ with respect to the relative toxic action of colchicine and these make a great difference in the inhibitions not only of metaphase but of prophase as well.

Prophasic arrangements that are held over from the previous telophase are not disturbed in plants by concentrations that induce c-mitosis, e.g., *Dipcadi*.[56] Yet this arrangement is upset in neuroblast cells with concentrations that give typical arrested mitosis,[39] while in mammals, prophase appears to be the most resistant period.[15, 29, 61, 63]

Earlier opinion regarding prophase as always normal in the presence of colchicine must be modified. More information is needed at this critical and difficult stage. Depending upon concentration and the particular material treated, prophase stages are influenced by colchicine.

2.4: Colchicine Metaphase

Again and again, after experiments with animals and with plant cells, the same conclusions were reached: colchicine changed the nuclear processes at metaphase. With few exceptions, agreement is unanimous, and the opinions are usually formed around the following explanations: (1) The metaphasic arrest arises when the spindle fiber mechanisms are partially or totally destroyed.[62, 56, 25, 27, 4, 80, 58, 77, 75, 39] (2) Chromosomes lose their metaphasic orientation when the spindle fibers become disengaged from the chromosomes.[34, 87, 90, 85, 7, 26, 22] (3) The spindle mechanisms are inhibited by colchicine; therefore, nuclear mitoses are arrested at metaphase.[29, 5, 93, 33, 40, 1, 79, 39] While three similar cases are presented, each thesis leads to the same general conclusion: the metaphasic arrest. That is why agreement in the final analysis is so excellent considering the many different biological specimens studied. Universally every one's attention is directed first to the chromosomal pattern at metaphase arrested by colchicine (Fig. 2.1*C*, 2.4*D*, and 2.8*A*) that is quite different from the normal metaphasic orientation (Fig. 2.4*A*). Spindle mechanisms enter the discussion only after the first impressions of chromosomal patterns have been obtained. Accordingly, our discussion is first directed to the chromosomal patterns of arrested metaphase. After these have been compared, it would appear consistent to discuss and analyze the spindle mechanisms that must operate in the production of c-mitosis. The spindle mechanism will be considered in Chapter 3.

2.4–1: Types of arrested metaphases. The regular metaphasic figures and equatorial plate orientations are replaced by different chromosomal patterns (Figs. 2.7*A*, 2.8*A*, and 2.4*D*). Such distributions are induced by colchicine, and these arrangements are not wholly random ones.[1, 79] Characteristic stages repeat often enough that a classification (Fig. 2.5) is possible.[1] If we disregard spindle action for the moment, the arrested metaphases may be grouped into two major categories: (1) the *oriented* metaphase (Fig. 2.5, *above*), (2) the *unoriented* metaphase (Fig. 2.5, *below*). There are subtypes for each group which will be considered under the special headings that follow.

Analysis of the pattern will be made on the basis of interacting factors that create the special type of arrested metaphase, while direct reference to spindle mechanisms will be deferred for the moment. The classification shown in Figure 2.5 was made from stained cells by cytological methods not thoroughly reliable in differentiating the fibers.[1] For this reason, criticism[79] has been made regarding assumptions involving spindle mechanisms, specifically with reference to the distorted star metaphase. Even though this classification was developed by a chromosomal pattern, an insight into c-mitosis and the arrested metaphasic types can be gained by such comparisons.

Colchicine penetrates the cell very rapidly. Effects may be noticed within seconds after the drug contacts the nucleus. C-mitosis in *Allium* develops permanently and completely within fifteen minutes.[88] Rate of penetration, as well as concentration, is very important. The

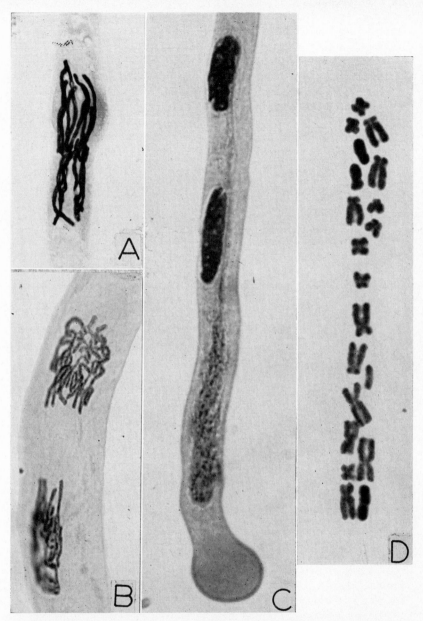

Fig. 2.4—Pollen tube cultures treated and untreated. **A.** A metaphase of generative cell of **Lilium michiganensis** without treatment. One per cent agar and 7 per cent sucrose, stained with iron alum haemotoxylin. **B.** Anaphase, **Polygonatum commutatum** untreated. Stained with acetocarmine. **C.** Two microgametes and tube nucleus. **D.** Arrested metaphase, c-pairs, caused by adding 0.01 per cent colchicine to culture media. The duplications among c-pairs indicate polyploidy. There are 20 c-pairs but only 10 types for the entire group. Centromeric locus shown by incision along chromosomes. Stained with acetocarmine. (Eigsti, 1940)

mitotic stage on hand when colchicine reaches the nucleus may determine the metaphasic type.

Since the action is reversible,[56] cells may recover from the action of the drug. Arrested types appearing during the recovery sequence[79] on the way to complete bipolar mitosis are as significant as those showing up when the drug is acting upon the mitosis.[1]

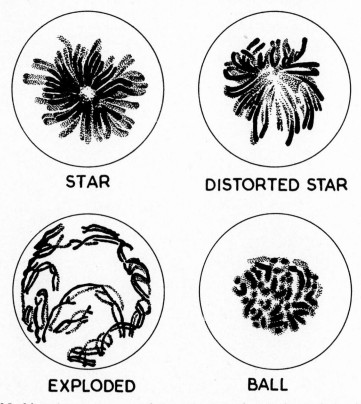

STAR   DISTORTED STAR

EXPLODED   BALL

Fig. 2.5—Schematic representations of the main types of arrested metaphases. (After Barber and Callan)

Length of exposure and concentration are directly related to the pattern that will develop.[7] A given situation must be noted with reference to these two factors.

Then, as was mentioned before, concentration, exposure, mitotic stage, kind of cell, recovery, active treatment, and general growth conditions become critical to the formation of an arrested metaphasic pattern whether oriented or unoriented.[1] Even though the interacting factors are several, the number of metaphasic types is surprisingly limited. In light of the complex interaction, it would seem that the kinds of metaphase that could develop would be more extensive.

2.4–2: The oriented arrested metaphase. In 1889, Pernice[78] sketched the first star metaphase, a distinctive oriented type induced by colchicine.[36] Next, these were reported in 1936[61] among tissues of mice and carcinomatous tissue cultures,[62] and since then the oriented star metaphase has been published many times, from a great variety of biological specimens.

The frequency of star metaphases is far too regular to be ascribed to a random occurrence.[1, 79] The chromosomes are all drawn to one focal point with the proximal portions extended outward resembling a star, and the type was named accordingly. The centromeric portions of the chromosomes are congregated at this one focal point[8] (Figs. 2.5, *upper left,* and 2.7B–F).

Two sets of data from similar materials, *Triton vulgaris*[1] and *Triturus viridescens,*[79] respectively, are pertinent to the matter of origin of the star. Larval cells of *Triton* were kept in solutions and were then removed from time to time, fixed, and stained for chromosomal pictures. The star, or oriented, metaphases, exceeded the unoriented types in the first fixations, at three hours (Table 2.2). The *Triturus* corneal cells, fixed and stained at intervals during recovery from the effects of drug, do not show the star metaphases at their peak until twenty-four hours have elapsed (Table 2.2).

Two critical experiments performed with neuroblastic cells in the grasshopper explain some of these differences.[39] Strong concentrations applied when the cell was at metaphase led to a star metaphase (cf. Chapter 3; Fig. 3.20). This action occurred after a particular mitotic stage had been reached. Another route was used to produce the star in neuroblastic cells, viz., application of lower dosage (1.9×10^{-6} M) at late prophase. Two sets of factors were operating: the concentration and the mitotic stage. In one instance a metaphasic stage was used, and in the other, prophase. Each required a different concentration. In the *Triton* materials, strong concentrations acted early, yet in *Triturus,* the stars accumulated later as cells were recovering from a previous strong dose. We shall return to this problem again under the subject of spindle mechanisms.

Multiple stars in single cells are commonly found in *Allium* root tips when cells recover.[56, 65] In similar instances, the "multiple" stars (Fig. 2.6) are to be seen in the *Tubifex* eggs.[95] Among the *Triturus,* recovery stages at six days show multiple stars (Fig. 2.7). Multiple stars are formed in connection with transition stages from the full c-mitosis to the complete recovery of the bipolar mitosis.[56]

Distorted star metaphases[1] are asymmetrical figures (Fig. 2.5). The origin of distorted star metaphase is controversial, and although they

TABLE 2.2
ARRESTED METAPHASES—TREATMENT AND RECOVERY
I. COLCHICINE TREATMENT STUDY: *Triton vulgaris*; EPIDERMAL CELLS OF LARVAE
(After Barber and Callan, 1943)

Frequency of Different Types of Cell (Means of Counts From 3 Larvae)

Duration of Treatment (*hours*)	Prophase	Bipolar Meta-phase	Star Meta-phase	Un-oriented Meta-phase	Total Meta-phase	Anaphase
0	22.3	25.0	. . . .	. . . .	25.0	30.7
3	24.0	15.7	7.7	6.3	29.7	20.0
6	20.3	15.0	16.3	10.7	42.0	15.7
12	27.0	12.3	20.7	66.3	99.3	8.3
24	17.7	5.0	6.7	175.3	186.0	6.7
48	12.0	0.3	1.7	83.3	85.3	4.3
72	2.3	. . . .	. . . .	9.7	9.7	1.0

II. COLCHICINE RECOVERY STUDY: *Triturus viridescens*; CORNEAL TISSUES
(After Peters, 1946)

Differential Count Expressing Percentage of Mitotic Types During Recovery

Recovery Time (*hours*)	Metaphase, Anaphase, Telophase	Unoriented Metaphases	Star Metaphases
8	2+	92+	5+
24	8+	69+	20+
72	79+	5+	16+

were among the first cases known,[24] less exact knowledge of their formation is at hand than for the star metaphase.

Outside the star or the distorted star, isolated chromosomes are regularly observed. This formation accounts for "lost" chromosomes frequently described in plant and animal tissue-culture cells.[15, 70]

2.4–3: Unoriented metaphases. Chromosomes scattered in the cytoplasm after a nuclear membrane disappears have been thoroughly described in plants[72, 34, 25, 73, 56, 76, 86, 27, 80, 40, 65, 77, 75, 22, 83] and animals.[29, 61, 62, 13, 24, 32, 87, 90, 1, 79, 28, 53, 39] The descriptive expression *exploded metaphase* is appropriate (Figs. 2.4D, 2.7A, and 2.8A). There is a complete lack of the usual equatorial metaphase orientation, hence the epithet *unoriented* (Fig. 2.1*C*, 2.4*D*, and 2.8*A*).

The exploded metaphases were described from cells of mice treated with strong doses of sodium cacodylate.[30] Therefore, a reappearance with colchicine tended to call attention to similarities between the two substances.[33]

Among regenerating liver cells following hepatectomy, the exploded metaphase is very characteristic (Fig. 2.8*A*). The investi-

Fig. 2.6—Cell of **Allium** root tip with an excessive number of chromosomes. Fixed after treatment for 208 hours, with 0.05 per cent colchicine in nutrient solution. The cells are beginning recovery; multiple star metaphases are present. Later cell plates form between the groups reducing one large cell to a number of smaller cells. Cf. Chapter 3. (After Mangenot)

gators[12, 13] described the unusual arrangement as though the individual chromosomes "repulsed one another." These widely scattered chromosomes in a single cell were equally impressive from other animals, the tissue cultures, and special cases, e.g., *Siredon*,[24] *Triton*,[1] *Triturus*,[79] and *Orthoptera*.[87] With plants, *Allium* root tips have been a favorite source for these types, but pollen tubes show unusual scattering of the c-pairs through the length of a single tube (Fig. 2.4*D*).

A specific concentration (2.5×10^{-6} *M*) applied at late prophase created the exploded metaphase in grasshopper neuroblastic cells. Similarly, critical dose-time requirements were necessary to produce an arrested exploded metaphase in the regenerating cells of liver (hepatectomized rats).[11, 13] Supralethal doses did not induce maximum arrested metaphases or exploded metaphases. There is then an optimum dose required for this type. Apparently this same rule holds for pollen tubes, because maximum scattering throughout the tube occurred only under given conditions of concentration and favorable pollen tube growth.[34] There are other cases bearing on this point.

Prophase-metaphase arrangements of chromosomes as an unoriented type are frequently observed (Fig. 2.2B). The spleen of *Siredon* yielded these types among the first colchicine-arrested mitoses ever studied (Fig. 2.2).[24, 84] Perhaps a more logical descriptive term would be *arrested prophase,* since the prophase orientation is maintained as the nuclear membrane disappears. No sign of spindle movement is detected. The chromosomes may revert to the interphase from a prophase-metaphase. During periods as long as five days after injection, the prophase-metaphase appears in *Siredon* (Fig. 2.9). Representative cases in animals are noted for this type.[16, 92] Following anaphasic treatment the intermingling of two sets of chromosomes leads to a similar prophase-metaphase grouping,[39] so that treatment at prophase or at anaphase might give this unoriented association.[39]

Ball metaphases[1] are distinctly clumped types (Figs. 2.2, 2.5). In fact, the clumped c-mitosis observed in *Spinacia,*[7] *Lepidium,* and *Petroselinum*[83] are typically ball metaphases. A toxic action is undoubtedly responsible for the particular apparent fusion of unoriented chromosomes. The next step in progressive development is either the degeneration after pycnosis or recovery to an interphasic stage. *Triton* material was represented with more ball metaphases than any other unoriented type. Even though chromosomes appear clumped, an individuality may be maintained as was pictured for cells of mice by the lacmoid-acetic method applied to a ball metaphase.[33] Many of these mitoses undergo destruction eventually in warm-blooded animals.[61] Lysis or degeneration after a ball metaphase may account for the destruction noticed in *Tubifex.*[53, 54, 55]

Ball metaphases are regularly produced in pollen tube cultures when the concentrations exceed .01 per cent in culturing media.[34] Clumping at the early stages followed by pycnosis and eventual lysis forms the regular course taken by the ball metaphase in pollen tube cells. Similar degeneration and settling of chromosomes in neuroblastic cells indicate destructive action as accompanying this particular unoriented type.

Much discussion has been directed to the distributed c-mitosis, a type that can be clearly demonstrated in pollen tubes when the c-pairs group into two clumps (Fig. 2.4D). The chromosomes are c-pairs, and separation may or may not be equal in number. The

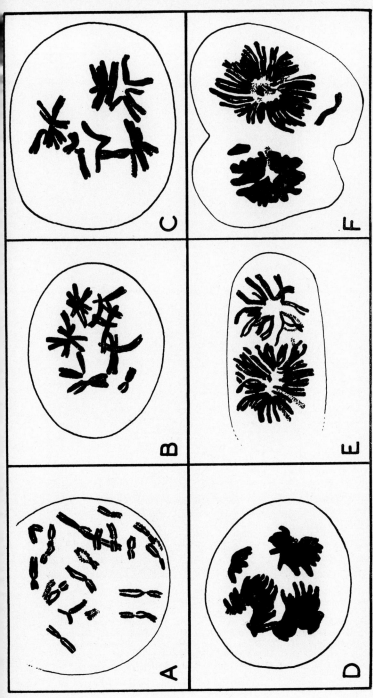

Fig. 2.7—Redrawn from photomicrographs of whole mounts from the cornea of **Triturus viridescens**. Cells treated with colchicine according to a schedule, then allowed to recover. Views show cells in various stages of recovery after treatment. **A.** Six days after recovery. An exploded metaphase, c-pairs similar to pollen tube and **Allium** root tip figures. **B.** Multiple stars six days after recovery, some c-pairs isolated from stars. **C.** Two centers of focus; some evidence of fibers observed on slides but only the position shows spindle action. Diploid number of chromosomes could be determined. **D.** Polyploid cell, five days after recovery; several anaphasic groups, multipolar spindle. **E.** Two metaphase groups, a distributed c-metaphase would give rise to such numbers. **F.** A diploid and tetraploid cell; each has a single chromosome outside the main group, six days after recovery. (After Peters)

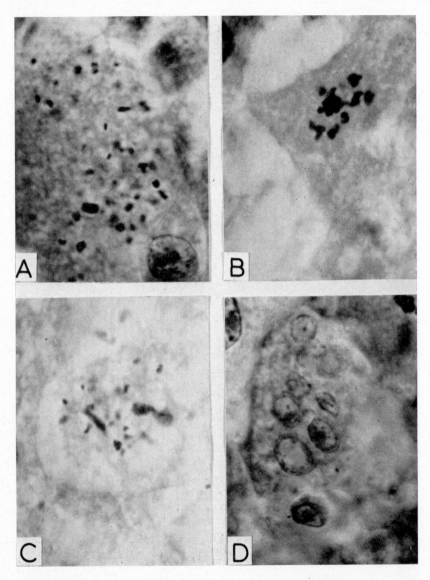

Fig. 2.8—Stages of restitution in exploded metaphases in the regenerating liver of rats injected with colchicine. Feulgen-fast green staining. **A.** Eight hours after colchicine. Typical exploded metaphase, without spindle. Scattered and shortened chromosomes. **B.** Sixteen hours. Chromosome agglutination and lengthening. **C.** Sixteen hours. Some suggestion of catachromatic changes. **D.** Thirty hours. Formation of large micronuclei; these originate by the catachromatic changes of agglutinated groups of chromosomes. (Original photomicrographs. Courtesy of A. M. Brues, Univ. of Chicago)

best classification for the distributed c-mitosis, or bi-metaphase,[79] is a subtype of the exploded metaphase. A somatic meiosis is not conceivable for the pollen tube, yet the distributed c-mitosis is like the cases upon which evidence for somatic meiosis has been built.

Seven years after the distributed c-mitosis was first published and illustrated[34] the term was coined.[75] This is preferable to *somatic meiosis*.[94] An unfortunate confusion in terms arises because one word has been used in two different instances to describe entirely different processes: The word *pseudoanaphase*[7] is used for the distributed, so-called bipolar arrangement of the c-pairs. In another instance, *pseudoanaphase* is synonomous with colchicine-anaphase.[65] The word should

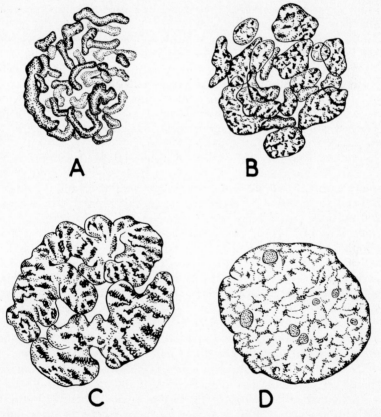

Fig. 2.9—Stages of recovery of arrested prophases in epidermal cells of **Siredon** after colchicine treatment. (Compare with Fig. 2.2A). Acetocarmine smear. **A.** Slight swelling of the chromosomes which have retained their prophasic disposition. **B, C.** Gradual loosening of the chromatic material of similar chromosomes: catachromasis. **D.** Restitution nucleus, formed by the fusion of the swollen chromosomes, which is already noticeable in **C.** (After Ries)

be dropped in favor of (1) *distributed c-mitosis,* and (2) *colchicine-anaphase.* Our preference for distributed c-mitosis instead of somatic meiosis has already been given. Since all factors related to the distributing action cannot be logically considered here, they will be reviewed later.

2.4–4: *Chromosomal evolution in plants.* Chromosomes persist individually ten times longer when colchicine is present than during ordinary mitosis.[93] Their intactness as measured in *Tradescantia* is maintained for 23 minutes normally, but treated cases extend this intactness period to 249 minutes. Of course, concentration plays an important role; however, optimum doses give this extensive period of intactness. A comparative estimate of metaphasic delay is gathered from inspection of records that show total time chromosomes remain intact.[93]

Estimated time given for neuroblastic cells also indicates a delay, but the extent of retardation is calculated in a different manner. The interval is seven to nine times longer with colchicine. Again the concentrations are all-important for any calculation.[39]

Specific measurements for pollen tube cultures, with colchicine in sucrose-agar, are from five to seven times that of the control. Treated and untreated populations were compared for the total period of chromosomal intactness.[34]

An analogy may be drawn with normal-speed motion pictures that are slowed down five to ten times their regular speed. Chromosomes normally go through metaphase, anaphase, and telophase at a speed of 20 minutes. With colchicine, this process is drawn out to 200 minutes. Such delay affects the sequence of chromosomal evolution. The number of chromosomal changes from prophase through telophase is not different, but the span of time which is longer, 200 rather than 20 minutes, accentuates the changes made in the longer period. Now one begins to realize how impressive a definite sequence of chromosomal forms becomes; this is characteristic enough to be outlined.

This extension in time is the reason for a comparison that is usually made between chromosomal evolution under colchicine in plants and the "terminalization of chiasmata" at meiosis.[56]

During a regular nuclear mitosis the process of chromosomal change is so rapid that one loses sight of the uncoiling and the straightening or evolution of the chromosome. There is a threshold for chromosome contraction that is independent of the c-mitosis. The contraction is related to c-mitosis but is autonomous.[77] Some studies indicated that the longer time allowed a greater contraction since super-contraction was caused by excessive coiling.[7]

The first sequence in chromosomal evolution is seen at the late prophase and early metaphase, while chromosomes are strongly cleft, and two chromatids are coiled about each other in a relational coil (Fig. 2.10). The entire chromosome is straightened so that relational coiling is easily perceived. Through the whole process of uncoiling, the delayed metaphase permits observation at each stage. Since both arms are held at one point, the centromere, the description of uncoiling is made easier. Uncoiling, then, is the first step and begins when the nuclear membrane disappears, unless action takes place earlier in a precocious uncoiling, as was reported in the section above under actions during prophase. The first step in the evolution toward a c-pair is passed when the major relational coiling has been removed (Fig. 2.10).

Next, the further reduction is similar to the terminalization of the chiasmata. The contacts of chromatids occurring originally at several points, finally slip off at the end (Fig. 2.10*B*). The movement begins at the centromere and proceeds to the end of each chromosome. The last contact is at the very end of each chromosome. If both ends are in contact, the characteristic figure-8 obtains (Fig. 2.10*B*). Should one end lose contact, and the other remain attached, a forceps type develops (Fig. 2.10*C*). All the while uncoiling takes place, the chromosomes are shortening. Usually the reduction is to one and one-half times the regular length.[77] In one instance, actual measurements for chromosomes of *Petroselinum* were 4.0 microns for control and 1.5 microns for colchicine-treated chromosomes at c-metaphase.[83]

Finally the last stage is reached, when both ends separate and move out as if there were actual repulsion of the two arms (Fig. 2.10*C*). The cruciform type has been seen a number of times in plant,[56] insect,[87] and mammalian cells cultured *in vitro*.[90] Mammals receiving colchicine via injection have not generally shown cells with the cruciform type. A maximum contraction is attained and the c-pair is held together only at the centromere (Figs. 2.4*D* and 2.10*C*). Thus the two chromatids starting from pro-metaphase as a cleft structure relationally coiled, are reduced until only the ends are in contact. After these are released, there develops the typical X-shaped structures (Fig. 2.10*C*). This sequence has taken a longer time than the control because an intactness period is ten times longer than untreated mitosis.

A stickiness of chromosomes prevents the X-shapes, or cruciform. Such physical changes are important to the falling apart of the c-pairs.[77]

Straightened chromosomes that are clearly marked at the centromere (Fig. 2.4*D*) improve the cytological and morphological studies of chromosomes. Not only the comparative sizes of chromosomes within a set can be judged (Fig. 2.4D), but the relative differences between the two arms of a chromosome can be estimated.[34] For these reasons the pretreatment of chromosomes by colchicine was suggested[76] and there followed an important advancement in cytological technique which now makes it possible to study chromosomes, particularly among root tips, with much greater accuracy.[17, 9, 74, 69] Scattered chromosomes in the pollen tube led to the discovery of the natural polyploid *Polygonatum commutatum*.[34] If the chromosome pairs are studied, duplication of a haploid set is obvious (Fig. 2.4D). Since the generative nucleus is haploid, there should theoretically be only one of each chromosomal type. But each type was repeated, typical of tetraploids (Fig. 2.4D). Then any related diploid should have only one of each type. This was found by extending the study to other representatives of the genus. The colchicine technique was useful for this cyto-taxonomic study.[34].

2.4–5: Duration of colchicine-mitosis in animal cells. Degenerative changes are frequent in arrested metaphases of animal cells, especially in mammals. Their mechanism, which may be of some importance when colchicine is utilized in the treatment of abnormal growth (cf. Chapter 10) is not clearly understood. As explained in further chapters, colchicine has been extensively used as a tool for the study of growth. It is impossible to reach precise conclusions if the duration of a given c-mitosis is not known. Direct observations can be made only in limited cases excluding all sectioning materials. From the study of sections, it appeared from the early work that within 24 hours or less, an arrested metaphase either recovered, or underwent destruction.[29, 61]

In cold-blooded animals, colchicine is probably metabolized much more slowly (cf. Chapter 7). In *Siredon,* after a single injection, a great number of arrested mitoses could be seen in the spleen (Fig. 2.2). This was apparent five days after the injection, and lasted for about ten days.[24] In *Triturus,* seven days after colchicine had been applied to the cornea, abnormal mitoses with scattered contracted and unoriented chromosomes have been reported (Fig. 2.7).[79]

However, a precise study of the duration of colchicine-mitoses in the larva of *Xenopus* led to the conclusion that destruction took place much sooner. This was calculated by an indirect method.[63] From data of short treatments with colchicine and from direct observation, it was found that epidermal mitoses lasted about 100 minutes. It was further assumed that the normal prophase duration of about 25 minutes was not modified by colchicine. In colchicinized animals the relations between the numbers of prophases and colchicine-metaphases and the average duration of each should be equal.

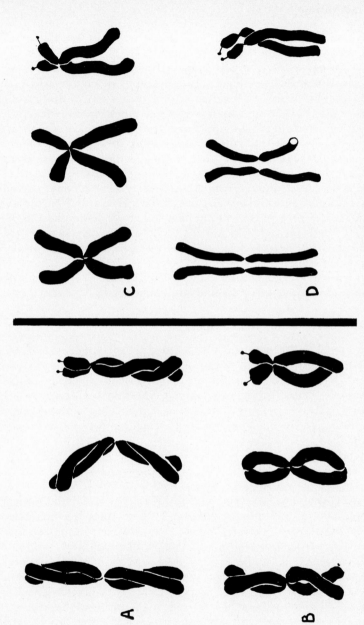

Fig. 2.10—Evolution of c-pairs in **Allium**. **A.** Relational coiling of the cleft chromosomes. **B.** Uncoiling has reduced the number of turns for each segment giving a figure-8 and a forceps type. **C.** Cruciform c-pairs held only at centromere. Arms expanded or spread apart. **D.** A colchicine anaphase marked by the chromosomes lying like "a pair of skis." (After Levan)

It was found that the arrested mitoses lasted from 5 hrs. 26 min. to 14 hrs. 20 min., and later were destroyed.

The spleen of *Siredon* was crammed with arrested mitoses five days after colchicine treatment. If the figures given above are accepted, the correlation of the two sets of data — (1) duration of c-mitoses and (2) the appearance of large numbers five days after treatment — naturally raises some questions that appear important. In *Xenopus,* while cellular degeneration may be rapid, the percentage of metaphases remains very high as long as three days after colchicine. In *Siredon,* it is possible that in the spleen only the intact cells remain visible, the others being washed away by the blood stream, so the results are not as contradictory as they seem at a first glance.

It is thus most probable, from what is known about the pharmacology of colchicine (cf. Chapter 7), that in warm-blooded animals, and particularly in mammals, arrested metaphases are destroyed in less than ten hours. This is in agreement with the histological evidence of nuclear degeneration,[29, 61] and must be kept in mind when colchicine is used as a tool for the study of growth.

2.5: Processes Leading to Interphase

Chromosomal formation is not stopped by colchicine. Under certain conditions the process is slowed down or the delay is so pronounced that there is an appearance of its formation being stopped. For example, many prophase-metaphase types are essentially arrested prophases. Also we pointed out how colchicine might stop chromosomal formation during prophase and turn the process back to interphase.[93, 39]

There are three ways in which chromosomes change to interphasic dispersal under the influence of colchicine — exclusive of recovery, which we will discuss in a subsequent section. They are: (1) the just-mentioned prophase reversal to interphase;[39, 93] (2) the changes from any of the arrested metaphases,[1, 22, 34] i.e., prophase-metaphase, ball metaphase, exploded metaphase, star and distorted star metaphases; and (3) a full c-mitosis through c-anaphase and c-telophase transformations.[56, 65]

Basically, the physical change that takes place in the chromosome does not differ much in either of the three routes taken. Therefore a general description of this process shall include the changes[22] common to plants and animals. Moreover, the process is not very different from a regular telophasic transformation found in a normal nuclear mitosis.[93] In all probability the unraveling, loss of chromaticity, and general physical changes are very similar.[7] Colchicine does not prevent the return of chromosomes to interphase and similarly it does not prevent chromosomal formation.[7] But colchicine does one thing important at this stage; it desynchronizes the separation of the chromosomes.[34, 56, 76, 46, 23] Or we may say the coordinated processes of anaphasic separation of all chromosomes at one particular moment are very badly upset.

Colchicine does not inhibit the uncoiling or the stage of *katachromasis*,[93] the return to interphase. The drug in certain concentration does slow down the uncoiling process in *Tradescantia* since it takes 60 minutes for uncoiling with 0.05 per cent colchicine and 77 minutes in 0.1 per cent contrasted with 35 minutes among untreated cells. There is one other relation of interest: The ratio of time for chromosomal formation, *anachromasis*, to chromosome uncoiling, *katachromasis*, is about 2:1 in regular mitosis. Colchicine-treated mitoses maintain this 2:1 ratio, i.e., 121:60 in colchicine and 97:35 for untreated cells. The significance of these corresponding figures is not understood.

The loss of chromatin, despiralization, and vesiculating stages[34] in the presence of colchicine are much the same as in normal plant cells. A solid chromosome becomes perforated, and two twisted coils appear. The chromosome is reduced to a zigzag thread. There is a fusion of chromosomes that lie close by and the final stages appear as a reticulated network with nucleoli[3] and a membrane surrounding the chromatin. Whether the change begins (1) from prophase, or (2) from arrested metaphase, or (3) through c-anaphase, the general despiralization, sometimes called unraveling, dechromatization, or katachromasis, is similar (cf. Chapter 3).[34, 56, 93, 65, 7]

A full c-mitosis implies that the c-pairs of chromosomes "fall apart" like "pairs of skis"[73, 72] in the cytoplasm (cf. Chapter 3; Fig. 2.10). *Allium* root tips (Fig. 2.10D), particularly, demonstrate this stage except when stickiness holds them together. Thus the c-anaphase can be observed without question.[56, 65, 1, 79] Such separation is evidence that the restitution nucleus shall carry the tetraploid number of centromeres.

Desynchronization is most easily observed if the chromosomes can be compared at a given moment. For example, Figure 3.7 shows a c-anaphase pair at the bottom, whereas above, c-pairs are clearly in X's and held together.[7] This has been shown over and over, from plants and animals, at arrested metaphase.[56, 88, 65] Within one set, single chromosomes, and others in c-pairs, have been noticed to revert[22] to interphase.

C-anaphase is more distinct in some plants, but the distinction is by no means valid for differentiating animals from plants.[87, 85, 3, 2, 1, 79, 56] Tetraploid restitution nuclei have been observed for many kinds of animal cells treated with colchicine.

Tetraploid numbers would also develop in animals if colchicine hit a cell in regular anaphase, because the two groups of chromosomes intermingle, fuse, and form a restitution nucleus.[39] This was demonstrated in grasshopper neuroblastic cells. This is basic to the development of triploid animals by treating egg cells at second maturation anaphase.[68]

Pycnotic changes are very common when chromosomes revert to the interphase. This is especially so in mammals where destruction is the fate of most arrested metaphases.[29, 33, 61] Toxic or strong concentration induces pycnosis. What structural changes occur are difficult to determine. Such changes are discussed under the section of chromosomal alteration.[29, 33]

2.6: Alterations of Chromosome Structure

The most frequent change of the chromosomes in arrested animal mitoses is an abnormal thickness and shortness.[79] This is especially evident in arrested and exploded metaphases of mammalian cells. The shortening may be the consequence of an excessive coiling. Very often these chromosomes degenerate, losing all visible structure; only irregular clumps of basophilic material remain scattered in the cytoplasm, and these in turn fall to pieces.[33] Agglutination and fusion are also quite frequent (Fig. 2.8B, 2.8C).[29, 61, 12, 13, 24, 15] These have been observed in cells where the colchicine action was incomplete and where the spindle was apparent,[15] a fact suggesting that the alkaloid modifies the chromosomes themselves.

In mammals, the colchicine-mitoses with short and clumped chromosomes are more frequent when the dose of alkaloid is high.[61] Animals injected with colchicine show mitotic abnormalities that vary from cell to cell. As an example, the tubules of the kidney contain cells with exploded metaphases and shortened chromosomes, while the cells of the renal pelvis show ball metaphases.[32] Short chromosomes are seen in cells of regenerating liver[12] when treated with colchicine according to specific schedules of time and concentration. Similar shortening also appears following bile duct ligature,[28] and in carbon tetrachloride poisoning.[18] Such changes were also observed in cells of human tissues poisoned with colchicine.[33] The junior author had the unique experience of following the successive changes in cells of the human body in a clinical case. This occurred when an individual suffering from an overdose of colchicine was brought to the hospital in which the junior author was a staff member. These effects are described in detail in Chapter 7.

There is no clear evidence that their structure is damaged. In mammalian cells, pycnotic, ball, or star metaphases may often proceed to normal telophase, although many degenerate, the whole cell being then rapidly destroyed.[61] There is no clear indication that the chromosomes are the first to be involved in the cellular death. Their eventual disintegration is probably a consequence of cytoplasmic or metabolic changes. A better understanding of these would be of great physiological interest, for it appears that among the warm-blooded species of vertebrates the chromosomes are unable to remain for more than a few hours in a cell with arrested mitosis. Quantitative data on this problem have been given in a preceding paragraph; it would be necessary to know what the biochemical changes are which lead to the destruction of the nuclear structures, and in what way this is related to the prolongation of metaphase.

Breakages such as transverse division of chromosomes in plants have been reported.[51] A number of other observations have been made along this line, but no tests have been performed to demonstrate that colchicine increases their frequency. Broken chromosomes and fragments are observed in untreated cells.

2.6–1: The destruction of chromosomes in Tubifex. Colchicine is regarded as a destructive mitotic poison, leading to degenerative changes of the nucleus in *Tubifex*,[53, 54, 55] as opposed to the inhibitive mitotic poisons which prevent cell division mainly by disturbing the spindle mechanism. *Tubifex* is very favorable for the study of early development and cytoplasmic division, but the "numerous and very small chromosomes are unfavorable for cytological analysis,"[95] so this may explain the great discrepancies between these findings and those of workers using different cells.

When the egg of *Tubifex* is treated by colchicine during its first cleavage, the spindle gradually fades away as it does in other objects. Then the chromosomes become progressively pycnotic and lose all visible structure. In the second cleavage, or after longer colchicine treatments, a total disappearance of the chromosomes was observed. [53, 54, 55, 95] The cells became empty; no more nuclear material could be stained by any method. More than seventy per cent of the eggs, twelve hours after colchicine, had such empty cells. But a few hours later, new nuclear structure appeared. First were seen protoplasmic condensations which did not stain with the Feulgen reaction. Then scattered Feulgen-positive masses appeared in the cytoplasm (Fig. 2.11). They seemed structureless but bore some resemblance to the small nuclei which are found in the control eggs. It is suggested that some synthesis of thymonucleic acid takes place in the cytoplasm.

The accompanying Figure 2.11 shows pseudonuclei in *Tubifex*. Among *Amphibia* after colchicine, podophylline, and benzanthracenequinone, evidence has been presented of a "multiplication of nuclear material without mitosis."[54]

One may, nevertheless, conclude that in animal cells other than *Tubifex*, chromosomes disintegrate only when extensive degenerative changes alter the whole cell. Contrary to plant cells, which may undergo subsequently several colchicine-mitoses, animal cells either remain arrested at prophase-metaphase or metaphase, or recover from the action of the drug and, exceptionally, become polyploid. This is true whether in protozoa, invertebrates, amphibians, or mammals; tissue cultures show that colchicine is no more a chromatin poison in animals than in plants. Nor does it appear to affect other nuclear

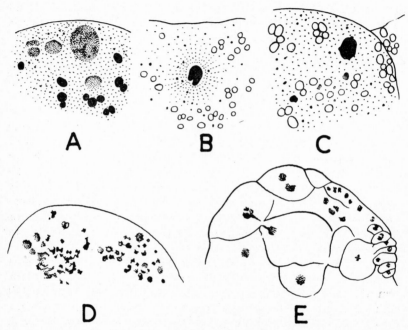

Fig. 2.11—Action of colchicine on the nuclei of developing eggs of **Tubifex**. **A.** After 44 hours, no nucleus is visible. Several cytoplasmic condensations (stippled) are notice-able. Yolk platelets are black. **B, C.** Formation of "pseudonuclei" (black). These are Feulgen-positive, apparently unstructured masses. **D.** Numerous pseudonuclei in an egg treated for 70 hours with colchicine. **E.** Control egg at the same stage as **D.** Note that colchicine has suppressed the cleavage clearly visible in **E.** (After Woker)

structures; there is no mention of any nucleolar changes apart from their possible multiplication in relation to polyploidy. Changes in the nuclear sap will be discussed later.

2.6–2: Colchicine and X-ray combined. Neoplastic tissues have been subjected to X-ray and colchicine,[59] but small attention was given to the relation between c-mitosis and the pretreatments that influence the effect of X-ray in normal cells (cf. Chapter 10).

Allium root tips pretreated with 0.05 per cent colchicine and then subjected to irradiation showed one-third as many chromatid aberra-tions among colchicinized root tip cells as the controls.[14]

The mutation process[23] was measured by pretreating barley seed twenty-four hours before irradiation. A series of solutions (0.1, 0.05, 0.01, 0.005, 0.001 per cent) of colchicine were used just prior to treatment with 5000, 10,000, 15,000 r units, respectively.[43] A treatment with colchicine prior to irradiation causes a decrease in the viridis mutants, but an increase in the rare and very rare mutations. There was no significant change in the albinos.[23]

It was concluded that the mutation process is considerably altered by the application of colchicine to the seedlings previous to irradiations according to the schedules given above.[43]

2.7: Reiteration of the C-mitosis

Cells of *Allium* with sixteen chromosomes as the diploid number accumulate chromosomes in hundreds, even more than a thousand per cell. These large numbers are striking. Obviously more than one doubling has taken place. If we plot the progression, it becomes clear how such high numbers accumulate. If the number of basic sets in a somatic cell is 2, then the chromosome number is $2 \times$ the haploid number per set, i.e., $2 \times 8 = 16$ for *Allium*. When one c-mitosis has been completed, the doubling produces 32, or four sets of 8 each. The second c-mitosis doubling 32, creates a cell with 64 chromosomes, or 8 sets of 8 chromosomes per set. We may let n equal the number of c-mitoses completed. Then $2^{(n+1)}$ represents the number of basic sets. Multiply these factors by the number of chromosomes per set. If cell A has completed 6 c-mitoses, then $n = 6$ and the number of sets of chromosomes becomes $2^{(6+1)}$ or 2^7, or $128 \times 8 = 1024$ chromosomes after 6 c-mitoses. Therefore, the c-mitotic cycles occur in a definite order.[56]

The number of chromosomes that may be packed into one cell is an interesting question. When the total exceeds 500 per cell, recovery of the bipolar mitosis does not occur.[56] Divisions of 64 may recover regularly, but numbers over 100 often show twisted spindles among recovering cells. The high numbers are found most generally in the embryonic vascular cells, notably the area where lateral root initials develop.[57, 65]

Short exposures of seven minutes to one hour permit one c-mitosis while more cycles follow in the longer exposure, i.e., 24- and 72-hour treatments.[56] A tetraploid cell begins the second c-mitosis after 30 hours and an octaploid c-mitosis at 72 hours.[46]

There is a correlation between the number of c-mitoses per cell and the region of the root.[56, 65, 40, 57] If an *Allium* root is divided into five or six regions and chromosome numbers tabulated, the greater percentage of cells with increased numbers occurs in the older parts of the root while cells very near the tip retain diploid numbers.

A distribution study for seven root tips showed that the regions away from the tip contained largest number of polyploid cells.

Reiteration of the c-mitosis in animals is limited by other factors, such as toxicity to cells exposed over a long time. Also the balance may be upset by increase in chromosomes per cell, so that only cells with tetraploidy or octoploidy may survive. High numbers per cell in animals have not been found as a consequence of c-mitosis.

2.7–1: Recovery in plants. One remarkable feature about colchicine is the ability of cells once stepped up to higher chromosome numbers, to recover and thereafter produce new cells with the increased number.[56, 65, 40] In other words, tetraploid cells induced by colchicine, if removed to water, will resume nuclear mitosis with the new increased numbers.

A second notable point in the recovery process is the change taking place when cells with high chromosome numbers begin the renewal of the regular mitosis. If one hundred or more chromosomes have aggregated in one cell and colchicine is removed, soon the chromosomes gather into small groups giving the effect of many star metaphases. Each of these groups may be the focal point around which a new cell is formed (Fig. 2.6). By a process of multipolar divisions the large numbers in a cell become reduced to smaller numbers.[66]

The length of treatment at a given concentration determines the speed of recovery based upon the types of metaphase chromosome formations observed. A one-hour treatment of *Spinacia* in 0.25 per cent shows complete recovery in 48 hours. A five-hour treatment at 0.25 per cent requires 63 hours for recovery.[7]

2.7–2: Recovery in animals. Interphase from star metaphase without an anaphasic movement took place in corneal epithelial cells as these tissues recovered from a strong dosage under a short exposure period.[79] Multiple stars appeared after five and six days from the time of the last application of colchicine.

Siredon cells show another phenomenon reported many times in other material, the swelling of chromosomes and cytoplasm. The immobile chromosomes seem to swell while in a scattered arrangement.[84] This is similar to reversal of prophase; later the chromosomes fuse into an interphasic nucleus (Fig. 2.9). Similar reconstructions during recovery are to be found in regenerating liver cells of the rat (Fig. 2.12).[13] A progressive fusion of micronuclei reduces the number until trinucleate and binucleate cells develop. Tissue cultures show comparatively the same micronuclear development.[15, 90]

Partial c-mitoses and multiple stars are common during recovery as observed in neuroblasts.[79] The multiple stars are evidence that recovery processes are underway.

2.7–3: *Consequences of c-mitoses: polyploidy in plants.* The artificial induction of polyploidy by colchicine was not a new discovery in plant science. Doubling of chromosomes was demonstrated in plant cells as early as 1904.[82] During a long and successful teaching career, Professor C. F. Hottes, University of Illinois, repeatedly outlined cytophysiological methods for inducing polyploidy in root tip

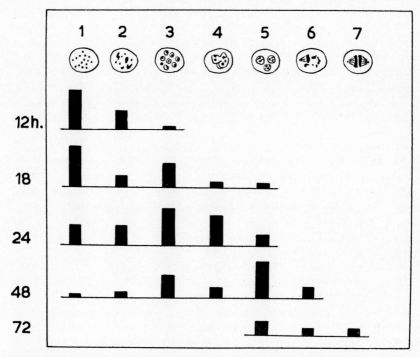

Fig. 2.12—Regenerating liver of the rat, after a single injection of colchicine. Schematic drawings of the various types of restitution nuclei: (1) exploded metaphase with scattered chromosomes, (2) fusion of some of these chromosomes, (3) micronuclei, (4) fusion of the micronuclei (compare with Fig. 2.4), (5) three nuclei, (6) abnormal mitosis with partially inactive spindle, (7) normal mitosis. The percentages of these types of cellular changes at various intervals after colchicine are expressed by the black rectangles. Normal mitoses are only found 72 hours after the injection, and restitution appears to proceed by the fusion of the micronuclei. (After Brues and Jackson)

cells. Specific polyploid plants were induced by regeneration techniques with mosses in 1908 by the Marchals. Later, polyploids were created among the flowering plants by Winkler in 1916 and similar work was continued by Wettstein, Jorgensen, Lindstrom and Koos, and Greenleaf from 1924 to 1934. An early suggestion for inducing polyploidy by temperature change was made by John Belling in 1925.[6] The temperature shock technique was later standardized successfully for maize in 1932,[82] after which time other laboratories followed Randolph's general method. This is a brief history of polyploidy through artificial means before the colchicine era began. That important period made work with colchicine more fruitful than it otherwise would have been. Sudden attention to colchicine almost blotted out the facts that polyploidy induced by several techniques had been well developed before 1937.

The vast literature[35] dealing with polyploidy in plants is discussed in subsequent chapters.

2.7–4: Polyploidy in animals. Polyploidy in animals has also received attention for a long time but success with artificial induction has been limited. The introduction of colchicine did not achieve the success found among many projects with plants.

Temperature shock-cold treatments with newly fertilized eggs of *Triturus viridescens*[38] were more successful than the application of colchicine to these animals. The procedures with colchicine were not efficient, at least when compared with treatment of plants; much was to be desired for work with animals.

Newly fertilized eggs of rabbits were treated with weak solutions of colchicine.[81] Other animals, frogs,[44, 50] *Triturus,*[79] *Triton,*[1] *Xenopus,*[63] *Artemia,*[3] silkworm,[48] *Habrobracon,*[49] *Drosophila,*[42, 10] chickens,[47] *Amoeba,*[20] were tested with colchicine for polyploidy. Generally colchicine has failed in comparison with the induction of polyploidy in plants.[38]

One remarkable series of experiments demonstrated in *Amoeba sphaeronucleus* how polyploid unicellulars could be created by colchicine.[20] This had no effect unless injected into the cytoplasm at metaphase, with a micropipette. Actual counting of chromosomes was not possible but there resulted larger cells with a larger nucleus. These, however, at each division built one normal and one abnormal nucleus, a fact suggesting triploidy. Supposedly polyploid nuclei were transplanted into enucleated fragments of normal amoebae and vice versa. It was observed that the size of the unicellular was directly related to the size of nucleus. The opposite was also true, and a normal nucleus grafted in a "polyploid" cytoplasm was observed to swell considerably. Cytoplasm and nucleus underwent several divisions and then recovered their normal volume of the original species. If the normal nucleus was grafted into a fragment of a polyploid cell, growth was resumed normally. These experiments have been illustrated by a remarkable series of cinemicrographic documents. They have provided new insight on nuclear-cytoplasmic relationship and the possibility of observing colchicine effects in cells, the membranes of which are impermeable to the drug.

A different attack was tried by taking advantage of the fact that colchicine coming in contact with egg cells in the second maturation division would arrest the anaphase stage thereby creating a diploid egg cell. If this cell united with a haploid sperm, it could give rise to a triploid individual.[19] The reasoning was logical enough and colchicine could be introduced at the proper moment through the admittance of sperm and colchicine by artificial insemination methods. Whether sufficient dosage of drug was given shrouds these tests with doubt.

Experiments with frogs in 1947[44] encouraged the trial of introducing colchicine at the time of fertilization, since larvae from eggs treated at fertilization seemed to be polyploid judging from the size of cells and nucleus. The idea was extended to other animals, notably rabbits and pigs.[45, 68] Certain principles were substantiated by these tests, viz., that the application of colchicine at the precise moment of fertilization would bring triploidy in the zygote, because a doubled egg cell would unite with a haploid sperm.

Techniques were developed to inseminate artificially rabbits and pigs,[45] by adding colchicine to sperm material. Proper concentrations were determined by laboratory tests. Suspected triploid offspring were studied cytologically and a conclusion was reached that egg cells were doubled by this procedure. One rabbit that deviated from diploids showed 66 chromosomes among certain mitotic cells of testicles.[68] There were other diploid cells in this test with 44 chromosomes. Thus the individual may have started as a triploid zygote with reduction as development proceeded. These results were, however, by no means conclusive. Previous accounts as well as these above have been criticized and not without some basis.

Similar experiments were done with pigs.[44, 45] Among 31 offspring from artificial inseminations, one differed from the rest as well as from diploid pigs. This male animal showed consistent mitotic figures with 47 chromosomes,[68] a good triploid, that originated when a diploid egg of 32 chromosomes and a haploid sperm carrying 15 chromosomes united. These techniques are new and merit further attention for theoretical studies of polyploidy among animals.[45]

REFERENCES

1. BARBER, H., AND CALLAN, H. The effects of cold and colchicine on mitosis in the newt. Proc. Roy. Soc. London. B 131:258–71. 1943.
2. BARIGOZZI, C. L'azione della colchicina sulla morfologia e sulla struttura dei cromosomie, studiata nelle cellule somatiche di *Artemia salina* Leach. Chromosoma. 2:293–307. 1942.
3. ————, AND FANTONI, L. L'azione della colchicina sul Nauplius di *Artemia salina* Leach. Monit. Zool. Ital. 53:69–74. 1942.

4. BEAMS, H., AND EVANS, T. Some effects of colchicine upon the first cleavage in *Arbacia punctulata*. Biol. Bull. 79:188–98. 1940.

5. ————, AND KING, R. An experimental study on mitosis in the somatic cells of wheat. Biol. Bull. 75:189–207. 1938.

6. BELLING, J. Production of triploid and tetraploid plants. Jour. Hered. 16:463–66. 1925.

7. BERGER, C., AND WITKUS, R. A cytological study of c-mitosis in the polysomatic plant *Spinacia oleracea*, with comparative observation on *Allium cepa*. Torrey Bot. Club Bull. 70:457–67. 1943.

8. BERGNER, A. Colchicine derivatives. III. Effect on mitotic activity of mouse spermatogonia. Cancer. 3:134–41. 1950.

9. BHADURI, P. A study of the effects of different forms of colchicine on the roots of *Vicia faba* L. Jour. Roy. Micr. Soc. III. 59:245–76. 1939. Improved smear methods for rapid double staining. Jour. Roy. Micr. Soc. 60:3–7. 1940.

10. BRAUNGART, D., AND OTT, G. A cytological study of the effect of colchicine on *Drosophila melanogaster*. Jour. Hered. 33:163–65. 1942.

11. BRUES, A. (*see* Ref. No. 4, Chap. 1. 1936). The mechanisms of cell division. Ann. N. Y. Acad. Sci. 51:1406–8. 1951.

12. ————, AND COHEN, A. Effects of colchicine and related substances on cell division. Biochem. Jour. 30:1363–68. 1936.

13. ————, AND JACKSON, E. Nuclear abnormalities resulting from inhibition of mitosis by colchicine and other substances. Amer. Jour. Cancer. 30:504–11. 1937.

14. BRUMFIELD, R. Effect of colchicine pretreatment on the frequency of chromosomal aberrations induced by X-radiation. Proc. Nat. Acad. Sci. 29:190–93. 1943.

15. BUCHER, O. Zur Kenntnis der Mitose. VI. Der Einfluss von Colchicin und Trypaflavin auf den Wachstumsrhythmus und auf die Zellteilung in Fibrocytenkulturen. Z. Zellforsch. 29:283–322. 1939. Hemmt oder fördert Colchicin die Zellteilung? (Nach Untersuchungen an in vitro gezuchten Kaninchen-Fibrocyten). Rev. Suisse Zool. 52:535–50. 1945. Zur Analyse von kerngrossen Frequenzkurven. Experientia. 8:201–4. 1952.

16. BUREAU, V., AND VILTER, V. Action de la colchicine étudiée sur les cellules epithéliales de l'Axolotl. C. R. Soc. Biol. Paris. 132:553–58. 1939.

17. BURRELL, P. Root tip smear method for difficult material. Stain Tech. 14:147–49. 1939.

18. CAVALLERO, C. Les glandes endocrines au cours de la grossesse. Étude cytophysiologique faite à l'aide de la réaction colchicinique (stathmocinétique) de Dustin. Arch. Int. Méd. Exp. 14:125–35. 1939.

19. CHANG, M. Artificial production of monstrosities in the rabbit. Nature. 154:150. 1944.

20. COMANDON, J., AND DEFONBRUNE, P. Action de la colchicine sur *Amoeba sphaeronucleus*. C. R. Soc. Biol. Paris. 136:410–11; 423; 460–61; 746–47; 747–48. 1942.

21. COOK, J., AND LOUDON, J. (*see* Ref. No. 9, Chap. 1. 1951).

22. D'AMATO, F. The effect of colchicine and ethylene glycol on sticky chromosomes in *Allium cepa*. Hereditas. 34:83–103. 1948a. Cytological consequences of decapitation in onion roots. Experientia. 4:388–90. 1948b. Preprophase inhibition of mitosis in root meristems. Caryologia. Pisa. 1:109–21. 1949.

23. ————, AND GUSTAFFSON, A. Studies on the experimental control of the mutation process. Hereditas. 34:181–92. 1948.

24. DELCOURT, R. Contribution à l'étude des réactions cellulaires provoquées par la colchicine. Le choc caryoclasique chez les amphibiens. Arch. Int. Méd. Exp. 13:499–515: 719–83. 1938.

25. DERMEN, H. A cytological analysis of polyploidy induced by colchicine and by extremes of temperature. Jour. Hered. 29:210–29. 1938. (*see* Ref. No. 10, Chap. 1. 1940).

26. DEYSSON, G. Phénylurethane and colchicine. C. R. Acad. Sci. Paris. 220:367–69. 1942. Colchicine, ether, chloroform. C. R. Acad. Sci. Paris. 219:289–91. 1944. Sur l'effet tropocinétisant des agents mitoclasiques. Bull. Soc. Bot. France. 95:205–11. 1948a. Contribution à l'étude du syndromes mitoclasique. Paris: Centre de Documentation Universitaire. France. 1948b.

27. DRAGOIU, J., AND CRISAN, C. Contributions à l'étude de l'action de la colchicine sur les racines des végétaux *Allium cepa* et *Phaseolus vulgaris*. Bull. Acad. Méd. Roumaine. 4:326–38. 1939.
28. DROCHMANS, P. Personal communications.
29. DUSTIN, A. (*see* Ref. No. 12, Chap. 1. 1934). L'action de la colchicine sur les tumeurs malignes. Leeuwenhoek Vereeniging. 4th Conf. 1935. La colchicine, réactif de l'imminence caryocinétique. Arch. Portugaises Sci. Biol. 5:38–44. 1936. Nouvelles applications des poisons caryoclasiques à la pathologie expérimentale, à l'endocrinologie et à la cancérologie. Le Sang. 12:677–97. 1938. L'action des arsenicaux et de la colchicine sur la mitose. La stathmocinèse. C. R. Assoc. des Anat. 33:204–12. 1938. A propos des applications des poisons caryoclasiques à l'étude des problémes de pathologie experimentale, de cancérologie et d'endocrinologie. Arch. Exp. Zellforsch. 22:395–406. 1939.
30. ————, AND GRÉGOIRE, C. (*see* Ref. No. 13, Chap. 1. 1937).
31. ————, HAVAS, L., AND LITS, F. (*see* Ref. No. 14, Chap. 1. 1937).
32. ————, AND ZYLBERZAC, S. Étude de l'hypertrophie compensatrice du rein par la réaction stathmocinétique. Note préliminaire. Bull. Acad. Roy. Méd. Belg. VIe Sér. 4:315–20. 1939.
33. DUSTIN, P., JR. L'activité du Laboratorie d'Anatomie Pathologique de la Faculté de Médecine de l'Université Libre de Bruxelles, sous la direction du Professeur Albert-Pierre Dustin, de 1929 à 1939. Arch. Med. Belg. 1:157–67. 1946. Some new aspects of mitotic poisoning. Nature. 159:794–97. 1947.
34. EIGSTI, O. (*see* Ref. No. 15, Chap. 1. 1938). Methods for growing pollen tubes for physiological and cytological studies. Proc. Okla. Acad. Sci. 20:45–47. 1940a. The effects of colchicine upon the division of the generative cell in *Polygonatum*, *Tradescantia*, and *Lilium*. Amer. Jour. Bot. 27:512–24. 1940b. A cytological investigation of *Polygonatum* using the colchicine pollen tube technique. Amer. Jour. Bot. 29:626–36. 1942a. A comparative study of the effects of sulfanilamide and colchicine upon mitosis of the generative cell in the pollen tube of *Tradescantia occidentalis* (Britton) Smyth. Genetics. 27:141–42. 1942b. Chromosomal cycle delay by colchicine treatment. Amer. Jour. Bot. 36:796. 1949.
35. ————, AND DUSTIN, P., JR. (*see* Ref. No. 16, Chap. 1. 1947, 1949).
36. ————, ————, AND GAY-WINN, N. (*see* Ref. No. 17, Chap. 1. 1949).
37. ————, AND TENNEY, B. Colchicine – a report on experiments. Univ. Okla. Press, Norman, Okla., 40 pp. 1942.
38. FANKHAUSER, G. The effects of changes in chromosome number on amphibian development. Quart. Rev. Biol. 20:20–78. 1945.
39. GAULDEN, M., AND CARLSON, J. Cytological effects of colchicine on the grasshopper neuroblast *in vitro*, with special reference to the origin of the spindle. Exp. Cell Res. 2:416–33. 1951.
40. GAVAUDAN, P. Essai d'explication du mécanisme de rotation de l'axe de caryocinèse et du plan de cytodiérèse dans la cellule végétale soumise à l'action des substances modificatrices de la caryocinèse. C. R. Soc. Biol. Paris. 136:419–20. 1942. Pharmacodynamie de l'inhibition de la caryocinèse. A. Marchand. Librairie le Francois, Paris, P. 337. 1947.
41. ————, GAVAUDAN, N., AND POMRIASKINSKI-KOBOZIEFF, N. (*see* Ref. No. 20, Chap. 1. 1937).
42. GELEI, G., AND CSIK, L. A colchicin hatasa a *Drosophila melanogaster*. Magyar Biol. Inst. Muukai. 11:50–63. 1939.
43. GUSTAFSSON, A., AND NYBOM, N. Colchicine, X-rays and the mutation process. Hereditas. 35:280–84. 1949.
44. HÄGGQVIST, G. Polyploidy in frogs, induced by colchicine. Proc. Kon. Nederl. Akad. Wetensch. 51:3–12. 1948. Über polyploide Saugetiere. Verhdl. Anat. Gesellsch. 48 Versamml. Kiel. Pp. 39–42. 1951.
45. ————, AND BANE, A. Studies on triploid rabbits produced by colchicine. Hereditas. 36:329–34. 1950a. Chemical induction of polyploid breeds of mammals. Kungl. Svenska Vetenskapakad. Handl. IV. Ser. 1:1–11. 1950b. Kolchizininduzierte Heteroploidie beim Schwein. Kungl. Svenska Vetenskapakad. Handl. 3:1–14. 1951.

46. HAWKES, J. Some effects of the drug colchicine on cell division. Jour. Genet. 44:11–22. 1942.
47. HIGBEE, E. Effects of colchicine experiments on chicken. Anat. Rec. 84:483. 1942.
48. HIROBE, T. Polyploid silkworm induced by colchicine treatment upon eggs. Jap. Jour. Genet. 15:69–74. 1939.
49. INOBA, F. Impaternate females of the parasitic wasp, *Habrobracon,* produced by colchicine treatment. Proc. Imp. Acad. Tokyo. 16:11–13. 1940.
50. JAHN, U. Induktion verschiedener Polyploidiegrade bei *Rana temporaria* mit Hilfe von Kolchizin und Sulfanilamid. Mikr.-anat. Forsch. 58:S. 37–99. 1952.
51. KARPECHENKO, G. On the transverse division of chromosomes as a result of colchicine treatment. C. R. Dokl. Acad. Sci. URSS. 29:404–6. 1940.
52. KRYTHE, J., AND WELLENSIECK, S. On the influence of colchicine upon the anthers of *Carthamus tinctorius* L. Proc. Ned. Akad. Wetensch. Amsterdam. 45:283–87. 1942.
53. LEHMAN, F. Über die entwicklungphysiologische Wirkung des Colchicins. Arch. Julius Klaus-Stift. 21:304–7. 1946.
54. ———, AND ANDRES, G. Chemisch induzierte Kernabnormalitäten. Rev. Suisse Zool. 55:280–85. 1948.
55. ———, AND HADORN, H. Vergleichende Wirkungsanalyse von zwei antimitotischen Stoffen, Colchicin und Benzochinon, am *Tubifex*-Ei. Helv. Physiol. et Pharm. Acta. 4:11–42. 1946.
56. LEVAN, A. (*see* Ref. No. 26, Chap. 1. 1938). The effect of acenaphthene and colchicine on mitosis of *Allium* and *Colchicum.* Hereditas. 26:262–76. 1940. The macroscopic colchicine effect — a hormonic action? Hereditas. 28:244–45. 1942. Notes on the cytology of *Dipcadi* and *Bellevallia.* Hereditas. 30:219–24. 1944. The influence on chromosomes and mitosis of chemicals, as studied by the *Allium* test. Hereditas. Suppl. Vol. Pp. 325–37. 1949. Colchicine-induced c-mitosis in two mouse ascites tumours. Hereditas. 40:1–64. 1954.
57. ———, AND LOTFY, T. Naphthalene acetic acid in the *Allium* test. Hereditas. 35:337–74. 1949.
58. ———, AND ÖSTERGREN, G. The mechanism of c-mitotic action. Observations on the naphthalene series. Hereditas. 29:381–443. 1943.
59. LEVINE, M. Colchicine and X-rays in the treatment of plant and animal overgrowths. Bot. Rev. 11:145–80. 1945.
60. ———, AND GELBER, S. The metaphase stage in colchicinized onion root-tips. Torrey Bot. Club Bull. 70:175–81. 1943.
61. LITS, F. (*see* Ref. No. 27, Chap. 1. 1934). Recherches sur les réactions et lésions cellulaires provoquées par la colchicine. Arch. Int. Méd. Exp. 11:811–901. 1936.
62. LUDFORD, R. (*see* Ref. No. 28, Chap. 1. 1936).
63. LÜSCHER, M. Die Entstehung polyploider Zellen durch Colchicinbehandlung im Schwanz der *Xenopus*-Larve. Arch. Julius Klaus-Stift. 21:303–5. 1946a. Die Hemmung der Regeneration durch Colchicin beim Schwanz der *Xenopus*-Larve und ihre entwicklungsphysiologische Wirkungsanalyse. Helv. Physiol. et Pharm. Acta. 4:465–94. 1946b. Hemmt oder fördert Colchicin die Zellteilung in regenerierenden Schwanz der *Xenopus*-Larve. Rev. Suisse Zool. 53:481–86. 1946c.
64. LYSENKO, T. The situation in biological science: Verbatim report of the proceedings of the Lenin Academy of Agricultural Sciences of the U.S.S.R. Foreign Languages Publishing House, Moscow. P. 631. 1949.
65. MANGENOT, G. Action de la colchicine sur les racines d'*Allium cepa.* Hermann and Cie., Paris. 120 pp. 1942.
66. MARTIN, G. Action de la colchicine sur les tissus de topinambour cultivé in vitro. Rev. Cytol. et Cytophysiol. Vég. 8:1–34. 1945.
67. MASCRE, M., AND DEYSSON, G. Les poisons mitotiques. Biol. Méd. 40:1–54. 1951.
68. MELANDER, Y. Chromosome behavior of a triploid adult rabbit. Hereditas. 36:335–41. 1950. Polyploidy after colchicine treatment in pigs. Hereditas. 37:288. 1951.
69. MEYER, J. Colchicine-Feulgen leaf smears. Stain Tech. 18:53–56. 1943.

70. MÖLLENDORFF, W. v. Zur Kenntniss der Mitose. VIII. Zur Analyse des pathologischen Wachstums hervorgerufen durch Chloralhydrat, Geschlechtshormone und cancerogene Kohlenwasserstoffe. Zellforsch. 29:5, 706–9. 1939.

71. MOL, W. DE, AND WESTENDORFF, W. Morphologische und cytologische Abweichungen bei *Bellevallia* usw. durch Colchicin, sowie der theoretische und praktische Wert der Colchicin-Behandlung im Vergleich zu dem Werte anderer Mittel. Cellule. 48:261–76. 1940.

72. NEBEL, B. Cytological observations on colchicine. Collecting Net. 12:130–31. 1937.

73. ———, AND RUTTLE, M. (*see* Ref. No. 32, Chap. 1. 1938).

74. NICHOLS, C. Spontaneous chromosome aberrations in *Allium*. Genetics. 26:89–100. 1941.

75. NYBOM, N., AND KNUTSSON, B. Investigations on c-mitosis in *Allium cepa*. Hereditas. 33:220–34. 1947.

76. O'MARA, J. Observations on the immediate effects of colchicine. Jour. Hered. 30:35–37. 1939.

77. ÖSTERGREN, G. Elastic chromosome repulsions. Hereditas. 29:444–50. 1943. Colchicine mitosis, chromosome contraction, narcosis and protein chain folding. Hereditas. 30:429–67. 1944.

78. PERNICE, B. Sulla cariocinesi delle cellule epiteliali e dell' endotelio dei vasi della mucosa dello stomaco e dell' intestino, nello studio della gastroenterite sperimentale (nell' avvelenamento per colchico). Sicilia Med. 1:265–79. 1889.

79. PETERS, J. A cytological study of mitosis in the cornea of *Triturus viridescens* during recovery after colchicine treatment. Jour. Exp. Zool. 103:33–56. 1946.

80. PIETTRE, L. Modifications obtenues par l'action directe de la colchicine sur des inflorescences de Crucifères et des fruits de Papavéracées. C. R. Acad. Sci. Paris. 211:803–5. 1940.

81. PINCUS, G., AND WADDINGTON, C. The effects of mitosis-inhibiting treatments on normally fertilized precleavage rabbit eggs. The comparative behavior of mammalian eggs *in vivo* and *in vitro*. Jour. Hered. 30:514–18. 1939.

82. RANDOLPH, L. An evaluation of induced polyploidy as a method of breeding crop plants. Amer. Nat. 75:347–63. 1941.

83. REESE, G. Beiträge zur Wirkung des Colchicins bei der Samenbehandlung. Planta. 38:324–76. 1950.

84. RIES, E. Die Bedeutung spezifischer Mitosegifte für allgemeinere biologische Probleme. Naturwiss. 27:505–15. 1939.

85. SAX, K., AND SWANSON, C. Differential sensitivity of cells to X-rays. Amer. Jour. Bot. 28:52–59. 1941.

86. SHIMAMURA, T. Cytological studies of polyploidy induced by colchicine. Cytologia. 9:486–94. 1939. Studies on the effect of centrifugal force upon nuclear division. Cytologia. 10:186–216. 1940.

87. SOKOLOW, I. Einfluss des Colchicins auf die Spermatogenialmitosen bei den Orthopteren. C. R. Dokl. Acad. Sci. URSS. 24:298–300. 1939.

88. STEINEGGAR, E., AND LEVAN, A. (*see* Ref. No. 42, Chap. 1. 1947, 1948).

89. SUITA, N. Studies on the male gametophyte in angiosperms. V. Colchicine treatment as a proof of the essential function of the spindle mechanism in karyokinesis in the pollen tube. Jap. Jour. Genet. 15:91–95. 1939.

90. TENNANT, R., AND LIEBOW, A. Actions of colchicine and ethylcarbylamine on tissue cultures. Yale Jour. Biol. and Med. 13:39–49. 1940.

91. VAARAMA, A. Morphological and cytological studies on colchicine-induced *Ribes nigrum*. Acta Agralia Fennica. 67:55–92. 1947. Spindle abnormalities and variation in chromosome number in *Ribes nigrum*. Hereditas. 35:136–62. 1949.

92. VILTER, V. Inhibition colchicinique de la mitose chez les Mammifères. C. R. Soc. Biol. Paris. 138:605–6. 1944.

93. WADA, B. Lebendbeobachtungen über die Einwirkung des Colchicins auf die Mitose, insbesondere über die Frage der Spindelfigur. Cytologia. 11:93–116. 1940. Eine neue Methode zur Lebendbeobachtung der Mitose bei den *Tradescantia*-Haarzellen. Cytologia. 13:139–45. 1943. Further studies on the effect of colchicine upon the mitosis of the stamen-hair in *Tradescantia*. Cytologia.

15:88–95. 1949. The mechanism of mitosis based on studies of the submicroscopic structure and of the living state of the *Tradescantia* cell. Cytologia. 16:1–26. 1950.

94. WILSON, G., AND CHENG, K. Segregation and reduction in somatic tissues. Jour. Hered. 40:3–6. 1949.

95. WOKER, H. Phasenspezifische Wirkung des Colchicins auf die ersten Furchungsteilungen von *Tubifex*. Rev. Suisse Zool. 50:237–43. 1943. Die Wirkung des Colchicins auf Furchungsmitosen und Entwicklungsleistungen des *Tubifex*-Eies. Rev. Suisse Zool. 51:109–71. 1944.

CHAPTER 3

Spindle and Cytoplasm

3.1: Colchicine and Spindle Fibers

More metaphases than anaphases or telophases collect in tissues treated with colchicine, creating an impression that chromosomes appear stranded between the two poles. Obviously colchicine blocks the mechanism that regularly moves them to the respective poles (Fig. 3.1*A,B*). Interference seems to be localized at the spindle fiber; consequently, arrested metaphases pile up in greater numbers per given area than do the other mitotic stages.[28, 58, 1]

A disproportion of metaphases was pictured by Pernice in 1889. His illustrations[35, 34] show many arrested metaphases with very few anaphases; the contact between the drug and intestinal cells of the dog blocked mitosis (Fig. 1.4).

If the spindle fiber is the substrate where colchicine acts — and there are many data to support this assumption — then cytological and biochemical methods should show us more clearly what reactions occur. The basic cause for a mitotic arrest undoubtedly is to be found in the chemistry and physiology of the spindle fiber and attending mechanisms.[31]

Provisionally, let us say that colchicine alters rather than totally destroys the spindle substance. Such assumptions are consistent with cytological tests. It is known that arrested metaphases fail to show the usual spindle fibers as linear structures; therefore, conversion of a fibriform element into a corpuscular one becomes a tempting suggestion, with attractive possibilities for explaining, at one level, how the spindle fiber and colchicine interact.[73, 38, 47, 95, 72, 37]

Molecules of colchicine reacting with a molecular system of spindle substrate have been considered as one of the basic relationships between the two substances[55, 38, 39, 57, 73] Such an explanation can be given on a quantitative basis. The destruction or inhibition of the fiber then appears to be a quantitative reaction, because the concentration of colchicine is a critical factor.

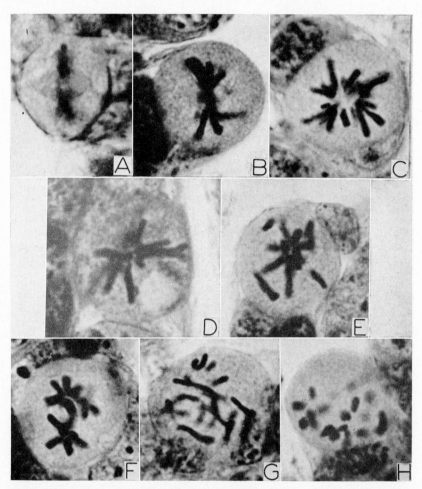

Fig. 3.1—Photomicrographs from embryo of grasshopper, sectioned 13 microns, stained with iron hematoxylin. **A.** Untreated cell at metaphase, spindle fibers differentiated. **B.** Cell treated, 25×10^{-6} M, 30-minute exposure; spindle fibers reduced by treatment but chromosomes not dispersed. **C.** Concentration of, 2.5×10^{-6} M, 90 minutes; star metaphase with some spindle activity. **D.** Clear spherical area, which is not stained, is the hyaline globule, that increases when spindle substance disappears as a result of treatment with colchicine. **E.** Chromosomes outside the star, 120 minutes, with 2.5×10^{-6} M concentration. **F.** Multiple stars, three in one cell, 2.5×10^{-6} M, 180 minutes. **G.** Exploded c-metaphase derived from prometaphase treatment, 2.5×10^{-6} M, 15 minutes. **H.** Chromosomes shortened after 180 minutes, 2.5×10^{-6} M, settle to bottom of cell. (Photographs provided through courtesy of Drs. M. Gaulden and J. Carlson. Adapted from **Experimental Cell Research** 2:416–33, 1951.)

Wide ranges of concentration induce a wide variety of reactions. These range from extremely minute changes involving the spindle orientation, the *tropokinesis*,[38] to the full c-mitosis, *stathmokinesis*, obtained by strong doses.[28, 38, 73, 25] These two reactions represent the extremes, between which there can occur many intermediate changes.

Before proceeding further, we should recall the old argument about spindle fiber reality as opposed to "artefact." If we are dealing with a specific molecular problem, the possibility that spindle fibers are artefacts would seriously influence our proposition. Perhaps the whole concept would be annulled. But excellent results, obtained from treated and untreated cells and from living and fixed materials, have opened up new approaches. Hence, the argument that spindle fibers are not real is almost extinct. An entirely new series of studies with phase contrast microscopes, polarization microscopes, cinematography, and other techniques has shown that fixed and stained fibers are similar to the living functional linear structures.[47] Colchicine has been employed most effectively in these studies.

A high specificity can be demonstrated between colchicine and spindle fibers.[15, 59, 9, 88, 54] Moreover, this specificity can be quickly destroyed if the chemical structure of the drug is changed only slightly. Pharmacobiologists have known for a long time that certain derivatives such as colchiceine are less active pharmacologically than colchicine. Numerous chemical derivatives of colchicine are accurately known by chemists and these have become available to biologists.[80] For example, isocolchicine is a transformed molecule of colchicine, that involves a shift in the position of keto and methoxyl groups on ring C. By this change the specificity between spindle fiber and colchicine is reduced.[88] Isocolchicine is one hundred times less active in producing a c-mitosis than colchicine.

The specificity between colchicine and spindle appears to be on the order of the enzyme and substrate specificity.

Admittedly, the spindle fiber mechanism is complex, highly organized, and delicately coordinated. But much is understood of this mechanism in animals and plants. Cytologists agree that two sets of fibers are formed at each regular mitosis: the continuous and the chromosomal.

The reaction between colchicine and the several components of the spindle appears, then, to have a quantitative basis. Some portions of the spindle can be inactivated leaving other portions activated. Such fractionating possibilities have been demonstrated,[55] and this fact merits attention.

3.2: Spindle Inhibition

Every mitotic cycle builds anew the spindle fibers. Cytoplasmic separation, a function of cytokinesis, is closely coordinated with the fiber and spindle functions.[94] Colchicine prevents the formation of a spindle at prophase, precludes a nuclear mitosis, delays chromosomal separation, inhibits daughter nuclei, and effectively blocks cleavage processes.

Among plants, the inhibition starts at the polar cap stage when polarity makes an appearance.[95] The first sign that colchicine acts upon a spindle is noticed at the polar cap stage.[95] Among animals, the preliminary spindle inhibition is an interference with the development of the astral rays, and functioning of the centriole outside the nucleus.[5] The initial inhibiting influence is seen at the time nuclear membranes are about to disappear and the centrioles begin their movement.

The prophase orientation of chromosomes in animal cells may or may not be destroyed by colchicine. Likewise, plant cells, e.g. in *Dipcadi,* have a prophase orientation that is determined from the previous telophase. These arrangements are not disturbed by colchicine. Thus, colchicine may inhibit the spindle without changing a basic chromosomal arrangement at prophase,[55] although strong solutions may interfere with the orientation before membranes disappear.

The bipolar mitosis is effectively prevented by colchicine acting at late prophase, and progressive changes from interphase into prophase are not inhibited by colchicine.

Undoubtedly there is an action upon resting cells if strong concentrations are used.[67, 68] Nuclear poisoning,[12] intranuclear precipitates,[44] chromatin condensation,[13] pycnotic destruction,[28, 31, 24] and nuclear degeneration[60] before mitotic arrest, are possible actions of colchicine. Deeply stained inclusions in cells of Amphibia were observed after strong treatments.[66] In most cases concentrations above the threshold for c-mitosis induce the changes. Neuroblastic cells of grasshopper, usually very responsive at prophase, metaphase, and anaphase, require a tremendous concentration ($1000 \times 10^{-6}\ M$) at interphase or late telophase.[37]

The mitotic stage at which colchicine is most effective in lowest concentration, is late prophase. There is no doubt that colchicine interferes with transformations of karyolymph, because the regular linear arrangements of fibers do not develop. These structures normally are formed 20 minutes after disappearance of the nuclear membrane; but in the presence of colchicine, fibers do not form. Instead, there is formed a hyaline globule in grasshopper neuroblastic cells, which is nonfibrous.

Similarly for *Tradescantia,* fibers do not develop at prophase with concentrations of 0.05 per cent or 0.1 per cent colchicine.[95] There are other cases, but these two are enough to prove that the first stage of spindle inhibition sets in at prophase.

Full strength solutions applied at prophase cause total inhibition; no vestige of the mitotic spindle can be observed. Partial inactivations are only found at the threshold levels.[73] The continuous fibers and astral rays rather than chromosomal fibers are then the ones inhibited during a partial inactivation. That is, enough colchicine is present to inhibit the exterior spindle, but the interior spindle develops. Such partial inactivation leads to a star metaphase.

Spindle material may be converted into such bodies as hyaline globules,[37] (Fig. 3.1*D*), the lakelike substance in *Arbacia*[5] (Fig. 3.5), achromatic sphere of *Allium*[29, 7] (Fig. 3.6), or the deformed atractoplasm among *Tradescantia.*[95] All these structures are closely associated to karyolymph; consequently, the inhibiting process of a normal spindle fiber is in reality transformation to another form of substrate.

Electron microscopic analysis of colchicine-treated polar cap stages in *Allium* indicated a "solubilization" and "fragmentation" of fibrous strands. These changes are interpreted as spindle fiber transformations. Submicroscopic interpretations are difficult, but the evidence is consistent with other microscopic data.[82]

A primary effect of colchicine is the inhibiton of a mitotic spindle.[7] Secondary effects stemming from this action are colchicine pairs, chromosomal changes, desynchronization of mitotic processes, delayed separation of chromosomes, and restitution nuclei instead of daughter nuclei.[7]

Originally the term *colchicine-mitosis* designated an "effect of colchicine on the course of mitosis" that is entirely specific.[55] Additionally, in a colchicine-mitosis the spindle apparatus is totally inactivated, and this causes completion of a "chromosome mitosis without nuclear or cellular mitosis." [55]

3.3: Destruction of the Spindle Fibers

That colchicine inhibits the spindle at late prophase is well established. Less familiar are the facts about colchicine when applied to a mitotic spindle that has developed as far as anaphase (Fig. 3.2*s–v*).

To establish these facts, special techniques had to be developed. Individual cells must be observed at the critical stage, anaphase, and the chemical must be applied at a precise moment when the mitosis has reached a certain stage. Fortunately, several excellent methods for plants and animals[47, 5, 95, 64, 37] have been developed, and we may now learn what happens when the drug is added to a cell after a spindle has formed.

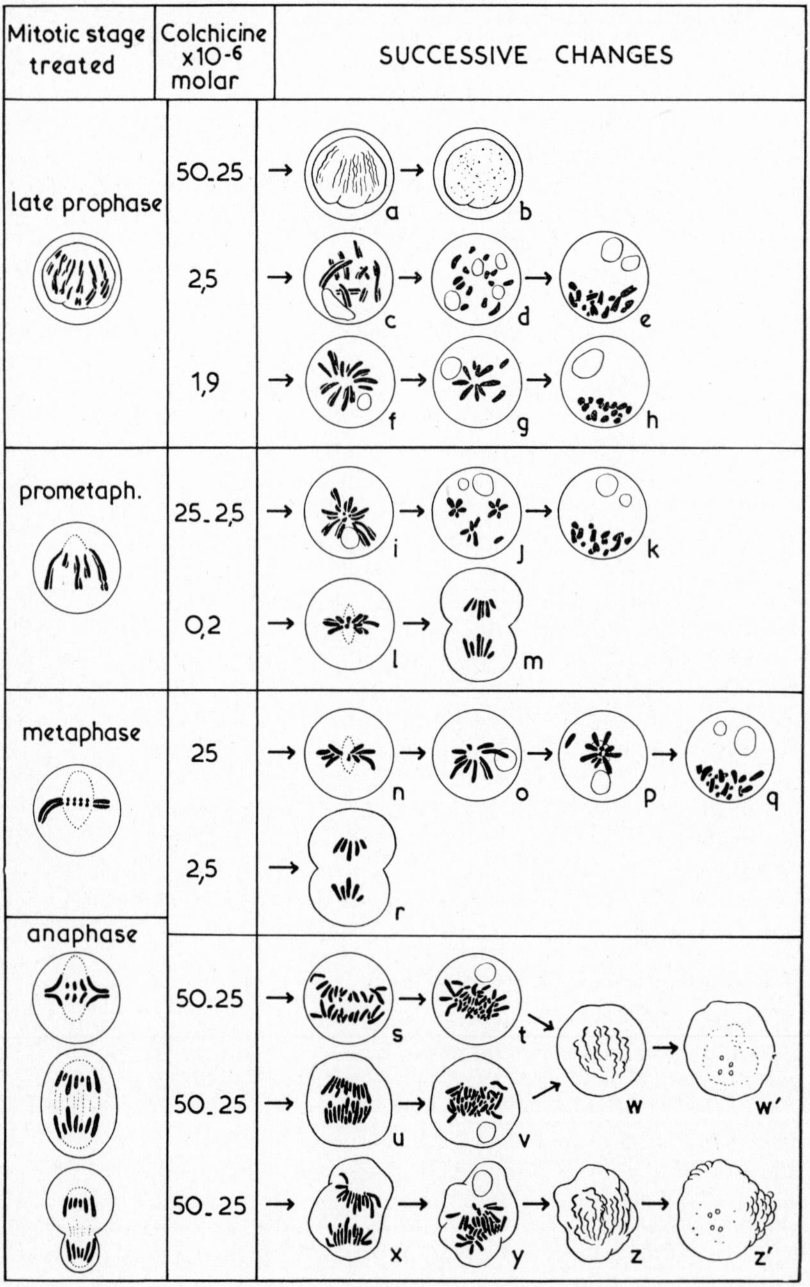

Mitotic stage treated
Colchicine x10-6 molar
SUCCESSIVE CHANGES
late prophase
50.25
2,5
1,9
a
b
c
d
e
f
g
h
prometaph.
25.2,5
0,2
i
j
k
l
m
metaphase
25
2,5
n
o
p
q
r
anaphase
50.25
50.25
50.25
s
t
w
w′
u
v
x
y
z
z′

The spindle fibers at anaphase can be destroyed by the proper concentration of colchicine. Thus, in addition to an inhibitive action upon a spindle at the start of the mitotic cycle, the spindle fibers can be reduced after they have been formed (Fig. 3.1A–G). The destructive action at anaphase follows a regular order, and there is a quantitative as well as a qualitative basis for the change.

3.3—1: Neuroblast cells of grasshopper. The technique developed by Professor J. Carlson, University of Tennessee, and used effectively in cooperative research with Dr. M. E. Gaulden, Oak Ridge Laboratories, Tennessee, has given a new insight to the relationship between colchicine and spindle fibers. Continuous observations upon living cells, together with the application of the chemical at a specific stage and in variable concentrations, have been a valuable addition. In fact, the answer to our question about anaphase and colchicine demands this kind of special method for watching an action upon the fiber (Figs. 3.1 and 3.2).

Cells at early, middle, and late anaphase were chosen. Strong concentrations (50 and 25 $\times$ 10^{-6} M) were used, and in each instance the spindle was "impaired almost immediately"[37] (Fig. 3.2t). The chromosomes stopped in their movement to the poles; the two groups intermingled, fused, and formed into a single telophasic nucleus (Fig. 3.2s–w'). This restitution nucleus was tetraploid, since the anaphasic separation of centromeres had taken place before the drug was applied. Four nucleoli appeared instead of two, and the "uncoiling" processes were only slightly delayed by colchicine (Fig. 3.2w'). Spindle fibers were destroyed at anaphase.

When the concentration was reduced to 2.5 $\times$ 10^{-6} M for the same stage, an anaphase, no detectable results were observed. The chromosomes continued to move to the respective poles. Yet this same concentration invoked a definite reaction at an earlier mitotic stage, i.e., late prophase or pro-metaphase (Fig. 3.2c).[37]

Fig 3.2—Mitotic stage when treatment began, shown in right column. Concentrations are expressed in molarity. Successive stages are lettered a to z'. a and b: prophase reversions occurring 10 to 20 minutes after treatment with this strong concentration. Chromatin resembles early prophase. c to e: chromosomes lie at random, no spindle formed, exploded c-metaphases, chromosomes continue to shorten, then clump together in groups at bottom of cell, hyaline globules formed in d rise to top of cell. f to h: the evolution of a star metaphase. i to k: star metaphase that becomes increased to multiple star and lost chromosomes. l to m: weak solutions do not fully inhibit spindle but reduce the size. n to q: the metaphasic spindle is reduced, hyaline globules form in o, chromosomes settle to bottom and globules rise in cell. r cell divides when concentration is too weak to destroy spindle completely. Compare figure r and c, that received same concentration, but applied at different stages. Anaphase spindles are reduced if concentration is 25×10^{-6} M or more. Chromosomes fuse and intermingle in t and v, hyaline globule forms in stages t, v, and y. Four nucleoli in w' and z' indicate a tetraploid restitution nucleus. These stages show the interaction of concentration, stage of mitosis, and length of exposure. (Diagrams adapted from M. Gaulden and J. Carlson, **Experimental Cell Research** 2:416–33, 1951)

A fully formed metaphasic spindle was reduced by weaker concentrations than those necessary for anaphase. Specific concentrations applied to the fully formed metaphasic spindle led directly to a star metaphase (cf. Chapter 2). These stars formed by treated metaphases persisted for five or six hours. During this time the Brownian movement shown by the mitochondria was actively increasing. While the activity of the protoplasmic material was increasing, the metaphasic spindle fibers were being reduced.

With further reduction of concentrations and with application to metaphase, no obvious reduction of the spindle was obtained. This concentration ($2.5 \times 10^{-6} M$) had no effect on anaphase, but produced a slight retardation of the spindle at metaphase. Yet this same concentration applied to earlier stages, the prophase, induced visible and truly inhibitive effects. No visible changes were observed at full metaphase by the concentration $1.9 \times 10^{-6} M$.

Pro-metaphase, an earlier stage than metaphase, responded (Fig. 3.2i–k) immediately to a strength ($2.5 \times 10^{-6} M$) that was without detectable action at anaphase. The spindle formed at late prophase was immediately reduced, and the chromosomes scattered in the cytoplasm: a typical exploded metaphase. Doses without influence at anaphase and with only slight effectiveness at metaphase were totally effective at pro-metaphase, or late prophase (Fig. 3.2c–e).

Reduction to a concentration of $1.9 \times 10^{-6} M$, effective at metaphase and now applied at prophase, created the star metaphase. Under these conditions, several focal points for the star remained after treatment (Fig. 3.2f,g). Hence, this concentration usually led to the multiple star metaphase (Fig 3.2j). The particular concentration inducing stars was effective only at prophase. Now, compare the difference between an effective concentration at prophase, $.2 \times 10^{-6} M$, with the concentration required to reduce the anaphasic spindle,[37] $25 \times 10^{-6} M$. The difference is significant.

Since, as one approaches interphase from anaphase, correspondingly weaker concentrations are required, it becomes a point of interest to note requirements for detectable results at interphase, or resting stage, or even late telophase. The concentration was raised to $1000 \times 10^{-6} M$ before any changes were noticed, and then the toxic action as well as pycnotic changes were the only results obtained. From all these tests there appears to be a critical point in the mitotic cycle when spindle fibers can be reduced with a minimum concentration.[37] That stage is late prophase and pro-metaphase.

Three important conclusions were reached:[37] (1) Effectiveness in destroying the spindle or interference with its further development depends upon concentration; the greater the concentration, the greater the effectiveness upon the spindle, within certain limits. (2)

A greater concentration is necessary to destroy the more advanced spindle, i.e., at anaphase, than a spindle at an early stage, pro-metaphase. (3) The form of a particular spindle is directly related to the characteristic type of metaphasic pattern that will develop after treatment such as the star, multiple star, ball, exploded, or other arrested metaphase.[37] Configurations depend upon stage at time of treatment, concentration, and duration of treatment or recovery.

After sober reflection upon these conclusions no one can disregard the importance of a specific concentration, the type of cell, and, most interesting of all, the particular mitotic stage at the time the drug enters the cell. Specificity between chemical and spindle fiber is supported by these investigations.

3.3—2: Staminal hair cells of Tradescantia. Techniques with the *Tradescantia* material were used quite as effectively as with the neuroblastic cells just reviewed. The central feature and main advantage lie in the possibility of applying colchicine at a particular stage and following the progressive development of mitosis thereafter. *Tradescantia* staminal hair cells have been a favorite material for mitotic studies *in vivo* for a long time. The first studies to be conducted with colchicine and plant cells were accomplished with the staminal hair cells.[72]

Colchicine applied to a cell when the spindle was well developed stopped further development and reduced the spindle within a short time. A deformed atractoplasm appeared in the cell after destruction of fibers by the chemical. Stronger concentrations were necessary to induce changes if the spindle was very far along in development. As the drug began its action, Brownian movement on the spindle was increased, indicating that the colchicine was acting upon the fibers. This action took place suddenly, as the chemical reached the cell.

Phragmoplasts, which are spindle materials of cytokinesis, were stopped in their further development and also reduced by colchicine. A cell wall partly developed from each side of the cell can be stopped by the drug.

At metaphase, activity upon the spindle is immediate. The c-pairs are formed as the spindle fibers are destroyed. Within 13 minutes, granular changes upon the spindle showed that action had set in. Within 1 hour and 36 minutes, the entire group of chromosomes returned by a precocious reversion to an interphase. Such quick results required strong solutions (2 per cent). Generally, lesser concentrations (0.05 per cent and 0.1 per cent) were used to effect spindle fibers.

Regardless of the stage from prophase to anaphase, even as late as the phragmoplast, an application of colchicine stopped movement, destroyed the spindle, and returned the chromosomes to interphase

by regular uncoiling processes, similar to the regular telophasic transformations. During later stages a "cytoplasmatization" of spindle or
"fluidity" was created.[72] By this process the spindle was transformed.

Metaphasic spindles were destroyed in pollen cells of *Ephedra*.
The concentration was a strong one (2 per cent), and reversion to
interphase was rapid. The total time for a cell to proceed through
a regular mitosis was no different from the time taken for a reversion. A full c-mitosis would have taken a longer time. This rapid
conversion back to interphase led to the conclusion that colchicine
did not delay the mitotic cycle. Preliminary results unpublished by
the authors show that concentration is a most important consideration for *Ephedra* as well as other cells. Reversions can proceed very
rapidly under the action of colchicine.[47]

The data from *Tradescantia* and neuroblasts confirm an opinion
stated earlier that the destructive action is quite as notable for colchicine as its inhibitive activity. The main difference lies with the
concentration. Stronger solutions are required to destroy a fiber at
anaphase than to inhibit its formation during prophase. That is
why a broad range of concentrations is imperative to obtain a full
picture of c-mitosis.

3.3–3: Arbacia punctulata. Colchicine applied to eggs of *Arbacia*
at a specific time after fertilization, showed a disintegrating action upon
the astral ray.[5] They faded out shortly after the drug entered the cell,
and a "lakelike" body appeared at one end of the mitotic figure (Fig.
3.3). The chromosomes were massed in the center of the cell. If the
drug entered the cell when two polar regions had already developed,
then two lakelike bodies were seen, one at each end. Finally, a still
later stage showed the chromosomes in two anaphasic clumps and a
lake area encircled the entire figure.

There is a critical time beyond which the colchicine does not stop
cleavage, but then a fluidity may be developed around each set of
chromosomes even though separate cells were formed.

The disintegration of amphiasters was rapid, and restitution nuclei
were formed after a scattering of chromosomal portions was obtained.
The destruction of the mitotic spindle at metaphase blocked cleavage
effectively. Thus, the spindle components are vitally important to
cleavage. The independence of the spindle action and a rhythm of
viscosity changes of the cortical layers, independent of mitosis, have
been demonstrated. The two processes may go on simultaneously.
These have been shown by methods for observing the changes at the
outer layer of the cytoplasm.[20, 72]

There can be no doubt that spindle fibers already formed can be
destroyed. The specificity between drug and fiber is necessary for such
action. A confirmation from materials representing diverse biological

sources has been effectively concluded. Therefore, colchicine acts either by an inhibition before mitosis or by destruction after spindles have been formed.

3.3–4: The polarization microscope. Submicroscopic structures were followed with an improved polarization microscope adapted for specific biological purposes. The birefringence pattern is clear because

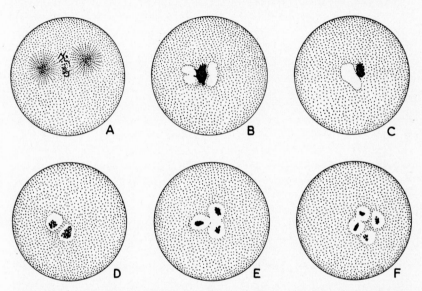

Fig. 3.3—Effects of colchicine upon first cleavage in **Arbacia punctulata**. The area where colchicine causes spindle destruction is a "lakelike" body. Compare **A**, the control, with **B**, a treated metaphase. **A.** Spindle fibers of untreated egg at metaphase. **B.** Colchicine applied when egg was at metaphase, both polar areas laked and chromosomes are clumped. 0.0002 molar concentration of colchicine in sea water applied 10 minutes after fertilization, temperature 22° to 24.4°C. **C.** Prophase when treated causing liquefaction of spindle and asters at one side. **D.** Spindle destroyed, chromosomes separated, but no cleavage furrows. **E.** Three groups of chromosomes. **F.** Four groups of chromosomes with laked areas around each group. (Drawings adapted from photomicrographs by Beams and Evans, 1940)

spindle fibers are optically anisotropic. The fibers, therefore, shine brightly, as compared with a dark grey for the chromosomes.

The disappearance of the spindle was correlated with the disappearance of the birefringence pattern. Therefore, as colchicine acted upon the spindle, a reduction was noticed by a definite fading out of the light pattern. Obviously the fibers changed their form under an attack by the chemical. This general procedure made it possible to perform some critical experiments.[47]

The first maturation division of the egg, the metaphasic spindle of a marine annelid worm, *Chaetopterus pergamentaceus*, was chosen for these experiments.[47] Normal metaphasic patterns are well known for this species at 25°C. Thus it was possible to judge the exact time when a fully formed metaphasic spindle could be expected. Accordingly, at this stage, the spindle fibers shone brightly and chromosomes were less brilliant against the light background of spindle fibers when viewed through this polarization microscope.

An egg cell in metaphase immersed in colchicine-sea water, showed

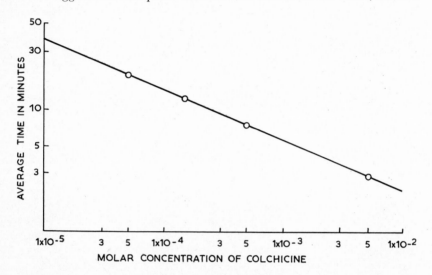

Fig. 3.4—The average time for disappearance of metaphasic spindle of **Chaetopterus** egg, disappearance measured by polarized light pattern. The stronger the concentration, the shorter the time for complete disappearance of spindle. Temperature of sea water 25°C. (Adapted from Inoue, **Experimental Cell Research** Suppl. 2:305–18. 1952)

a steady disappearance of the spindle. This meant that colchicine was destroying an already formed metaphasic spindle. The rate for a disappearance was directly correlated with concentration. In line with previous data, then, the greater the concentration, the more rapid the destruction of the spindle. Figure 3.4 shows these relationships clearly. For example, in one test, the disappearance of spindle occurred in 30 minutes with the concentration 5×10^{-4} M. But an increasing concentration (5×10^{-3} M) reduced the same stage of a spindle within 3 minutes. Moreover, these observations were made by continuous records from living cells and not fixed structures.[47]

By an entirely new technique the destructive action of colchicine was traced from a fully formed metaphase spindle to the complete disappearance. Finally, the quantitative relation between concentration and disappearance supports the proposition that specificity has a quantitative basis.

Several other similar observations were made at the same time spindle disappearance was studied. The continuous fibers are the first to disappear along with the astral rays. These observations confirmed previous work. Accordingly, the last fibers to lose their birefringence were the chromosomal fibers. These data also fit other results. The order in which the component spindles disappear is important to an explanation for the star metaphase. Active chromosomal fibers and suppressed continuous fibers create the star figure.

While stronger solutions cause the most rapid disappearance of the spindle, the shortening of the spindle during its disappearance is not the same for each strength. Rapid destruction showed very little shortening, whereas weak solutions, which require a long time, showed much shortening during destruction. The shortening process carried the chromosomes up to the periphery of a cell. While this reduction in length of spindle occurred, the chromosomes were always maintained at a midway point between two poles. At the same time chromosomes retained their metaphase position on the equator.

Another important detail was noticed just before the final disappearance of the metaphasic spindle. The chromosomal fibers were the last to disappear, and as soon as the last vestige of spindle faded out, the chromosomes scattered. Their position in the equatorial plate evidently was maintained by chromosomal fibers. Thus chromosomal fibers are responsible for equatorial orientation. Chromosomal fibers once destroyed caused a scattering of the chromosomes and a typical exploded metaphase.

Spindle retardation, measured in millimicrons, showed that changes in spindle measured against time, and plotted accordingly, showed a rapid decrease at first then a slowing down of this process (Fig. 3.5). An exponential decay curve was obtained for this activity.

Confirmation of an action of colchicine along similar lines was obtained by a phase contrast microscope in which no spindle fibers were detected 24 hours after treating testis cells of *Melanoplus differentialis* with colchicine.[90] By other methods and with different chemicals, the spindle fibers were studied as bodies that operated during a mitosis. These could be destroyed, or transformed into other structures. The net result was c-mitosis.[46]

Fibers that appeared anisotropically active, linearly differentiated with micellar particles arranged end to end, changed in their structural pattern. Birefringence showed that colchicine destroyed the fibrous arrangement progressively, step by step. First the continuous fibers and asters disappeared, then the chromosomal fibers. These critical tests with a polarization microscope deal a solid blow to the argument that spindle fibers are cytological artefacts. Not only can the spindle fibers be demonstrated by a light pattern but their changes under an influence of colchicine are traceable. Finally a quantitative relation between concentration and rate of spindle reduction has been established (Figs. 3.4 and 3.5).

3.4: Changes in Spindle Form

The *Allium* root tip cells treated by the research group at Brussels showed that a differentially stainable body was formed in the col-

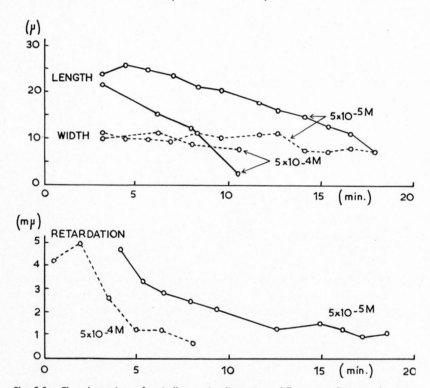

Fig. 3.5 — The shortening of spindle as it disappears differs according to the concentration. The strong solutions cause rapid disappearance and not much shortening of spindle. The width does not change as much as length of spindle. Measurements of retardation in millicrons show rapid retardation at first, then gradual slowing toward the end. Top group shows decrease in length compared to width for two concentrations. Bottom group indicates the sharp drop at the beginning and slower rates of retardation until final disappearance. (After Inoue)

chicinized cells.[29] The chromosomes were clustered about this body (Fig. 3.6). Such structures persist through the interphase and become prominent in the large amoeboid restitution nuclei (Fig. 3.6).

Although the relation to spindle was not suggested until later,[63, 85] the role of the deformed spindle has been mentioned for a number of cases. Specifically, this was called the achromatic sphere and the pseudospindle. Related to this same structure from observations with neuroblasts is the hyaline globule.[37]

These bodies do not show polarity, their staining properties are distinct from cytoplasm, and their relationship to spindle material or karyolymph is a good one. It was believed that the c-pairs regularly

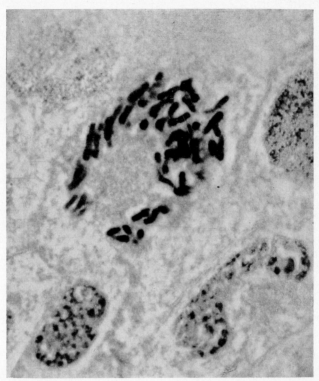

Fig. 3.6—Cell of **Allium** root treated with colchicine showing the spindle substance around which chromosomes are grouped. Another amoeboid nucleus shows the influence cf this substance. (Photomicrograph made from slide of the A. P. Dustin Collection, University of Brussels. An unpublished photo similar to diagrams by Havas, Dustin, and Lits, 1937)

associated around the pseudospindle, and that this structure accounted for the exploded metaphase. Indeed the chromosomes were distributed by this body, and the specific distributed c-mitosis was seemingly related to the pseudospindle, but no further direct associations can be made.[37, 95, 61] Different subjects tend to show different kinds of material. The clear area around chromosomes[17] and the lakelike bodies of *Arbacia* may all be related to these deformed spindle materials.

Some materials, such as *Spinacia*[7] and *Lepidium*,[77] do not show the body. Not all cells of *Allium* develop the achromatic sphere. There may be some progressive relational development, or a specific concentration may be required for producing the achromatic sphere and other similar bodies. That a definite progressive stage is followed was carefully shown by the work with neuroblasts.

Until the final answer is obtained, our present observations have led to the idea that fibriform materials, that is, substrate making the spindle fibers, are converted into a corpuscular form instead of the usual fibrillar arrangements. Colchicine plays a role in directing the spindle fiber substance into these modifications noticed for many cells. The course of development of the spindle to its disappearance in neuroblasts and the progressive enlargement of the hyaline globule as the spindle fibers disappear, point to the fact that a spindle material is converted into another form and this form is shown by the hyaline globule. Such a body has definite optical characters, size relationships, and is, in fact, a structure that must be given serious consideration as a changed form of spindle substrate.

If the globules form at prophase, then karyolymph is suspected to be the original material. When metaphasic and anaphasic stages are studied, the spindles have been developed and quite another view comes into focus. In such cases, colchicine progressively reduces or destroys the spindle, and globules form as spindles disappear. Such globule formation requires a longer time at metaphase or anaphase than at prophase. Again, both concentration and stage of spindle are important factors in converting the spindle into globules[37] (cf. Subsection 2.4–3).

When 25 and 50×10^{-6} M colchicine solutions are applied during anaphase, the spindle disappears and a hyaline globule forms[37] (Fig. 3.1D). The globule occupies a position near one of the poles. The formation of a globule, as the drug acts, leads to a correlation between spindle and globule. Since concentrations determine spindle destruction, the globular formations are likewise dependent upon concentration. These facts are clear.

In agreement with reports on the hyaline globule specifically noted in treated neuroblasts, a similar structure, the achromatic sphere, has characteristics in common with the hyaline globules. Very likely these are similar, just as the spindle fibers of mitoses in cells of plants and animals have certain similar properties. Characteristics of the hyaline globule are: (1) it is spherical; (2) diameters vary from 3 to 15 microns; (3) rate of formation is related to speed of spindle destruction; (4) it is opaque, homogeneous, of high viscosity, not surrounded by membrane, and is optically indistinguishable from karyolymph or spindle; (5) it tends to lodge at top of cell while chromosomes settle to bottom.[37] Finally after all these characteristics are cited, the fact remains that in colchicine-treated neuroblasts, the hyaline globule increases when disorientation of chromosomes and spindle destruction take place. Observations such as these support the idea that, as colchicine acts, spindle structure becomes altered rather than annihilated.

The spindle fiber analyzed by electronic microscopy can be described as compound, measuring from 600 to 800 Å at the polar cap stage.[82] When colchicine is applied to *Allium* root tip cells for 30 minutes, the fibers lose their compactness. After one-hour exposures the fibers are disoriented and fragmented. After 2 hours the fibers appear swollen as well as increasingly fragmented. In the untreated cell, fibers remain as such regardless of the type, whether they be chromosomal fibers, continuous fibers, or fibers of the polar cap stage. With long exposure to dilute solutions or short exposure to stronger concentrations, a decided swelling and a tendency toward "solubilization" of their substance were apparent.[82]

3.5: The Arrested Metaphase and Spindle Mechanisms

Interaction between colchicine and spindle fibers ultimately determines the arrested metaphase. The two types, oriented and unoriented,[2] both depend upon several variables existing during a treatment or during a recovery from the drug. As mentioned before, concentration of colchicine, mitotic stage at time of action, length of exposure, recovery processes, type of cell, and conditions favorable to mitosis, all play an important role in the production of the particular arrested metaphase, whether oriented or unoriented.[37]

A pattern such as the star metaphase (Fig. 3.1C) is far too regular to be regarded wholly as a random occurrence. During a recovery, the star is characteristic, as is also the multiple star (Fig. 3.1F). These types do not reach a peak in a recovery until some time has elapsed between application and the dissipation of drug. A majority of the bipolar mitoses follow the star metaphases, thereby indicating that recovery was nearing completion. The star metaphases are the last colchicine effects to appear during recovery. The *Triton* material that was fixed[2] directly out of colchicine and stained at three hours and at succeeding intervals, shows that stars appear at once and build up much faster than in *Triturus*.[74] When the stars reach a peak in *Triton,* unoriented types, rather than bipolar mitoses, become the most prominent mitotic figures.

Any pattern, whether star or exploded metaphase, should be regarded as a response to colchicine, operating primarily through the spindle fibers. Two basic components are accepted as established for plants and animals; these are (1) continuous fibers and (2) chromosomal fibers (Fig. 3.1). Sometimes these two are called the exterior and interior spindles,[5] or the centrosomic and centromeric spindles.[74]

The birefringence pattern for a metaphasic spindle[47] in *Chaetopterus* egg, disappearance due to the action of colchicine, registers the fading of continuous fibers and astral rays first, while the chromosomal fibers are the last to disappear. Action upon astral rays before the interior portions has been demonstrated with other material.[98] Hence, data on the living cell and on fixed tissue are in accord as to the action upon the several parts of the total spindle.

Acenaphthene is 1000 times slower in action upon a spindle than colchicine.[55] This slower activity permits a better analysis, because the exterior spindle is destroyed before the interior. Colchicine acts so totally and abruptly that this delicate difference is frequently overlooked. Until the threshold concentrations are employed, a partial action showed that colchicine in dilute solution, like acenaphthene, destroyed the exterior spindle before the interior. That is, continuous fibers are first to be affected. This experience is like dissecting an organism into its essential parts.[55]

Certain concentrations of colchicine applied to the metaphasic spindle in neuroblasts cause star formations (Fig. 3.1). The continuous fibers are inactivated, but chromosomal fibers remain intact. The centromeric portions of chromosomes are drawn to one focal point (Fig. 3.1). There, however, is another way to produce a star metaphase in neuroblastic cells. To obtain the correct concentration for prophasic treatment, enough colchicine is used to inhibit the continuous fiber in its development, but such a concentration does not act in the same manner on the chromosomal fiber. These interactions lead to a star metaphase.

Now a final explanation for *Triton*[2] and *Triturus*[74] appears to be at hand. *Triton* cells removed from colchicine show star metaphases at 3 hours, build up to a peak within 12 hours, and are succeeded by unoriented metaphases. Colchicine acts progressively more strongly as the peak is being built. During the action, continuous fibers were destroyed before chromosomal fibers, giving cause for stars in *Triton* cells. Finally, the whole spindle was inactivated when colchicine reached full effect and unoriented types took precedence (cf. Chapter 2). Inspection of data from *Triturus*[74] leads to another observation. The stars appear later, and after the peak is reached, the bipolar mitoses occupy the prominent position among dividing cells. As recovery was taking place, the colchicine was becoming more dilute. At a certain point the continuous fibers were inhibited but not the chromosomal fibers. Then at last, both continuous and chomosomal fibers developed, and bipolar mitosis predominated among the dividing cells. Among cells of *Triton* the stars appear as the effect of colchicine begins. The stars were the "arrivals" in this case. While *Triturus* cells developed, the star showed that the effect of colchicine was "departing."

We may conclude that the star forms when centriole, centromere, and chromosomal fibers interact while continuous fibers are suppressed. A mitotic polar metaphase appears much the same as the star, but the latter has very small, if any, stainable achromatic core. The size differences have been demonstrated in several instances.[74, 8, 37]

Chromosomes occasionally fall outside the star cluster. Lagging chromosomes may be observed in untreated cells. Neuroblasts, treated with very weak solutions of colchicine, consistently show lagging chromosomes. The lost chromosome is confirmation that a partial spindle inactivation takes place when these particular types form.[69]

Multiple stars (Fig. 3.2*j*) are basically the same as the single star, except for several focal centers instead of one. If two or more chromosomes fell outside the first star, a second could form. This type is most common when cells are recovering in *Allium* root tips. Increasing the number of chromosomes shows a corresponding increase in the number of multiple stars. Multiplex stars have been demonstrated in both plants and animals, during recovery as well as during active treatment. *Triturus* showed the bimetaphase and trimetaphase, equivalent to multipolars, five to six days after recovery.[74]

Distorted stars[2] are not proved as easily as the star formation. Two explanations have been given. One, the action is a response of centromeres and a centrosomic center, but the staining procedures did not bear out these assumptions. Two, the hyaline globule which forms when spindle fibers disappear, becomes wedged between the chromosomes, distorting the star.[37] Either explanation may be considered valid until more information is at hand.

Unoriented metaphases, such as ball, clumped, prophase-metaphase, or exploded types, do not show activity on the chromosomes or any part thereof. The term *unoriented* is entirely appropriate[2] for such figures (Fig. 3.1*G*, 3.2*d*).

An exploded or scattered arrangement has been observed in many plants and animals (cf. Chapter 2). If the disappearance of a metaphasic spindle is followed by the birefringence pattern,[47] one may assume some mechanical explanation for the exploded type, for as soon as the spindle disappears completely, the chromosomes seem to scatter as if they were held on the equatorial plate to the very last moment. Disappearance of the continuous fibers did not permit the scattering. Not until chromosomal fibers disappeared did the chromosomes disperse. This confirms that the exploded metaphase originates when both chromosomal and continuous fibers are destroyed. Such observations support the concepts that a full c-mitosis may involve an

exploded metaphase and that complete spindle inactivation is fundamental to the unoriented type or full c-mitosis.

Presence of the pseudospindle[61] or the achromatic sphere[85, 7] (Fig.
3.9) has helped to explain the scattered arrangement in some cases,
notably in *Allium* root tips (Fig. 3.7). C-pairs are closely appressed
around an achromatic sphere. But comparable cells in regenerating
liver exhibit excellent exploded metaphases without a stainable
sphere. Other scattered types are not comparable to the special case
of *Allium*.

The assumption[2] that a single centrosomic spindle operates in
pushing the chromosomes to the periphery of the cell is hardly ten-
able, for staining has not proved the case, nor have the other techniques subtantiated such mechanisms. It would hardly be consistent to
classify as an unoriented type, one that had such a mechanism as a
central spindle pushing the chromosomes to the edge.

Whatever the final answer will be as to their disposition, they
seem profusely scattered, and seem to lie in the cytoplasm as if each
repulsed the other.

The exploded metaphases are a striking type.[14, 16] They would
seem to result from the total inactivation of both the continuous and
the chromosomal fibers.

The ball metaphase is more common than the exploded metaphase; it increases in frequency as the concentration increases. A
toxic or poisoning action is logically the basis of a ball metaphase.
The chromosomes are definitely unoriented and are often massed in
a clump. For that reason the c-mitosis has been called *clumped,* a type
related to the ball metaphase.[33, 77]

Prophase-metaphase formations (Fig. 3.2) are more nearly described by the term *arrested prophase* (cf. Chapter 2), for they represent
leftover prophasic arrangements. With no spindle action, chromosomes remain stranded in a pre-prophasic arrangement.[33] In fact there
is complete inactivation. Prophase orientations are not necessarily
disturbed by colchicine, as noted for *Dipcadi*.[55] Here the chromosomes
are disposed in a pattern determined by the previous telophase. If
the concentration is partially inactivating, a star metaphase results;
total inactivation leads to the prophase-metaphase type.[24, 78] The prophase-metaphase merges into the ball metaphase and clumped metaphase depending on the concentration. There may be return by recovery to a multinucleate cell. The prophase-metaphase and clumped
c-mitosis seem to be more characteristic of meristematic cells of stems
than of roots.[96]

Distributed c-mitoses have attracted much attention because they
were described as a "somatic meiosis" (cf. Chapter 2). These are a
subtype of the exploded metaphase. The main difference between
exploded and distributed metaphase is seen in the disposition of the

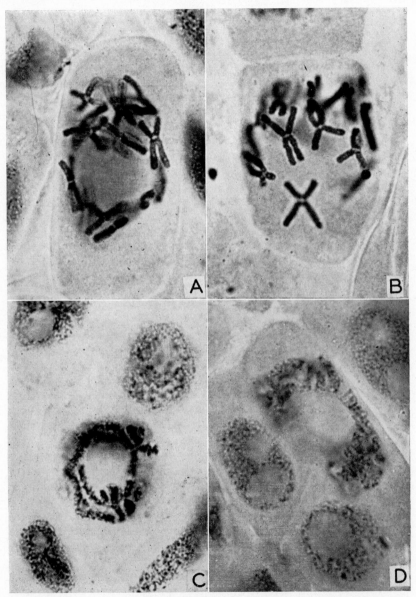

Fig. 3.7—**Allium** root cells treated with colchicine. **A.** Cruciform c-pairs associated around the spindle substance. At bottom of group one pair is completely separated in c-anaphase. The timing of separation is upset as well as delayed. **B.** C-pairs with arms fully repulsed. A light, unstained area surrounds the chromosome. **C.** Chromosome reverting to interphase; dechromatization has occurred. Chromosomal framework associated with the central substance. **D.** An amoeboid restitution nucleus around the pseudospindle or achromatic sphere. The end of at least one c-mitosis. (Photomicrographs furnished by courtesy of Dr. C. A. Berger, Fordham University, N. Y. After Berger and Witkus, 1943)

c-pairs. Polar groupings of c-pairs typify the distributed metaphase, whereas exploded metaphases are nonpolar. Unquestionably, the distributed c-metaphase was clearly illustrated in pollen tubes.[33] The distributions were equal and unequal. They were not conceived as a somatic meiosis. In root tips, naphthalene acetic acid and colchicine increased the number of distributed c-mitoses compared with either chemical alone. Other chemicals increase this type even more than colchicine.

3.6: Spindle Disturbance and Cytological Standards

Spindle disturbances in plants may be classified in three categories:[73] (1) full inactivation, stathmokinesis,[28] (2) partial inactivation, merostathmokinesis,[38] (3) slight disturbance in orientation, tropokinesis.[38, 25] All these types are produced by colchicine, as already pointed out. If one wishes to make comparative studies with other chemicals known to influence mitosis, well-defined cytological standards of judgment are needed to classify reactions as either disturbed or normal. If the reaction is disturbed, it is important to distinguish the type according to velocity or strength of reaction. The most reliable criteria appear to be those based upon tests at telophase, rather than at earlier stages.[73]

Abnormal chromosomal distributions may be caused by spindle disturbances in three degrees: first, multipolar; second, apolar; and third, unipolar. When three or more groups of chromosomes join so as to form discrete groups, partial spindle disturbances are obvious. These were carefully noted under the general type, merostathmokinesis,[38] or under the present classification as multipolars. However, complete destruction or inactivation leaves one single group, or there may be two groups with no evidence of spindle function. This is the apolar distribution. Another specialized disturbance is the close gathering at one focal point described before as the star metaphase; this type becomes unipolar at telophase.[73]

Colchicine (0.005 per cent) applied to *Allium* root tips for 46 hours, increases the percentage of tropokineses. The controls may show as many as 10.5 per cent, but treated root tips raised the frequency to 21.3 per cent. These disturbances are the first-order changes occurring at threshold concentration,[25] and are the first signs of spindle disturbance.

3.7: Cytoplasmic Division

Nuclear mitosis and the completed process of cell division are not synonymous, because the nuclear processes and cytoplasmic processes taken together make up cell division. Truly, karyokinesis (nuclear mitosis) and cytokinesis (cytoplasmic processes) are very highly integrated, and are closely coordinated processes.[6] One cannot always mark the separation between the processes. For this reason and perhaps others, biologists use the term *mitosis* as completely synonymous with cell division, when mitosis is only one aspect of a dividing cell.[46]

When colchicine acts during a division, the significance of what has been noted for mitosis and cell division becomes apparent. The multiplication of chromosomes continues in the presence of the drug at a certain concentration, whereas the total absence of spindle fibers prevents the movement of chromosomes to the respective poles. Inhibition of fibers has one drastic effect on the cytoplasmic phases of cell division: the cytokinetic processes are completely eliminated. Among animal cells the cleavage processes are somewhat specific and respond to colchicine in a unique fashion. These aspects are discussed in the next section. In plants no cell plate is formed, and phragmoplasts are prevented. For organization purposes these are discussed separately from animal cells.

3.7—1: Cleavage processes in animals. Marine eggs have been subjects for studying the mechanism of cell division since the pioneering work of Hertwig, Boveri, and Wilson. The sea urchin, *Arbacia punctulata,* was therefore a logical selection for Nebel and Ruttle[72] when, in 1937, they wanted to analyze more completely the activity of colchicine. They established that $10^{-4}M$ concentrations block cleavage. Even a concentration of 0.0002 M inhibits cytoplasmic division[5] if applied 22 minutes after fertilization at 22° to 24.4°C. At this time eggs are in prophase, metaphase, or early anaphase, and spindle mechanisms are inhibited or destroyed by colchicine (Fig. 3.3).

If nuclear mitosis passes a certain stage, cleavage is not stopped by these concentrations. Therefore, a critical point is reached beyond which destruction of spindle apparently has no effect. These points emphasize a close integration between nuclear mitosis and cytokinesis. [20, 97, 98]

Specific objectives were outlined to determine precisely up to what stage or stages in the mitotic cycle treatment was effective in blocking cleavage and at which stage colchicine was no longer effective. The results showed that suppression of cleavage by colchicine follows a particular course on the basis of fertilized eggs of *Arbacia punctulata.*[5] The eggs were allowed to stand 10 minutes after fertilization; then different lots were placed in colchicine at 2-minute intervals during a 60-minute period. By this test, a lapse of 22 minutes between fertilization (22° to 24.4°C.) and the addition of colchicine was found as the critical period, because cleavages were not blocked after that time (Fig. 3.3). The mitotic stages most generally present at this time were prophase, metaphase, and possibly early anaphase, each of which was affected by colchicine. These stages regularly precede the usual furrowing process by about 10 to 14 minutes. Therefore, after the critical mitotic stage, anaphase was passed, the furrowing process started, and after that point colchicine did not inhibit cleavage of the cell into two parts.

Similar results were obtained from tests[20] using the starfish, *Asterias forbesii;* the sea urchin, *Arbacia punctulata;* sea urchins from Bermuda, *Tripneustes esculentus* and *Lytechinus variegatus;* and the sea slug, *Chromodoris* sp. In all cases, the key for inhibiting cleavage was anaphase. The concentrations varied, but otherwise the general plan was very similar for all tests. Once the eggs passed metaphase, cleavage could not be altered by dosages of colchicine that destroyed the mitotic spindle. If threshold concentrations were used at metaphase, furrowing almost divided the egg, and a regression then set in. This showed that the final closing of cytoplasm is distinctly a process dependent upon the spindle. Cases such as these emphasize the interdependence between karyokinesis and cytokinesis as processes of cell division that involve nucleus and cytoplasm.

Cytological evidence for action by colchicine is obtained from the lakelike bodies appearing where astral rays and spindle fibers normally should be found[5] (Fig. 3.3). One lake body indicates prophase; two, one on either side of a clumped mass of chromosomes, point to action at metaphase; and two clusters of chromosomes can be taken as evidence for disturbed anaphase. All these prevented cleavage.

Furrowing is dependent upon viscosity changes, and once processes begin, apparently colchicine does not stop cleavage. In an effort to correlate such changes with the cleavage process, centrifugal experiments were run, but not all results are in agreement.[7] The additional evidence [97] for viscosity or rigidity relationships and nuclear mitosis as well as cytoplasmic division are discussed under the mechanisms in the last chapter.

A demonstrated fact emerges that cleavage is averted if achromatic figures are destroyed before a certain mitotic stage has been reached. Of course, concentration variabilities are important, but the blocking process appears to be an "all-or-nothing" effect; therefore, either nuclei divide and there follows a cytoplasmic division, or an arrested mitosis precludes daughter cell formation. For example, chromosomes, scattered as a result of colchicine, form micronuclei, and no cytoplasmic division takes place.[5, 16, 14] On the other hand, recovery among a number of star metaphases may eventually lead to the cytoplasmic division, because spindle inactivation is not complete.

Depending upon concentration, cleavages may be retarded or stopped (Fig. 3.3). The germ cell of *Triturus helveticus* L. does not cleave if a 1:500 colchicine solution is used.[83] Regeneration of the spindle may determine the course of cytokinesis. These data have been limited mostly to eggs, where the principles of cytokinesis in relation to the mitotic mechanism are better observed than among other animal cells. Further data on the action of colchicine on eggs are to be found later (cf. Chapter 8).

In those cases where a lowered viscosity is related to mitosis, it is assumed that the gelation-solation phases are influenced.[4] If solation conditions destroy spindles, then lowered viscosity acts accordingly. Spindles are inhibited because colchicine acts upon a mechanism that changes the solation conditions. But viscosity changes may be secondary effects while other mechanisms operate before cytoplasmic changes take place.[97]

Birefringence tests show that the normal variations of the cortical layer of eggs of the sea urchin, *Psammechinus miliaris,* presumably sychronized with spindle and monaster expansion, are entirely independent.[70] The spindle and viscosity changes in the cortical layers may go on simultaneously, yet remain independent. Rhythmical surface changes of eggs of *Tubifex* were not modified by arrest with colchicine. This further substantiates the premise that cytoplasmic processes are not entirely controlled when the mitosis is controlled.

In the neuroblastic cell, lowering of cytoplasmic viscosity was visible through the increased activity of mitochondria.[39] Brownian movements were used to indicate the changes. Chromosomes settled to the lower half of the cell when spindles were completely destroyed. Disappearance of the spindle and a more rapid Brownian movement were correlated. The notable decrease in viscosity was suggested as a consequence of a decrease in the content of ribonucleic acid and phosphorus at the time colchicine acts upon mitosis.[39]

3.7—2: Cell plate formation in plants. The continuous fibers form the spindle of cytokinesis upon which the cell plate forms. Between the spindle and cell wall a phragmoplast completes the fibrous structure and the cell plate across the cell.[6, 95] Since colchicine destroys or prevents continuous fibers, there is no spindle of cytokinesis or phragmoplast.

During recovery and regeneration of the spindle, various abnormalities may be seen, but these processes are characteristic only in relation to recovery and reversible effects of which the cells are capable after colchicine.

By the special techniques for applying colchicine at certain stages, the phragmoplast has been tested specifically with regard to the role of the drug acting upon such structures already formed.[95] If the phragmoplast is in formation, colchicine can reverse the process, changing the fibers back to a fluid stage, a kind of cytoplasmatization. Even rudimentary cell plates and the beginnings of septa from each side are arrested. Under these conditions further development is arrested, and chromosomal bridges extend between the cells.[95]

Direct destructive action upon cell plates was recorded also in wheat root tip cells. Generally, the absence of spindle determines the formation of a restitution nucleus precluding any form of cyto-kinesis as well as daughter nuclei.[33, 55, 89, 61, 62] The interrelation between cytokinesis and mitosis is shown by the effects of colchicine.

By centrifuging root tips treated with colchicine, a much greater displacement of chromosomes against the centrifugal wall was found among treated cells than among the controls. The action of the drug was interpreted as an effective lowering of cytoplasmic viscosity.

Allium root tips treated with colchicine at varying exposures were centrifuged to determine changes in structural viscosity of the achro-matic figure. The decrease in viscosity was indicated. Moreover, there was a low viscosity at eight hours, when c-mitosis was at a peak. After return to normal bipolar mitosis the viscosity showed increases paralleling these recovery processes.

Another view somewhat opposed to that expressed above has been presented. Since the spindle fibers are inhibited and no achromatic figure is present to hold the chromosomes in position, greater dis-placement may take place regardless of viscosity change. The centri-fuge tests merely show that the spindle fibers are lacking. Supporting this view are the observations on cyclosis in *Elodea,* which does not seem to be changed by colchicine.

Additional tests showing changes in viscosity among plant cells are reviewed in Chapter 4.

3.7—3: Cytoplasmic constituents and cell organites. The centro-some, a self-perpetuating body outside the nucleus, becomes involved with spindle destruction. Its activities are depressed along with those of the spindle mechanism. Several centrosomes may accumulate within a cell treated with colchicine, hence the formation of multiple stars. Each star probably represents a centrosomic body. These were carefully demonstrated in *Triturus viridescens.*

A confusion arises from the mitochondrial picture and colchicine. Some say these bodies are affected by the drug;[10] others report no change.[24] The concentrations as well as materials vary widely, but it would seem that some consistent reaction might be obtained. How-ever, until now we can only review the pro and con. Modifications involving fragmentation, dispersion, reduction, as well as minor morphological changes have been seen after colchicine treatments directed to: (1) Flexner-Jobling carcinoma of rat, (2) liver cells of rat,[41, 42] (3) cells of certain orthoptera, *Gyrllus assimilis* and *Melanoplus differentialis.*[26] No mitochondrial modifications are re-ported for neuroblasts in *Chortophaga viridifasiata,*[31] an observation coinciding with a phase contrast observation of *Siredon* erythro-blastic prophase-metaphases made by the junior author (un-published).

Root meristematic mitochondria tended toward constrictions and fragmentations after exposures to colchicine for more than 25 hours (0.005 *M* colchicine) (Fig. 3.9). Shorter exposures, 13 hours, were less effective. The relation between viscosity and mitochondrial shapes was believed valid.[79] The mitochondria were demonstrated in *Allium* (Fig. 3.9) in which cases mitochondria did not penetrate the achromatic sphere (Fig. 3.9) (pseudospindle) about which the c-pairs seemed to collect.[61]

While the Golgi bodies have not received the attention given other cytoplasmic organites,[36] fragmentation and scattering of these bodies were induced in adult mice by 0.1-mg. colchicine injections.[43]

Metabolic aspects of cytoplasm were demonstrated among tissue cultures by differential staining with methylene blue (1:10,000). The arrested mitoses remained colorless while the cytoplasm of resting cells was diffusely stained. Untreated cells in division are also colorless because methylene blue is reduced more rapidly when cells are dividing.[59] This suggests that arrested metaphase reduces methylene blue like a regularly dividing cell. This metabolic activity may provide an explanation for the eventual destruction of arrested mitoses in animal cells[59] (cf. Chapter 2).

"Bleb" formation occurred at cellular surfaces among grasshopper neuroblasts[37] when mitosis was arrested. Also, notable cytoplasmic agitations were seen among fibroblasts treated with colchicine and studied by cinematographic projection.[17] These observations call attention to an unusual activity when cytoplasmic division is pre-vented by colchicine. This agitation has been described by others using treated tissue cultures.[59, 68] Changes at cell surfaces can also be induced by many other substances, such as mustard gas and ultra-violet radiations.[59]

Some observed cases do not indicate direct action by colchicine. The marine eggs of *Psammechinus miliaris* observed for birefringence characteristics indicated that actions in the cortical layers were inde-pendent of mitotic arrest.[70] *Tubifex* eggs provided additional cases for observing the relation between changes in cytoplasmic viscosity and mitotic cycles.[98]

3.8: Reversible Characteristics of the Spindle

Let us summarize what has been detailed from Chapter 2 up to this point. If we compare a colchicine-mitosis (c-mitosis) with a regular mitosis, our first impressions might well be the following: c-mitosis is mitosis without metaphase, anaphase, and telophase;

c-mitosis precludes cytokinesis; c-mitosis leads to a restitution nucleus; c-mitosis prevents daughter nuclear formations; c-mitosis stops the formations of daughter cells from a mother cell. Our summary implies — and similar implications can be found in the literature[64] — that, whereas during c-mitosis the notable stages of a normal mitosis are omitted, whereas a single nucleus is formed instead of two, and whereas one cell begets one cell, the whole c-mitotic process appears to be a quicker and shorter one. Seemingly, the reason for this is that the arrested metaphase is a bypass method ultimately short-circuiting, by the influence of colchicine, true division of a cell. But in reality, these apparent abbreviations that would seem to shorten c-mitosis, require more time than a regular mitosis covering similar chromosomal transformations. For example, one c-mitosis takes 430 minutes compared with 155 minutes for a normal mitosis.[95] Furthermore, during the 155 minutes, chromosomes become involved in metaphase, anaphase, and telophase. During the 155 minutes, two cells each with a nucleus are derived from a mother cell and one nucleus. In other words, a c-mitosis (430 minutes) that gives an impression of a shorter procedure by omissions, actually takes 2.8 times longer than the corresponding control (155 minutes).

These comparative figures are accurate measurements from continuously recorded cases of individual living cells, passing through the entire cycles of c-mitosis and mitosis, respectively. Contrary to these time sequences, *Ephedra* pollen cells showed no difference between treated and untreated cells.[64] However, changes may have influenced these time sequences, so that transformations from prophase to interphase took place without a delayed metaphase.[64]

As pointed out in Chapter 2 and summarily stated above, a time scale comparison between c-mitosis and normal mitosis is like projecting a moving picture in slow motion. Action for 155 minutes is stretched out to 430 minutes. Now, most of this extra time is taken up while the chromosomes appear to lie scattered in the cytoplasm, unoriented because colchicine inactivated the spindle fibers, in contrast to the metaphase-anaphase stages that are oriented and activated by spindle mechanisms. We may refer to this phase as the "intactness period" of the chromosomes. Chromosomes retain an individuality, an intactness, ten times longer under colchicine than do those of the control culture, because, out of 430 minutes, 249 are relegated to an intactness period, against 23 out of the 155 in a control cell. Remembering that such data are taken from living cells continuously observed and recorded, these facts are significant.

After a c-mitosis is accomplished, the restitution nucleus forms a single unit that combines the chromosomes which regularly become distributed equally among two daughter nuclei.[55] Of course, a *"pre-*

cocious reversion" from c-metaphase or earlier arrested stages as well
as a recovery in due course of time, often true for animals[58, 16, 24, 76,
78, 91, 83] but not limited to them, creates a restitution nucleus or
daughter nuclei with diploid numbers of chromosomes (centromeres), because in these cases a c-anaphase does not obtain, under
conditions of *reversion* or recovery, from an arrested stage. However,
doubling of chromosomes can and does take place among animal cells.
[51, 76, 86, 11, 3, 4, 2, 83, 22, 74, 65, 81, 48] Although this process of duplication
is more common to plants treated with colchicine, neither situation
should be regarded as typical for one group or the other. Such gen-
eralizations lead to false conclusions.

Three statements concisely express the primary concepts: (1)
c-mitosis creates a polyploid restitution nucleus via c-metaphase-c-ana-
phase-c-telophase processes; (2) c-mitosis by *precocious reversion* from
c-metaphase, or earlier arrested stage, may with exceptions, lead to a
nonpolyploid restitution nucleus; (3) c-mitosis may after due time recover from the arrested stage and develop regular anaphase, instead
of the c-anaphase, thus leading to diploid daughter nuclei.

Greater than all these remarkable features is the underlying biological principle of reversibility. When the cell, in contact with the
drug for a given time, is removed from the influence of colchicine,
either by actual transfer or by allowing dissipation of chemical during
a recovery period, the characteristics of reversibility come into focus.[55]

Cells treated with optimal dosages that induce a c-mitosis creating the polyploid nucleus, recover so that a normal mitosis may follow with a fully functional bipolar spindle. That is, a restitution
nucleus can regenerate a bipolar spindle after the effects of colchicine are removed.[28]

Regeneration among the restitution cells is permanent, and cells
develop spindle mechanisms in each succeeding division with metaphase, anaphase, telophase, and, of course, the doubled number of
chromosomes. This new divisional process continues thus, as long
as the cell lineage retains power to divide. Polyploidy is thereby maintained and continued without attending cytogenetic changes, except
for those effects related to an increasing number of chromosomes per
cell.[55] No one has demonstrated by careful cytogenetic methods that
colchicine at optimal doses for a c-mitosis leading to polyploidy, also
increases the frequencies of mutations or chromosomal changes.[33, 92]
Caution at this point is advised because mutations and chromosomal
changes may occur independently of colchicine but simultaneously
with a treatment.[33]

The capacity of the cell to recover after a treatment, to regenerate
a bipolar spindle following a c-mitosis, to reverse the inactivating
effects of colchicine upon spindle; these are, in our opinion, the most

striking and significant biological characteristics demonstrated when dividing cells of animals and plants come in contact with optimal doses of colchicine.

3.8—1: Recovery in plants. Allium root tips transferred to pure water after specific exposures to colchicine are excellent materials for tracing recovery of the spindle mechanism. Very slight toxicity, if any, results from an exposure sufficient to inactivate the spindle completely. Usually 12 to 24 hours in water give adequate time for first recovery stages.[55, 75, 38, 61, 74, 21, 25]

The regeneration of spindle runs a characteristic course, probably representative of many plant cells. But most work has been done with *Allium cepa* L. specifically, and with root tips rather than stem tips, generally. By a *characteristic course* is meant the sequence of chromosomal groups from full c-mitosis to partial c-mitosis, then to bipolar spindles. During this course the obvious abnormalities appear in terms of normal mitosis.[33, 40, 55, 27, 75, 38, 61, 45, 7, 21, 56] First, the chromosomes group into what may be called multiple star formations (Figs. 3.6 and 3.8). There is no connection between the various stars of a single cell. The chromosomes may be somewhat clumped together. Shortly thereafter, asymmetrical and loose spindles appear.

Cells with unusually high numbers are followed in the transition to normal mitosis. Extremely large cells with high numbers appeared in tissue cultures of plant cells.[62] The first hint that a cell is on the road to recovery shows in the telophasic stage. Chromosomes are not condensed into one nucleus when first observed. Later each nucleus becomes perforated and filled with canals. Next the grouping of nuclei of a large cell is like a multiple cell,[61] containing as many as twenty stars.[55] Perhaps each star represents a regenerating spindle area. When telophase sets in, fibers running between each group lead to cell wall formation (Fig. 3.9). Thus, the large restitution nucleus containing many chromosomes, becomes divided into as many as 20 small cells.[61, 62]

The obvious reduction to many small units means reduced chromosomal numbers. While this is "somatic reduction," it does not correspond to reduction through meiosis, except in the numerical changes. Certainly no qualitative genetic reduction takes place such as occurs in meiotic processes.[56]

After 36 hours most cells have run their normal course. A diagram correlating length of exposure to time for regeneration and completed recovery, has been constructed.[55] The exposures, covering 7 to 30 minutes, require between 12 to 24 hours for the first spindle regeneration, and 36 hours for regular spindle. An increasing exposure, 2 to 72 hours, retards spindle regeneration to 24 hours, and delays complete recovery to 36 and 48 hours. This means that the longer the exposure, the longer the time for recovery.

Another view is obtained from the 1-hour and 5-hour treatments with *Spinacia* root tips. In these cases metaphases were plotted during recovery. Complete recovery occurred within 48 hours if exposure was 1 hour, but 63 to 66 hours were required for a 5-hour exposure.[7]

Cytological consequences in relation to treatment have been analyzed. The first tetraploid cell begins a second cycle after 30 hours,[45]

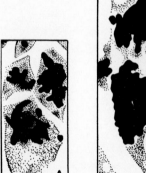

Fig. 3.8—Recovery stages in cells of roots of **Triticum** treated with colchicine. **A.** Multipolar groups of chromosomes, unequal numbers. **B.** Cell with a larger number of chromosomes showing that several cycles of c-mitosis had been accomplished. Upon recovery, cell plates may form between groups. **C.** A large cell cut into several smaller ones, a characteristic recovery pattern. **D.** One cell divided into at least six cells upon recovery from the effects of colchicine. These cells do not survive but are replaced by diploid, tetraploid, or octoploid cells. (Drawings adapted from photomicrographs of Beans and King, 1938. Their Figures, 31, 32, 34, 35)

octoploids at 72 hours,[61] and after 96 hours, 16-ploid cells, or 128 chromosomes, were in division.[61]

If one studies the entire root, some new facts come to our attention that are more meaningful than any absolute ratio between time and number. Euploid numbers, multiples of 8, predominate so that usually the count reads 16, 32, 64, 128, etc. There are very few polyploid cells near the root tip; in fact, after 72 hours diploid cells persist a little farther from the tip. Tetraploid and octoploid cells persist in even larger numbers. At the region farthest from the tip, where lateral root initials are found, giant lobed nuclei were plentiful.[61] These cells were crowded with chromosomes having as high as 1000 c-pairs.[55, 56] In these cases no regeneration of the cell took place. As a rule, the nearer the root tip, the lower the chromosome number. Or in other words, a greater percentage of cells with high numbers is found in older portions of the root.

Just how far this accumulation can continue with hope for reversibility to normal was answered by an elaborate test that required a series extending over a long time. About 500 chromosomes is the upper limit beyond which no recovery can be expected, but 128 and 64 make the most rapid recovery to bipolar spindle.[55]

Lethal or toxic effects have been disregarded, but the drug has a growth-depressing influence if shoot growth is the index. The effects

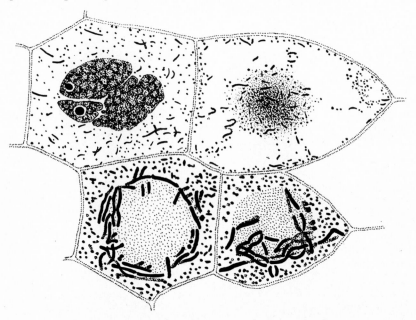

Fig. 3.9—**Allium** root cell treated with 0.05 per cent colchicine 32 hours, then fixed and stained with iron alum haemotoxylin. The lower cells show chromosomes around the pseudospindle. Shortened mitochondria do not penetrate the area of the pseudospindle. Large restitution amoeboid nucleate cell not in c-mitosis. (Adapted from Mangenot, 1942)

of the poison may be expressed in growth differences between treated and control plants. Controls had leaf shoots 34 cm. long on the seventh day; .01 per cent of the treated plants grew to 15 cm. (about one-half), and 0.1 per cent of the plants were reduced one-fourth, to 8 cm.[55]

3.8—2: Recovery in animals. Recovery analyses in animals present difficulties not met in plant cells because animal cells are not able to survive as long.[28, 98, 58] A c-mitotic dose frequently becomes lethal to the animal, an effect that precludes recovery. Another difficulty is the variation in toxicity between animals as well as the differences when dealing with warm-blooded and cold-blooded animals, and/or tissue cultures.[53, 93]

Among the first experiments at Brussels, 24 hours was considered a recovery time in mammals, and at 48 hours [28, 58, 31] normally dividing cells were in abundance. Many cells degenerated before 24 hours. Results with *Siredon* and *Xenopus* have been discussed in Chapter 2.

Generally, 5 to 10 hours represented the duration of arrested mammalian mitoses, while in cold-blooded vertebrates mitoses may remain arrested for several days.

Certain trends are seen not only in the recovery figures with *Triturus viridescens,*[74] but also in the recovery frequencies in corneal tissues.[18, 50] A cornea is treated and then allowed to recover. The maximum arrested metaphases observed at the first fixation (8 hours) are an unoriented type (92 per cent) which means that both continuous and chromosomal fibers are inactivated. Only 5 per cent of the figures are stars and 2 per cent bipolar mitoses. The next fixation shows a drop in unoriented metaphases and an increase in stars, 69 per cent and 20 per cent, respectively. Bipolar mitoses increase to 8 per cent. Finally at 72 hours, only 5 per cent of the figures are unoriented while the stars maintain their numbers up to 16 per cent, and most remarkable is the increase in bipolar mitoses to 80 per cent. The picture at 72 hours is a reversal compared to the 8-hour fixation.

Diploid, tetraploid, and octoploid mitoses definitely show that animal cells can be made to double the number of chromosomes.[74, 24, 2] A few anaphase bridges, fragments, as well as chromosomes were found outside the nucleus.[74] As late as 168 hours, some bimetaphases, or the "distributed" c-mitoses, were found in *Triturus,* also some trimetaphases that present a multipolar picture.[74]

Conclusions drawn from studies of the recovery pattern are that (1) chromosomal fibers recover first — otherwise stars would not be first to rise and fall; (2) the continuous fibers follow the chromosomal in recovery; (3) the interaction between two kinds of spindle fibers and the centromeres determines the metaphasic type to be expected; and (4) animal cells may develop into polyploid cells capable of dividing upon recovery.

The nuclear figures were followed during recovery in rats having received single injections following partial hepatectomy.[16] The regenerating liver offered special advantages for the tracing of these stages; a definite series was noticed.[16]

At 12 hours, there were two changes: (1) the chromosomes thickened and shortened, while (2) a gradual clumping was seen. At 18 hours, the cells were full of miniature nuclei, the micronuclei. Some swelling accompanied the clumping.

Between 18 and 48 hours, some amoeboid patterns emerged. These were obviously a result of fusing micronuclei.[14, 15, 16] Perhaps the related and progressive stages were the binuclear and trinuclear stages.

First signs of partial spindles were seen at 48 hours. This is evidence that recovery or reversibility was taking full effect, so that by 72 hours a complete spindle was reformed.

Reversibility is seen in animal cells, but the recovery is complicated by other effects in addition to arrested mitosis. This is particularly true in mammals, where considerable destruction of arrested metaphases takes place not giving time for the spindle to recover before the chromosomes are irreversibly altered.

3.9: Summary

In this chapter and in the preceding one, selected works were correlated to describe, first, the action upon nuclear mitosis as observed through chromosomal patterns and, second, the spindle mechanisms fundamental to arrest by various techniques. We are aware that little attention was given to the mechanism of action, theoretical aspects, and problems of c-mitosis, all of which are suggested by the data.

The action of colchicine involves the cell as a whole and, for animals, the correlated activity of tissues. Before a discussion of the problems can be made most effectively, other aspects must be viewed. Therefore the mechanisms of action as well as the very important problem of mitotic poisons are grouped together in Chapter 17. Here it is hoped that some of the important issues raised by the action of colchicine on plant and animal cells can be brought into a synthesis, the *problems of c-mitosis.*

REFERENCES

1. ALLEN, E., SMITH, G., AND GARDNER, W. Accentuation of the growth effect of theelin on genital tissues by arrest of mitosis with colchicine. Anat. Rec. 67: Suppl. 1:49. 1936. Accentuation of the growth effect of theelin on genital tissues of the ovariectomized mouse, by arrest of mitosis with colchicine. Amer. Jour. Anat. 61:321–41. 1937.
2. BARBER, H., AND CALLAN, H. (*see* Ref. No. 1, Chap. 2. 1943).
3. BARIGOZZI, C. (*see* Ref. No. 2, Chap. 2. 1942).
4. ————, AND FANTONI, L. (*see* Ref. No. 3, Chap. 2. 1942).
5. BEAMS, H., AND EVANS, T. (*see* Ref. No. 4, Chap. 2. 1940).
6. ————, AND KING, R. (*see* Ref. No. 5, Chap. 2. 1938).
7. BERGER, C., AND WITKUS, E. (*see* Ref. No. 7, Chap. 2. 1943).
8. BERGNER, A. (*see* Ref. No. 8, Chap. 2. 1950).
9. BHADURI, P. (*see* Ref. No. 9, Chap. 2. 1939, 1940).
10. BOAS, F., AND GISTL, R. Über einige Colchicinwirkungen. Protoplasma. 33:301–10. 1939.
11. BRAM, A. Zum Verhalten der Mitochondrien bei Einwirkung verschiedener Pharmaka. Acta Anat. 13:385–402. 1951.
12. BROCK, N., DRUCKREY, H., AND HERKEN, H. Über Kerngifte und Cytoplasmagifte. Arch. Exp. Path. 193:679–87. 1939.
13. BRODERSEN, H. Mitosegifte und ionisierende Strahlung. Strahlenther. 73:196–254. 1943.
14. BRUES, A. (*see* Ref. No. 11, Chap. 2. 1951).
15. ————, AND COHEN, A. (*see* Ref. No. 12, Chap. 2. 1936).

16. ————, AND JACKSON, E. (*see* Ref. No. 13, Chap. 2. 1937).
17. BUCHER, O. (*see* Ref. No. 15, Chap. 2. 1939, 1945, 1952).
18. BUSCHKE, W., FRIEDENWALD, J., AND FLEISCHMANN, W. Studies on the mitotic activity of the corneal epithelium. Methods. The effects of colchicine, ether, cocaine and ephedrine. Bull. Johns Hopkins Hosp. 73:143–68. 1943.
19. COOK, J., AND LOUDON, J. (*see* Ref. No. 9, Chap. 1. 1951).
20. CORNMAN, I., AND CORNMAN, M. The action of podophyllin and its fractions on marine eggs. Ann. N. Y. Acad. Sci. 51:1443–87. 1951.
21. D'AMATO, F. (*see* Ref. No. 22, Chap. 2. 1948a, 1948b, 1949).
22. DAVID, M. Action of colchicine and acenaphthene on the spermatogenesis of orthopterous insects of genus *Stauroderous* Boh. C. R. Acad. Sci. Paris. 221:185–186. 1945.
23. DE CASTRO, D. Nota acerca da accão da colquicina sobre o centromera. Agron. Lusitana. 4:61–70. 1942.
24. DELCOURT, R. (*see* Ref. No. 24, Chap. 2. 1938).
25. DEYSSON, G. (*see* Ref. No. 26, Chap. 2. 1948).
26. DOOLEY, T. The influence of colchicine upon the germ cells of insects (Orthoptera), with special reference to mitochondria and dietyosomes. Trans. Amer. Micr. Soc. 60:105–19. 1941.
27. DRAGOIU, J., AND CRISAN, C. (*see* Ref. No. 27, Chap. 2. 1939).
28. DUSTIN, A. (*see* Ref. No. 29, Chap. 2. 1934, 1936, 1938, 1939).
29. ————, HAVAS, L., AND LITS, F. (*see* Ref. No. 14, Chap. 1. 1937).
30. ————, AND ZYLBERSAC, S. (*see* Ref. No. 32, Chap. 2. 1939).
31. DUSTIN, P., JR. (*see* Ref. No. 33, Chap. 2. 1946, 1947).
32. EHRENBERG, L., AND LOFGREN, N. Colchicine-protein complexes demonstrated by the diphtheria toxin-antitoxin precipitin reaction. Svensk. Kem. Tid. 57:183–85. 1945.
33. EIGSTI, O. (*see* Ref. No. 34, Chap. 2. 1938, 1940). Colchicine — a bacterial habitat. Amer. Jour. Bot. 33:4. 1946.
34. ————, AND DUSTIN, P., JR. (*see* Ref. No. 16, Chap. 1. 1947, 1949).
35. ————, ————, AND GAY-WINN, N. (*see* Ref. No. 17, Chap. 1. 1949).
36. FOSTER, C. Effect of colchicine on Golgi bodies. Nature. 153:556–57. 1944.
37. GAULDEN, M., AND CARLSON, J. (*see* Ref. No. 39. Chap. 2. 1951).
38. GAVAUDAN, P. (*see* Ref. No. 40, Chap. 2. 1942, 1947). La pathologie expérimentale de la caryocinèse et de la cytodiérèse. Bull. Musée Hist. Nat. Marseille. 1:13–40. 1941. Étude quantitative de la mito-inhibition dans la cellule végétale. C. R. Soc. Biol. Paris. 137:342–43. 1943.
39. ————, DODÉ, M., AND POUSSEL, H. L'importance de la notion d'activité thermodynamique en toxicologie et en pharmacodynamie — Rec. Trav. Scient. Stat. d'Ess. Bouchet (Trav. de Toxic, et Pharm. Cell.). 1:5–22. 1945.
40. ————, AND GAVAUDAN, N. Modifications numériques et morphologiques des chromosomes induites, chez les végétaux, par la colchicine. C. R. Soc. Biol. Paris. 126:985. 1937. Mécanisme d'action de la colchicine sur la caryocinèse des végétaux. C. R. Soc. Biol. Paris. 128:714. 1938.
41. GIORDANO, A., AND GRAMPA, G. Mitosen bei experimenteller Leberregeneration unter Colchicin-Wirkung. Zentralbl. Allg. Path. 85:25–29. 1950.
42. GRAMPA, G. Azione citoplasmatica della colchicina nel fegato normale e in rigenerazione sperimentale. Studia Ghisleriana. (Studi Medeci Biologici) Ser. III. 1:1–10. 1949. Osservazioni col microscopio a contrasta di fase sul condrioma delle cellule epatiche in rigenerazione sperimentale. Boll. Soc. Ital. Biol. Sper. 27:808–10. 1951.
43. GUYER, M., AND CLAUS, P. Destructive effects on carcinoma of colchicine followed by distilled water. Proc. Soc. Exp. Biol. and Med. 43:272. 1939.
44. HAAS, H. Über die Beeinflussung des Zellkerns durch Pharmaka. Arch. Exp. Path. 197:284–91. 1941.
45. HAWKES, J. (*see* Ref. No. 46, Chap. 2. 1942).
46. HUGHES, A. The effect of iodoacetamide upon cell division in tissue cultures of the chick embryo. Jour. Roy. Micr. Soc. 69:215–24. 1949. Mitotic cycle. Academic Press, New York, 1952.

47. INOUE, S. A method for measuring small retardations of structure in living cells. Exp. Cell Res. 2:513–17. 1951. The effect of colchicine on the microscopic and submicroscopic structure of the mitotic spindle. Exp. Cell Res. Suppl. 2:305–18. 1952.

48. JAHN, U. (*see* Ref. No. 50, Chap. 2. 1952).

49. KANTER, M. Der Einfluss des Colchicins auf die Zellteilung lebender Amphibien. Z. Anat. 115:273–86. 1950.

50. KAUFMANN, B., GAY, H., AND HOLLAENDER, A. Distribution of mitoses in the corneal epithelium of the rabbit and the rat. Anat. Rec. 90:161–78. 1944.

51. KEPPEL, D., AND DAWSON, A. Effects of colchicine on the cleavage of the frog's egg (*Rana pipiens*). Biol. Bull. 76:153–61. 1939.

52. KING, R., AND BEAMS, H. A comparison of the effects of colchicine on division in protozoa and certain other cells. Jour. Cell. and Comp. Physiol. 15:252. 1940.

53. LEHMANN, F., AND HADORN, E. (*see* Ref. No. 55, Chap. 2. 1946).

54. LETTRÉ, H. Zur Chemie und Biologie der Mitosegifte. Angew. Chemie. 63:421. 1951. Über Synergisten von Mitosegiften. V. Mitt. Versuche zur Aufhebung der synergistischen Wirkung durch Phosphagen. Naturwiss. 38:13. 1951. Über Mitosegifte. Ergebn. Physiol. 46:379–452. 1950.

55. LEVAN, A. (*see* Ref. No. 56, Chap. 2. 1938, 1940, 1942, 1944, 1949, 1954).

56. ————, AND LOTFY, T. (*see* Ref. No. 57, Chap. 2. 1949).

57. ————, AND ÖSTERGREN, G. (*see* Ref. No. 58, Chap. 2. 1943).

58. LITS, F. (*see* Ref. No. 61, Chap. 2. 1934, 1936).

59. LUDFORD, R. (*see* Ref. No. 28, Chap. 1. 1936).

60. LUSCHER, M. (*see* Ref. No. 63, Chap. 2. 1946a, 1946b, 1946c).

61. MANGENOT, G. (*see* Ref. No. 65, Chap. 2. 1942).

62. MARTIN, G. (*see* Ref. No. 66, Chap. 2. 1945).

63. MASCRE, M., AND DEYSSON, G. (*see* Ref. No. 67, Chap. 2. 1951).

64. MEHRA, P. Colchicine effect on the mitotic division of the body nucleus in the pollen grains of some *Ephedra* Sps. Proc. Nat. Inst. Sci. India. 12:333–40. 1946.

65. MELANDER, Y. (*see* Ref. No. 68, Chap. 2. 1950, 1951).

66. MILLS, K. Variations in the rate of mitosis in normal and colchicine-treated tadpoles of *Rana pipiens* and *Amblystoma jeffersonianum*. Jour. Morph. 64:89–113. 1939.

67. MISZURSKI, B. Effects of colchicine on resting cells in tissue cultures. Exp. Cell Res. Suppl. 1:450–51. 1949.

68. ————, AND DOLJANSKI, L. Effect of colchicine on resting cells in tissue culture. Proc. Soc. Exp. Biol. and Med. 64:334–36. 1947.

69. MÖLLENDORFF, W. v. (*see* Ref. No. 70, Chap. 2. 1939).

70. MONROY, A., AND MONTALENTI, G. Cyclic variations of the submicroscopic structure of the cortical layer of fertilized and parthenogenetic sea urchin eggs. Nature. 158:239. 1946.

71. NEBEL, B. (*see* Ref. No. 72, Chap. 2. 1937).

72. ————, AND RUTTLE, M. (*see* Ref. No. 32, Chap. 1. 1938).

73. ÖSTERGREN, G. (*see* Ref. No. 77, Chap. 2. 1943, 1944). Cytological standards for the quantitative estimation of spindle disturbances. Hereditas. 36:371–82. 1950.

74. PETERS, J. (*see* Ref. No. 79, Chap. 2. 1946).

75. PIETTRE, L. Action de la colchicine sur les végétaux. C. R. Soc. Biol. Paris. 131:1095–97. 1939.

76. PINCUS, G., AND WADDINGTON, C. (*see* Ref. No. 81, Chap. 2. 1939).

77. RESSE, G. (*see* Ref. No. 83, Chap. 2. 1951).

78. RIES, E. (*see* Ref. No. 84, Chap. 2. 1939).

79. RYLAND, A. A cytological study of the effects of colchicine, indole-3-acetic acid, potassium cyanide and 2, 4-D on plant cells. Jour. Elisha Mitchell Sci. Soc. 64:117–25. 1948.

80. SANTAVY, F. Isolierung neuer Stoffe aus den Knollen der Herbstzeitlose, *Colchicine autumnale* L. Pharm. Acta Helv. 25:248–65. 1950.

81. SCHREIBER, G., AND PELLEGRINO, J. Analise citologica e cariometrica da ação da colchicina sobre a espermatogenese dos Hemipteros. Mem. do Inst. Oswaldo Cruz. Rio de Janeiro. 49:513–42. 1951.

82. Sedar, A., and Wilson, D. Electron microscope studies on the normal and colchicinized mitotic figures of the onion root tip, *Allium cepa* L. Biol. Bull. 100:107–15. 1951.
83. Sentein, P. Mode d'action da la colchicine sur la caryocinèse de *Molge palmata*. C. R. Soc. Biol. Paris. 137:133–34. 1943. Les effets mitoclasiques chez quelques Vertébrés. C. R. Soc. Biol. Paris. 139:294–95. 1945. Action de la colchicine et de l'hydrate de chloral sur l'oeuf de *Triturus Helveticus* L. en développement. Acta Anat. 4:256–68. 1947. Les transformations de l'appareil achromatique et des chromosomes dans les mitoses normales et les mitoses bloquées de l'oeuf en segmentation. Arch. Anat. Hist. Embryol. 39:377–94. 1951.
84. Setala, K. Colchicine as carcinogenic agent in skin carcinogenesis in mice. Distribution of carcinogenic hydrocarbons in the mouse skin applied during life and death. Ann. Med. and Biol. Fenniae. 26:126–30. (Index Analyticus Cancer. 20:305.) 1948.
85. Shimamura, T. (*see* Ref. No. 86, Chap. 2. 1939, 1940).
86. Sokolow, I. (*see* Ref. No. 89, Chap. 2. 1939).
87. Soyano, Y. Physiological and cytological relations between colchicine and heteroauxine. Bot. Mag. Tokyo. 54:141–48. 1940.
88. Steinegger, E., and Levan, A. (*see* Ref. No. 42, Chap. 1. 1947, 1948).
89. Suita, N. (*see* Ref. No. 89, Chap. 2. 1939).
90. Tahmisian, T. Mechanism of cell division. I. The living spindle. Proc. Soc. Exp. Biol. and Med. 78:444–47. 1951.
91. Tennant, R., and Liebow, A. (*see* Ref. No. 90, Chap. 2. 1940).
92. Vaarama, A. (*see* Ref. No. 91, Chap. 2. 1947, 1949).
93. Verne, J., and Vilter, V. Étude de l'action de la colchicine sur les mitoses des fibroblastes cultivés *in vitro*. Concentrations dites fortes. C. R. Soc. Biol. Paris. 133:618–21. 1940a. Mécanisme d'action de la colchicine, employée en concentrations faibles, sur l'évolution de la mitose dans les cultures de fibroblastes *in vitro*. C. R. Soc. Biol. Paris. 133:621–24. 1940b.
94. Vilter, V. Inhibition colchicinique de la mitose chez les Mammifères. C. R. Soc. Biol. Paris. 138:605–6. 1944.
95. Wada, B. (*see* Ref. No. 93, Chap. 2. 1940, 1949, 1950).
96. Walker, R. The effect of colchicine on somatic cells of *Tradescantia paludosa*. Jour. Arnold Arb. 19:158–62. 1938.
97. Wilbur, K. Effects of colchicine upon viscosity of the *Arbacia* egg. Proc. Soc. Exp. Biol. and Med. 45:696–700. 1940.
98. Woker, H. (*see* Ref. No. 95, Chap. 2. 1943, 1944).

CHAPTER 4

Cellular Growth

The senior author observed unusual "spearlike" tips forming on *Allium* roots immersed in a 0.01 per cent solution of colchicine. After 24 hours startling changes in the roots were noted[35] (cf. Chapter 2). *Colchicine-tumor,*[79] the name given to this growth, is appropriately descriptive. Similar anomalies were observed earlier by Nemec and others.[35] This growth pattern can also be reproduced with chemicals other than colchicine or by certain physical treatments.[79, 44] Although the c-tumors were not new to biology, the revival of interest in colchicine brought them to the attention of many experimenters.[34, 33, 93, 86, 44, 37, 59, 55, 133, 115, 111, 90, 88, 62, 154, 128, 18, 4, 10, 8, 21]

Roots with c-tumors may have some cells with many chromosomes within the single cells, because polyploidy is a consequence of c-mitosis. The correlation between larger leaves, stems, seeds, and flowers, and increasing numbers of chromosomes is well established. [135, 152] This concept influenced the first conclusion that c-tumors were directly correlated with the polyploid cells. On the contrary, an enlargement of root tips is not the result of polyploid cells induced by the drug, even though polyploid cells may be created at the same time the c-tumor is formed.[82] The c-mitosis and c-tumor are independent processes.[82]

Now we know that in similar manner, enlarged cells may be induced in various parts of plants.[106] All these anomalous formations induced by colchicine are the result of changing the growth pattern. [62, 90] Such structures as pollen tubes,[35, 60, 137] stylar cells of the flower, [148] hair cells of stem and root,[53, 55, 115] hypocotyl, and other somatic cells all show particular enlargements after treatment with colchicine. They are in contrast to the untreated or normal cells that enlarge by a cell tension that shows distinct polarity. By a broad interpretation, all deviations expressed as growth patterns and appearing as a response to colchicine will be classified as c-tumors, in spite of the fact that this name originally designated a specific kind of root tip enlargement after treatment with colchicine.

The processes of meiosis and gametophytic development are changed by colchicine.[2, 9, 29, 79, 114, 124, 122, 148] Response depends upon the concentration, stage of development when colchicine reaches the cell, length of exposure, and, of course, concentration. As might be expected, the spindle is inhibited, but there are also other changes that accompany the colchicine-effect.[1] For that reason the problem of a "colchicine-meiosis" [79] is included in this chapter along with the action upon embryo sac development[48] and pollen tube studies.[35]

Colchicine acts upon cells during their differentiation processes. One noticeable change is found in the cell walls.[53] Their chemical composition is altered also, and various physical marks show that action of colchicine is not limited to the mitotic spindle or upon certain cytoplasmic constituents.[53] Enough data are at hand to prove that differentiation processes in plants are modified by colchicine.[35, 53, 156, 151]

Among unicellular organisms, processes of division, enlargement, and differentiation, are closely integrated within one cell. For that reason one would expect to find the results from a colchicine exposure difficult to interpret. Conceivably, all three processes go on within one cell at the same time; hence, colchicine may act upon each phase in a specific manner, yet simultaneously. If this interpretation is correct, the confusing picture drawn from the literature dealing with colchicine and microbiological materials may be partly explained by the inability to distinguish the specific process being studied, whether a cell division, cell enlargement, or differentiation and maturation. There is general agreement that the actions reported in this research are contradictory. Under some conditions, however, colchicine is effective if introduced to specific microbiological cultures within certain concentrations.

A mechanism for action of colchicine upon processes of growth and differentiation is difficult to visualize. Nevertheless, there should be some aspects of metabolism that might help toward the solution of this problem.[103, 16, 89, 77, 155, 142, 130, 99, 56, 46, 47, 48, 45] Generally, the work with physiology[101, 99] has been done with such isolated processes as enzyme reactions[127] or respiration[110] under a restricted set of conditions for experimental material. At least a start has been made in this direction, but more can be done in the future.

4.1: Colchicine Tumors in Roots, Hypocotyl, and Stems

The root tumor forms at the region of elongation, a section between the meristematic area and the differentiated cells of a root[90, 35, 79, 82, 62] (Fig. 2.1). Normally cells elongate linearly to the axis of the root. They seem to show a polarity in this respect. When colchicine is present, an enlargement of the cell takes place in all directions. That is, an isodiametric expansion occurs, rather than a polarwise elongation. The volumes of cells from a c-tumor are about the same as the volumes of elongated cells in untreated roots.[62] Therefore, the direction of growth is modified, but not necessarily the total amount of expansion.[62]

Cells of the cortex become inflated.[79] This leads to a swelling at the particular place along the root. Longitudinal and cross sections of treated and untreated roots within five or six layers of cells show where the change occurs, and reveal particularly the difference in the shape of individual cells. These comparative studies confirm the opinion that direction of growth is altered when colchicine is present. The action is not unique for colchicine. Growth-promoting substances, as naphthaleneacetic acid (NAA) and indolebutyric acid, induce tumors.[97, 90, 91, 42, 27, 7, 34, 44, 79, 81, 59, 61] Acenaphthene, another compound that has a c-mitotic potential, may cause tumors on roots.[108] Not all compounds that create tumors arrest mitosis. In fact, certain phytohormones that do not stop mitosis may induce root tip enlargements. The idea of an autonomy of c-mitosis and c-tumors gains support from these general observations with several chemicals.[82]

Specific thresholds below which no tumors form, are demonstrable for colchicine. Concentration specificity is shown also by NAA.[81] If two solutions, colchicine and NAA, are combined, the threshold concentration does not change.[81] There is no evidence that two solutions, each capable of inducing tumors alone, will in combination lower the threshold value. Thus, the mechanism for creating the tumor may be different for these particular substances.[81] The threshold changed, however, when sulfonamide (2 per cent prontosil) was added to colchicine.[4, 69]

The combined solutions of *meso*-inositol and colchicine prevented the usual production of a c-tumor with roots of *Allium*.[18] Apparently this antagonism by *meso*-inositol operates at 19°C. since a repetition at 26°C. did not reveal such antagonism.[26] The critical role of temperature is seen in pollen tube enlargements, where the maximum width induced by colchicine occurs only at a specific temperature.[127] Above or below that optimum the pollen tubes are close to normal dimension in spite of the same concentration of colchicine present in each test.

Venom from bees was demonstrated to have an antagonistic action upon the formation of root tumors by colchicine.[59] The specific differences between kinds of plants was also shown. Tomatoes were more sensitive than wheat seedlings. A 69 per cent reduction of tumors was obtained for tomatoes and 47 per cent with wheat.[59, 61]

Ethyl alcohol changes the c-mitotic threshold for *Allium* root cells from 0.006 per cent, when colchicine alone is used, to 0.01 per cent if alcohol (0.5 per cent) is added. If the concentration of alcohol is increased to 2 per cent, other poisonous actions occur. Alcohol acts as an antidote with respect to c-mitosis and the c-tumor.

When two chemicals work together to accelerate an activity beyond the effect obtainable by each chemical independently, the response is known as a synergism. Colchicine and numerous other chemicals have been tried for their synergistic action.[78] Some give accelerated response and others do not. Phenylurethane along with colchicine increases the action of drug upon roots of *Allium*.[30]

Tissue cultures of *Helianthus tuberosus* were handled by combined treatments of heteroauxin (10^{-9}) and colchicine (10^{-6}). Small doses of colchicine enhance the action of heteroauxin because the tissues seem to divide more actively and huge cells with many chromosomes develop as a result. A stimulating action seems evident from these experiments. Increasing the concentration of colchicine leads to repetitive c-mitoses and an inhibition of cellular multiplication among the tissues.[91]

Generally, favorable conditions for growth increase the promotion of a tumor from a specific treatment.[84] The range in concentration is fairly broad, but there are limits marked by minimum and maximum concentrations. The formation of tumors within certain limits is proportional to concentration. Finally, the thresholds for c-mitosis and c-tumors are close to each other with some indication that the threshold for the latter process is lower than that for c-mitosis.[82]

As soon as the independence of c-mitosis and c-tumor was suspected, a specific experiment was designed to test autonomy.[79] Root primordia of *Allium fistulosum* were subjected to intense X-ray treatment. Consequently, the mitotic capacity of meristematic cells was destroyed. Following X-irradiation, bulbs were placed over colchicine, and typical c-tumors formed with no evidence for several days thereafter of c-mitoses in these roots. We may conclude, therefore, that enlargement occurs without a simultaneous division of cells. Polyploidy following a c-mitosis is not necessary for tumor formation.[79]

Swelling at the hypocotyl when seedlings were soaked in colchicine gave the first evidence that tumors were in no way related to c-mitosis or induced polyploidy. Although cells in the hypocotyl are not meristematic, they are capable of elongating or expanding. Colchicine causes an isodiametric expansion of cells much the same as among cortical cells in roots.[62]

The tumor formation is proportional to concentration within certain limits.[55] Different species show different degrees of response to the same concentration. Another factor is the specific moment when seedlings are placed in colchicine.[115] If the seedling has not yet elongated, there is swelling throughout the entire hypocotyl. But the seedling that has already elongated, let us say to 23 mm. before treatment begins, shows practically no swelling at the hypocotyl.[115] All these points fall in line with the proposition that tumor formation is basically a growth response to colchicine (Fig. 4.1).

Stems of *Tradescantia* cut from the plant and placed in colchicine show extreme swelling at the node where leaves are attached.[148] The nodal enlargements are in every respect comparable to root and hypocotyl tumors. A petiolar swelling also may occur if expanding leaves are placed in colchicine.

The growth responses observed for roots and stems raised the question of a possible hormone action. However, the standard tests for measuring phytohormone potency gave negative results.[34, 90, 59] No

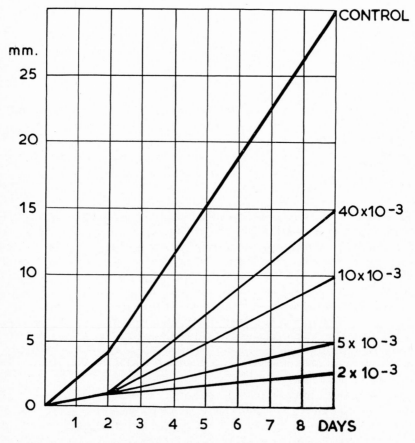

Fig. 4.1—Elongation of hypocotyl of **Lepidium** seedlings. Reduction in length is proportional to concentration of colchicine. (Adapted from Gremling)

responses were obtained from colchicine applied to the *Avena, Helianthus,* and *Pisum* tests.[115] Colchicine is not a phytohormone, but the basic relation between growth responses shown by tumors and the reactions noted for phytohormones in causing cell enlargement is not understood. There are numerous cases reported where colchicine changed growth rates.

Resistance to colchicine by cells of *Colchicum* was demonstrated under the section dealing with c-mitoses. A similar resistance can be proved with colchicine and tumor formation. Enough species of *Colchicum* were tried to give conclusive proof of a resistance.[88, 79, 9, 84] Not all plants supposedly containing colchicine are resistant as tested by the tumor test.[88] The resistance shown by tumor experiments is not proof of a c-mitotic resistance, and vice versa. This point was not always appreciated because the independence of the two processes was not understood until specific tests were finished.

Golden hamsters showed resistance to colchicine under laboratory conditions.[107] This specific resistance may be explained in the following way: Animals inhabiting regions where *Colchicum* is found would come in contact with seeds, fruits, leaves, and corms of the plant and would consume amounts of varying strength. Enough colchicine would be present to kill susceptible individuals, while others might survive. Therefore, by selection in nature the hamster may have acquired this specific resistance.

4.2: Effects of Colchicine on Pollen Tubes, Hair Cells, and Other Parts of Plants

The number of chromosomes per pollen tube does not increase after c-mitosis in the generative cell.[35, 137] An enlarged pollen tube is independent of the action of colchicine upon the nucleus. When a pollen grain germinates in artificial media, a tube grows out and away from the grain (Fig. 4.2). Such filaments are very narrow and elongation of the tube is polarwise. Colchicine decreases the length and increases the width of a tube. An enlargement even greater than the grain itself may occur (Fig. 4.2). These are the pollen tube tumors. A stimulation has been reported when hormones are added to cultures with colchicine.[76, 150]

A lateral expansion is comparable to the isodiametric extension of root or hypocotyl cells. The tubes seem to "bloat" or inflate like balloons (Fig. 4.2F). Since there is no bursting, the increase must take place by an orderly deposition of cell wall material forming the tube.[35] Colchicine causes these pollen tube enlargements. When the concentrations are of low dosage, a stimulation is observed.[150, 76]

An interaction between concentration and temperature condition was expressed in measurements with calculated averages of pollen

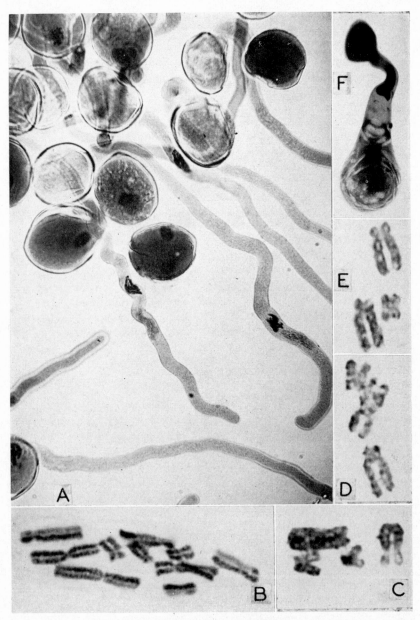

Fig. 4.2—Pollen tubes of **Polygonatum pubescens** from cultures in sucrose agar, treated with colchicine and untreated. **A.** Control culture, pollen tube with generative cell in metaphase, stained with iron acetocarmine. **B.** Colchicine mitosis of a diploid species, n-10, to be compared with Figure 2.4D of Chapter 2, the tetraploid species, n-20. **C, D, E.** Reversion to interphase; c-pairs are not separated completely at centromeric region. **F.** Pollen tube c-tumor that is a response to colchicine independent of any polyploidy. Tube wall staining shows depositions not commonly observed in control. Stained with iron alum haemotoxylin. (Eigsti, 1940)

tube widths.[127] Five-and-one-half-hour cultures at 25°C. had tubes with a 30 per cent increase in width over the control. No such significant differences in width were found at 20°C. or 30°C. Although the mean tube length was less than control for all temperature levels, only at the optimum, 25°C., was maximum width obtained.[127] The concentration of drug, 0.01 per cent, remained the same for all tests. No similar increase in width was found upon adding 3-indoleacetic acid, vitamin B_1, or NAA to the culturing medium.

Pollen from *Colchicum autumnale* L. was tested for response to colchicine. Germination was depressed by concentrations ranging from 1.0 to 0.1 per cent.[60] Tumors were observed comparable to those in pollen samples from species not known to produce colchicine, and thus a resistance such as was shown to c-mitosis and c-tumor has not been demonstrated for the case of the pollen tube tumors. The response from these tests is of further interest in light of the report that bees carrying pollen from flowers of *Colchicum* yield honey that is poisonous due to a high colchicine content.[146] From this indirect evidence it would thus seem that the pollen contains the drug. The quantities of colchicine which are carried in the flowers are described in Chapter 5.

Epidermal protuberances on roots, the root hairs, involve no mitotic stages.[53] These cells are suitable for testing the action of colchicine upon enlargement of root hairs. Eight species of plants were included in a study to measure differences in root hair development between control and treated cases.[53]

Bulbous tips appeared in contrast to the normal long, thin filamentous root hairs. The polyploid condition is not involved since the nucleus does not divide. Here again is evidence for an independence between the c-tumor and c-mitosis. Sometimes the end of a particular hair becomes forked.[53]

Other plant parts, the stem, leaf, and flowers, have hairlike cells. For *Helianthus,* a protuberance quite different from the normal is produced following treatment with colchicine.[73]

Staminal hair cells of *Rhoeo discolor* form a chain of cells like beads.[29] Colchicine causes the distal cell to enlarge considerably beyond the normal size. Each cell successively from the tip to base is enlarged, but the size decreases progressively from the tip to the basal cell. The largest cell, an end cell, is also the youngest. Maximum increase is then proportional to the age of the cell; younger cells expand more than older ones.[29]

The stylar portion of a pistil is elongate and is composed of elongated cells. Flowers of *Tradescantia* treated with colchicine before the pistil develops, show modification of these floral parts.[148] Short, stubby pistillate structures replace the long filamentous styles. The number of cells does not change, but the manner in which elongation proceeds becomes considerably altered. Cross sections as well as longitudinal views are very instructive.[148]

Floral parts from *Carthamus tinctorius* follow similar patterns of induced changes when treated with colchicine before the flowers mature. Blunt, wrinkled petals and short, single gynoecia with woolly hairs replace the pointed, elongate petals, double gynoecium, and stiff, pointed hairs of normal flowers.[73]

Enough data have been collected to confirm the fact that colchicine alters the way in which cells enlarge.[147] Growth by increase in volume is modified under specific conditions, and this may be related to changes in viscosity of cytoplasm caused by colchicine.[28, 32, 68, 37, 39, 126, 88, 98, 103]

To explain the mechanism for a c-tumor, certain parallels were drawn between viscosity changes in the cytoplasm and dissociation of the cytoplasmic proteins.[103] Colchicine caused a decrease in viscosity that was correlated with the formation of the c-tumor in *Allium*. In this explanation, a dissociation was the primary causal factor. A similar mechanism was described in connection with the c-mitosis.[103]

The idea of a narcosis was also introduced to account for a c-tumor, but instead of there occurring a narcotized cell division, it is the growth process by cell enlargement that is influenced by colchicine.[108] In regard to this hypothesis and the preceding one, much additional information is needed for a full explanation of the action of the drug during cell enlargement.

4.3: Colchicine-Meiosis and Gametophytic Development

In pollen mother cells or megaspore mother cells that are in contact with colchicine at the time of reduction division, the meiotic stages are converted into a "colchicine-meiosis."[79] Only at this time can such a process as c-meiosis take place (Fig. 4.3). Earlier, that is, during divisions in the archesporium, and in later cycles, when microspores or generative cells divide, the processes become true c-mitoses.[79] Since the c-meiosis represents a special case, primarily because meiosis is a particular kind of division, it is discussed in this chapter with other aspects of growth and reproduction. Obviously the spindle inhibition is common to both c-mitosis and c-meiosis; so also are the c-pairing phenomena (Table 4.1), a secondary action of the suppressed spindle, and the "c-bivalents" accompanying c-meiosis. These and related characteristics of c-meiosis occur only during a certain time in the reproductive cycle (Figs. 4.3 and 4.4; Tables 4.1 and 4.2).[79, 29, 124, 148]

To help visualize how essential a timing sequence is in producing the c-meiosis, a survey of the particular cell, treated stage, and expected results are given in Table 4.2. From this outline one can see

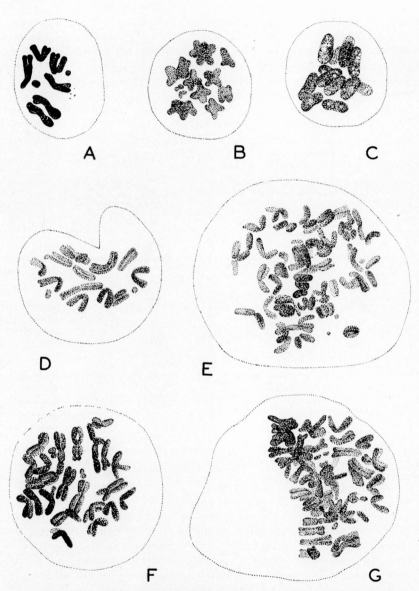

Fig. 4.3—Pollen mother cells of **Tradescantia palludosa**. Control and treated cultures. **A.** Untreated microspore. **B.** Univalents induced by colchicine. **C.** Desynaptic metaphases, four days after treatment was made. **D.** Diploid microspore from a treatment that became effective at the second meiotic division. **E.** Octoploid microspore 21 days after treatment; time of treatment 48 hours, then time allowed for recovery, two meiotic divisions inhibited, and one premeiotic c-mitosis. **F.** Tetraploid microspore, 12 days after treatment. **G.** Hexaploid microspore, an unequal division that is similar to a distributed c-mitosis. (After Walker)

that action during division leading up to meiosis creates octoploid or tetraploid pollen mother cells.[79] In contrast, activity during meiotic divisions I and II creates tetraploid monads, and activity at division II only, diploid monads. Monadal formation is a special feature of the c-meiosis. The monads replace the usual tetrads of microspores forming at the close of a meiosis.[29, 148, 122, 79]

Since archesporial divisions become regular c-mitoses, these are not described in great detail here, except to say that one c-mitosis in this

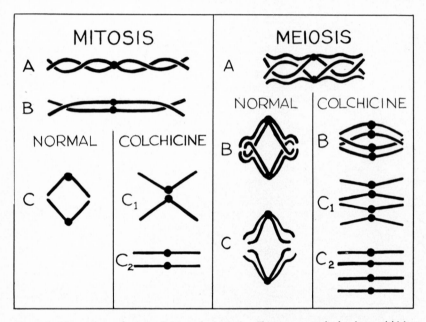

Fig. 4.4—Comparison of a c-meiosis and c-mitosis. The stage reached when colchicine becomes effective determines the action in meiosis. (After Levan)

tissue gives rise to tetraploid pollen mother cells, and that two c-mitoses bring about the octoploid condition. Beyond this degree of polyploidy the meiotic processes are so upset that no further action of colchicine can be obtained at meiosis. The premeiotic stages of *Allium cernuum* with diploid, tetraploid, and octoploid numbers 7, 14, and 28 pairs, respectively, were observed and followed up to the first meiosis.[79] Already at tetraploid stages, the polarities of meiotic spindles were irregular. The multiple spindle aspects during recovery from a c-mitosis were noticed at meiosis if the previous c-mitotic cycles of archesporial cells caused polyploidy.

Pairing of homologous chromosomes and chiasmatal formation formed during prophase are decisive functions before a regular meiosis or a c-meiosis begins. Colchicine reduces the pairing as shown by the reduction in chiasmata and increased frequency of univalents.[2] The calculations from several independent studies confirm the action on pairing. *Allium cernuum* rarely showed univalents in controls, but among treated cases, 8 cells out of 31 had no bivalents. Moreover, no cell among 31 pollen mother cells studied had more than 5 bivalents when the total with full pairing could have been 7.[79] Among *Tradescantia*, 12 univalents (Fig. 4.3C) were produced by a full c-meiosis. Similar cases are reported with other species.

The terminalization of chiasmata is different when colchicine is present; therefore, there is reduction in chiasmata as well as change in the kind of chiasmata (Table 4.3).[2] Whether crossing-over is changed has not been tested genetically, but the cytological picture seems to warrant a conclusion that cross-overs would occur in places they are not generally expected.

If recovery sets in while the univalents are distributed through the cell, there is no congregation into the equatorial plate. But the

TABLE 4.1
RELATION BETWEEN TREATMENT AND STAGE
(After Levan)

Developmental Stage	Stage Treated	Results Obse ved
Archesporium...............	division I division II	tetraploid pollen octoploid pollen
Pollen mother cell............	resting stage prophase	no effect abnormal asynapsis irregular bivalents
Pollen mother cell............	meiosis I meiosis II	tetraploid monad diploid monad
Pollen.....................	resting stage first division	no effect diploid pollen

univalents collect at poles where the particular chromosomes happen to lie. On the other hand, bivalents, if they have persisted, upon recovery orient in the equator.

Unlike the tendency toward supercontraction at the metaphase of a c-mitosis, the c-meiotic chromosomes do not show the usual contraction.[79] In fact, they are less contracted; this is a very striking action induced by colchicine. Such lack of contraction is correlated with a decrease in the frequency of chiasmata. These are the major effects noted when colchicine acts during premeiotic stages. Full action upsets the meiosis so that abnormal metaphase I and irregularities occur in subsequent stages.

If prophases have proceeded normally, pairing is regular, but colchicine introduced at the metaphase stage reduces spindle fibers. Under these conditions, the bivalents remain scattered in the cytoplasm, and the separation of two homologous chromosomes proceeds

TABLE 4.2

RELATION BETWEEN TIME OF TREATMENT AND RESULTS
(After Dermen)

Days After Treatment	Results
4	meiotic chromosomes in short broken chains; reduction of chromosomes not noticed
5 or 6	diploid and tetraploid pollen mother cells
8	tetraploid and octoploid pollen mother cells
11	polyploid microspores
12	failure at meiosis I and II; haploid, diploid, tetraploid microspores

where each pair happens to lie. Since each homologous chromosome of the pair is cleft and clearly separated, except at the region of the centromere, a colchicine-anaphase I is characterized by two cruciform "c-pairs" lying close to each other. The straight, cruciform anaphase I chromosomes are a contrast to normal ones at this stage.

As the first telophase begins, chromosomes lose their staining capacity, the chromatids remain connected at the centromere, and the usual transformation to interphase between the meiosis I and II takes place.[114] The outlines of chromosomes are difficult to trace at this stage and can be overlooked, making it appear that division II begins without an intervening interphase, a prophase II, or a metaphase II.

When the second c-meiotic division begins, chromosomes condense and assume a prophase appearance. The contraction of the chromatid proceeds in a prophase II. During this time the relic spiral disappears and a chromosome of c-metaphase II comes into the picture. These chromosomes are held together at the centromere up to late prophase; then they are straightened, and as fairly long chromosomes they separate from each other completely. The second c-metaphase II merges with the second c-anaphase II. All the chromosomes remain within one cell, so that instead of a tetrad of 4 cells, a monad results with all 4 sets of chromosomes contained within one cell (Fig. 4.3). The monad is tetraploid. C-telophase II concludes the c-meiosis with unraveling and loss of the stainable structure.[114]

The full c-meiosis has been sketched briefly without taking into consideration deviations and abnormalities caused by different concentrations, exposure, and stage at which the drug acts. Abnormal diploid, tetraploid, hexaploid, and octoploid microspores may be found, as was noticed for *Tradescantia* and *Rhoeo* (Fig. 4.3).[29] Polynucleate cells were produced from certain members of the *Aloinae*[122] and these cases arose from a treatment that probably began in prophase of meiosis.

Reduction divisions in *Carthamus tinctorius* L. were treated by a special technique in which the entire inflorescence was treated.[73] Under these conditions 10 to 17 pollen grains appeared within a single pollen mother cell (Fig. 4.5). Most grains had a nucleus, except for the very small grains. In view of the fact that this species is dicotyledonous, while the major descriptions of c-meiosis were made from monocotyledonous types, these differences may be in order. The simultaneous formation of tetrads within a pollen grain of the dicotyledons may account for the variations. *Carthamus* and *Allium* show certain fundamental differences.

The aftereffects of colchicine point out a possible influence upon pairing at meiosis in *Antirrhinum* as long as 6 weeks and possibly

TABLE 4.3

ACTION OF COLCHICINE ON CHIASMATA IN *Fritillaria*

(After Barber, 1940)

Treatment	Total Number	Percentage Proximal Locations	Percentage Medium Locations	Percentage Distal Locations
Control.........	215	92	6.9	1.1
0.5%..........	127	62	25.5	12.5
0.25%..........	80	70	17.5	12.5

up to 15 weeks after treatment of the plant.[129] An increase in univalents was 37 per cent among the treated plants compared with control.[129] A time lapse of such long duration between treatment and the colchicine-effect is of particular interest. Whether the colchicine is retained in the plant or the chromosomal mechanism is specifically affected was not determined. Similar meiotic irregularities were found

in treated plants of *Ribes* that remained diploid, and thus meiotic irregularities induced by colchicine would seem to be carried along,
not entirely explainable by tetraploidy.[143]

    Colchicum autumnale L. is a sterile plant in middle and southern
Japan. Cytological analysis showed many irregularities during meiosis
of these plants.[138] In contrast to these figures, the root tip mitoses

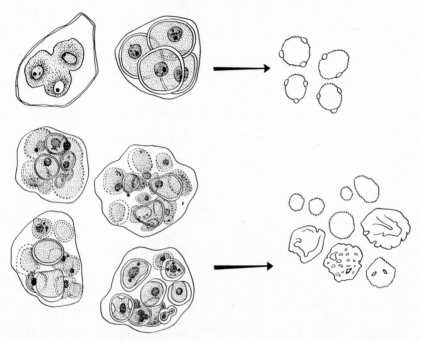

Fig. 4.5—**Above.** Untreated pollen mother cells and pollen. **Below.** The large multicellular pollen mother cells and abnormal pollen grains of **Carthamus tinctorius.** Flowers
treated in an early stage of development. (After Krythe)

were regular. The pollen grains from *Colchicum* were irregular, being
monosporic, disporic, trisporic, or tetrasporic. Many grains carried
fragments. The interpretation made from these studies was to the
effect that colchicine contained in the cells of *Colchicum* created an
autotoxicosis that led to sterility in this species.

    Irregular pollen and poor germination were not reported for a
European representative of *C. autumnale* L. used for pollen tube
germination.[60] In this instance the pollen tubes that formed did not
show a resistance to the presence of colchicine added to the medium.
There was no evidence that the pollen of *Colchicum* carried the drug
within the protoplasm of the grains since responses obtained were
reportedly the same as pollen tubes of other species not known to
produce colchicine, e.g., *Polygonatum*[35] and *Antirrhinum.*[127]

If the microspore nucleus is treated with colchicine, a typical c-mitosis appears. Since the haploid numbers prevail, an otherwise precise picture of the c-mitosis can be obtained. A diploid uninucleate pollen grain is formed after the c-mitosis (Fig. 4.3).

When monad microspores with numbers higher than haploid divide without colchicine, some interesting cells are formed. These may be regarded as an aftereffect of colchicine. Multipolar divisions are common, and in particular, a tripolar division gives rise to a huge grain, with two vegetative cells appressed close to the wall, and one generative cell. On occasion, two generative cells are formed.[79] These conditions are similar to the recovery phases described in earlier chapters.

Pollen grains of *Polygonatum* with one generative cell, a haploid, and a tube cell were tested for c-mitotic characteristics (Fig. 4.2).[35] The method of testing is described in detail in Chapter 16. In Chapters 2 and 3, illustrative material was drawn from pollen tube c-mitosis, but here it is pertinent to point out that the c-mitosis in this structure never exceeds the diploid number. Very rarely do the c-pairs become completely separated, so reversion to the interphase goes from an arrested metaphase rather than through c-anaphase. Enough tests have been run to report conclusively that there is a termination to c-mitosis and, unlike the divisions in root tips that continue to build high numbers, multiple-ploidy has never been found in pollen tubes with *Polygonatum* or reported from other sources. Then the microgametophyte never exceeds diploidy.

In the case of embryo sac development in *Tradescantia,* the nuclei that regularly divide during the process of gametophyte formation seem to build up the amount of chromatin, although as is expected, no spindle forms with colchicine. Therefore, the chromosomes remain together. The size of the large nucleus, the size of the embryo sac, and a tendency toward cell formation lead one to infer that c-mitoses proceed to but do not go beyond the eight-cell condition, normal for an embryo sac in *Tradescantia* (Fig. 4.6). Aside from the c-mitotic aspect, the unusual increase in the embryo sac beyond that for the control is of interest in light of our discussion about the action of colchicine on growth processes involving increase in volume.[148]

The ovules of *Carthamus tinctorius* did not develop into seeds, and no descriptive cytology accompanied the successive stages that must have taken place when colchicine acted while the embryo sac stages were in formation. This would be of interest for a comparison with *Tradescantia.*[73, 95]

4.3–1: Gametophytes of mosses, liverworts, and ferns. In 1908, a series of experiments with mosses demonstrated that polyploidy could be induced artificially. The Marchals used regenerative tissues to isolate polyploid races. Three decades elapsed between the first work early in the twentieth century and the next significant colchicine experiments.[64] Colchicine has been tried recently for a number of mosses, using protonemata and propagula, treating the tissues in special culturing media. Size differences between colchicine-treated and untreated cells have been used as criteria for the changes in number of chromosomes (Table 4.4).

Diploid gametophytes of the male and female thalli from *Marchantia polymorpha* were made by colchicine.[9] Chromosomal check showed that the numbers were increased. Another hepatic, *Pallavacinia* spp., was subjected to colchicine.[157] Again new patterns of growth showed that changes were induced. One may assume that the number of chromosomes was increased, although the modification in cellular form without a corresponding increase in chromosomes makes

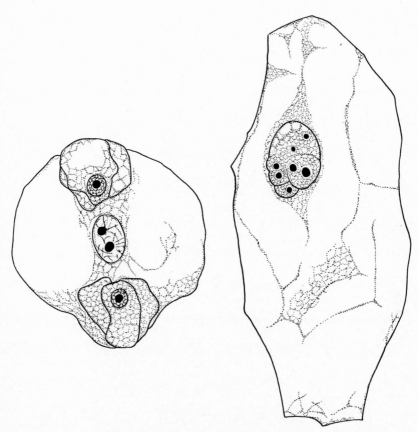

Fig. 4.6—Embryo-sac stages of Tradescantia. Untreated stage with cells distributed in the sac and a smaller cavity. Treated stage with all nuclear material grouped in the center of sac. The size is not a response to polyploidy. (After Walker)

TABLE 4.4
ACTION OF COLCHICINE ON ALGAE AND GAMETOPHYTES OF MOSSES,
LIVERWORTS, AND FERNS

Species	Results	Reference
Aulacomnium androgynum	morphological changes	4–64
Cladophora spp.	cross wall thickened	4–53
Closterium spp.	temporary inhibition	4–80
Dryopteris felix-mas	morphological changes	4–117
D. subpubescens	abnormal sperms	4–94
Gonium spp.	temporary inhibition	4–80
Goniopteris prolifera	abnormal sperms	4–94
Hormidium spp.	leukophytic isolate	4–125
Hydrodictyon spp.	cellular changes	4–53
Marchantia polymorpha	diploid gametophytes	4–9
Micrasterias thomasianas	no c-mitosis	4–67
Nitella mucronata		cf.4–88
Nostoc commune		cf.4–88
Oedogonium spp.	polyploids	4–140
Oedogonium	cellular wall changes	4–53
Pallavacinia	morphological changes	4–157
Polystoma	temporary inhibition	4-80
Spirogyra spp.	plastid changes	4–158 4–68
Ulva spp.	temporary inhibition	4-80

it less certain than previously believed possible for chromosomal numbers to be increased as cell form changed.

Fern prothalli and sporogenous tissues were tested for the induction of polyploidy following colchicine.[117] Evidences of changes in numbers were obtained for several species of ferns. In another application of colchicine to growing prothallia regularly producing spermatozoids, some unusually large sperms were obtained. Also some changes in the shape of cells were noticed along with the increases in size. Dilute solutions were used for early stages of germination of the prothalli.

Information at hand shows that the gametophyte stages of green plants can be doubled in manner similar to the sporophytic cells, notably among the seed plants.

4.4: Microbiological Data

Controlled cultures using unicellular organisms are admirably suited for experiments with colchicine. A wide concentration range may be used because the strongest dosages show a minimum toxicity. Furthermore, the experimental subjects are numerous considering the bacteria, yeasts, filamentous fungi, algae, and protozoa. Considerable preliminary work has been started, but contradictory conclusions and no small amount of confusion still exist.

In some cases the methods are not clearly described, nor are they carefully planned. Modifications such as concentration, media, and exposure would prove helpful. The interpretations have been very narrow, and patterned generally after the known action of colchicine upon the nucleus of vascular plants and multicellular organisms. As an illustration, the doubling of chromosomes is a remarkable action with vascular plants, and it would be helpful to know more about the hereditary materials in bacteria, but colchicine can hardly resolve the problem of chromosomes in bacteria when cytologists have had such great difficulties in demonstrating structures in untreated cultures.

Yeast cells that have an advantage over bacteria in size of internal structures have been tested with colchicine. The results can not be considered decisive. Even among the algae where chromosome numbers for species have been established, there are no clear cytological data to prove that the number of chromosomes can be doubled by colchicine. There is discussion of haploids, diploids, and tetraploids among fungi, but present work with colchicine does not provide answers either through demonstration of chromosomes or by genetic evidence.

Changes in the sizes of cells within a culture and direct action upon the growing organism indicate that the drug has some influence upon growth processes related to increase in size. Of course, these changes are not transmitted to succeeding generations. The mechanism of growth by cellular enlargement can not be analyzed from such tests. Metabolism of bacteria in relation to colchicine represents an unexplored field. Preliminary work has been done. In 1907, interesting work was done on temperature and toxicity using cultures of *Paramecium*.[58] Otherwise, this field of experimentation has been overlooked.

Finally the processes of differentiation and cellular structure are influenced by colchicine. Fungi and algae show evidence that during the process of cell wall formation the action of colchicine modifies structure.[53] These aspects are treated in a subsequent section of this chapter.

4.4–1: Bacteria. Tests with colchicine have included a range of species.[19, 149, 17, 159, 37, 113, 66, 51, 134, 63, 41, 109, 35, 25, 13, 14, 43, 144, 104] Some report no reaction and others claim that colchicine acts upon growth by inhibition. Toxicity was also noted (Table 4.5).

Certain species of bacteria tolerate high concentrations of colchicine in the medium. One source of powdered colchicine had bacteria present in the material; small quantities of powder added to sterile solutions of colchicine showed species of *Agrobacterium*.[35] For a number of species of microorganisms, colchicine without any additional nutrient supported bacterial growth. It was a habitat for bacteria. Undoubtedly these forms were able to use colchicine as a food.

The bacteria growing in a medium of strong dosage (1 per cent) produced aberrant cells larger than the initial culture, but no continuation of these types has been possible. An increase in size may represent a condition similar to the cell enlargements for vascular plants. These are not hereditary changes. Single cell isolations have not been reported. It would be of interest to know more about these types. They should be singled out for subculture, since mass transfer for isolating the particular deviates has objections. Some morphological alteration temporary for a specific culture undoubtedly has been obtained. Increases amounting to 40 per cent were measured for *Bacillus mesentericus*.[113]

Polynuclear cells in *Escherichia coli* cultures were reported but no follow-up of this work has been discovered.[134] Apparently a repetition has not been accomplished.

In a metabolism test, respiration was inhibited in *Micrococcus aureus*. A growth stimulation was obtained for *Photobacterium phosphoreum*.[104] No changes were observed in the desoxyribose nucleic acid and the ribose nucleic acid when cultures of *Micrococcus aureus* were used.[17] This is a sample of the fragments of information; more are tabulated elsewhere (Table 4.5).

4.4–2: Yeasts and other fungi. The common brewers' yeast, *Saccharomyces cerevisiae,* has been tested by more independent workers than any other of the microorganisms. A variety of concentrations of colchicine were used and different techniques for culture, as well as staining to determine cytological changes were tried.[116, 5, 4, 83, 41, 126, 54, 39, 144, 75, 9, 6, 119, 52, 132, 145]

A wide choice of responses is at hand, ranging from reports of no action to those citing definite cytological change demonstrated by special staining methods. Dumbbell-shaped nuclei were seen after a 96-hour treatment with 0.1 per cent colchicine. Other workers were unable to obtain these same results (Table 4.6).

TABLE 4.5

ACTION OF COLCHICINE ON BACTERIA

Species	Results	Reference
Agrobacterium spp.	growth not inhibited	4–35
Bacillus mesentericus	size increase 40%, growth changes	4–113
Bacterium megatherium	negative results	4–149
Bacterium spp.	no action	4–66
Bacterium spp.	indecisive results	4–43
"Bacteria"	no action	4–144
"Coliform bacteria"	mutations	4–109
Escherichia coli	polynuclear cells	4–134
E. coli phage		4–25
Micrococcus spp.	inactive	4–19
M. aureus	negative results	4–19
Micrococcus spp.	morphological changes	4–149
M. aureus	respiration inhibited	4–17 4–159
Mycobacterium tuberculosis	stimulates cells, prevents variants	4–63
Photobacterium phosphoreum	growth increases	4–104
Proteus vulgaris	inhibition	4–37
Streptococcus catarrhalis	toxic action	4–149
S. hemolyticus	inhibition	4–37

Camphor induced giantlike cells now called the "camphor forms." In old cultures these appear with low frequency. A few were found after treatment with colchicine, but their frequency was not high enough to warrant the conclusion that colchicine had the same capacity as camphor to produce giant forms.[4]

In light of the known antagonistic action of ethanol as discovered for cells of *Allium*, the production of alcohol by the yeast cell itself may serve as a kind of antidote or protection against colchicine.[82] These facts have not been verified with experimental data.

Brewing tests did not bring out specific differences between treated and control cultures of *Saccharomyces cerevisiae*.[82] The usual sedimentation, foam head, and other comparative values revealed no changes induced by colchicine. Methylene blue was decolorized more rapidly as evidence of some basic metabolic change.

There is a possibility that colchicine may serve as a source of energy. Another conclusion led to the idea that the drug serves as a buffer against the toxic substances accumulating in an active culture. Filamentous fungi from a variety of families[9] have been tested for possible induction of polyploidy. A polyploid strain of *Penicillium notatum* was isolated in one laboratory.[52] This new strain was supposed to yield more penicillin than the original strain. The polyploids were obtained by another group who rechecked these specific types. Polyploidy and increased penicillin was not confirmed (Table 4.6).[119]

TABLE 4.6

ACTION OF COLCHICINE ON YEASTS AND OTHER FUNGI

Species	Results	Reference
Allomyces javanicus	changes induced	4–6
Aspergillus spp.	mutants	4–132
Botrytis cinerea	hypertrophy of hyphae	4–145
Coprinus radians	conidia influenced	4–144
Diaporthe perniciosa	no conidial formation	4–145
Mucor sp.	no change	4–9
Penicillium notatum	polyploids	4–52
P. notatum	no polyploids	4–119
Psilocybe semilanceolata	conidia changed	4–144
Saccharomyces cerevisiae	no changes noted	4–4 4–83 4–144 4–75 4–5
S. cerevisiae	cytological changes	4–126
	cells enlarge	4–39
	methylene blue decolorized more rapidly	4–41
	stimulation	4–116
	inhibition	4–54
Stropharia merderia	conidia changed	4–144
Verticillium dahliae	no conidial formation	4–145
"Wide range of families"	no change	4–9

Hypertrophy of the hyphae and failure to form conidia were regularly noted among several species of fungi, but doubling of chromosomes or evidence of polyploidy was never demonstrated. Possible mutagenesis[123] was reported for *Streptomyces griseus*. Concentrations ranging from 0.5 to 1.0 per cent introduce changes in growth patterns that resemble the tumors previously reviewed. No better specific information is at hand for the yeasts and fungi than for bacteria. That mycelial growth may be influenced is probable, but polyploidy or induction of mutations is extremely doubtful (Table 4.6).

Colchicine increases the frequency with which resistant sporangia of *Allomyces javanicus* developed mixed thalli from the sporophytic generation. When germinating zygotes were treated, some nuclei were thought to have been converted into polyploids. The cytological records of chromosomes were not available to confirm the polyploidy.[6] A series of treatments involved the use of colchicine and sodium nucleate, so the specific action of colchicine may be in some way related to the use of the sodium nucleate.

4.4–3: Algae. The first artificially induced polyploid among plants might well be credited to Gerassimov who treated *Spirogyra* by temperature shock and apparently succeeded in increasing the volume of the nucleus. This was done in 1901. A confirmation made some years later strongly supports the thesis that *Spirogyra* cells were doubled. One might hope that colchicine would be useful in repeating this classical experiment by chemical means, or at least demonstrate that the drug is not effective. The results with algae and colchicine are not any farther along than those with the other specimens of fungi.[140, 158, 125, 65, 67, 180, 9, 88] The treatment of *Spirogyra* with colchicine should be tried with a wide range of concentrations and cytological control.

A polyploid strain of *Oedogonium* was said to be obtained from treatment with colchicine, but no exact cytological data went with the report to prove the doubling of chromosomes had taken place.[140]

Temporary inhibition of mitosis in cells of *Micrasterias thomasianas* was recorded in cultures. The general conclusion was reached that colchicine was ineffective except for some temporary changes in plastid structure.[67] Unfortunately, only limited ranges of concentrations of colchicine were employed for the *Micrasterias* work. Some dosages may be more effective than others.

Leukophytic variants were isolated from colonies of *Hormidium* sp. treated with colchicine.[125] Several generations of subculture brought a return to the chlorophyllous type. If a change was induced, the weakness of a non-green variant did not permit a survival in competition with unchanged chlorophyllous types.

Plastid changes are to be expected in the treated generation. Whether or not changes are retained upon transfer to culture without colchicine remains unconfirmed. Supposedly the elasticity of plastids in *Spirogyra* changes under the influence of colchicine.[158]

Inhibitions at higher concentrations were secured with *Gonium* and *Polystoma*. Upon recovery the cells remained diploid as far as the investigators were able to judge. Some action seems to have been registered upon the zoospores and zygotes of the green alga *Ulva*.[80]

Studies dealing with the cell wall and colchicine are of interest from the view of differentiation. Cell structure and composition of the wall are modified by colchicine (Table 4.4).

4.4–4: Protozoa. A number of investigations[3, 11, 20, 24, 49, 57, 58, 71, 118, 136, 144] on various aspects of colchicine and the protozoa, as well as regenerative studies[136] have been published since 1938. As long ago as 1907, the action of colchicine on *Paramecium* was studied in relation to toxicity and temperature changes.[58] Increasing toxicity with raising the temperature was demonstrated by this early work. No one has repeated these studies in the modern period, but most have been concerned with cell division and problems of polyploidy. Undoubtedly the influence of cytology and genetics preconditioned much of the experimentation since 1937.

The species of protozoa tried for response to colchicine show that strong solutions can be tolerated at 22° to 24°C. Fission occurs for a number of species.[71] The microinjections of colchicine give further information on the penetrability of the drug that may influence the reaction. Failure of the drug to penetrate the cell may be one key in explaining the resistance to colchicine of protozoa as a group.

Some retardation in growth and changes in new cells developing within a culture containing colchicine have been recorded. As a general rule, the direct action of the chemical upon the cell or nucleus has not been demonstrated. Some increases in "radio-sensitivity" accompanied the pretreatment by colchicine.[57] In this case the cells appeared to be more sensitive to action of the X-ray after a treatment.[57]

Table 4.7 may be used as a reference for a survey of work completed upon the protozoa as a group.

4.5: Differentiation Processes

After a treatment with colchicine the new leaves, developing when growth is resumed, appear wrinkled and distorted. Apparently the drug has directly or indirectly caused these new types. Some changes are a result of chimeras which are discussed in connection with polyploidy, yet other very similar anomalies cannot be correlated directly with an increase in the number of chromosomes. These cellular and

TABLE 4.7

ACTION OF COLCHICINE ON PROTOZOA

Species	Results	Reference
Amoeba proteus	fission not inhibited with 2% solution	4–71
A. sphaeronucleus	microinjection inhibits division of nucleus	4–20
Chilomonas spp.	fission not inhibited	4–71
Chlamydomonas spp.	not effective on division	4–49 4–83 4–144
Chlamydomonas spp.	growth retarded	4–24
Euglena spp.	ineffective	4–71 4–144 4–83
Oxytricha spp.	no action	4–71
Paramecium spp.	raising temperature increases toxic action of colchicine	4–58
P. caudatum	fission not retarded	4–71
P. caudatum	growth retarded	4–3
P. caudatum	radiosensitivity increased	4–57
P. multimicronucleatum	no action	4–71
Peranema	fission	4–71
Plasmodium relictum	no retarding action	4–11
P. vivax	no action	4–118

anatomical variations are probably a direct action from the drug by other means than nuclear changes.[153] As an example, the c-tumor response occurs from contact with colchicine. Yet more difficult to explain are the changes that persist into several generations of propagation.[40] Vegetative propagations that continue the anatomical variations are not as difficult to explain as variations that reportedly persist or occur after several generations of seed propagation.

Not so much attention has been directed to the cell wall and related problems of differentiation as to nuclear aspects, i.e., c-mitosis.[35] Colchicine causes modification of cytoplasmic and cellular processes.[131] Sufficient evidence is at hand to make this assumption. The actions of c-mitosis, the c-tumor, and differentiation are independent although very closely related to each other. For example, the nearly simultaneous action upon division, enlargement, and differentiation can conceivably take place when unicellulars are subjected to colchicine. At least the processes may merge into each other so closely that separating the actions becomes difficult or nearly impossible.

Analysis and reports from widely different sources are brought together in this section that treats the microscopic, microchemical, and gross anatomical changes in plants.[22, 121, 50, 53, 151, 105, 112, 135]

4.5–1: Microscopic and microchemical data. The cell walls of treated plants show different types of depositions which form striations.[53] These are regularly observed for pollen tubes growing in media containing colchicine. When stained, their distinction becomes more clear. The submicroscopic structure of pollen tube walls has not been studied. Data are accumulating from other sources that point up the possibilities in this field.[73]

Excellent photomicrographs showed that the cells of algae were changed after growing in media carrying colchicine.[53] The newly formed portions of cells in *Oedogonium* showed swelling and local thickenings inside the cell (Fig. 4.7). These were scattered without regular order along the wall. Inner cell walls of *Cladophora* became thicker than controls, showing that unusual depositions had occurred (Fig. 4.8). Finally, the regular network characteristic for *Hydrodictyon* became distorted through swelling of the middle parts of connecting cells (Fig. 4.9). Also the points of contact were enlarged. These three cases comparing treated and untreated cells leave no doubt that colchicine exerts a strong influence during cellular differentiation.[53]

The root hairs grown in cultures containing colchicine (0.25 to 0.5 per cent) offer a comparable source for analysis of cell wall structure. Earlier we described the tumors that were formed on root hairs. Now microscopic and microchemical study has correlated the cell structure with the form taken under treatment. After the cell walls were stained with chloro-zinc-iodide and these structures viewed with polarized light, the irregularly deposited micelles were in distinct contrast to regular arrangements viewed in untreated root hairs. Photomicrographs with polarized light are instructive for these comparisons.[53]

Pollen mother cells developing in colchicine (*Carthamus tinctorius* L.) were protoplasmically interconnected at the points where cells touched each other.[73] Later, as pollen grains formed, one large cell was composed of numerous pollen grains within a common wall (Fig. 4.10). Another developmental feature was the wall intrusion which was essentially an excessive deposition of a callous-like material on the inner wall (Fig. 4.10). The origin and nature of these developments are unknown, but the change is an effect of colchicine.

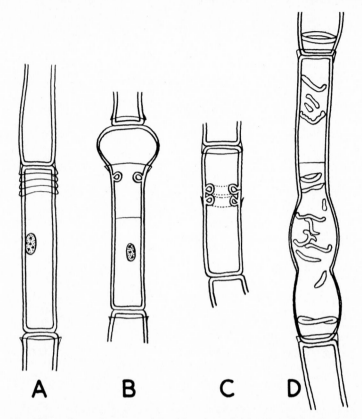

Fig. 4.7—**Oedogonium** cultures, treated and untreated. **A.** Untreated cell showing the usual ring and cellular striations. **B.** Enlargement caused by colchicine, indentation of cellular layers a result of treatment. **C.** Inner cell thickening, and depositions. **D.** Enlargement of the cell from treatment and irregular depositions. (After Gorter)

An interesting vascularization following recovery from colchicine has been described for the huge cells in *Allium* roots that form in the differentiated pericycle at points where lateral roots originate. Scalariform vessels developed and a unique tumor was left buried in the root.[156] Nuclear contents that were estimated to contain over 1000 chromosomes as a result of 6 or more c-mitoses disappeared during the differentiation process. A complex series of pretreatment with NAA (0.0002 per cent) and colchicine (0.25 per cent) interspersed with recovery periods preceded this development. No one can doubt that an interesting problem of differentiation is presented by this work.

Stomatal development regularly proceeds from an embryonic mother cell and eventually forms the guard cells,[139, 151, 88] with associated subsidary components. Independently, several investigations have shown that colchicine interferes with this differentiating process.[74] These stomatal anomalies, brought into focus by reports from such cases as pollen tube walls, root hairs, algal and fungal cell walls, as well as other differentiating cells, afford added evidence that colchicine acts in some way upon cells that are differentiating. This is the first time that so many diverse instances of the action of colchicine have been brought together under one discussion. These problems deserve attention. We have not exhausted the list of instances that may have further bearing on this aspect.

4.5—2: Gross anatomical variations. When the outer layer of cells, the epidermis, has a different number of chromosomes from those of cells deeper in the leaf, some distortions become evident. These cases are well documented and belong to problems in polyploidy. Less known and understood are the cases that cannot be readily explained by chromosomal numbers.[153] A few of these instances are described here.

New shoots of *Ligustrum* arose after treatment with colchicine.[82] The leaves were darker green, appeared to be thicker, and answered the description of an induced polyploid. These characters were transferred several times by vegetative propagation. The chromosomal numbers did not correlate with these differences.

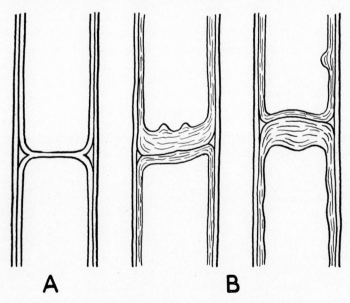

A　　　　　　　**B**

Fig. 4.8—The end walls of **Cladophora** with extra depositions in treated cases, **B**, compared with control, **A**. (After Gorter)

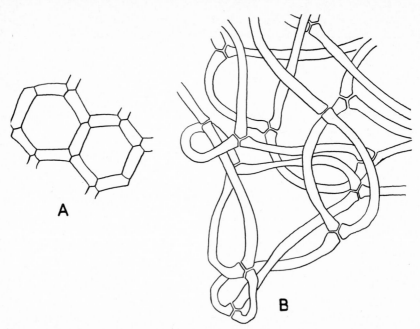

Fig. 4.9—The network of **Hydrodictyon** becomes distended and unorganized by treatment with colchicine. **A.** Control cells. **B.** Treated cellular network. (After Gorter)

Sugar beets developed after a treatment showed consistent size increase for roots, but polyploidy was not found with these particular cases. Larger roots are regularly developed in known triploid and tetraploid progenies.[79] Barring some error in method, the explanation for larger beets falls outside the scope of polyploidy. Perplexing variations appeared in subsequent progenies of sorghum plants that were treated with colchicine. Chromosomal numbers were diploid, so polyploidy was not correlated with these types. Additional progenies from treated F_1 plants were significantly lacking in uniformity as compared with untreated cases. These variants were not classified with aberrants reported previously and described above, i.e., the *Ligustrum* variations, because while the lack of uniformity followed a segregation pattern, the control material did not show a similar segregation.[82] Although no explanation was given, the hereditary mechanism was not ruled out as a possible cause. The instance is cited in this discussion primarily to emphasize that results from treating colchicine are not in every case quickly disposed of as the effect of a c-mitosis, leading to polyploidy which in turn is the explanation for new variants. That colchicine has caused a more basic deviation not correlated with a doubling of chromosomes seems quite reasonable even though the full explanation remains in question.

A survey of the literature[36] on colchicine hints that more examples could be obtained in which colchicine induces changes not directly correlated with a change in the number of chromosomes. Obviously hundreds of polyploids have been induced by colchicine. Yet, alongside these majority reports come the difficult cases that appear as anomalous anatomical and morphological deviations. These are certainly problems for future study.

4.6: Metabolism and Colchicine

Physiological studies with colchicine that had some relation to c-mitosis were touched upon briefly in Chapter 3. At the basis of cellular changes such as c-tumors and cell differentiation there must also be physiological processes involving action of colchicine. These are difficult to evaluate. However, tests have been run that show colchicine has a capacity to influence certain metabolic processes as understood by special tests.[141, 102, 92]

Enzymatic reactions performed *in vitro* proved that the transformation of starch by malt diastase was accelerated. The basis for stimulation of this order was not explained, although as a constituent of the reaction medium, colchicine favored the rate of enzymatic action. Increasing the concentration of colchicine increased the rate of reaction correspondingly.[127]

Diastase activity was scored by quantitative measurements of the increase in sugar (Benedict's solution). Control values were given at 100.0, and if the reaction time was accelerated, the value accordingly fell below 100.0. With each tenfold increase in concentration the rate was increased. Values of 84.0 ± 2.5, 78.9 ± 2.5, and 70.3 ± 1.7 were obtained for three concentrations, 10 p.p.m., 100 p.p.m., and

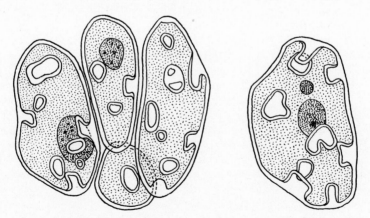

Fig. 4.10—Cellular intrusions among the pollen mother cells of *Carthamus tinctorius* caused by treatment with colchicine. (After Krythe)

1000 p.p.m., respectively. In other words, a control solution that reduced 25 cc. of Benedict's solution in a certain time was equal to 100 and the solution (1:1000) with colchicine showed a value of 70.3 ± 1.7 because the time taken to reduce the standard amount was shortened, as expressed by these values.[127]

These data are interesting when correlated with reports of stimulation in growth through seed and shoot treatments.[70] Colchicine may act upon enzymes in such a way as to accelerate the transfer of starch to sugar, which processes may in turn stimulate growth.

Excised roots of maize treated with colchicine showed lowered rates of respiration and dipeptidase response. Also, the elongation of individual roots was retarded. Since conditions vary from test to test the comparisons may not be wholly alike.[110]

Virus tumor tissues (Black's original R_1 strain from *Rumex acetosa* L.) were treated with a wide range of concentrations (0.00001 to 100.0 p.p.m.) of colchicine.[101] Growth was stimulated with concentrations of 0.02 to 0.2 p.p.m. with maximum acceleration at 0.1 p.p.m. Increasing the concentrations beyond a point of stimulation brought inhibition. The maximum uptake of oxygen occurred at 0.1 p.p.m. This value was estimated at 25 per cent above the control. Growth was measured over a period of 3 weeks and respiration tests ran for 3 hours. Curves were plotted to show the similarities and differences.[101]

Decreases in structural viscosity paralleled the formation of c-tumors in root tips of *Allium;* the decreases were most pronounced at 24 hours.[103] Changes in cytoplasmic proteins were correlated with changes that led to formation of tumors.

Rates of plasmolysis among *Elodea* were changed by a pretreatment with colchicine.[88] Not only the time for changing the form of cytoplasm but the shape of structures formed after plasmolysis was different in controls and treated cells.

REFERENCES

1. AMERIO, G., AND DALLA, N. Studi di citologia sperimentale: l'effeto di agenti chimici et fisici diversi sopra la struttura della cellule vegetale. Ist. Lombardo Rendic. III. 75:109–18. 1942.
2. BARBER, H. The experimental control of chromosome pairing in *Fritillaria.* Jour. Genet. 43:359–74. 1942.
3. BARROS, R. A colchicina eos Paramecios. Univ. São Paulo Bol. Fac. Filos. Cien. e Letras III Biol. Geral. 17:97–116. 1940.
4. BAUCH, R. Beziehungen zwischen polyploidisierenden, carcinogenen und phytohormonalen Substanzen. Auslösung von Gigas-Mutationen der Hefe durch pflanzliche Wuchsstoffe. Naturwiss. 30:420–21. 1942. Sulfonamides as antagonists to the polyploid effect of Colchicine. Naturwiss. 33:25–26. 1946. Sulfonamide und Colchicin. Ein botanischer Beitrag zum Sulfonamidproblem. Die Pharmazie. 4:1–7. 1949.
5. BEAMS, H., *et al.* Cytological studies on yeast cells with special reference to the budding process. Cytologia. 11:30–36. 1940.
6. BENEKE, E., AND WILSON, G. Treatment of *Allomyces javanicus* var. Japonesis Indoh with colchicine and sodium nucleate. Mycologia. 42:519–22. 1950.

7. BERGER, C., AND WITKUS, E. A cytological study of c-mitosis in the polysomatic plant *Spinacia oleracea*, with comparative observation on *Allium cepa*.
Torrey Bot. Club Bull. 70:457–67. 1943. Further studies of the cytological
effects of combined treatments with colchicine and naphthaleneacetic acid.
Amer. Jour. Bot. 36:794–95. 1949.

8. BHADURI, P. Effects of different forms of colchicine on roots of *Vicia faba*
L. Jour. Roy. Micr. Soc. 59:245–76. 1939.

9. BLAKESLEE, A. The present and potential service of chemistry to plant
breeding. Amer. Jour. Bot. 26:163–72. 1939. Effect of induced polyploidy
in plants. Amer. Nat. 75:117–35. 1941.

10. BOAS, F., AND GISTL, R. Über einige Colchicinwirkungen (Protoplasma. 33:
301–10. 1939). Abstr. Bot. Zentralbl. 33: (12) :82. 1940.

11. BOATNEY, R., AND YOUNG, M. The effect of colchicine on bird malaria. Jour.
Parasit. 25:446–47. 1939.

12. BOND, L. Colchicine stimulation of seed germination in *Petunia axillaris*.
Jour. Hered. 33:200–201. 1942.

13. BONNETTI, E., AND ILLENYI, A. Die Wirkung des Colchicins auf den Bakte-
rienstoffwechsel. Zentralbl. Bakter. 2–3:114. 1941.

14. BOYD, J., AND BRADLEY, P. On the assessment of the influence of chemical
compounds on bacteriophage multiplication. Brit. Jour. Exp. Path. 32:
397–407. 1951.

15. BOYLAND, E., AND BOYLAND, M. The action of colchicine and *B. typhosus*
extract. Biochem. Jour. 31:454. 1937.

16. BRUMFIELD, R. Effect of colchicine pretreatment on the frequency of chromosomal aberrations induced by X-radiation. Proc. Nat. Acad. Sci. 29:190–93.
1943.

17. CAFIERO, M., AND ZAMBRUNO, D. Sul' azione della colchicina sulla moltiplicazione della *Staphylococcus aureus*. Boll. Soc. Ital. Biol. Sper. 24:1326–27.
1948.

18. CHARGAFF, E., *et al.* Inhibition of mitotic poisoning by meso-inositol. Science.
108:556–58. 1948.

19. CHODAT, F., AND MARTIN, G. Sur l'inefficacité de la colchicine dans un pro-
cessus purement nucléaire. C. R. Soc. Phys. et Hist. Nat. Genève. 55:70–71.
1938.

20. COMMANDON, J., AND FONBRUNE, P. DE. Action de la colchicine sur *Amoeba
sphaeronucleus*. Obtention de variétés géantes. C. R. Soc. Biol. Paris.
136:410–11, 423, 460, 746, 747, 763. 1942.

21. CONSTANTIN, T. Mitogenesis and colchicine in the onion root. Bull. Histol.
Appl. Physiol. Path. Tech. Microscop. 17:97–108. 1940.

22. Cormack, R. Intercellular inclusions in white mustard roots induced by colchicine treatment. Nature. 163:362–63. 1949.

23. CORNIL, L. Action of colchicine in aqueous solution on germination of wheat.
C. R. Soc. Biol. Paris. 138:932–33. 1944.

24. CORNMAN, I. Disruption of mitosis in *Colchicum* by means of colchicine.
Biol. Bull. 81:297–98. 1941. Susceptibility of *Colchicum* and *Chlamydomonas*
to colchicine. Bot. Gaz. 104:50–61. 1942. Alleviation of mitotic poisoning
by glucose. Jour. Cell. and Comp. Physiol. 35:301–2. 1950.

25. CZEKALOWSKI, J., AND DOLBY, D. Effect of enzyme inhibitors on the genesis
of phage. Nature. 163:719–20. 1949.

26. D'AMATO, F. The effect of M-inositol on c-mitosis and c-tumor reaction.
Caryologia. Pisa. 1:358–61. 1949. The quantative study of mitotic poisons.
by the *Allium cepa* test. Data and problems. Protoplasma. 39:423–33. 1950.

27. ————, AND AVANZI, M. Reazioni di natura auxinica ed effetti rizogeni in
Allium cepa L. Studio cito-istologico sperimentale. Nuovo Giornale Botanico
Italiana N. S. 55:161–213. 1948.

28. DANGEARD, P., *et al.* Étude relative à l'action de la colchicine sur la cyclose
cytoplasmique. C. R. Soc. Biol. Paris. 141:1055–57. 1947.

29. DERMEN, H. Colchicine, polyploidy and technique. Bot. Rev. 6:599–635.
1940. A cytological analysis of polyploidy. Jour. Hered. 29:210–29. 1938.

30. DEYSSON, G. Action simultanée du phényluréthane et de la colchicine sur
les méristèmes radiculaires d'*Allium cepa*. C. R. Acad. Sci. Paris. 220:367–69.

1945. Contribution à l'étude du "syndrome mitoclasique." Centre de Documentation Universitaire, Paris. 1948. Pharmacodynamic study of cellular division. Rev. Gen. Sci. 56:152–60. 1949.

31. DEYSSON, G., AND DEYSSON, M. Action of meso-inositol on growth and mitosis of higher plants. Bull. Soc. Chim. Biol. Paris. 32:268–75. 1950.

32. DOUTRE, L., AND BIRABEN, J. Pharmacodynamic activity of colchicine as a medicament for cancer. Action on cytoplasmic cyclosis. Jour. Méd. Bordeaux. 124:463–65. 1947.

33. DRAGOIU, I., AND CRISAN, C. The action of colchicine on the roots of the plants (*Allium cepa* and *Phaseolus vulgaris*). Bull. Acad. Méd. Roumaine. 4:326–38. 1939.

34. DUHAMET, L. Recherches sur l'action de l'hetero-auxine et de la colchicine sur la croissance de racines isolées de *Lupinus albus.* Rev. Cytol. et Cytophysiol. Vég. 8:35–75. 1945.

35. EIGSTI, O. A cytological study of colchicine effects in the induction of polyploidy in plants. Proc. Nat. Acad. Sci. 24:56–63. 1938. The effects of colchicine upon the division of the generative cell in *Polygonatum, Tradescantia,* and *Lilium.* Amer. Jour. Bot. 27:512–24. 1940. Colchicine — a bacterial habitat. Amer. Jour. Bot. 33:4. 1946.

36. ———, AND DUSTIN, P., JR. Colchicine bibliography. Lloydia. 10:65–114. 1947. Colchicine bibliography III. Lloydia. 12:185–207. 1949.

37. EULER, H. Factors affecting the pyruvic acid content of rat blood. Arkiv. Kemi. Mineral. Geol. 20A. No. 12. 10 pp. 1945. Growth ergones and antiergones. Svensk. Kem. Tid. 58:180–87. 1946. Action of colchicine and X-rays. Influence of saponin and digitalis glycosides on seed germination and mitosis. Arkiv. Kemi. Mineral. Geol. 22A. No. 14. 10 pp. 1946.

38. ———, AND PERJE, M. Action of vitamins and antivitamins on seed germination and mitosis. Arkiv. Kemi. Mineral. Geol. 20A. No. 2. Chem. Abst. 41:2125. 1945.

39. ———, et al. Changes produced in yeast cells by Röntgen rays and chemical substances. Z. Physiol. Chem. 277:1–17, 18–25. 1942.

40. FRANZL, R., AND CHARGAFF, E. Bacterial enzyme preparations oxidizing inositol and their inhibition by colchicine. Nature. 168:955–57. 1951.

41. FREI, W., AND BRUNNER, T. Beziehungen zwischen Zellteilung und Oxydation bei Bakterien. Schädigung der aeroben und anaeroben Oxydation von Bakterien mit Cyankali, Pyridin, Colchicin und Ultraviolettstrahlen. Helv. Physiol. et Pharm. Acta. 5:252–64. 1947.

42. FUNKE, G. Growth of water plants in solutions of phytohormones and other substances. Proc. Ned. Akad. Wetensch. 45:937–43. 1942–43.

43. GAROFALO, F. L'azione della colchicina. Boll. Soc. Ital. Biol. Sper. 22:394–95. 1946.

44. GARRIGUES, R. Effects of colchicine and chloral on the roots of *Vicia faba.* Rev. Cytol. et Cytophysiol. Vég. 4:261–301. 1940. Colchicine. La Nature. 1945:244–46. 1945.

45. GAVAUDAN, P. Pharmacodynamie de l'inhibition de la caryocinèse. Librairie le François, Paris. 1947.

46. ———, AND BREBION, G. The scale of functional inhibitions in the plant cell. Mem. Services Chim. État. Paris. 35:No. 3, 73–78. 1950.

47. ———, AND GAVAUDAN, N. Mécanisme d'action de la colchicine sur la caryocinèse des végétaux. C. R. Soc. Biol. Paris. 128:714–16. 1938.

48. ———, et al. La toxicologie générale et la notion d'activité thermodynamique. Mem. Services Chim. État. Paris. 31:384–423. 1944. L'importance de la notion d'activité thermodynamique en toxicologie et en pharmacodynamie. Rec. Trav. Scient. Station d'Ess. Bouchet. 1:5–22. 1945.

49. ———, AND KOBOZIEFF, N. Action of colchicine on caryokinesis and cytodieresis in *Chlamydomonalineae.* C. R. Soc. Biol. Paris. 127:790–93. 1938.

50. GEISSLER, G. Knob formation on onion roots by mitosis poisons, growth and germination inhibitors. Naturwiss. 37:563–64. 1950.

51. GOHAR, M., AND MAKKAWI, M. Antibacterial action of colchicine and colchiceine. Jour. Pharm. and Pharmacol. 3:415–19. 1951.

52. GORDON, W., AND McKECHNIE, J. Autopolyploidia induced in *Penicillium notatum* by colchicine. Anales Farm. Bioquim. Buenos Aires. 17:12–17. 1946.
53. GORTER, C. De invloed van colchicine op den groei van den celwand van wortelharen. Proc. Kon. Nederl. Akad. Wetensch. 48:3–12. 1945.
54. GRACE, N. Note on sulfanilamide and other chemicals that act as plant growth-promoting substances. Can. Jour. Res. 16:C, No. 3, 143–44. 1938.
55. GREMLING, G. Troubles morphologiques determinés par la colchicine chez les végétaux. Assoc. France Avanc. Sci. 63rd Session, Liege. Pp. 595–607. 1939.
56. GUINOCHET, M. Modifications of the physiochemical reactions of the plant cell, caused by mitosis-inhibiting substances. C. R. Acad. Sci. Paris. 210:579–80. 1940.
57. HALBERSTAEDTER, L., AND BACK, A. Influence of colchicine alone and combined with X-rays on *Paramecium*. Nature. 152:275–76. 1943.
58. HAUSMANN, W., AND KOLMER, W. Über die Einwirkung kolloidaler Gifte auf Paramacien. Biochem. Z. 3:503–7. 1907.
59. HAVAS, L. Is colchicine a "phytohormone"? Growth. 2:257–60. 1938. Parthenocarpy and accompanying hormonal syndromes induced by unrelated chemicals. Nature. 157:629–30. 1946. Problems of growth studied with the aid of colchicine in plants and animals. Ann. Soc. Roy. Sci. Med. et Nat. Bruxelles. 1:57; cf. Chem. Abst. 42:4676c. 1948. Hormone-mimetic and growth effects of colchicine in plants. Exp. Cell Res. Suppl. 1:597–601. 1949. Effect of bee-venom on colchicine-induced tumors. Nature. 166:567–68. 1950.
60. ———, AND BALDENSPERGER, A. The oncological aspect of the "immunity" of *Colchicum* to colchicine. Science. 114:208–10. 1951.
61. ———, AND FELFOLDY, L. Fasciations and kindred teratisms induced in plants by polyploidogenic agents. Magyar. Biol. Kut. Muukai. 17:131–40. 1947.
62. HAWKES, J. Some effects of the drug colchicine on cell division. Jour. Genet. 44:11–22. 1942.
63. HEISE, F., AND STEENKEN, W. Growth and virulence of tubercle bacilli. A study of the effect of vitamin B_1, and B_6, riboflavine, colchicine, phthiocol and thyloquinone. Amer. Rev. Tuberc. 44:635–36. 1941.
64. HEITZ, E. Moosmutationen 1. Spontane und durch Colchicin ausgelöste polyploide Mutanten dei *Aulacomnium androgynum* (L.). Arch. Julius Klaus-Stift. 20:119–25. 1945. Über "Colchicinmuster." 8. Jahresber., Schweiz. Ges. Vererbungsforsch. Arch. Julius Klaus-Stift. (¾), pp. 497–99. 1948.
65. JAKOB, H. Influence de la colchicine sur le développement de certaines algues d'eau douce. C. R. Acad. Sci. Paris. 230:1203–5. 1950. Action de la colchicine sur certaines algues d'eau douce et comparison avec l'action des substances metaboliques en provenance d'algues. Rev. Gen. Bot. 58:348–52. 1951.
66. JENNISON, N. The inactivity of colchicine for bacteria. Jour. Bact. 39:20–21. 1940.
67. KALLIO, P. The significance of nuclear quantity in the genus *Micrasterias*. Ann. Bot. Soc. Zool. Bot. Fenn. 24:1–122. 1951.
68. KARTASHOVA, N. Treatment of vegetable cells with colchicine. C. R. Dokl. Acad. Sci. URSS 46:372–74. 1945.
69. KAYSER, F., AND BESSON, S. Action of sulfonamides and colchicine on development of pea roots. C. R. Soc. Biol. Paris. 142:84–86. 1948.
70. KING, C. Changes of carbohydrates of germinating wheat seeds in manganese sulfate, indoleacetic acid and colchicine media. Bot. Bull. Acad. Sinica. 1:9–24. 1947.
71. KING, R., AND BEAMS, H. Comparison of the effects of colchicine on division in protozoa and other cells. Jour. Cell. and Comp. Physiol. 15:252–54. 1940.
72. KOSTOFF, D. Induction of polyploidy by pulp and disintegrating tissues from *Colchicum* sp. Nature. 143:287–88. 1939.
73. KRYTHE, J. The effect of colchicine on the anthers of *Carthamus tinctorius* L. Proc. Acad. Sci. Amsterdam. 45:283–87. 1942.
74. LANG, K., *et al.* Über die Hemmung von Desoxyribonucleotide spaltenden Fermenten durch Colchicin. Experientia. 5:449. 1949.

75. LAUR, C. Experimental study of the action of colchicine on certain phases of cellular development. Ann. Anat. Path. 15:792–99. 1938.

76. LEE, T., AND HWANG, T. Growth stimulation by manganese sulfate, indole-3-acetic acid and, colchicine in pollen tube growth. Acta Brev. Sinensia. 8:21–22. 1944.

77. LEFEVRE, J. Actions similaires sur les mitoses végétales de l'anéthol et des substances du groupe de la colchicine. C. R. Soc. Biol. Paris. 133:616–18. 1940.

78. LETTRÉ, H.Über Mitosegifte. Ergebn. Physiol. 46:379–452. 1950. Über Synergisten von Mitosegiften V. Mitt. Versuche zur Aufhebung der synergistischen Wirkung durch Phosphagen. Naturwiss. 38:13. 1951.

79. LEVAN, A. The effect of colchicine on meiosis in *Allium*. Hereditas. 25:9–26. 1939. The effect of acenaphthene and colchicine on mitosis of *Allium* and *Colchicum*. Hereditas. 26:262–76. 1940. The macroscopic colchicine effect — a hormonic action? Hereditas. 28:244–45. 1942.

80. ―――, AND LEVRING, T. Some experiments on c-mitotic reactions with *Chlorophyceae* and *Phaeophyceae*. Hereditas. 28:400–408. 1942.

81. ―――, AND LOTFY, T. Naphthalene acetic acid in the *Allium test*. Hereditas. 35:337–74. 1949.

82. ―――, AND ÖSTERGREN, G. The mechanism of c-mitotic action. Observations on the naphthalene series. Hereditas. 29:381–443. 1943.

83. ―――, AND SANDWALL, C. Quantitative investigations on the reaction of yeast to certain biologically active substances. Hereditas. 29:164–78. 1943.

84. ―――, AND STEINEGGAR, E. The resistance of *Colchicum* and *Bulbocodium* to the c-mitotic action of colchicine. Hereditas. 33:552–66. 1947.

85. LEVINE, M. The effect of colchicine and acenaphthene in combination with X-rays on plant tissue. Torrey Bot. Club Bull. 72:563–74. 1945. Action of colchicine on cell division in human cancer, animal and plant tissues. Ann. N. Y. Acad. Sci. 51:1365–1406. 1951.

86. ―――, AND LEIN, J. The effect of various growth substances on the number and the length of roots of *Allium cepa*. Amer. Jour. Bot. 28:163–68. 1941.

87. LOO, T., AND TANG, Y. Growth stimulation by manganese sulphate, indole-3-acetic acid, and colchicine in the seed germination and early growth of several cultivated plants. Amer. Jour. Bot. 32:106–14. 1945.

88. MAIROLD, F. Studien an colchicinierten Pflanzen. Protoplasma. 37:445–521. 1943.

89. ―――, AND WEBER, F. *Matricaria chamomilla* durch Colchizinierung ohne Strahlenblüten. Phyton. 2:271–75. 1950.

90. MANGENOT, G. Substances mitoclasiques et cellules végétales. État actuel de la question d'après les travaux publiés jusqu'à la fin de 1940. Rev. Cytol. et Cytophysiol. Vég. 5:169–264. 1941. Action de la colchicine sur les racines d'*Allium cepa*. Hermann and Cie., Paris. 120 pp. 1942.

91. MARTIN, G. Action de la colchicine sur les tissus de topinambour cultivé *in vitro*. Rev. Cytol. et Cytophysiol. Vég. 8:1–34. 1945.

92. MARTINEZ, L. Influence of various alkaloids on the growth of wheat seedlings. Farmacognosia. Madrid. 9:231–46. 1949.

93. MASCRE, M., AND DEYSSON, G. Les poisons mitotiques. Biol. Méd. 40:1–54. 1951.

94. MEHRA, P. Colchicine effect on the mitotic division of the body nucleus in the pollen grains of some *Ephedra* Spp. Proc. Nat. Inst. Sci. India. 12:333–40. 1946. Colchicine effect and the production of abnormal spermatozoids in the prothalli of *Dryopteris subpubescens* (Bl.) C. Chr. and *Goniopteris prolifera* Roxb. Ann. Bot. 16:49–56. 1952.

95. MOL, W. DE. Colchicine treatment of *Scilla* to produce polyploids. Papers Mich. Acad. Sci. 35:3–7. 1951.

96. MUNTZING, A., AND RUNQUIST, E. Note on some colchicine-induced polyploids. Hereditas. 25:491–95. 1939.

97. NAUNDORF, G., AND HAASE, E. The auxin metabolism of polyploid plants after colchicine treatment. Naturwiss. 31:570. 1943.

98. NEBEL, B. Cytological observations on colchicine. Collecting Net. 12:130–31. 1937.

99. ――――, AND RUTTLE, M. Action of colchicine on mitosis. Genetics. 23:161–62. 1938.

100. NEWCOMER, E. Colchicine as a growth stimulator. Science. 101:677–78. 1945.

101. NICKELL, L. Effect of certain plant hormones and colchicine on the growth and respiration of virus tumor tissue in *Rumex acetosa.* Amer. Jour. Bot. 37:829–35. 1950.

102. NIHOUS, M. Toxic effect of aqueous solutions of colchicine on the germination of *Pisum sativum.* C. R. Soc. Biol. Paris. 138:128. 1944.

103. NORTHEN, H. Alterations in the structural viscosity of protoplasm by colchicine and their relationship to c-mitosis and c-tumor formation. Amer. Jour. Bot. 37:705–11. 1950.

104. OBATON, F. Influence de la colchicine sur le développement de *Photobacterium phosphoreum.* C. R. Acad. Sci. Paris. 208:1536–38. 1939.

105. OLLIVIER, H. Étude cyto-toxicologique de l'influence de divers agents physiques et chimiques sur les plantules de blé. Rev. Can. Biol. 7:35–159. 1948.

106. O'MARA, J. Observations on the immediate effects of colchicine. Jour. Hered. 30:35–37. 1939.

107. ORSINI, M., AND PANSKY, B. The natural resistance of the golden hamster to colchicine. Science. 115:88–89. 1952.

108. ÖSTERGREN, G. Narcotized mitosis and the precipitation hypothesis of narcosis. Mécanisme de la Narcose. Colloques Internat. Centre Nat. Recherche Scient. 26:77–87.

109. PARR, L. A new "mutation" in the coliform group of bacteria. Jour. Hered. 29:381–84. 1938.

110. PATTON, R., AND NEBEL, B. Preliminary observations on physiological and cytological effects of certain hydrocarbons on plant tissues. Amer. Jour. Bot. 27:609–13. 1940.

111. PIETTRE, L. Action of colchicine on plants. C. R. Soc. Biol. Paris. 131:1095–97. 1939.

112. POSTMA, W. Opermerkingen over de cytologie van normale en van met colchicine behandelde *Cannabis*-planten. Erfelijkheid in Praktijk. 4:171–73. 1939.

113. POTTZ, G. Effects of colchicine on bacteria. Proc. Okla. Acad. Sci. 22:139–41. 1941.

114. PRAAKEN, R., AND LEVAN, A. Notes on the colchicine meiosis of *Allium cernuum.* Hereditas. 32:123–26.

115. REESE, G. Beiträge zur Wirkung des Colchicins bei der Samenbehandlung. Planta. 38:324–76. 1950.

116. RICHARDS, O. Colchicine stimulation of yeast growth fails to reveal mitosis. Jour. Bact. 36:187–95. 1938.

117. ROSENDAHL, G. Versuche zur Erzeugung von Polyploidie bei Farnen durch Colchicin-behundlung sowie Beobachtungen an polyploiden Farnprothallien. Planta. 31:597–637. 1941.

118. RUHE, D., *et al.* Studies in human malaria. XIV. The ineffectiveness of colchicine, S. N. 12,080, S. N. 7266 and S. N. 8557 as curative agents against St. Elisabeth strain vivax malaria. Amer. Jour. Hyg. 49:361. 1949.

119. SANSOME, E., AND BANNON, L. Colchicine ineffective in inducing polyploidy in *Penicillium notatum.* Lancet. 251:828–29. 1946.

120. SANTAVY, F. Polarografie a spektrografie kolchicinu a jeho derivatu. Publ. Fac. Med. Brno. 19:149–72. 1945.

121. SASS, J., AND GREEN, J. Cytohistology of the reaction of maize seedlings to colchicine. Bot. Gaz. 106:483–88. 1945.

122. SATO, D. The effect of colchicine on meiosis in *Aloinae.* Bot. Mag. Tokyo. 53:200–7. 1939.

123. SCHULDT, E., AND GOTTLIEB, D. Colchicine as a mutagenic agent for *Streptomyces griseus.* Ill. Acad. Sci. Trans. 43:51–52. 1950.

124. SHIMAMURA, T. Effect of acenaphthene and colchicine on the pollen mother cells of *Fritillaria* wild var. *Thunbergie* Baker. Jap. Jour. Genet. 15:179–80. 1939. Studies on the effect of centrifugal force upon nuclear division. Cytologia. 10:186–216. 1940.

125. Siebenthal, R. A leucophytic clone of *Hormidium* derived from a culture treated with colchicine. C. R. Soc. Phys. et Hist. Nat. Genève. 58:187–92. 1941.

126. Sinoto, Y., and Yuasa, A. Karyological studies in *Saccharomyces cerevisiae*. Cytologia. 11:464–72. 1941.

127. Smith, P. Studies of the influence of colchicine and 3-indole acetic acid upon some enzymatic reactions. Proc. Okla. Acad. Sci. 21:105–8. 1941. Studies of the growth of pollen with respect to temperature, auxins, colchicine and vitamin B₁. Amer. Jour. Bot. 29:56–66. 1942.

128. Soyano, Y. The hypertrophy in roots induced by several chemicals. Bot. Mag. Tokyo. 34:185–95. 1940.

129. Sparrow, A. Colchicine-induced univalents in diploid *Antirrhinum majus* L. Science. 96:363–64. 1942.

130. Sreenivasan, A., and Wandrekar, S. Biosynthesis of vitamin C during germination. I. Effect of various environmental and cultural factors. Proc. Indian Acad. Sci. 32B:143–63. 1950.

131. Stalfelt, M. Effect of heteroauxin and colchicine on protoplasmic viscosity. Proc. 6th Internat. Congress Exp. Cytology (1947). Exp. Cell Res. Suppl. 1:63–78. 1949.

132. Steinberg, R., and Thom, C. Mutations and reversions in reproductivity of *Aspergilli* and nitrite, colchicine and d-lysine. Proc. Nat. Acad. Sci. 26 (6): 363–66. 1940.

133. Steineggar, E., and Levan, A. The cytological effect of chloroform and colchicine on *Allium*. Hereditas. 33:515–25. 1947. The c-mitotic qualities of colchicine, trimethyl colchicine acid and two phenanthrene derivatives. Hereditas. 34:193–203. 1948.

134. Sterzl, J. Morphological variability of the nuclear substance and genetic changes induced by colchicine in "*Escherichia coli*." Nature. 163:28. 1949.

135. Straub, J. Quantitative und qualitative Verschiedenheiten innerhalb von polyploiden Pflanzenreihen. Biol. Zentralbl. 60:659–69. 1940.

136. Sturtevant, F., *et al.* Effect of colchicine on regeneration in *Pelmatohydra oligactis*. Science. 114:241–42. 1951.

137. Suita, N. Studies on the male gametophyte in angiosperms. V. Colchicine treatment as a proof of the essential function of the spindle mechanism in karyokinesis in the pollen tube. Jap. Jour. Genet. 15:91–95. 1939.

138. Takenaka, Y. Notes on cytological observations in *Colchicum*, with reference to autotoxicosis and sterility. Cytologia. 16:95–99. 1950.

139. Tonzig, S., and Ott-Candela, A. L'azione della colchicina sullo sviluppo degli apparati stomatici. Nuovo Gior. Bot. Ital. 53:535–47. 1946.

140. Tschermak, E. Durch Colchicinbehandlung ausgelöste Polyploidie bei der Grünalge *Oedogonium*. Naturwiss. 30:638–84. 1942.

141. Ubatuba, F. Inhibition of growth of oat rootlets. Rev. Brasil Biol. 5:263–74. 1945.

142. Umrath, K., and Weber, F. Elektrische Potentiale an durch Colchicin oder Heteroauxin hervorgerufenen Keulenwurzeln. Protoplasma. 37:522–26. 1943.

143. Vaarama, A. Permanent effect of colchicine on *Ribes nigrum*. Hereditas. Suppl. Abst. 680–81. 1949.

144. Vandendries, R., and Gavaudan, P. Action de la colchicine sur quelques organismes inférieurs. C. R. Acad. Sci. 208:1675–77. 1939.

145. Vanderwalle, R. Observation sur l'action de la colchicine et autres substances mitoinhibitrices sur quelques champignons phytopathogènes. Bull. Soc. Roy. Bot. Belg. 72:63–67. 1939.

146. Vietez, E. Palynological observations on some Spanish honeys. Torrey Bot. Club Bull. 77:495–502. 1950.

147. Wada, B. Lebendbeobachtungen über die Einwirkung des Colchicins auf die Mitose, insbesondere über die Frage der Spindelfigur. Cytologia. 11:93–116. 1940.

148. Walker, R. The effect of colchicine on microspore mother cells and microspores of *Tradescantia paludosa*. Amer. Jour. Bot. 25:280–85. 1938. The

effect of colchicine on somatic cells of *Tradescantia paludosa*. Jour. Arnold Arb. 19:158–62. 1938. The effect of colchicine on the developing embryo sac of *Tradescantia paludosa*. Jour. Arnold Arb. 19:442–45. 1938.

149. WALKER, A., AND YOUMANS, G. Growth of bacteria in media containing colchicine. Proc. Soc. Exp. Biol. and Med. 44:271–73. 1940.

150. WANG, F. Effects of auxin, colchicine and certain amino acids on the germination of *Lotus corniculatus* pollen. Biochem. Bull. China. 38:1–3. 1944.

151. WEBER, F. Spaltöffnungsapparat-anomalien colchicinierter *Tradescantia*-blatter. Protoplasma. 37:556–65. 1943.

152. WEICHSEL, G. Polyploidie, veranlasst durch chemische Mittel, insbesondere Colchicinwirkung bei Lebuminosen. Zuchter. 12:25–32. 1940.

153. WEISSENBOCK, K. Studien an colchizinierten Pflanzen. I. Anatomische Untersuchungen. Phyton. 1:282–300. 1949.

154. WERNER, G. Untersuchungen über die Möglichkeit der Erzeugung polyploider Kulturpflanzen durch Colchicinbehandlung. Zuchter. 11:51–71. 1940.

155. WEYLAND, H. The action of chemicals on plants and its significance in medicine. Z. Krebsforsch. 56:148–64. 1948.

156. WITKUS, E., AND BERGER, C. Induced vascular differentiation. Torrey Bot. Club Bull. 77:301–5. 1950.

157. WOLCOTT, G. The effect of colchicine on a hepatic. Jour. Hered. 32:67–70. 1941.

158. YAMAHA, G., AND UEDA, R. Über die Wirkung des Kolchizins auf *Spirogyra*. Bot. and Zool. Syokubuta Oyobi Dobuta. 8:1709–14. 1940.

159. ZAMBRUNO, D. Azione della colchicina, della narcotina, e dell'androstendione sulla moltiplicazione delle *Staphylococcus aureus*. Giorn. Batt. Immul. 34:55–57. 1946.

CHAPTER 5

Sources of the Drug

5.1: Scope of Study

In this chapter we shall discuss the pharmacognosy of *Colchicum* and other plants that produce colchicine. Origins, geography, history, commerce, cultivation, preparation, and applications to biology are explained in greater detail for *Colchicum* than is usual in standard works for pharmacists.

The Greek words *pharmakon,* meaning *drug* or *medicine,* and *gnosis,* a knowing, are combined to form the term *pharmacognosy.* Literally, the meaning is a knowledge of drugs. This word is not so old as the study of drugs since it was introduced in 1815 by Seydler through his work, *Analecta Pharmacognostica.* A much older name for this subject is *materia medica,* and while this is still preferred in medicine to *pharmacognosy,* pharmacists prefer the latter word. The two are not entirely synonymous, for the newer term has a more limited meaning. Biologics, such as vaccines, sera, and similar compounds, do not fall within the scope of pharmacognosy but are a part of materia medica. On the other hand, compounds such as waxes, gums, oils, resins, spices, and fibers are included with drugs.

There was much discussion in centuries past as to whether *Colchicum* should be an official drug in the standard formularies of various nations. At certain times *Colchicum* was made official, then dropped, only to be taken up again in a later issue of the formulary. Its extremely poisonous nature and the lack of proper methods to assay the drug caused much of the trouble. It was realized that *Colchicum* was a good cure for gout. Medical men also realized the danger associated with administering the drug. The expressions *official* or *nonofficial, acceptance* or *rejection,* are based on the inclusion of a drug in standard pharmacopeias of a particular government. The drug may be official for one country and not another. Today, the standardization of colchicine is accurate, and the drug is official in every national work on pharmacy.[80] Because of its availability, *Colchicum luteum* is permitted as a substitute for *C. autumnale* in India.[11] The standards of the *British Pharmacopoeia* do not permit the use of *C. luteum,* because the amount of colchicine in raw material is not high enough.

5.1–1: Geographical distribution. Figure 5.1 gives the location of the important species of the genus *Colchicum,* outlining the main areas where species are native. Taxonomists recognize 65 species in this genus,[68] but during the earlier centuries all autumn-flowering species were grouped in the *C. autumnale* type. Actually, the official species is distributed over Europe; line 55 outlines this area on the map (Fig. 5.1). The majority of species described on the map flower in the fall and produce seed in the spring. Another species known to antiquity is *C. variegatum,* number 61. The distribution of *C. luteum,* number 1, is the easternmost representative. All are limited to the Northern Hemisphere and none are reported in the Americas.

5.2: Problems in Pharmacognosy

Maintaining quality, protecting the consumer, preventing fraud, and regulating traffic become the responsibility of trained pharmacognosists.[16, 19] During earlier centuries, physicians had to use *Colchicum* according to their judgment. At times this duty was a heavy responsibility (cf. Chapter 1). Even today the problem is not completely solved, for it has been discovered that U.S.P. colchicine may contain another compound, desmethylcolchicine.[24] The substance has biological activity; therefore, purification of so-called pure colchicine is recommended if carefully controlled experiments are to be undertaken.

The preparation of the drug from the fresh state before drying, or through processes of drying, must be correct in order to avoid changes in these complex compounds. Colchicine in solution must not be exposed to sunlight. Slicing, washing, and exposure to insects or bacteria can also introduce changes.

Four principal techniques are used to evaluate drugs. These are (1) organoleptic, (2) microscopic and microchemical, (3) physicochemical, and (4) biological methods. Each particular test is described in the formularies or standard works on assay of drugs. Many of the methods have been applied to colchicine.

5.3: Plants Containing Colchicine

One species is famous in every pharmacist's handbook for the production of colchicine. There are many other species that have a capacity for synthesizing the compound in parts of plants. All species of the genus *Colchicum* analyzed to date yield colchicine.[3, 27, 70] An extensive list of them has been collected (Table 5.1). Two genera, *Merendera* and *Colchicum,* have been used interchangeably. Species

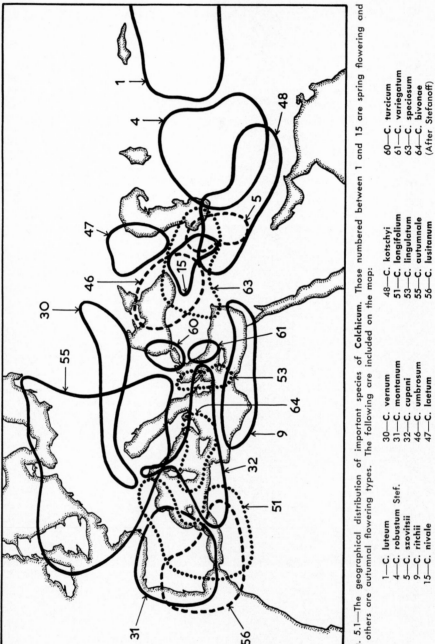

Fig. 5.1—The geographical distribution of important species of **Colchicum**. Those numbered between 1 and 15 are spring flowering and all others are autumnal flowering types. The following are included on the map:

1—C. luteum	30—C. vernum	48—C. kotschyi	60—C. turcicum
4—C. robustum Stef.	31—C. montanum	51—C. longifolium	61—C. variegatum
5—C. szovitsii	32—C. cupani	53—C. lingulatum	63—C. speciosum
9—C. ritchii	46—C. umbrosum	55—C. autumnale	64—C. bivonae
15—C. nivale	47—C. laetum	56—C. lusitanum	(After Stefanoff)

of each are found in the northwestern Himalayan area. Both drugs are on sale in the bazaars of the Orient.[17]

Isolated substances from *Colchicum autumnale* and related species have been studied extensively by Professor F. Santavy and his colleagues at the Medical-Chemical Institute of the Polacky University of Olomouc, Czechoslovakia. An up-to-date summary was prepared by Professor Santavy exclusively for this book. Accordingly Tables 5.2 and 5.3 combine the significant details from their numerous published and unpublished works.

The chemical structure of substance F as listed has been determined as desacetyl-N-methyl-colchicine, and differs from colchicine by the loss of the carboxy-group attached to the nitrogen ring as can be seen in the structural diagrams of Chapter 6. Since this compound F has strong c-mitotic properties and is less toxic than the parent alkaloid when used with animals, the further examination of related substances would appear to be worth considerable exploration. A compound "Demecolcin," marketed by Ciba of Basel, Switzerland, has been studied extensively and a preliminary survey shows useful applications to some types of malignant growth. These data are found in references to papers by Bock and Gross (1954), Meier, Schar, and

TABLE 5.1

PRINCIPAL PLANT SOURCES OF COLCHICINE

Colchicum autumnale L.	*Tofieldia glacialis* Gaud.
C. montanum L.	*T. calyculata* Whlnd.
C. arenarium Waldst. and K.	*Veratrum album* L.
C. neapolitanum Ten.	*V. nigrum* L.
C. alpinum DC.	*Anthericum ramosum* L.
C. luteum Baker	*Hemerocallis fulva* L.
C. multiflorum Brot.	*Ornithogalum umbellatum* L.
Merendera bulbocodium Ram.	*O. comosum* L.
M. caucasica Biel.	*Tulipa silvestris* L.
M. persica Bois and Kotsch.	*Asphodelus albus* Willd.
Gloriosa superba L.	*Fritillaria montana* Hoppe.
Merendera sobolifera Fisch.	*Lloydia serotina* Salib.
Bulbocodium ruthenicum Bung.	*Muscari tenuiflorium* Tausch

TABLE 5.2

SURVEY OF PLANTS EXAMINED FOR THE PRESENCE OF COLCHICINE AND RELATED SUBSTANCES SUMMARIZED BY DR. F. SANTAVY

Plant	Starting Material and References	Substances Isolated or Otherwise Identified													
		Substances of Neutral and Phenolic Properties							Substances of Basic Properties				Substances of Glucosidic Properties		
		Colchicine	B	C	D	E_1	I	Colchiceine	F	S	U	Ta	Colchicoside	To	M
Colchicum autumnale L.	seeds[61,63,84,85,88,100,101,106]	+++	+++	++			+++		+++	+++	+++		+		
	bulbs[61,83,89,98,96]	+++++	+++		++	++		++	++++++			+		+	+
	flowers[51,61,99]	+++++				+									
	leaves, pericarp[24,33,90,98]	+++++		+		+			+++	++					
C. speciosum Stev.	bulbs[3,64,70,82,86,87]	+++++													
	flowers[87,90]	+++++													
C. arenarium W.K.	bulbs[64,92]	+++++		+											
C. cilicum Hayek	bulbs[64]	+++++													
C. variegatum L.	bulbs[90]	+++++													
C. vernum Ker-Gawl	bulbs[33,95]	+++++					+								
C. agrippinum Baker	bulbs[95]	+++++													
C. neapolitanum Tenore	bulbs[92]	+++++ (?)													
C. montanum L.	bulbs[92]	+++++ (?)													
C. alpinum D.C.	bulbs[92]	+++++ (?)													
C. multiflorum	bulbs[92]	+++++ (?)													
C. luteum Baker	bulbs[90]	+++++													
C. kesselringii	leaves[38]	++++													
C. hierosolymitanum Feinbr.	bulbs[90,105]	+++++ (?)							+						
C. ruthenicum	leaves[33]	++++							++++						
C. bornmuelleri	bulbs[64]	++++		+											
C. autumnale album	bulbs[64]	++++		+											
C. autumnale major	bulbs[64]	++++		+											
C. autumnale minor	bulbs[64]	++++		+											

TABLE 5.2 (continued)

Plant	Starting Material and References	Substances Isolated or Otherwise Identified														
		Substances of Neutral and Phenolic Properties							Substances of Basic Properties				Substances of Glucosidic Properties		
		Colchicine	B	C	D	E₁	I	Colchiceine	F	S	U	Ta	Colchicoside	To	M
C. autumnale var. Lilac Wonder	bulbs[64]	+							+						
C. autumnale var. The Giant	bulbs[64]	+							+						
C. autumnale var. Violet Queen	bulbs[64]	+++							+++						
C. autumnale flore pleno	bulbs[90]	+++++	++	++			++								
Merendera sobolifera C.A.M.	bulbs[90,95]	+++++													
M. attica Boiss et Sprun	bulbs[95]	+++													
M. bulbocodium Ram	bulbs[17]	+++	+	+											
M. robusta	leaves[38]	++		+											
M. caucasica Spreng	bulbs[90]	+				+	+		+						
Androcymbium gramineum McBride	bulbs[56,90] flowers, leaves[90]	+++++	+++	+++											
Gloriosa superba L.	bulbs[12,94,103,104]	+++++													
G. rothschildiana O'Brien	bulbs[6,94]	+++													
G. simplex	bulbs[94]	−													
Tulipa silvestris L.	bulbs[33,95]	−													
Hemerocallis fulva	bulbs[33,64]	−													
Ornithogallum caudatum Ait.	bulbs[33,90]	−													

These plants do not contain other substances with a tropolone ring.

NOTE: Due to the lack of starting material, a number of plants could not be analyzed by us for the presence of all the substances identified in meadow saffron.

[145]

TABLE 5.3

SUBSTANCES ISOLATED FROM MEADOW SAFFRON (*Colchicum autumnale* L.) AND THEIR MOST IMPORTANT PHYSICAL AND CHEMICAL PROPERTIES SUMMARIZED BY DR. F. SANTAVY

Isolated Compounds	Formula	M.P.	$[\alpha]_D$ in $CHCl_3$	Reaction With Concentrated H_2SO_4	Tropolone Ring	Number of Methoxyls	Number of Phenol Groups	Number of Acetyl Groups	Sugar Residue	Acetyl Derivative Formula	Acetyl Derivative M.P.	Acetyl Derivative $[\alpha]_D$ in $CHCl_3$	Starting Material and References
Neutral and Phenolic Compounds													
Colchicine	$C_{22}H_{25}O_6N$	157°	−121°	yellow	+	4		1*					whole plant[61,63,93,96–101]
B	$C_{21}H_{23}O_6N$	266°	−171°	yellow	+			1*					whole plant[61,93,96–101]
C	$C_{21}H_{23}O_6N$	180°	−132°	yellow	+	3	1			$C_{23}H_{25}O_7N$	231°	−92°	seeds[24,61,100,101] bulbs[61,93,96]
D	$C_{21}H_{23}O_6N$	236°	+294°	red-violet		3		1		$C_{23}H_{25}O_7N$	232°	+283°	whole plant[61,93,96,97,99–101]
E_1	$C_{21}H_{23}O_6N$	180°	−130°	yellow	+	3	1	1		$C_{23}H_{25}O_7N$	194°	−125°	flowers[61,99] leaves[98] pericarp[98]
I	$C_{22}H_{25}O_6N$	186°	+307°	orange		4		1					whole plant[61,93,96,97,99–101]
J	$C_{22}H_{25}O_6N$	278°	−445°	orange		4							whole plant[61,93,96,97,99–101]
Ka	?	214°	−140°	yellow	+								seeds[101]
N	?	256°	−143°	colorless	+	4		1			229°	−110°	flowers[99]
O	$C_{22}H_{25}O_6N(?)$	229°	−226°	orange		4		1					flowers[99]
P	?	198°		yellow									bulbs[96]
R	?			yellow	+	3	1	1		$C_{23}H_{25}O_7N$	124°	−260°	bulbs[96]
Colchiceine	$C_{21}H_{23}O_6N$	177°	−256°	yellow	+	3	1	1					flowers,[99] bulbs[96]
Basic Compounds													
F (Demecolcin)	$C_{21}H_{25}O_5N$	186°	−127°	yellow	+	4				$C_{23}H_{27}O_6N$	231°	−240°	whole plant[61,63,93,96,97,99–101]
H–3	?	185°	−117°	yellow	+++								bulbs[96]
S	$C_{20}H_{23}O_5N$	138°	−117°	yellow	+	3				$C_{22}H_{25}O_6N$	202°	−218°	whole plant[63,96,98,99,101]
U	$C_{19}H_{21}O_5N$			yellow	+++	3	1			$C_{23}H_{25}O_7N$	229°	−93°	whole plant[96,99,101]
Ta	$C_{21}H_{25}O_5N(?)$	135°	−211°	yellow	++	3							bulbs[96]

TABLE 5.3 (*continued*)

Isolated Compounds	Formula	M.P.	$[\alpha]_D$ in CHCl₃	Reaction With Concentrated H₂SO₄	Tropolone Ring	Number of Methoxyls	Number of Phenol Groups	Number of Acetyl Groups	Sugar Residue	Acetyl Derivative Formula	Acetyl Derivative M.P.	Acetyl Derivative $[\alpha]_D$ in CHCl₃	Starting Material and References
Glucosidic Compounds													
Colchicoside	C₂₇H₃₃O₁₁N	218°	−360° (water)	yellow	+	3		1	1	C₃₅H₄₁O₁₅N	177°	−57°	seeds[83]
M	C₂₇H₃₃O₁₁N	314°		red-violet		3		1	1	C₃₅H₄₁O₁₅N	304°	−244°	flowers[99]
To	C₂₆₋₂₇H₃₁₋₃.₅O₉N(?)	234°	−65° (pyridine)	yellow	+	3		1	1				bulbs[96]
Other Compounds													
Apigenin	C₁₅H₁₀O₅	350°								C₂₁H₁₆O₆	185°		flowers,[99] bulbs[61,93,96,97,99-101]
Phytosterol-mixture		136°	−36°										whole plant[61,93,96,97,99-101]
Benzoic acid	C₆H₆O₂	122°											
Salicylic acid	C₆H₆O₃	156°											whole plant[61,93,96,97,99-101]
2-Oxy-6-methoxy-benzoic acid	C₈H₈O₄	133°											seeds[18]
Fatty acid-mixtures													bulbs, seeds[61,93,96,97,99-101]
Saccharose	C₁₂H₂₂O₁₁	187°	+67° (water)										
Asparagine													bulbs[102]

* Formyl

Neipp (1954), Moeschlin, Meyer, and Lichtman (1954), and Santavy, Winkler, and Reichtstein (1953).*

Probably the best method of detecting colchicine is the polarographic technique used to great advantage by Santavy and his colleagues.[61] By these newer methods, other compounds have been identified in the seed, corm, and flowers. A section is devoted to this problem.

5.3–1: Colchicum autumnale L. We mentioned earlier the unusual character of this autumn-flowering crocus. Not many plants bloom in the fall and mature seeds the following spring. Since the flowering and fruiting cycle is directly correlated with development of corm and seed, and since colchicine production is related to these processes, knowledge of development is important. The content of colchicine will vary from season to season, and with different environmental conditions. Seeds are a rich source of colchicine after maturation. The corms reach a peak of colchicine about June or July. A vast amount of information has been reported over a period of 20 centuries, yet it is surprising to learn how few textbooks bring together a complete report on comparative morphology, anatomy, and physiology in relation to drug production. More than passing attention will be given to such details in this chapter.[34]

The corm has two coverings when dug in early summer, the outer brown membranous and an inner reddish-yellow layer. Beneath these coats lies a yellow body that composes the bulk of the corm and most of the tissues that yield colchicine. The corm is conical, somewhat rounded on the surface, and flattened on one side. At the base of the flattened area a smaller corm, or bud, fits into a groove or depression. When this young bud begins development, the larger, parental corm usually carries the maximum colchicine per dry weight of body.

A bud develops in July, and during August or September stalks of flowers appear. Floral activity is the first index that the young corm has been active. Violet and reddish flowers in a cluster ranging from two to six break through the membranes of the corm just described and appear above ground. Corms that are not placed in the

---

* H. Bock and R. Gross, "Leukämie und Tumorbehandlung mit einem Nebenalcaloid aus *Colchicum autumnale* (Demecolcin)." *Acta Haematol.* 11:280–300. 1954.

R. Meier, B. Schar, and L. Neipp, "Die Wirkung von Demecolceinamiden an Zellen *in vitro.*" Experientia. 10:74–76 . 1954.

S. Moeschlin, H. Meyer, and A. Lichtman, "Ein neues Colchicum-Nebenalcaloid (Demecolcin Ciba) als cytostaticum myeloischer Leukämien." Schweiz. Med. Wschr. 83:990. 1953.

F. Santavy, R. Winkler, and T. Reichstein, "Zur Konstitution von Demecolcin (Substance F) aus *Colchicum autumnale* L." Helvetica Chim. Acta. 36:1319–24. 1953.

soil develop flowers when the time is right. They do so without attention as to water or nutrition. For this reason unusual attention is given to the corm for ornamental purposes.

Each flower measures 10 to 20 cm. from base to tip of petal. The six stamens and six floral parts are united in a tube from the top to the carpels below. Three carpels of an ovulary show the relation to the liliaceous group. At the base of the long tube is the superior, syncarpous ovulary. Regularly, the corm is deep enough in the soil so that about one-half of the flower is above the surface; thus, the ovulary is well beneath the soil surface. Following fertilization, the ovules begin a development that proceeds during the entire winter.[7] A progression of development and colchicine content was noted over the long period of time that elapses from fertilization to maturation. Pollination development begins soon after, but the content of colchicine is low. There is not much increase during the early stages. In other words, the increase in the winter is very small compared to the gain that occurs in content of colchicine as seeds mature. The total time studied extended from August of one year to April of the next.[7, 8, 62]

In early spring the fruit capsule rises out of the soil. Expanding leaves accompany the fruit development. In the vicinity of Olomouc, Czechoslovakia, the green capsules contain small, watery ovules until about the middle of May. From May to July the content of colchicine increases from 0.2 to 0.5 per cent. As capsules mature, the walls split and seeds fall out.[7]

5.3–2: Colchicum luteum Baker. Because of its availability in India, the Indian pharmacopeia accepts this spring-flowering species as a source for colchicine.[11, 45, 54]

The product called colchicine is Surinjan-i-talkh. Undoubtedly this drug has been used for many years, certainly before the present studies of pharmacognosy were conceived in their present level. Collection of the corm for colchicine must be coordinated with the flowering and fruiting cycles. Each corm is inclosed in membranous layers, under which lies a hard, white bud. The daughter corm that produces the next season's plant is found in a groove at the base of the parent corm.

At altitudes of 7000 ft., the buds develop early in March or late February. Flowers appear when the snow melts; the plant is one of the earliest to flower in the area. The common name for the species is *Kashmir hermodactyl.*

A scape bearing golden flowers, two or three per cluster, emerges from the corm. Fruiting stalks develop soon after pollination. The capsules mature, and leaves form. Finally the seeds mature, and a cycle is thus completed within one season, from March to May.

5.3–3: Other sources for colchicine. Numerous sources of colchicine exist in nature (Table 5.1), and undoubtedly more will be discovered. A notable case is *Gloriosa superba* producing 0.3 per cent colchicine compared with 0.5 per cent for *C. autumnale.* The unusual demand for colchicine made by plant breeders should stimulate search for other sources.[54] These are the problems that pharmacognosists are surveying, particularly in areas where plants have not been thoroughly studied.

When colchicine is extracted from *Colchicum,* other compounds appear in the residue, some of which have proved to be valuable. New products of biological interest might well be revealed through examination of the species that yield colchicine. By new methods of analysis a large amount of important work has been done in recent years with compounds of colchicine and its derivatives.[61]

5.4: Cultivation, Collection, and Preparation

An important source of raw material has come from the plants growing in natural habitats.[5] A large area in southeastern Europe supplied much raw material that was purified into colchicine and distributed throughout the world. About 1939 the sudden demand for large portions to be used by geneticists in creating polyploids created a shortage in the market. Almost simultaneously, the war interrupted production and trade in *Colchicum.* The prices increased and colchicine was difficult to obtain.

There are standard practices for cultivating most drug plants, and similar work has been done with *Colchicum.*[21] A general procedure is as follows: Seeds are sown in September, in moist, shady locations and are covered with a thin layer of soil. After germination the next spring, seedlings are set out 60 cm. apart. Cultivation practices are continued for three years. Corms are dug and prepared for the market.

If seed supplies are to be made from cultivated plants, four years of propagation are necessary. Actually a five-year cycle is required. A common practice involves the use of seeds produced in natural habitats. Seeds are collected by bagging the ripening capsules.

Another method for producing raw material under cultivation is to set out the corms that come through the regular corm and bulb markets. Or the corms may be dug in the wild state and transferred to a field for intensive cultivation. Production of colchicine is influenced by environment. A survey from 111 localities in Moravia showed that colchicine produced by seed varied from 0.6 to 1.23 per cent. An average of 0.8 per cent colchicine was obtained. [7, 8, 9]

Drug production can be increased by the application of fertilizer. Increases in colchicine per corm were made when P_2O_5 was added.[60] The methods for adding the fertilizer to soil and details of these tests have not been repeated or confirmed. These data are correlated with a variability in production of colchicine found for different localities.

Variation in production of colchicine appeared to be a function of size of seed (Fig. 5.2). The number of seeds per gram varied from 183 to 406. As the number of seeds increased, there was an increase in the percentage of colchicine per 100 grams of raw material. The size of seed is a response to environmental condition, and in turn the production of colchicine is changed by the seed form. Standards set for content of colchicine must account for variation in raw samples of *Colchicum*. Not enough attention has been paid to the relation between environmental conditions and production of colchicine.[69]

Colchicum luteum is collected from natural sites exclusively. The corms, rather than the seeds, serve as a source of colchicine. There are large areas of the northwestern Himalayas, notably in the grasslands, where the plants are abundant. Their locations are at levels from 4000 to 7000 ft. While the total content of colchicine is not as high for *C. luteum* as the officially recognized species, enough can be gathered to make this a valuable drug plant.

The dried whole corms are collected from March to May. By this time the fruits have matured and leaves have dried down. The corms are dug and prepared for market according to practices established by collectors who have been working at this trade for many years.

Altitude influences the production of colchicine in the seed more than in the corm, according to a study made in the European Alps for *C. autumnale*. Collections were made beginning at 50 m. and continuing in locations up to 2200 m. The content of colchicine in the seed sample was found to diminish with increasing altitude. The differences were not so great for the corm.[74]

5.5: The Crude Drug

Dried corms and seeds of *Colchicum* are official in standard pharmacopeias.[41] Since 1946, *C. luteum* has been accepted in the Indian standards. Dried corms are bitter and have a disagreeable odor. There are two drugs in the Himalayan collections known as the bitter and the sweet surinjan; the former is *C. luteum*.

Collections are made and corms sliced 2 to 5 mm. thick after drying. Each piece should be about 3 cm. wide. A black layer along the side becomes prominent. In transverse section the ground tissues

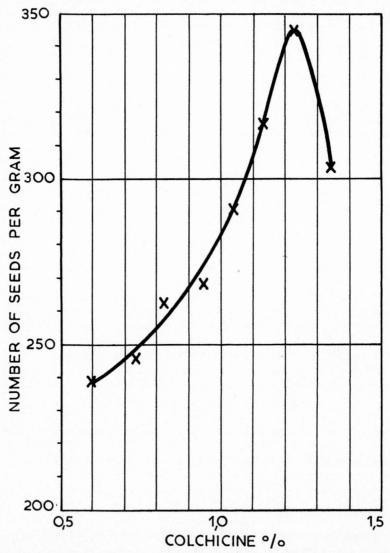

Fig. 5.2—Size of seed can be correlated with percentage of colchicine per gram. The smaller seeds yield more colchicine per gram of raw material. Environmental conditions influence the size of seeds. Larger yields occur when number of seeds per gram exceed 300. (Adapted from Buchnicek)

appear grayish at certain points; these mark the vascular bundles of the corm and are distinct features. In the apical and basal regions the pieces are subconical and plano-convex, respectively. The use of specific marks of identification help to prevent the substitution of material not genuine.

Histologically, the crude drug can be identified by the presence of typical cells. Epidermal cells are rectangular and polygonal, measuring 60 microns on the average. The walls are brown and thickened. Ground tissues are full of starch grains, usually simple; if compound, the components are from two to three parts. Vascular bundles run longitudinally through the corm and are of the collateral type. Xylem vessels are narrow, spiral, or annular, and about 30 mm. in diameter.

Seeds of *Colchicum* are subspherical, 2 to 3 mm. in diameter, having a dark brown and rough seed coat. A large, hard, yellow endosperm surrounding a small embryo is embedded near the surface of the seed. Strong HCl colors the endosperm yellow, indicating the presence of oils.[17, 18] The seeds are bitter, but they do not have the same disagreeable odor found with corms. Large enough amounts of colchicine are contained in seeds that poisonous effects can be produced if warm-blooded animals eat a certain quantity.

5.6: Compounds Isolated From *Colchicum*

From 1901 to 1949, many reports have been made to establish the amount of pure substance to be expected from a given amount of dried raw material. The corm, seed, fruit, and flowers have been studied, and variations recorded.[23, 66, 67] Some of the basic reasons for variation have been mentioned. There are sources of variation that occur because different methods of extraction and assay have been used.[4, 80] A survey of some of the literature shows the variety of methods that have been advocated and used.[2, 3, 5, 11, 14, 15, 18, 19, 22, 31, 33, 35, 37, 41, 42, 43, 52, 66, 73] Improvements in methods have come through the use of polarography and chromatography.[32, 61, 65] A large field of chemistry of plant products has been opened by the application of these new technics to drug plants. The idea that *Colchicum* produces only colchicine must be changed in light of the important compounds that appear with pure drug.[81]

The treatment of corms with boiling water during preparation for market causes water-soluble portions to leach out. Different solubilities and physical properties show that even the so-called pure drug is not a single compound. These impurities have been detected in pollen germination studies. Obviously very few biological experiments have been performed with pure colchicine. There are difficulties in making absolutely pure colchicine in large quantity.

In addition to the compounds obtained from the raw material, there are derivatives made in the laboratory by degradation work from the drug. Enough has been done to prove that specific chemical substances related to colchicine are obtainable. The details of such work are extended in the chapter dealing with chemistry of colchicine.

Santavy and his colleagues have isolated compounds from the corm, seed, fruit, and flowers. Their general method involves the extraction from dried powder of particular portions of the plant. Fats are extracted by petrol ether, followed by alcoholic extraction. The use of water, then ether, and finally chloroform brings out an extract demonstrated to have reducible substances when subjected to polarographic analysis. By chromatographic differentiation, specific and identifiable compounds have been reported. Details of the procedures are given in papers written by Santavy and his associates.[61] Isolated substances, the chemical and physical properties of which have been observed, are tabulated in Table 5.3. The work by F. Santavy and his group extends greatly our knowledge of the specific chemical components that may be obtained from the *Colchicum* plant. Classification is made by grouping substances as neutral and phenolics, basic and glucosidic compounds. The particular part of the plant used is listed so that others may repeat the isolation of similar compounds.

Substances A, B, C, D, E, F, G, J, and I have been derived from the corm, seed, fruit, and flowers. In some cases the substances have been found only in certain parts. Pure colchicine is identified as compound A. Desmethylcolchicine appears to be similar to compound C. Another material, colchicerin 3, corresponds to compound G. Biologically, these compounds have different toxicities and produce different effects upon mitosis. Compound F is less toxic than colchicine yet more active in blocking mitosis.

Sunlight induces changes in a solution of colchicine.[65] Irradiation changes the structure of colchicine to a product known as lumicolchicine. At present two kinds of lumicolchicine, I and II, are obtainable. Lumicolchicine I is identified with substances obtained from the seed and flower. Lumicolchicine II is similar to compound J. By irradiation and also through chemical treatment, compounds may be converted from one structure to another. These tests show that the stability of pure colchicine must be regarded as a possible source of variation in biological experimentation.

Only a small portion of this important development in pharmacognosy has been given here. The possibilities of undiscovered identifiable and active compounds open new fields for experimental work. Colchicine has proved to be a very unique substance. The discovery of related compounds synthesized by the plant is even of greater interest.

REFERENCES

1. ALBO, G. Sur la signification physiologique de la colchicine dans les différentes espèces de *Colchicum* et de *Merendera*. Arch. Sci. Phys. Nat. 12:227–36. 1901.
2. ANDERSON, A., *et al.* Modified assay methods for crude drugs involving the removal of interfering substances by enzymic digestion. I. Modified assay method

for *Colchicum* corm and seed. Jour. Amer. Pharm. Assoc. Sci. Ed. 37:319–21. 1948.

3. BEER, A., *et al.* Chemical study of *Colchicum speciosum* Stev. C. R. Dokl. Acad. Sci. URSS. 67:883–84. 1949.
4. BELLEAU, B. The biogenesis of colchicine. Experientia. 9:178. 1953.
5. BLAZEK, Z., AND SLOUF, A. The examination of the *Colchicum* seeds, fruits and leaves of the domestic origin. Hortus Sanitatis. 2:68–74. 1949.
6. BRYAN, J., AND LAUTER, W. A note on the alkaloid content of *Gloriosa rothchildiana* O'Brien. Jour. Amer. Pharm. Assoc. Sci. Ed. 40:253. 1951.
7. BUCHNICEK, J. Colchicin in reifenden Herbstzeitlosensamen. Pharm. Acta Helv. 25:389–401. 1950.
8. ————, AND SANTAVY, F. Mnozstvi kolchicinu v semenech ocunu zeme Moravskoslezske (Content of colchicine in the seeds of meadow saffron from Moravia and Silesia). Acta Acad. Sci. Nat. Moravo-Silesicae. 20:1–16. 1948.
9. ————, AND HEJTMANEK, M. Toxicita kolchicinu studovana na lebistes reticulatus. Zvlast. Otisk z Casopisu Biologicke Listy. 31:122–29. 1950.
10. CATTELAIN, E. La colchicine alcaloïde du *Colchicum autumnale*, extraction, propriétés, constitution. Jour. Pharm. et Chim. 3:162. 1926.
11. CHOPRA, R. (*see* Ref. No. 7, Chap. 1. 1933).
12. CLEWER, H., *et al.* The constituents of *Gloriosa superba*. Jour. Chem. Soc. 107:835. 1915.
13. COOK, J., AND LOUDON, J. (*see* Ref. No. 9, Chap. 1. 1951).
14. DAVIES, E. The assay of *Colchicum* by the phosphotungstic method. Pharm. Jour. 106:480–81. 1921.
15. ————, AND GRIER, J. Colchicine, its assay, isolation and special properties. Pharm. Jour. 109:210–11. 1922.
16. DOTT, D. The British Pharmacopoeia 1932. Pharm. Jour. 132:83–84. Chemist and Druggist. 120:102–3. 1934.
17. FOURMENT, P., AND ROQUES, H. *Merendera bulbocodium* Ram. Matière médicale, localisation et dosage de la colchicine. Bull. Soc. Pharm. Bordeaux. 65:26–31. 1927.
18. GAAL, G. The fatty oil of seeds of *Colchicum autumnale* L. Tarsasag Ertesitoje. 6:149–67. 1930.
19. GRIER, J. Investigation of *Colchicum* and its galenicals. Pharm. Jour. 111:87–89; 125–26. 1923.
20. GRIMME, C. The alkali and oil content of the seeds of the meadow saffron. Pharm. Zentralhalle. 61:521–24. 1920.
21. GUYER, R. Cultivation of medicinal plants in Scotland, past and present. Pharm. Jour. 106:146–49; 168–71; 190–92. 1921.
22. HEIDUSCHKA, A., AND MEISNER, N. Microchemistry of the alkaloids. Arch. Pharm. 261:102–17. 1923.
23. HOOPER, E., AND KING, K. The international standardization of *Colchicum* preparations. Pharm. Jour. 111:104–6. 1923.
24. HOROWITZ, R., AND ULLYOT, G. Desmethylcolchicine, a constituent of U.S.P. colchicine. Science. 115:216. 1952.
25. JANOT, M., AND CHAIGNEAU, M. Sublimation of alkaloids under reduced pressure. C. R. Acad. Sci. Paris. 225:1371–73. 1947.
26. JERMSTAD, A. Preparation of tinctures. Pharm. Acta Helv. 9:129–40. 1934.
27. KARAPETYAN, S. Dynamics of alkaloid transformation in *Colchicum speciosum*. C.R. Dokl. Acad. Sci. URSS. 71:97–99. 1950.
28. KARIYONE, T., AND FWA-TUNG, L. Crude drugs in Southern Asia. I. The use of areca alkaloids. Jour. Pharm. Soc. Japan. 64: No. 11A, 67. 1944.
29. KARSMARK, K. Tinctura colchici. Svensk. Farm. Tids. 28:97–100. 1924.
30. KASSNER, H. Comments on some tests and assays of the U.S.P.X. Jour. Amer. Pharm. Assoc. 19:135–41. 1930.
31. KING, J., JR. A colorimetric method for the estimation of colchicine. Jour. Amer. Pharm. Assoc. 40:424–27. 1951.
32. KIRKPATRICK, H. Polarographic study of alkaloids. Quart. Jour. Pharm. and Pharmacol. 19:526–35. (CA 41:3261) 1946.
33. KLEIN, G., AND POLLAUF, G. Microchemical detection of alkaloids in plants. The detection of colchicine. Oesterr. Bot. Z. 78:251–56. 1929.

34. KOLDA, J. Excretion of drugs in the milk. II. Biol. Listy. 12:236–67. 1926.
35. KOLTHOFF, I. The dissociation constants, solubility product and titration of alkaloids. Biochem. Z. 162:289–353. 1925.
36. KUHN, A., AND SCHAFER, G. Distribution of plant constituents in the capillary picture. IV. Capillary pictures of seed and fruit. Pharm. Ztg. 82:31–34. 1937.
37. LAUNOY, L. Sensitiveness of the general method for extracting alkaloids from water. C. R. Acad. Sci. Paris. 165:360–62. 1917.
38. LAZUREVSKII, G., AND MASLENNIKOVA, V. Investigation of colchicine-containing plants in Middle Asia. C. R. Dokl. Acad. Sci. URSS. 63:449–50. 1948.
39. LIPTAK, P. Localization of alkaloids in the seed of *Colchicum autumnale* L. Pharm. Monatsh. 8:125–26. 1927.
40. LOUDON, J., AND SPEAKMAN, J. The solubility of colchicine in water. Research. London. 3:583–84. 1950.
41. LYONS, A. Assay of *Colchicum* corm. Amer. Druggist. Feb. Pharm. Jour. 82:270. 1909.
42. MACK, H., AND FINN, E. A calorimetric method for the estimation of colchicine in pharmaceutical preparations. Jour. Amer. Pharm. Assoc. 39:532–34. 1950.
43. MARTINI, A. Contribution to the microchemistry of colchicine and atropen. Anales Asoc. Quim. Argentina. 31:62. 1943.
44. MASCRE, M., AND DEYSSON, G. Action mitoclasique de la desmethylcolchicine, comparée à celles du colchicoside et de la colchicine. C. R. Acad. Sci. Paris. 234:2480–82. 1952.
45. MEHRA, P., AND KHOSHOO, T. Observations on some colchicine-containing plants. Jour. Pharm. and Pharmacol. 3:486–96. 1951.
46. MOKRANTZA, M. A new reagent for the identification of various alkaloids. Bull. Soc. Chim. Ray. Yougoslav. 3:171–76. 1932.
47. MORRISON, J. Preliminary examination of the crystal structures of colchiceine and its copper salt. (Univ. Glasgow.) Acta Cryst. 4:69–70. 1951.
48. MUHLEMANN, H., AND TOBLER, R. Chromatographisch-titrimetrische Alkaloidgehaltbestimmung von Tinctura Colchici. Ph. H. V. und Semen Colchici Ph. H. V. Pharm. Acta Helv. 21:34–46. 1946.
49. NAKAYAMA, K. Habit and culture of *Colchicum* as the pharmaceutical plant. Agr. and Hort. Tokyo. 24:639–42. 1949.
50. National Formulary, 8th ed. Amer. Pharm. Assoc. Washington, D. C. 1946.
51. NIEMANN, E. Experiments on the use of flowers of *Colchicum autumnale* in place of semen colchici. Pharm. Acta Helv. 8:92–107. 1933.
52. NORTH, E., AND BEAL, G. The preparation, properties and uses of silicoduotungstic acid. Jour. Amer. Pharm. Assoc. 13:889–98; 1001–9. 1924.
53. OSOL, A., AND FARRAR, G. U. S. Dispensatory, 24th ed. J. B. Lippincott, Philadelphia, Pa. 1947.
54. PARTHASARATHY, N. An Indian source for colchicine. Curr. Sci. Bangalore. 10:446. 1941.
55. PASCHKIS, H. Pharmakologische Untersuchungen über Colchicin. Med. Jahrb. Vienna. Pp. 257–58. 1883.
56. PERROT, E. Une plante nouvelle à colchicine, le lofout lilacee saharienne. C. R. Acad. Sci. Paris. 202:1088–89. 1936.
57. ROBERG, M. Occurrence and distribution of saponins in seed drugs. Arch. Pharm. 275:328–36. 1937.
58. ROJAHN, C., AND HERZOG, H. Decrease in content of alkaloidal salt solutions and pharmaceutical tinctures in sun and ultra violet light. Pharm. Zentralhalle. 73:401–10. 1932.
59. ROSENTHALER, L. Microchemical behavior of the official alkaloids. Amer. Jour. Pharm. 101:821–29. 1929. Economic drug testing. XII. Pharm. Ztg. 76:288. 1931.
60. SALGUES, R. Influence of fertilizer on the yield and composition of some cultivated plants (medicinal plants). Ann. Agron. 8:537–51. 1938.
61. SANTAVY, F. Polarograficke stanoveni kolchicinu a kolchiceinu. Zvlast. Otisk z Cas. Lek. Ces. 81:1160–67. 1942. Polarografie a spektrografie kolchicinu a jeho derivatu. Publ. Fac. Med. Brno. 19:149–72. 1945. Isolace novych latek z ocunu jesennino. Chem. Listy. Rocnick. 42:177–80. 1948. Sur la variabilité

de la teneur en colchicine des semences de colchique. Pharm. Acta Helv. 23:380. 1949. Polarography and spectrography of colchicine, colchiceine, and similar substances. Collection Czechoslov. Chem. Commans. 14:145–55. 1949. Isolation of new substances from the flowers and pericarps of meadow saffron. *Colchicum autumnale* L. Coll. Czech. Chem. Comm. 15:552–69. 1950.

62. ————, AND BUCHNICEK, J. Sur la variabilité de la teneur en colchicine des semences du colchique. (*Colchicum autumnale* L.) Substances tirées du colchique et leurs dérivés. 9e Comm. Pharm. Acta Helv. 24:20–30. 1949.

63. ————, AND REICHSTEIN, T. Alkaloide der Herbstzeitlosenzwiebeln während deren Entwicklung: Substanzen der Herbzeitlose und ihre Derivate. XXV. Pharm. Acta Helv. 27:71–76. 1952.

64. ————, *et al.* Substances of *Colchicum autumnale* and their derivatives. XXI. Isolation of substances from the corms. Ann. Pharm. Franc. 9:50–59; cf. Chem. Abst. 45:4343a, 4888a. 1951.

65. SCHUHLER, H. Spectral and physiochemical properties of colchicine. C. R. Acad. Sci. Paris. 210:490–93. 1940.

66. SELF, P., AND CORFIELD, C. Determination of colchicine in *Colchicum* corm and seed and the official *Colchicum* preparations. Quart. Jour. Pharm. and Pharmacol. 5:347–56. 1932.

67. SEIFERT, R. Determination of colchicine in the drug and tincture. Deut. Apoth. Ztg. 58:77–78. 1943.

68. STEFANOFF, B. (*see* Ref. No. 41, Chap. 1. 1926).

69. SUZUKA, O., AND SAWAK, K. A study on the tetraploid *Datura stramonium* L. induced by colchicine. Jap. Jour. Pharmacog. 4:14–17. 1951.

70. TARAN, E. Chemical study of some alkaloid-bearing plants. IV. Alkaloids of Caucasian *Colchicum speciosum* Stev. Farmatsiya. No. 9–10, 38–40. 1940.

71. TRAUB, H. Colchicine poisoning in relation to *Hemerocallis* and some other plants. Science. 110:686–87. 1949.

72. UFFELIE, O. The determination of colchicine in *Colchicum* seed. Pharm. Weekblad. 81:419–26. 1946.

73. UMNEY, J. Notes on *Colchicum* seeds. Pharm. Jour. 95:393. 1915.

74. VENTURI, V. Colchicine content and toxicity of *Colchicum* seeds and corms collected at different heights. Jour. Pharm. and Pharmacol. 2:17–19. 1950.

75. VLES, F. Oxidation reduction potentials of nucleic-acid-colchicine mixtures. Arch. Phys. Biol. 17:Suppl. 50–52. 1944.

76. ————, AND SCHULER, H. Interpretation of the ultraviolet spectral absorption curve of colchicine. Arch. Phys. Biol. Vol. 99 and 100.

77. WEINLAND, R., AND HEINZLER, J. A new reagent for alkaloids. Sueddeutsche Apoth. Ztg. 61:46. 1922.

78. WEISSE, G. v., AND LEVY, M. Determination of the dissociation constants of some alkaloids. Jour. Chim. Phys. 14:261–84. 1916.

79. WERLE, E., AND POEWER, F. Monoamine oxidase in plants. Biochem. Z. 320:298–301. 1950.

80. WERTH, E. Crocus und *Colchicum*, zwei blütenbiologische Paradoxa. Deut. Bot. Gesell. Ber. 63:82–87. 1950.

81. ZEEHUISEN, H. Physical properties of some alkaloids. Arch. Exp. Path. Pharm. 86:342–72. 1920.

ADDITIONAL REFERENCES FOR TABLES 5.2 AND 5.3 NOT CITED ABOVE

82. BEER, A. A.: C. R. Dokl. Acad. Sci. URSS. 69:369. 1949. Chem. Abst. 44:2178 g. 1950.

83. BELLET, M. P. Ann. Pharm. Franc. 10:81. 1952.

84. GEIGER, P. L. Ann. Chem. Pharm. (later, Liebigs Ann.) 7:274. 1833.

85. HOUDÉ, A.: C. R. Acad. Sci. Paris. 98:1442. 1884.

86. KISSELEW, W. W., MENSCHIKOW, G. P., AND BEER, A. A. C. R. Dokl. Acad. Sci. URSS. 87:227. 1952.

87. MASINOVA, V., AND SANTAVY, F. Chem. Listy. In press.

88. OBERLIN, L. Ann. Chim. Phys. [3] 50:108. 1857.

89. PELLETIER, P. J., AND CAVENTOU, J. Ann. Chim. Phys. 14:69. 1820.
90. POTESILOVA, H., BARTOSOVA, I., AND SANTAVY, F. In manuscript.
91. RAFFAUF, R. F., FARREN, A. L., AND ULLYOT, G. E. Jour. Amer. Chem. Soc. 75:3854. 1953.
92. ROCHETTE. Union Pharm. 17:200. 1876; cited in Dragendorff, Die Heilpflanzen, p. 114, Stuttgart, 1898.
93. SANTAVY, F. Pharm. Acta Helv. 25:248. 1950.
94. ————, AND BARTEK, J. Die Pharmazie. 7:595. 1952.
95. ————, AND COUFALIK, E. Coll. Czeck. Chem. Comm. 16:198. 1951.
96. ————, HOSCALKOVA, Z., PODIVINSKY, R., AND POTESILOVA, H. Chem. Listy. In press.
97. ————, LANG, B., AND MALINSKY, J. Arch. Int. Pharmacodyn. 82:321. 1950.
98. ————, LIPOVA, J., AND COUFALIK, E. Ceskoslovenska Farmacie. 1:239. 1952.
99. ————, AND MACAK, V. Chem. Listy. 47:1215. 1953.
100. ————, AND REICHSTEIN, T. Helv. Chim. Acta. 33:1606. 1950.
101. ————, AND TALAS, M. Chem. Listy. 47:232. 1953.
102. STEIGER, A. Z. Physiol. Chem. 86:245. 1913.
103. SUBBARATNAM, A. V. Sci. Ind. Res. 11:446. 1952.
104. ————. Die Pharmazie. 8:1041. 1953.
105. WEIZMANN, A. Bull. Research Council Israel. 2:21. 1952.
106. ZEISEL, S. Monath. für Chem. 7:557. 1886.

CHAPTER 6

Chemistry

by James D. Loudon*

6.1: Extraction and General Properties

Colchicine is commonly extracted from the seeds and corms of the autumn crocus, *Colchicum autumnale,* Linn., but it is also present in numerous species of *Colchicum* (Albo[1]) as well as in other Liliaceae (Klein and Pollauf[2]). Extraction is effected by alcohol (Zeisel;[3] Chemnitius[4]) and the concentrates after dilution with water are freed from insoluble fats or resins. The aqueous solution is then repeatedly extracted with chloroform and the colchicine is recovered in the form of a crystalline addition complex with the solvent. From this the chloroform is distilled off in steam or alcohol and evaporation of the residual solution yields amorphous colchicine which may be crystallized from ethyl acetate as pale yellow needles (Clewer, Green, and Tutin[5]). Chromatographic purification of the chloroform solution on alumina greatly facilitates the procedure (Ashley and Harris[6]).

Pure colchicine, $C_{22}H_{25}O_6N$, forms fine, practically colorless needles, m.p. 155°; $[\alpha]_D^{13} - 119.9°$ (c = 0.878 in chloroform), as determined by Mr. T. Y. Johnston at Glasgow. It is readily soluble in alcohol, chloroform, or in cold water, but is less soluble in hot water or in cold benzene and is almost insoluble in ether. From these solvents there is a tendency to crystallize with solvent of crystallization which may markedly affect the melting point. Concentrated aqueous solutions deposit crystals of the sesquihydrate which, despite its relatively sparing solubility in water, does not crystallize from more dilute solution unless induced to do so by seeding (Loudon and Speakman[7]). Dilute mineral acids and alkalis color colchicine an intense yellow, while nitric acid (d,1.4) produces a violet color which slowly changes to yellow and finally to green: other color-reactions are de-

---

* Lecturer in Chemistry, University of Glasgow, Scotland.

scribed by Zeisel.[3] Although under suitable conditions colchicine forms precipitates with many of the usual alkaloidal reagents,[3] its classification as an alkaloid is questionable. It is essentially a neutral substance with a homocyclic ring-structure: on the other hand, it is associated in the plant with compounds of allied structure, some seven crystalline and kindred alkaloids being known (Santavy and Reichstein[8]).

6.2: The Functional Groups

Hydrolysis of colchicine by boiling with very dilute hydrochloric acid yields methyl alcohol and *colchiceine,* $C_{21}H_{23}O_6N$, which is acidic, gives a deep olive-green color with aqueous ferric chloride (distinction from colchicine), and on further hydrolysis with more concentrated acid yields equivalent amounts of acetic acid and *trimethylcolchicinic acid,* $C_{19}H_{21}O_5N$ (Zeisel[9]). This last compound is amphoteric and contains a primary amino-group (Johanny and Zeisel[10]); hence the two-stage hydrolysis may be represented as follows:

$$C_{19}H_{18}O_4 \, (OMe) \, (NH.COMe)$$
$$\rightarrow MeOH + C_{19}H_{18}O_4 \, (OH) \, (NH.COMe)$$
$$\rightarrow MeCO_2H + C_{19}H_{18}O_4 \, (OH) \, (NH_2).$$

Trimethylcolchicinic acid contains three methoxyl groups which, by prolonged hydrolysis, are demethylated and *colchicinic acid,* $C_{16}H_{15}O_5N$, is produced. Correspondingly in colchicine itself the presence of four methoxyl groups is shown by the usual Zeisel estimation.[9]

The four methoxyl groups and the acetylamido-group together account for five of the six oxygen atoms of colchicine. Since the sixth oxygen is unresponsive to carbonyl reagents, it was at one time thought to be part of a carbomethoxy group (–CO.OMe) or of an oxygen ring system. The former view is in harmony with the ready hydrolysis to colchiceine which has acidic character but which, on the other hand, also shows definite enolic properties and when methylated by diazomethane, yields two readily hydrolyzable *O*-methyl ethers, namely colchicine and iso*colchicine* (Meyer and Reichstein;[11] Sorkin[12]). Similarly trimethylcolchicinic acid reacts with benzenesulphonyl chloride to give two di(benzenesulphonyl) derivatives (Windaus[13]), in each of which one of the acyl groups is attached to nitrogen while the second appears to be attached to oxygen since fairly mild hydrolysis converts both compounds into the same *N*-benzenesulphonyl trimethylcolchicinic acid. This duplication of *O*-derivatives strongly suggests that in colchiceine and in trimethylcolchicinic acid there is a tautomeric enol system capable of giving rise to paired *O*-derivatives which are either steric or structural isomers. Accordingly the sixth oxygen atom is considered to reside in the carbonyl group of an enolone system in colchiceine and of a corresponding enolone-methyl-ether system in colchicine.

Although neither colchicine nor colchiceine reacts with the usual carbonyl reagents, hydrogenation results provide evidence of the presence of a carbonyl group in each. Bursian[14] found that with a platinum catalyst both compounds absorbed three moles of hydrogen and that thereby colchicine gave a mono-alcohol while colchiceine gave a diol. In each case therefore a new hydroxylic function has been produced and may well arise from reduction of a carbonyl group by one mole of hydrogen. The absorption of two further moles of hydrogen shows the presence of two olefinic groups, while the presence of yet a third olefinic group, which resists hydrogenation, was indicated by the interaction of *hexahydrocolchicine*, $C_{22}H_{31}O_6N$, with perbenzoic acid[14] or with monoperphthalic acid (Tarbell *et al.*[15]) to form an oxide, $C_{22}H_{31}O_7N$.

Summing up: The evidence suggests that colchicine is the methyl ether of an enolone which contains three additional methoxyl groups, an acetylated primary amino-group, and three non-benzenoid double bonds:

$$C_{16}H_9 \ (OMe)_4 \ (NH.COMe) \ (:O) \ (=)_3 .$$

6.3: The Structural Problem

The saturated hydrocarbon, $C_{16}H_{22}$, which corresponds to this assemblage of groups, fall short of the paraffin, $C_{16}H_{34}$, by six hydrogen molecules each of which in default indicates the presence of either a carbon ring or a benzenoid type of double bond. Four of the missing hydrogen molecules are at once accounted for by the demonstrable presence of a benzenoid ring; the remaining two must therefore denote two further ring systems. Colchicine is accordingly tricyclic and the respective rings, both in the alkaloid and in its degradation products, are designated by the letters A, B, and C.

6.3–1: Ring A. The presence of the benzenoid ring (A) is shown by the formation of 3:4:5-trimethoxyphthalic acid (I), or its anhydride, from colchicine and many of its derivatives on oxidation with hot alkaline permanganate (Windaus[16, 17]).

6.3–2: Ring B. The most penetrating insight into the molecular structure of colchicine is obtained through a series of degradation products (Windaus[17, 18]) derived from N-*acetyliodocolchinol*, $C_{20}H_{22}O_5NI$. This compound is formed from colchiceine by the action of iodine in the presence of alkali. It is definitely phenolic and is reduced by zinc and acetic acid to N-*acetylcochinol*, $C_{20}H_{23}O_5N$, which on methylation affords N-*acetylcolchinol methyl ether*. The latter still contains the acetylated primary amino-group and may be deaminated in several ways: (1) directly, by heating with phosphoric oxide in xylene (Cook and Graham;[19] Barton, Cook, and Loudon[20]) whereby two isomeric compounds, $C_{19}H_{21}O_4$, are formed and are named *deaminocolchinol methyl ether* and iso*deaminocolchinol methyl ether,* respectively; (2) by hydrolysis to the primary amine, *colchinol methyl ether*, followed by reaction with nitrous acid to form a carbinol

(I)

(Cohen, Cook, and Roe[21]) which on dehydration[20] yields the same pair of isomeric products; (3) by Hofmann degradation of colchinol methyl ether whereby only deaminocolchinol methyl ether has been isolated (Windaus[22]).

Barton, Cook, and Loudon[20] established the structure (II) for deaminocolchinol methyl ether and the structure (III) for the *iso*-compound on the following grounds. Both isomers afforded the same dihydride when hydrogenated in acetic acid with a palladium catalyst; they must therefore differ only in the location of a double bond which must be ethylenic in type. Deaminocolchinol methyl ether was oxidized with sodium dichromate in acetic acid to 2:3:4:7-tetramethoxyphenanthraquinone (VIII), together with a by-product which was recognized as an unsaturated ketone, $C_{19}H_{18}O_5$.

Formation of the quinone, which was identified by synthesis, establishes the presence of a (bridged) diphenyl system and fixes the methoxylation pattern. The nature of the three-carbon bridge in deaminocolchinol methyl ether (II) was next determined by oxidation with osmium tetroxide to a glycol (IV) which, by scission with lead tetra-acetate, yielded not the normally expected di-aldehyde (V) but a mono-aldehyde (VI) formed from (V) by internal condensation. This mono-aldehyde — later synthesized — was identified by oxidation to 2:3:4:7-tetramethoxyphenanthrene-10-carboxylic acid which was also synthesized. Similar stepwise oxidation of *iso*deaminocolchinol methyl ether (III) gave 2:3:4:7-tetramethoxy-9-phenanthraldehyde (VII), identical with a synthetic specimen.

These results leave little room for doubt that deaminocolchinol methyl ether and its *iso*-compound are correctly formulated. Moreover, Cook, Dickson, and Loudon[23] have shown that the synthesized

(II)   (IV)   (V)   (VI)

(III)   (VII)   (VIII)

parent hydrocarbon corresponding to (II; H for OMe) reproduces in all essentials the behavior just described and, further, that this hydrocarbon is isomerized to 9-methylphenanthrene by successive heating with hydriodic acid and zinc dust. Such isomerization accounts for the isolation of 9-methylphenanthrene by Windaus[22] during an attempt to demethoxylate deaminocolchinol methyl ether, and it con-

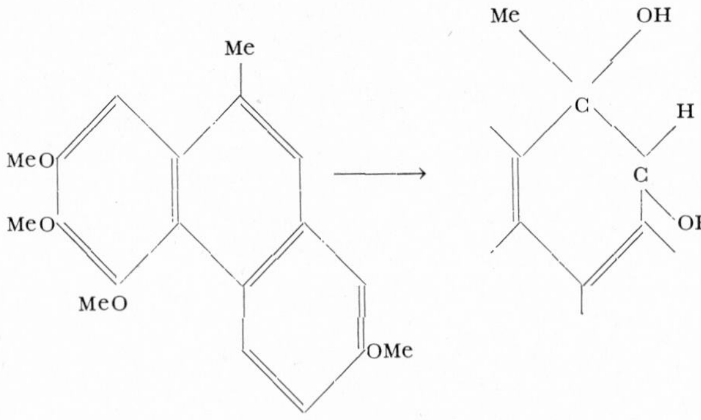

(IX)

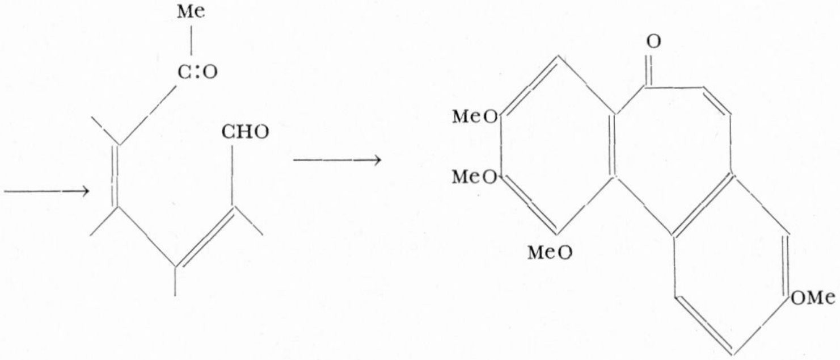

(X)

tributed to his formulating the latter compound as either 2:3:4:6- or 2:3:4:7-tetramethoxy-9-methylphenanthrene, each of which, when synthesized by Buchanan, Cook, and Loudon,[24] proved to be distinct from the degradation product. Tarbell, Frank, and Fanta,[25] who prepared deamino-iodocolchinol methyl ether from N-acetyliodocolchinol and oxidized it to a derivative of homodiphenic acid, likewise conclude in favor of a 7-membered ring B as in (II).

The first synthesis of a significant derivative of (II) was effected by Buchanan, Cook, Loudon, and MacMillan.[26] The sequence of reactions used for the ring-contraction (II) → (IV) was applied in the opposite direction to expand the central ring of 2:3:4:7-tetramethoxy-10-methylphenanthrene (IX). This took advantage of the known reactivity of the 9:10-double bond in phenanthrenes and hydroxylation, scission, and renewed cyclization led to an unsaturated ketone (X) identical with the one produced, as already mentioned, by oxidation of deaminocolchinol methyl ether. Moreover, by applying the same series of reactions to 2:3:4:7-tetra-methoxy-9-methylphenanthrene (XI) Cook, Jack, and Loudon[27] obtained an isomeric unsaturated ketone (XII). This was reduced to the saturated ketone (XIII) and thence by oximation and renewed reduction was converted to the (±)-amine (XVI). Optical resolution of this amine, through its salts with (+)-6:6'-dinitrodiphenic acid, afforded the (−)-base and hence the (−)-acetyle derivative and these respectively were identical with colchinol methyl ether and its *N*-acetyl derivative

(XI)   (XII)

(XIII)   (XIV)

as obtained by degradation of colchicine. [28] By a different route starting from the 9-monoxime of 2:3:4:7-tetramethoxyphenanthraquinone Rapoport, Williams, and Cisney also synthesized the (±)-amine (XIV) and showed it to be identical with racemized colchinol methyl ether.[29]

A second series of degradation products has a bearing on the structure of ring B. Windaus[13] found that *N*-benzoyltrimethylcolchicinic acid (prepared by di-benzoylation of trimethylcolchicinic acid and preferential hydrolysis of the *O*-benzoyl group) was oxidized by cold alkaline permanganate to two products, namely N-*benzoylcolchinic anhydride*, $C_{23}H_{21}O_7N$, and a corresponding lactone, N-*benzoylcolchide*, $C_{23}H_{23}O_6N$, which he formulated[22] as derivatives of 1:2-dihydro-2-methylnaphthalene. With the recognition of ring B as 7-

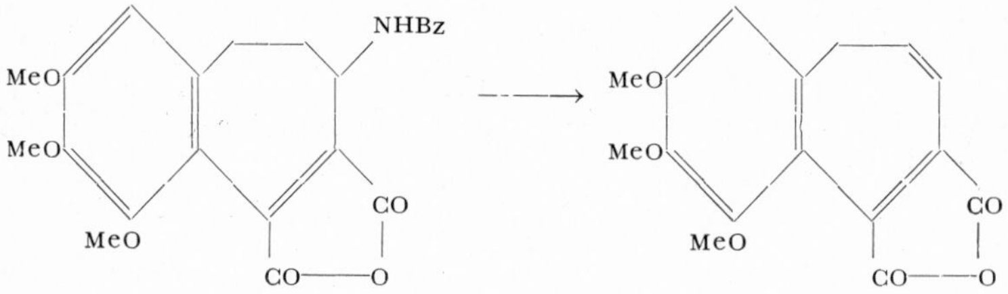

(XV)   (XVI)

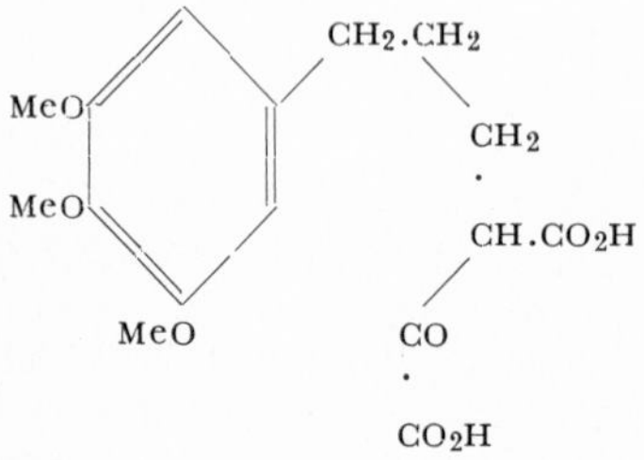

(XVIII 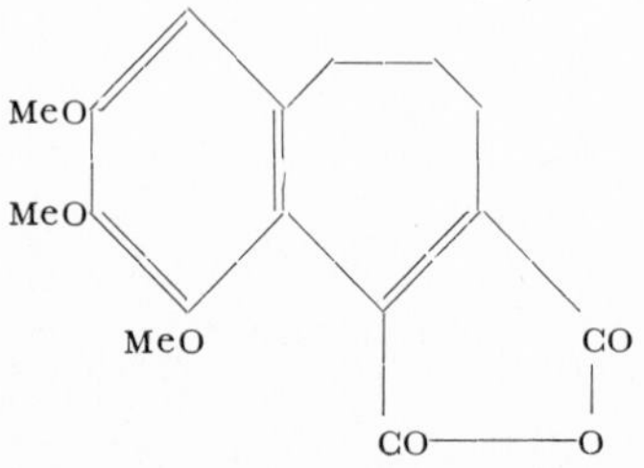)   (XVII)

membered in the colchinol series, it was at once evident that N-benzoylcolchinic anhydride might be better represented by formula (XV) and N-benzoylcolchide by a corresponding lactone structure. To test this view, Cook, Johnston, and Loudon[30] deaminated the anhydride and showed that the resultant deaminocolchinic anhydride was not identical with 6:7:8-trimethoxy-3-methylnaphthalene-1:2-dicarboxylic anhydride — as it would be on the Windaus formulation — nor indeed could it be a naphthalene derivative since it showed ethylenic behavior towards reduction. From the reduction products, Horning, Ullyot, and their colleagues[31] isolated a dihydride and established its structure as (XVII) by synthesis and cyclization of the oxaloacetic acid (XVIII). Thereby the 7-membered rings in N-benzoylcolchinic anhydride (XV) and its deamination product (XVI) are unequivocally proved.

Accordingly both lines of degradation — the first, through N-acetylcolchinol, involving a process which makes ring C benzenoid; the second producing N-benzoylcolchinic anhydride apparently by direct oxidation of ring C — consistently lead to the conclusion that ring B of colchicine is 7-membered.

6.3–3: Ring C. It will now be evident that the enolone properties of colchiceine derive from the third ring, namely ring C, and that the structure to be assigned to this ring must also interpret the conversion of colchiceine into *N*-acetyliodocolchinol. This transformation is empirically expressed by

$$C_{21}H_{33}O_6N + I \rightarrow C_2OH_{22}O_5NI + [CHO]$$

and the colchinol derivative so produced may be formulated as (XIX) which is in harmony with the observation that its methyl ether yields 4-iodo-5-methoxyphthalic acid on oxidation.[18, 32] Two further links between the structure of the alkaloid and that of colchinol are known. Cech and Santavy[33] obtained *N*-acetylcolchinol directly by oxidizing colchiceine with alkaline hydrogen peroxide. Again, colchicine (but

(XIX)

(XX)

not colchiceine) is isomerized when heated with sodium methoxide in methanol (Santavy;[34] Fernholz[35]) forming the methyl ester (*allo*-colchicine) of a carboxylic acid (*allo*colchiceine); and Fernholz[35] converted this acid into *N*-acetylcolchinol by the standard procedure: $RCO_2H \rightarrow RNH_2 \rightarrow ROH$. The structure of *allo*colchicine is therefore securely fixed as (XX).

Even before all of these facts were available, Dewar[36] suggested that ring C of colchiceine was tropolonoid and on this basis the structure of colchiceine is represented by the tautomeric system (XXI) ⇌ (XXII). The validity of this formulation is now generally accepted and an earlier formula, proposed by Windaus,[22] need not be discussed here.

6.4: Comparison With Tropolones

It is necessary, however, to refer briefly at this stage to some of the more general features of tropolone chemistry (for more compre-

(XXI)   (XXII)

hensive treatment, see Cook and Loudon[37]). Tropolone (2-hydroxy*cyclo*heptatrienone) and its derivatives have aromatic properties, the reactivity of the ethylenic and carbonyl functions being suppressed. Thus the compounds are substituted by electrophilic reagents but do not react with carbonyl reagents. The hydroxyl group is markedly acidic. Salt formation is accompanied by development or intensification of color, and coordination complexes are produced with ferric or cupric ions. Tropolone itself exhibits feebly basic properties and yields a hydrochloride and a picrate. Tropolone ethers resemble esters in their ready hydrolysis. With varying ease individual tropolones (or their ethers) are isomerized by hot alkali, the 7-membered ring undergoing contraction to the benzenoid structure of an appropriately substituted benzoic acid (or ester). Catalytic hydrogenation of tropolones is seldom simple. When complete, it yields octahydrides which are 1:2-diols, but it may involve loss of oxygen, and ketonic intermediates are frequently detectable.

The general analogy with colchiceine, implicit in this account of tropolone behavior, is borne out by more specific comparison. Like unsymmetrically substituted tropolones, colchiceine is known only as a single substance which yields two isomeric methyl ethers, colchicine and *iso*colchicine, corresponding to the tautomerides (XXI) and

(XXII). The ester-like properties of these ethers are revealed in their rapid hydrolysis to colchiceine and in their reactions with ammonia and amines whereby colchicamides are formed,[38] the reactive methoxyl group being replaced by an amine residue. Hydrogenation of colchiceine, or of colchicine, is complex,[14, 15, 39, 40, 41] but there is evidence that hexahydrocolchiceine is a 1:2-diol,[15, 42] and less fully hydrogenated material shows ketonic properties.[39] Polarographic measurements made by Santavy and by Brdicka,[43] and infrared absorption studies by Scott and Tarbell[44] confirm the similarity between colchiceine and tropolones. Moreover, *allo*colchicine (XX) is at once seen to be the benzenoid isomerization product of a methyl ether derived from either (XXI) or (XXII). Its production corresponds to that of methyl benzoate from tropolone methyl ether (Doering and Knox[45]) and explains the origin of the trimellitic acid (benzene-1:2:4-tricarboxylic acid) which Windaus obtained from colchicine by successive alkali fusion and oxidation.[16]

6.5: Structure of Colchicine

The tautomeric nature of colchiceine allows two possible formulations of colchicine, its methyl ether. It is not easy by chemical means to distinguish between these alternatives but the distinction can be made by X-ray crystallographic analysis. King, De Vries, and Pepinsky[46] in this way examined an addition complex of colchicine and methylene di-iodide and not only confirmed the tricyclic structure with its two fused 7-membered rings but also showed that colchicine is the particular methyl ether (XXIII). It follows that *iso*colchicine has the methyl ether structure corresponding to (XXII).

6.6: Miscellany

So far in this chapter discussion has been directed primarily to the evidence on which the structural formula of colchicine rests. There remain to be noted several reactions and items of chemical interest, which are either at present incompletely evaluated or only indirectly related to the alkaloid's structure. For instance it is known that nitration of colchicine yields a mononitro-colchicine, reducible to an aminocolchicine, but the seat of substitution in these derivatives is not yet definitely ascertained (Nicholls and Tarbell[41]). Bromination of colchicine yields mono-, di-, and tribromo derivatives (Zeisel and Stockert[47]). Bromination of colchiceine yields a tribromo acid which Lettré, Fernholz, and Hartwig[48] formulate as (XXIV) by analogy with the bromination of tropolones[49] and because the compound is readily decarboxylated to a tribromo derivative of *N*-acetyl-colchinol. Oxidation of colchicine with chromic acid in aqueous solution yields a ketone, namely oxycolchicine, $C_{22}H_{23}O_7N$, in which a methylene group of the alkaloid has been oxidized to carbonyl.[22, 50]

Molecular rearrangement is almost commonplace in colchicine's chemistry. It is inherent in the changes, already described, by which the 7-membered rings of the alkaloid or its derivatives become contracted to 6-membered rings. It is also encountered in formation of the carbinol (6.3) by the action of nitrous acid on colchinol methyl

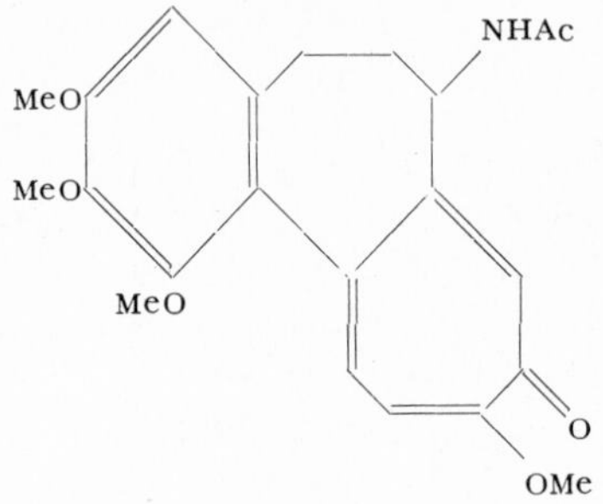

(**XXIII**)

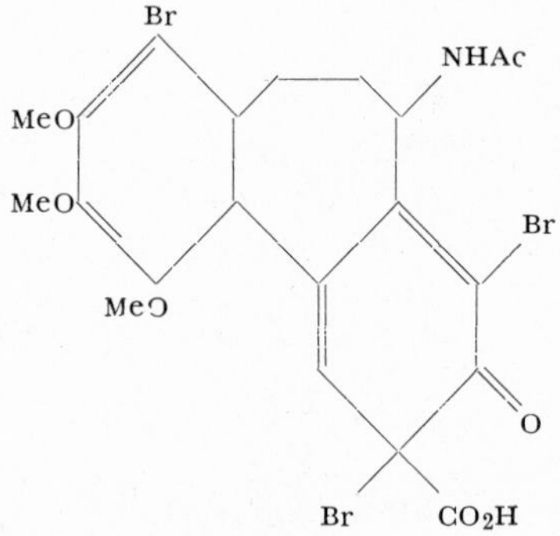

(**XXIV**)

ether and is again found in dehydration of this carbinol whereby deaminocolchinol methyl ether (and its isomeride) is produced. Both of these reactions are known to involve Demjanow-type rearrangements (Cook, Jack, and Loudon[51]) and through them ring B, initially 7-membered, is contracted and re-expanded in successive steps. Moreover, colchicine itself is sensitive to ultraviolet light and is isomerized in aqueous solution by sunlight. Thereby three isomerides, namely α-, β-, and γ-lumicolchicine are formed (Grewe and Wulf;[62] Santavy[53]) but their molecular structures remain undetermined.

Synthesis — the ultimate challenge of a natural product to the organic chemist — has still to be achieved for colchicine although, at the time of writing, preliminary work in this direction is engaging much attention.[54-59] The colchicine structure is novel chiefly in respect of the two fused 7-membered rings of its tricyclic system. These rings are retained in a compound, $C_{19}H_{26}O_3$, which Rapoport and Williams[38] prepared from colchicine by a series of hydrogenation reactions. In this product ring A of colchicine is unaltered, but rings B and C are fully reduced and devoid of substituent groups. Synthesis of this compound is potentially more simple, although also less significant, than that of colchicine itself. But even total synthesis of the alkaloid, when achieved, is unlikely to have more than academic importance: synthetic colchicine will not soon provide an economic replacement of the natural product. Here another issue is joined, for it may be possible from a study of the alkaloid and its immediate derivatives to discern some pattern of atoms or groups, which is associated with colchicine's effect on mitosis. By incorporating this molecular pattern in simpler and more accessible compounds it would then be possible to search on a rational basis for synthetic substitutes. Already several attempts have been made to achieve this end and some success has been claimed for compounds modeled on the earlier, partly erroneous formula of Windaus (see work by Lettré discussed in Chapter 17). As would be expected, tropolone derivatives have been investigated for their effect on cell mitosis. For instance, *p*-acetamidotropolone (XXV) — a compound possessing obvious structural similarities to colchiceine — was examined, in *Tradescantia* cells *in vivo*, by Wada[60] who records a strong radiomimetic

NHAc

O

OH

(**XXV**)

action and regards the compound as a possible mutagenic substance. Its effect, however, does not appear to be identical with that of colchicine.

As an aid to biological studies Raffauf, Farren, and Ullyot[61] have prepared C^{14}-labeled derivatives of colchicine by methylation of colchiceine with labeled diazomethane and by acetylation of desacetyl-colchicine with labeled acetyl chloride.

Mention was earlier made of congeners of colchicine (6.1). These include a demethylcolchicine — or "substance C" — in which one of the three methoxyl groups of ring A is demethylated. Horowitz and Ullyot[62] find what is probably the same compound present in U.S.P. colchicine to an extent of some 4 per cent. It is also interesting that Bellet[63-65] has isolated a glucoside, namely colchicoside, $C_{27}H_{33}O_{11}N$, from *C. autumnale* and that this glucoside may be hydrolyzed to, and synthesized from, "substance C" and glucose. The glucosidic link probably involves the oxygen atom which in ring A is adjacent to ring B. Santavy and his colleagues have improved the technique of isolating colchicine from *C. autumnale* and have examined its seasonal variation in the plant.[66] They also surveyed various *Colchicum* species for alkaloid content and found *C. arenarium* W.K. to be particularly rich in colchicine. Finally they have made considerable progress towards elucidating the structures of colchicine's co-alkaloids [8, 68] and it is already apparent that at least several of these are simple modifications of the structural pattern of colchicine.

REFERENCES

1. ALBO, G. Sur la signification physiologique de la colchicine dans les différentes espèces de *Colchicum* et de *Merendera*. Arch. Sci. Phys. Nat. 12:227–36. 1901.
2. KLEIN, G., AND POLLAUF, G. Der mikrochemische Nachweis der Alkaloide in der Planze. XII. Oesterr. Bot. Z. 78:251–56. 1929.
3. ZEISEL, S. Über das Colchicin. Monatsh. 7:557–96. 1886.
4. CHEMNITIUS, F. Zur Darstellung des Colchicins. Jour. Prakt. Chem. 118:29–32. 1928.
5. CLEWER, H. W. B., GREEN, S. J., AND TUTIN, F. The constituents of *Gloriosa superba*. Jour. Chem. Soc. 107:835–46. 1915.
6. ASHLEY, J. N., AND HARRIS, J. O. Purification of colchicine by chromatography. Jour. Chem. Soc. 1944. P. 677.
7. LOUDON, J. D., AND SPEAKMAN, J. C. The solubility of colchicine in water. Research. 3:583–84. 1950.
8. SANTAVY, F., AND REICHSTEIN, T. Isolierung neuer Stoffe aus den Samen der Herbstzeitlose *Colchicum autumnale* L. Substanzen der Herbstzeitlose und ihre Derivate. (12. Mitteilung) Helv. Chim. Acta. 33:1606–27. 1950. cf. Santavy, F. (14. Mitteilung) Pharm. Acta Helv. 25:248–65. 1950.
9. ZEISEL, S. Über Colchicin. Monatsh. 9:1–30. 1888.
10. JOHANNY, S., AND ZEISEL, S. Zur Kenntnis des Colchicins. Monatsh. 9:865–81. 1888.
11. MEYER, K., AND REICHSTEIN, T. Synthesis of 2-methoxymethylenephenanthrones and comparison with colchicine. Pharm. Acta Helv. 19:127. 1944.
12. SORKIN, M. *iso*Colchicin. Helv. Chim. Acta. 29:246–48. 1946.
13. WINDAUS, A. Untersuchungen über Colchicin. II. Sitzber. Heidelberg. Akad. Wiss., Math. Nat. Klasse. A. 1911. 2 Abh.
14. BURSIAN, K. Über das Colchicin. Chem. Ber. 71:245–57. 1938.
15. ARNSTEIN, H. R. V., TARBELL, D. S., SCOTT, G. P., AND HUANG, H. T. Studies in the structure of colchicine. The structure of ring C. Jour. Amer. Chem. Soc. 71:2448–52. 1949.
16. WINDAUS, A. Untersuchungen über Colchicin. I. Sitzber. Heidelberg. Akad. Wiss., Math. Nat. Klasse. A. 1910. 2 Abh.
17. ———. Untersuchungen über Colchicin. III. *Ibid*. A. 1914. 18 Abh.
18. ———. Untersuchungen über Colchicin. IV. *Ibid*. A. 1919. 16 Abh.

19. COOK, J. W., GRAHAM, W., AND (in part) COHEN, A., LAPSLEY, R. W., AND LAWRENCE, C. A. Colchicine and related compounds. Part III. Jour. Chem. Soc. 1944. Pp. 322–25.

20. BARTON, N., COOK, J. W., AND LOUDON, J. D. Colchicine and related compounds. Part V. The structure of Windaus's deaminocolchinol methyl ether. *Ibid.* 1945. Pp. 176–78.

21. COHEN, A., COOK, J. W., AND ROE, E. M. F. Colchicine and related compounds. Part I. Some observations on the structure of colchicine. *Ibid.* 1940. Pp. 194–97.

22. WINDAUS, A. Untersuchungen über die Konstitution des Colchicins. Annalen Chem. 439:59–75. 1924.

23. COOK, J. W., DICKSON, G. T., AND LOUDON, J. D. Colchicine and related compounds. Part VI. 3:4:5:6-Dibenzcyclohepta-1:3:5-triene. Jour. Chem. Soc. 1947. Pp. 746–50.

24. BUCHANAN, G. L., COOK, J. W., AND LOUDON, J. D. Colchicine and related compounds. Part IV. Synthesis of 2:3:4:5-, 2:3:4:6-, and 2:3:4:7-Tetramethoxy-9-methylphenanthrenes. *Ibid.* 1944. Pp. 325–29.

25. TARBELL, D. S., FRANK, H. R., AND FANTA, P. E. Studies on the structure of colchicine. Jour. Amer. Chem. Soc. 68:502–6. 1946.

26. BUCHANAN, G. L., COOK, J. W., LOUDON, J. D., AND MACMILLAN, J. Synthesis of colchicine derivatives. Nature. 162:692. 1948.

27. COOK, J. W., JACK, J., AND LOUDON, J. D., Synthesis of (±) -N-acetylcolchinol methyl ether. Chem. and Ind. 1950. P. 650.

28. ———, ———, ———, AND (in part) BUCHANAN, G. L., AND MACMILLAN, J. Colchicine and related compounds. Part XI. Synthesis of N-acetylcolchinol methyl ether. Jour. Chem. Soc. 1951. Pp. 1397–1403.

29. RAPOPORT, H., WILLIAMS, A. R., AND CISNEY, M. E. The synthesis of *dl*-colchinol methyl ether. Jour. Amer. Chem. Soc. 72:3324–25. 1950. *Ibid.* 73:1414–21. 1951.

30. COOK, J. W., JOHNSTON, T. V., AND LOUDON, J. D. Colchicine and compounds. Part X. Jour. Chem. Soc. 1950. Pp. 537–43.

31. HORNING, E. C., HORNING, M. G., KOO, J., FISH, M. S., PARKER, J. A., WALKER, G. N., HOROWITZ, R. M., AND ULLYOT, G. E. Colchicine. The structure of Windaus's anhydride. Jour. Amer. Chem. Soc. 72:4840–41. 1950.

32. GREWE, R. Über die Iod-methoxy-phthalsäure aus Colchicin. Chem. Ber. 71:907–11. 1938.

33. CECH, J., AND SANTAVY, F. The effect of hydrogen peroxide in alkaline medium on colchicine. Coll. Czech. Chem. Comm. 14:532–39. 1949.

34. SANTAVY, F. Remarques sur le formule de la colchicine. C. R. Soc. Biol. Paris. 140:932. 1946. *Idem.* Preparation de l'acide colchicique de la colchicine. Helv. Chim. Acta. 31:821–26. 1948.

35. FERNHOLZ, H. Über die Umlagerung des Colchicins mit Natriumalkoholat und die Struktur des Ringes C. Annalen der Chemie. 568:63–72. 1950; cf. Lettré, H. Zur Konstitution des Colchicins. Angew. Chem. 59A:218–24. 1947.

36. DEWAR, M. J. S. Structure of colchicine. Naure. 155:141–42. 1945.

37. COOK, J. W., AND LOUDON, J. D. The tropolones. Quart. Rev. 5:99–130. 1951.

38. (a) RAPOPORT, H., AND WILLIAMS, A. R. The degradation of colchicine to octahydrodemethoxydesoxydesacetamidocolchicine. Jour. Amer. Chem. Soc. 73: 1896–97. 1951. (b) HOROWITZ, R. M., AND ULLYOT, G. E. Colchicine. Some reactions of ring C. *Ibid.* 74:587–92. 1952. (c) UFFER, A. Über Colchiceinamide. Helv. Chim. Acta. 35:2135–39. 1952.

39. ARNSTEIN, H. R. V., TARBELL, D. S., HUANG, H. T, AND SCOTT, G. P. The structure of ring C of colchicine. Jour. Amer. Chem. Soc. 70:1669. 1948.

40. KEMP, A. D., AND TARBELL, D. S. Studies on the structure of colchicine. Reduction products from ring C. *Ibid.* 72:243–46. 1950.

41. NICHOLLS, G. A., AND TARBELL, D. S. Colchicine and related products. *Ibid.* 75:1104–7. 1953.

42. DEWAR, M. J. S. Structure of colchicine. Nature. 155:479. 1945.

43. SANTAVY, F. Polarography and spectrography of colchicine, colchiceine and similar substances. Coll. Czech. Chim. Comm. 14:145–55. 1949; cf. Brdicka, R. Arkiv. Kemi. Mineral. Geol. 26B. No. 19. 1948.

44. SCOTT, G. P., AND TARBELL, D. S. Studies in the structure of colchicine. An infrared study of colchicine derivatives and related compounds. Jour. Amer. Chem. Soc. 72:240–43. 1950.

45. DOERING, W. VON E., AND KNOX, L. H. Tropolone. Jour. Amer. Chem. Soc. 73:828–38. 1951.

46. KING, M. V., DE VRIES, J. L., AND PEPINSKY, R. An X-ray diffraction determination of the chemical structure of colchicine. Acta Cryst. 5:437–40. 1952.

47. ZEISEL, S., AND STOCKERT, K. R. Über einige bromhaltige Abkömmlinge des Colchicins. Monatsh. 34:1339–47. 1913.

48. LETTRÉ, H., FERNHOLZ, H., HARTWIG, E. Zur Kenntnis der Tribromocolchiceinsäure. Annalen. Chem. 576:147–54. 1952.

49. FERNHOLZ, H., HARTWIG, E., AND SALFELD, J-C. Einige Untersuchungen an Tropolonen und Vergleiche mit dem Colchicin. Annalen Chem. 576:131–46. 1952.

50. ZEISEL, S., AND FRIEDRICH, A. Über das Oxycolchicin. Monatsh. 34:1181–86. 1913.

51. COOK, J. W., JACK, J., AND LOUDON, J. D. Colchicine and related compounds. Part XII. Some molecular rearrangements. Jour. Chem. Soc. 1952. Pp. 607–10.

52. GREWE, R., AND WULF, W. Die Umwandlung des Colchicins durch Sonnenlicht. Chem. Ber. 84:621–25. 1951.

53. SANTAVY, F. Substanzen der Herbstzeitlose und ihre Derivate. XXII. Photochemische Produkte des Colchicins und einige seiner Derivate. Coll. Czech. Chem. Comm. 16:665–75. 1951.

54. BOEKELHEIDE, V., AND PENNINGTON, F. C. Coumarins as intermediates in the synthesis of colchicine analogs. Jour. Amer. Chem. Soc. 74:1558–62. 1952.

55. ANDERSON, A. G., AND GREEF, H. F. Synthesis of dimethyl 6,7,8,9,-tetrahydro-5H-cycloheptabenzene-5-acetate-6-propionate. Jour. Amer. Chem. Soc. 74:5203–4. 1952.

56. GINSBERG, D., AND PAPPO, R. Colchicine studies. I. Synthesis and reactions of 2-aryl*cyclo*hept-2-enones. Jour. Amer. Chem. Soc. 75:1094–97. 1953.

57. KOO, J., AND HARTWELL, J. L. Synthesis of 2:3:4-trimethoxybenzosuberene and 2:3:4:-trimethoxybenzosuberancarboxylic acids and esters. Jour. Amer. Chem. Soc. 75:1625–28. 1953.

58. TARBELL, D. S., HIRSCHLER, H. R., AND HALL, T. J. Syntheses in the thiochromanone field. Jour. Amer. Chem. Soc. 75:1985–87. 1953.

59. GUTSCHE, C. D., AND SELIGMAN, K. L. Preliminary experiments on the synthesis of colchicine: a method for synthesising ring B. Jour. Amer. Chem. Soc. 75:2579–84. 1953.

60. WADA, B. The effect of chemicals on mitosis studied in *Tradescantia* cells *in vivo*. I. p-Acetylaminotropolone. Cytologia. 17:14–34. 1952.

61. RAFFAUF, R. F., FARREN, A. L., AND ULLYOT, G. E. C^{14}-Labeled colchicine derivatives. Jour. Amer. Chem. Soc. 75:2576–78. 1953.

62. HOROWITZ, R. M., AND ULLYOT, G. E. Desmethylcolchicine, a constituent of U.S.P. colchicine. Science. 115:216. 1952.

63. BELLET, P. Le colchicoside. I. Ann. Pharm. Franc. 10:81–88. 1952.

64. ————, AMIARD, G., PESEZ, M., AND PETIT, A. Sur le colchicoside. II. Synthèse partielle et constitution. Ann. Pharm. Franc. 10:211–16. 1952.

65. ————, AND REGNIER, P. Colchicoside et colchicine. III. Sur quelques singularités de pouvoir rotatoire. Ann. Pharm. Franc. 10:340–44. 1952.

66. SANTAVY, F., AND REICHSTEIN, T. Alkaloide der Herbstzeitlosenzwiebeln (*Colchicum autumnale* L.) während deren Entwicklung. Substanzen der Herbstzeitlose und ihre Derivate. (25. Mitteilung) Pharm. Acta Helv. 27:71–76. 1952.

67. ————, CERNOCH, M., MALINSKY, J., LANG, B., AND ZAJICKOVA, A. Isolement des substances des bulbes des différentes espèces du genre Colchique. Substances tirées du Colchique et leurs dérivés. (21e Communication) Ann. Pharm. Franc. 9:50–59. 1951.

68. ————. Substanzen der Herbstzeitlose und ihre Derivate. XXVII. Beitrag zur Konstitution der Substanz F. Coll. Czech. Chem. Comm. 16:676–88. 1951.

CHAPTER 7

Pharmacology

7.1: Colchicine in Medical Therapeutics and Forensic Practice

The nineteenth century medical literature contains many references to *Colchicum* preparations.[18] These were widely used in the treatment of gout, a disease in which severe pain is associated with the deposition of uric acid crystals near the joints. It was logical to attempt to cure other painful joint ailments with the same drug, and references may be found dealing with the treatment of various types of "rheumatism." The medical interest in the drug had two very different consequences. Scientists took up precise pharmacodynamic experiments in order to reach a better understanding of the therapeutic effects of colchicine. Various animals and organs were treated with the drug, and important new facts were proclaimed in learned papers. A typical paper of this type is that of Jacobj, which summarizes all that was known of the drug in the 1890's.[35] Frequent reference will be made to it, and to a chapter contributed by Führner[27] in Heffter's textbook of pharmacology. Most of the contributions of the last century are now only of historical interest and will not be reviewed in this chapter. Today interest in colchicine pharmacology has been revived,[23] and it is apparent that many conclusions will have to be changed in the light of modern work. In 1952, it was stated that the mechanism of action of colchicine, from a pharmacological point of view, was "largely unknown."[23]

Another and more redoubtable consequence of the use of the drug against gout in the nineteenth century was the increasing number of cases of fatal human poisoning.[74, 44] While one author is claimed to have taken as much as 20 mg. of colchicine in an experiment to study the toxic reactions,[67] there are reports of severe physiological disturbances and even death in patients that had absorbed only a few milligrams of the drug.[15] It is quite difficult to compare all these findings, for the preparations of *Colchicum* may have been different. Even after the crystallization of the alkaloid by Houdé, preparations

[175]

were not standardized. Recent work reviewed in other chapters indicates the complexity of the alkaloidal content of *Colchicum* and the great differences in toxicity of substances chemically very close to colchicine.

Forensic medicine quite naturally was often interested in the problem of human poisoning, accidental or criminal. A vast amount of literature on this subject exists, but it has not been found necessary to include it in this book. However, one most important fact made clear in this field is the long persistence of the alkaloid in the body after death.[27] The problems of the metabolism of colchicine will be taken up further in this chapter.

All work on colchicine before 1934, excepting only that on blood-forming tissues and blood cells, which will be discussed later, was confined to pharmacological methods and chemical testing. No study of the morphological changes was made, and these remained unsuspected for a long time. The aim of this chapter is not to give a detailed study of the pharmacology of colchicine, but to place it in a new perspective, that of spindle-poisoning. The significance of this in a field apparently so distant from cytology can be illustrated by modern descriptions of death from colchicine poisoning. These will show some of the complexities of the pharmacology of that very ancient drug, *Colchicum*.

7.2: Colchicine Poisoning in Man

The junior author happened to make the first detailed post-mortem study after the discovery of the action of colchicine on cell division.[22] In 1941, a woman of 42, attempting suicide, swallowed 60 1-mg. pills of colchicine "Houdé." She lived eight days after this very high dose; delayed lethality is nearly always found in colchicine poisoning. Vomiting and diarrhea were prominent, the blood urea increased to 1.5 gm. per thousand, and there were nervous troubles which were considered to be evidence of polyneuritis. An important decrease in the number of white blood cells and of platelets was noticeable. A bone-marrow study was performed only two hours before death, that is to say, eight days after colchicine had started to act. The abnormal percentage of metaphases, mainly of the star type, illustrated that spindle activity had not yet entirely recovered (Fig. 7.1).

Microscopic evidence of this was found at the post-mortem examination.[22] Arrested metaphases could be seen in lymph glands, in the spleen, and in the Lieberkühn glands of the intestine. The histological changes in the liver were remarkable. Here, 4 per cent of all liver cells were in a condition of arrested metaphase. About 15 per cent of these mitoses were ball metaphases, while the others showed scattered chromosomes. Other findings interesting from the point of view of the general action of the alkaloid were hypertrophy of the adrenal cortex, where no mitoses were to be seen, hypertrophy of the Langerhans' islets, and hyperbasophilia of the anterior lobe of the pituitary. These were considered to bring evidence of an "alarm-reaction," that is to say, a nonspecific pituitary-adrenal stimulation. The kidneys did not show any particular changes, with the exception of a very small

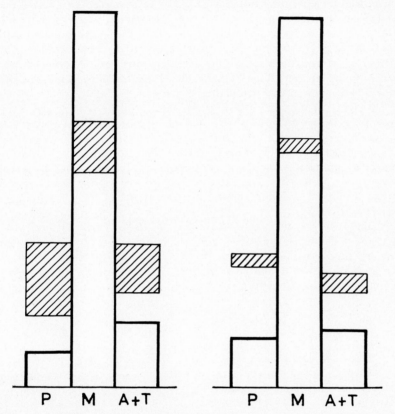

Fig. 7.1—Colchicine poisoning in man. Metaphasic arrest in the bone marrow. **Left,** granulocytes; **Right,** erythroblasts. The shaded areas indicate the normal repartition and variation in the percentage of each stage. (After P. Dustin[23])

number of mitoses. Mitoses arrested by colchicine could be found both in exocrine and endocrine tissues of the pancreatic gland.

The principal findings were (1) the persistence of mitotic changes long after the ingestion of colchicine, indicating that this substance is only slowly metabolized, (2) evidence of a general toxic reaction, and (3) considerable changes in the liver, where the proliferation of hepatic cells was made evident by the mitotic "stasis" produced by spindle destruction. These changes were considered at the time as evidence of mitotic stimulation by colchicine (cf. Chapter 9); they are probably only an indirect effect, the alkaloid having destroyed hepatic cells and later arrested the mitoses needed for regeneration.

One other similar pathological description has recently been published.[38] This was a case of acute poisoning. A five-year-old girl swallowed an unknown number of seeds. These were later identified as belonging to the genus *Colchicum*. Repeated vomiting and abdominal pain were the first signs of toxicity. The central temperature rose and the pulse became fast. Death followed in 38 hours. Cerebral edema was conspicuous. Small hemorrhagic dots were seen on the pericardium and the peritoneal serosa. The duodenal mucosa was swollen and dotted with many hemorrhagic zones.

Evidence of mitotic poisoning was visible in the liver, where some cells were in a condition of arrested metaphase. Others showed evidence of degenerative alterations. Arrested metaphases were conspicuous in the bone marrow; a small number could be found in the duodenal mucosa. Pycnotic destruction of lymphocytes in lymph glands, Peyer's patches, and the thymic cortex was probably the result of the combined action of the mitotic poison and of the general alarm-reaction.[69]

Colchicine was detected by a biological method, while chemical reactions remained negative. Large quantities were found in several organs, in particular the liver, the kidney, and the brain. Extracts from these tissues displayed a typical spindle-poisoning effect when brought into contact with chick fibroblast cultures.

In the complex changes which take place when a large dose of colchicine is absorbed in man, it is evident that some are related to the poisoning of cell division, for instance bone-marrow inhibition,[9, 68] while others, such as the destruction and regeneration of liver cells, and the evidence of stress, are of a more complex nature. Vomiting, which may appear shortly after the drug is taken, is one major sign of a series of disturbances which clearly have nothing to do with the cytological effects which have been studied so far. These will now be described from data on various mammals and vertebrates, before analyzing the changes possibly related to spindle inhibition. The important problem of the metabolism of colchicine in the body will be discussed in a later paragraph.

7.3: Disturbances Unrelated to Mitotic Poisoning

Vomiting, diarrhea, bloody stools, and a progressive paralysis of the central nervous system are the most evident signs of toxicity. Death occurs within several hours in warm-blooded animals, or several days in cold-blooded vertebrates, after injections of the largest doses. In 1906, colchicine was called "this most remarkable slow poison."[20] Progressive nervous paralysis leading to respiration arrest, appears to be the main cause of death, whatever the animal tested. Recent research has brought new emphasis on this nervous action of colchicine.[23]

7.3–1: Nervous system, central and peripheral. An experiment performed nearly 50 years ago gives a remarkable demonstration of the sensitivity of the nervous system towards colchicine. While the injection of even the largest doses killed a cat only after several hours, the intracerebral injection of the drug had a spectacular and rapid action. Very soon the blood pressure was found to increase, and the respiration became rapid and deeper. After 35 minutes, a sharp fall in the blood pressure indicated vasomotor paralysis. One hour after the injection, the animal died of respiratory paralysis.[20]

An important series of findings in rats and cats points to the nervous system as one of the principal causes of the various effects of colchicine poisoning. This work can only be summarized here.[23] Some of the most significant observations are listed. Vomiting cannot be, as was sometimes thought, the consequence of pathological modifications of the gastrointestinal tract brought about by mitotic arrest. The same is true for diarrhea, a frequent symptom, which would appear to be a consequence of intestinal congestion and ulcerations.[26] No diarrhea and almost no vomiting is found in animals injected with barbiturates, even when the dose of colchicine is lethal.

The central temperature falls sharply after colchicine. This may be partly a result of stress and nonspecific toxicity[14, 69] (Fig. 7.2), but the curves indicate that the decrease taking place in the first ten hours has another cause. This is now believed to be a central nervous effect.[23]

Another fact points in the same direction: Animals treated with colchicine display an increased sensitivity. While unanesthetized cats die only after eight to ten hours, the same dose of colchicine brought death in less than two hours when the animals had received barbiturates previously.[23] Barbiturate or ether anesthesia also proved to be abnormally dangerous in animals which had received the alkaloid first.

Arterial constriction leading to high blood pressure has been mentioned. Experiments of brain transsection in the cat demonstrated that this also was a consequence of a central nervous stimulation.[23]

However, other territories of the nervous system are affected by colchicine. The neuromuscular apparatus appears to be the most sensitive, though only after repeated administration of the alkaloid can the modifications be detected. An atrophy of the hind quarters of cats injected daily with 0.05 mg. per kg. of body weight was observed after two weeks. The leg muscles were converted into thin strands. There was no evidence of muscular damage. Abnormal responses to acetylcholine were observed. There was no true neuromuscular block.

Anesthetic properties have also been described; these are probably of central origin. Death often follows a period resembling narcosis. In the dog, this appears before the muscle paralysis. In cold-blooded animals, the nervous changes may be very slow to appear. In frogs

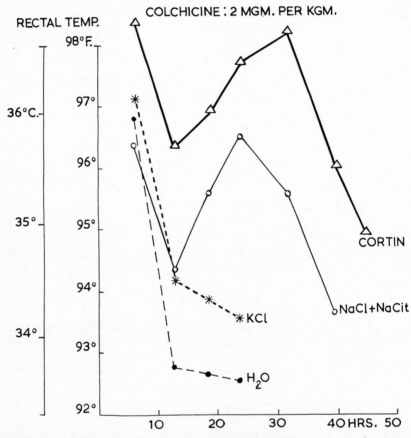

Fig. 7.2—Action of cortin and sodium on the temperature fall of rats after colchicine intoxication. (After Clark and Barnes[14])

kept at low temperature, reflexes disappear progressively, the corneal being the last, and this not until several weeks after an injection of colchicine.[27]

7.3–2: Striated muscle. Recent studies of the frog's sartorius muscle have brought new evidence of a muscular action of colchicine. In 1875, irreversible changes in striated muscles of frogs injected with a large dose were first reported.[27] Later "oxycolchicine" was shown to be extremely toxic in frogs.[35] If the injected animals leapt within a few minutes after the drug took effect, their legs remained stretched and exhibited fibrillary twitchings. The rectus abdominis muscle of the frog was also modified by colchicine, and contracture appeared after repeated stimulation.[43] This was considered to be a "Lundsgaard effect," identical with that induced by many substances interfering with glycolysis.

A detailed analysis of the sartorius muscle of frog treated with especially purified preparations of colchicine has brought to light many facts, which will be summarized here and which are illustrated by Figure 7.3. The curarized muscle preparation was subjected to supra-maximum electrical stimulation. Colchicine concentrations above 10^{-3} M produced a sustained increase in contractile force, which reached more than 60 per cent with 1.6×10^{-2} M. Larger doses resulted in contracture and failure to respond to stimulation. The increased contractility was paralleled by an increased demand for oxygen, which may be the double of the controls after two hours. Caffeine appeared to act synergically on this increase in oxidative processes, while metabolic inhibitors such as azide, fluoroacetate, and malonate prevented this action of colchicine. The rate of glycolysis was increased two to three times with colchicine concentrations of 6.4×10^{-2} M, as evidenced by the amount of lactate produced. Hydrolyzable, but not inorganic, phosphorus was also increased. These facts do not appear to point towards a change in ATP utilization. They resemble closely those of caffeine. The action of colchicine in increasing the available energy is called "relative rarity," and thus one more curious effect of the alkaloid appears to have been discovered.[23]

7.3–3: Smooth muscle and intestine. Conflicting reports have been published on this subject. The discovery that diarrhea is of central origin may be the explanation. A strong increase in the intestinal movements has been described in animals under ether anesthesia.[35] A similar effect has been found in frogs.[20] It was abolished by atropin. Increased tonus and automatic movements have also been described in spleen, uterus, and bronchioli. In the dog, the action on smooth muscle has been said to be immediate, resembling that of pilocarpin, and to be antagonized by atropin.[21] Quite different results have been reached by other workers on isolated intestine.[27, 59] The immediate effect was one of depression. The reactions towards adrenalin and atropin were not altered.

The local action on the intestine is paralytic, and was found to be related to the changes taking place in the mucosa, especially hemorrhage.[26] In a cat, injections of colchicine (1 mg. in saline) were made in ligated segments of the small intestine. A strong congestion and hemorrhages are to be seen locally within 24 hours. With larger doses,

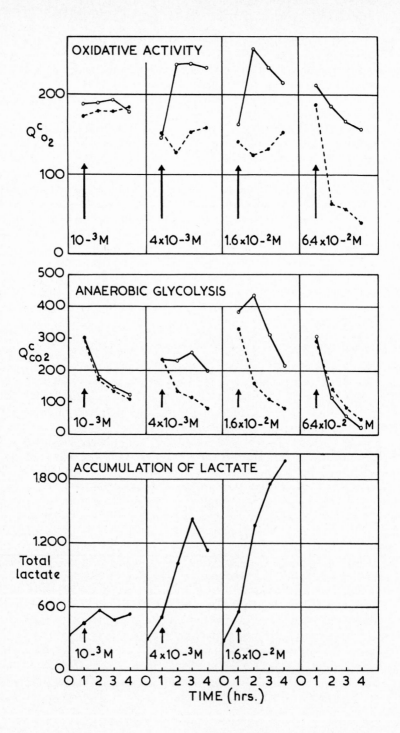

up to 5 mg. colchicine, the hemorrhages are apparent after 8 hours. This does not appear to be in any way related to a release of histamine,[3] which is one of the toxic actions of colchicine locally applied on the skin.[30]

Recent work[23] indicates that colchicine has no direct action on the smooth muscle of the intestine.

7.3–4: Heart and circulation. The heart is apparently insensitive to colchicine, either in frogs or in mammals. The isolated heart of the frog may beat in a 4 per cent solution of colchicine.[26] In mammals, the heart may go on contracting regularly for as long as two hours after death by colchicine poisoning.[61] As a consequence, blood pressure is only depressed immediately before death.

There is no general agreement about action on vasomotor nerves. While having no action on the heart's sympathetic fibers,[36] colchicine has been found to increase the hypertensive action of epinephrine in the rabbit under urethane anesthesia.[12] In a dog under chloralose anesthesia, a similar potentiating effect could be measured by changes in blood pressure and intestinal contraction.[58] This latter observation has not been confirmed, and only the excitatory actions of epinephrine on the vascular bed appear to be well proved.[23]

7.4: Disturbances Possibly Related to Mitotic Poisoning

Several remarkable effects of the alkaloid will be gathered under this heading. Our purpose is, when possible, to relate pharmacological effects to the histological changes resulting from spindle destruction. However, this is obviously far from being simple, and this paragraph should only be considered as a tentative grouping of cellular reactions. It will be noticed that the leukocytosis-promoting effect of colchicine, which nearly led to the discovery of its action on mitosis,[20, 21] is probably only remotely linked to mitotic arrest. Its origin may be the action of the drug on the central nervous system. However, it is associated with some of the first descriptions of tissues altered by colchicine, and has often been quoted as the origin of modern cytological work in this field. For this reason, the problem will receive more attention here.

7.4–1: Action on the blood. A substance that arrests for some hours the mitoses taking place in the bone marrow and destroys many of them, would be expected to depress blood formation. Extensive cellular destruction has been found in the bone marrow of mice.[47] Considerable congestion and a decrease in the number of nucleated cells are the consequence of this destruction. In some experiments, 20

Fig. 7.3—Action of colchicine on the isolated Sartorius muscle of the frog. Broken lines: controls. The oxidative activity and anaerobic glycolysis are measured on caffeinated muscle (1.9 x 10⁻³M). The lactate concentration is expressed in microgm/gm of muscle. (After Ferguson,[24] slightly modified)

per cent of all the nucleated cells of the marrow were arrested at metaphase.[77] That this actually decreases the output of young red blood cells was made clear by reticulocyte counts in the blood of rabbits. Normal animals and rabbits with phenylhydrazine-induced hemolytic anemia were utilized (Fig. 7.4 and 7.5). A sharp but transient fall in the percentage of reticulocytes is a convincing demonstration of the inhibition of blood formation.[22]

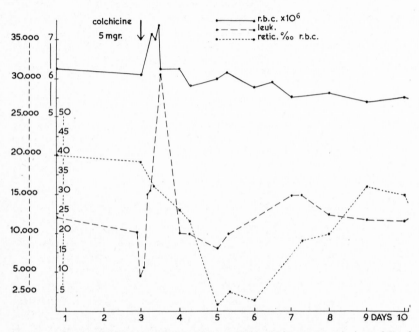

Fig. 7.4—Blood changes in the adult rabbit. Colchicine-leukocytosis and sharp fall of the numbers of reticulocytes (immature red-blood cells). The importance of the mitotic disturbances of the erythroblasts is evidenced by the slow return of the reticulocyte number to normal, and by a slight anemia. (Unpublished, after P. Dustin[23])

On the other hand, Dixon and Malden[21] discovered that in rabbits and dogs an injection of colchicine was followed by a considerable increase in the number of circulating white blood cells (Figs. 7.6 and 7.7). These authors, while reporting this curious effect, mentioned that 12 hours after the injection, the bone marrow of rabbits appears empty of most of its nucleated cells. This is in agreement with observations of bone-marrow aplasia, sometimes fatal, which have since been recorded in the medical literature (cf. Chapter 10).

The British authors[21] expressed their conclusions in a rather misleading way, to quote: "evidence is conclusive that colchicine is a powerful stimulant to the bone-marrow, since it turns out into the circulation all the elements including the erythroblasts, and leaves the

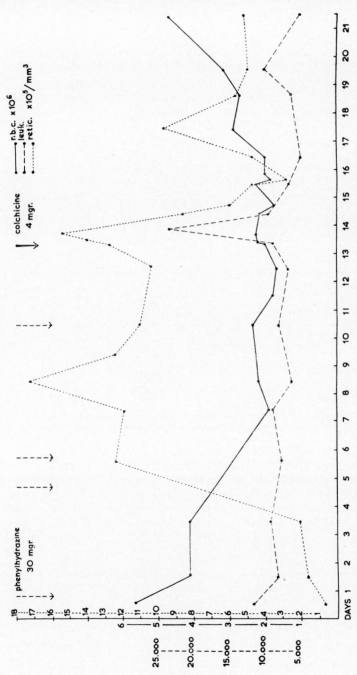

Fig. 7.5—Blood changes in an adult rabbit previously intoxicated by the hemolytic drug, phenylhydrazine. This has considerably increased the number of reticulocytes. The curve of this graph, contrary to Fig. 7.4, gives the number of reticulocytes per cmm. The injection of colchicine is followed by the usual leukocytosis and by a sharp but transient drop in the numbers of reticulocytes. This decreases later because the effect of phenylhydrazine fades off and the anemia disappears. (Unpublished, after P. Dustin[23])

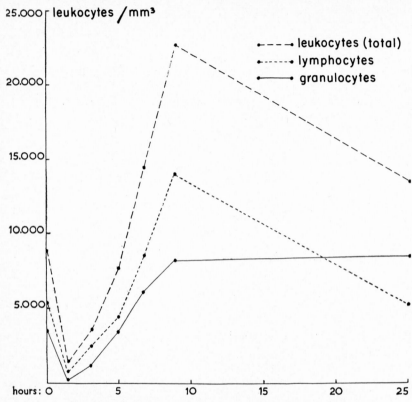

25.000 leukocytes /mm³

- - - → leukocytes (total)
- - - - → lymphocytes
──────→ granulocytes

20.000

15.000

10.000

5.000

hours: 0   5   10   15   20   25

Fig. 7.6—Modifications of the leukocyte count in the blood of a rabbit injected 7.8 mg/kg colchicine, after 5.2 mg/kg atropine sulfate. (After Dixon and Malden[21])

marrow relatively denuded of corpuscles."* This is no true stimulation, and the authors are more precise when in the same paper they mention that the cells "are swept out . . . of the bone-marrow . . . into the circulation" (see Table 7.1) .†

It appears evident, however, that these authors did observe some of the facts of mitotic arrest. But not being histologists, they failed to appreciate the exact significance of the facts. In 1906, Dixon[20] wrote:

A further effect of colchicine is to excite karyokinesis. This action on the marrow cannot be adequately determined at present, but it should not be regarded as specific to the leukocytes, but rather a type of the action which goes on to a greater or less degree in other tissues of the body, but is necessarily more easily investigated in the wandering cells of the blood.‡

*W. Dixon and W. Malden, "Colchicine, With Special Reference to Its Mode of Action and Effect on Bone-Marrow," *Jour. Physiol.*, 37 (1908) , p. 73.
† *Ibid.*, p. 62.
‡ W. Dixon, *A Manual of Pharmacology* (London: Arnold, 1906) , p. 96.

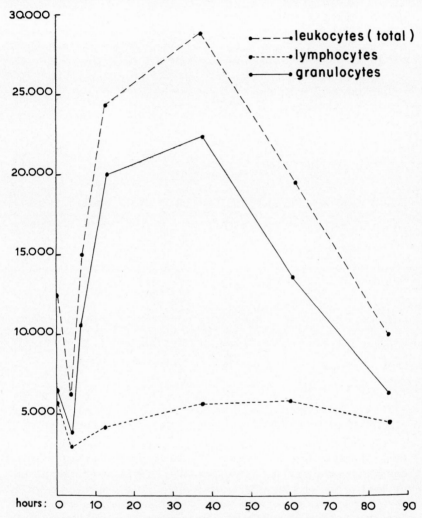

Fig. 7.7—Modifications of the leukocyte count of a dog injected 0.34 mg/kg colchicine.
(After Dixon and Malden[21])

In a later paper,[21] it is mentioned that after repeated injections of colchicine in rabbits, "sections of smears of the bone-marrow . . . exhibit proliferation . . . : *plentiful mitotic forms can occasionally be observed*" [our italics].*

There can be no doubt today that the significance of these histological changes was not grasped. These publications on colchicine pharmacology were widely quoted, and for 26 years text books

---

* *Jour. Physiol.*, 37 (1908) , p. 76.

mentioned that colchicine increased the numbers of leukocytes. Nobody appears to have been interested enough to study more precisely the bone-marrow changes, and it is only in 1934 that this was done.[47] Colchicine-mitosis was then discovered at once, for in the laboratory of A.P. Dustin, Sr., problems of mitosis and mitotic stimulation had been studied for many years, and the proper techniques had been developed.

TABLE 7.1

EFFECT OF COLCHICINE ON BLOOD COUNT IN RABBIT[*]

(Injection with 0.02 gm. colchicine made at 1:05 P.M.)

(After Dixon and Malden)

Cellular Types	Time of Blood Count				
	1 P.M.	1:30	3:00	5:00	9:15
Total leukocytes per cmm.....	8850	4600	6700	9650	20,000
Granulocytes (%) (pseudoeosinophils).........	37	16	50	36	16
Eosinophils.................	1	1	1	0.5	1
Mast cells.................	7	4	7	6.5	1
Myelocytes.....................	....	....	3	7.5	7
Monocytes.....................	10	4	7	4.5	4
Lymphocytes...............	45	75	32	45	71
Erythroblasts (per cent leukocytes)......	....	5	4	8	*41*

* Weight of rabbit, 1800 gm.

While the changes occurring in the blood-forming tissues were then described, first in mammals,[47] then in amphibia,[17] the Dixon and Malden experiments were repeated in rabbits by another author, unaware of the problems of mitotic regulation and poisoning.[16] The effect of repeated small (from 1 to 5 mg.) daily injections was studied. Immature white and red blood cells were found in the blood stream. The percentage of hemoglobin and the number of red blood cells progressively decreased. The marrow was very cellular, with leukoblastic areas far in excess of the erythroblastic ones. The following conclusion was reached, to quote: "Colchicine, undoubtedly, stimulates the formation of new cells in the marrow, and induces immature cells . . . to appear in the peripheral blood, but . . .its destructive powers outweigh its stimulant effect."[*] Here again, the action on the mitotic spindle was missed.[16]

*C. R. Das Gupta, "The Action of Leucopoietic Drugs," *Indian Jour. Med. Res.,* 26 (1939) p. 997.

At present, no clear relation can be discovered between the inhibition of mitotic growth and the colchicine-leukocytosis, and clearly new work is badly needed in this field. Some facts are of interest however.

It has been discovered that in leukemic patients and in normal men a single dose of colchicine (2 mg.) may increase considerably the number of platelets. The bone-marrow megakaryocytes do not change in number, but there is evidence of a greater platelet-building activity by their cytoplasm.[37, 41] In essential thrombopenia, where megakaryocytes are present but appear to be unable to produce platelets, this effect of colchicine was not found. It is evidently not related to mitosis, but may be similar to some other membrane changes induced by the alkaloid (Chapter 4).

Some recent work attempts to relate the bone-marrow changes and leukocytosis. This is often preceded by a transient period of leukopenia, which appears to have no causal influence on the leukocytosis.[77] Bone-marrow studies in mice and rabbits all confirm the increase of arrested metaphases, which is about 15-fold in the rabbit after 15 hours. The erythroblastic cells become progressively more numerous than the granuloblastic; the increase is from 10–15 per cent to more than 60 per cent in mice. The immature cells increase in proportion, because the adult cells leave the marrow. There is no visible relation between this phenomenon and the mitotic changes.[77] However, repeated daily injections of 12 μg. of colchicine increase considerably the number of leukocytes in the blood of mice (more than 250,000 per cmm.). It has been suggested[77] that these changes may be the consequence of a central nervous stimulation of the bone marrow. This is in line with more recent pharmacological data (see above) and merits close attention.

The following changes of blood cells after colchicine may be mentioned here, though an explanation is not evident. Young rats, aged 1 and 3 days, develop anemia, and a single injection decreases the red blood cell diameter.[71] These two facts may bear some relation to the decrease in the numbers of reticulocytes, which have a larger diameter than average red blood cells. An increase of "monocytoid" leukocytes in a case of fatal human poisoning[39] parallels the observation of abnormally great numbers of histiocytes in guinea-pig tissues after repeated injections.[56] Several important data on blood cells studied by culture *in vitro* with the help of colchicine will be reported in Chapter 9.

7.4–2: Skin, hair, and feathers. Colchicine arrests the mitoses in the hair follicles in mammals. Inhibition of hair growth can be seen in rats in the vicinity of colchicine injections, and loss of hair has been found in human intoxication.[44] In birds, similar changes may be expected to exist, but the following results are not necessarily the consequence of mitotic poisoning.

In hens, 1.5 mg/kg of colchicine causes death in 36 to 48 hours. The symptoms are those already described: diarrhea, vasomotor disturbances, and nervous paralysis. Injections of 1.2 mg/kg are not fatal. They cause a shedding of the feather buds in places where the feathers were removed 15 days previously.[2] The feathers which grow next have a white extremity. Two similar injections, 7 and 14 days later, give to these feathers a deep black barring. The other feathers of the animals darken. An analysis of the rate of growth of the feathers demonstrates that colchicine acts immediately and that it modifies the feather growth for 48 hours. It was demonstrated later[13] that the section of the spinal nerves could bring about similar changes of color. The authors are led to the conclusion that colchicine may act by affecting the nervous system, a conclusion remarkably in line with later research.[23]

7.5: Nonspecific Toxic Changes

In considering the modifications of an organism which has been injected or which has received by any route a substance as toxic as colchicine, nonspecific changes must be taken into account.[69] These may be difficult to separate from effects of the drug itself, and only future work will enable this aspect of the subject to become clearer. For instance, while the influence of the pituitary-adrenal system is known to be great in all types of "stress," there are only two papers on the action of colchicine in adrenalectomized animals.[24, 42] It was demonstrated that an important number of the nuclear pycnoses of thymus and lymphoid tissue are only indirectly the consequence of mitotic poisoning. Pycnosis is much less apparent in adrenalectomized animals.[42] No work has been reported on the general effects of the alkaloid after hypophysectomy. This should be important, considering the possibility of the pituitary gland taking part in some central nervous stimulation of leukocytosis.

The facts assembled here may only have a distant relation to stress and the alarm-reaction. It is known, however, from experimental work[38] and from human pathology[23] that this reaction can appear after colchicine. Also, several of the changes reported have also been observed after other mitotic poisons, chemically unrelated to colchicine.[73] It is logical to believe that they belong to the vast group of nonspecific tissue changes.[69]

7.5–1: The "hormone-mimetic" actions of colchicine. The idea of colchicine having some direct hormonal action was put forward by botanical work.[32] It led to some curious experiments which are important to consider when one knows how often the alkaloid has been used for the detection of hormone-stimulated growth (Chapter 9).

During the breeding season, the fish *Rhodeus amarus* displays brilliant red "nuptial colors," which are related to the expansion of chromatophores and to local hyperemia. These colors appear in animals treated with male hormones. Colchicine alone has the same effects.[32, 33] Nuptial colors are displayed by fish subjected for 10 minutes to a 1.5/1000 solution, or for 35 minutes to a concentration of 0.75/1000. Colchicine and hormones add their effects, and the full skin changes could be produced in 2 instead of 20 hours with hormone alone. The oxygen consumption of the animals was also increased.[50] However, the "endocrine" mechanisms of this action of colchicine may be questioned. In females of the same species, no increase in the size of the ovipositor was noted.[8] The changes of the male fishes, where vasomotor mechanisms play a great part, may have been either the consequence of a nervous action, or of the general toxicity of colchicine.

The possibility of stimulating the action of pituitary hormones by the alkaloid was strongly suggested by experiments on the ovulation of isolated ovaries of *Rana pipiens*. This was considerably accelerated, both in whole animals and on isolated ovaries (Fig. 7.8). The eggs were fertilizable, but none ever divided. Colchicine was believed to bring a "true potentiation" of the pituitary hormones controlling ovulation.[52] In the rabbit, however, no potentiation of the action of pregnant mare's serum, containing gonadotropic hormones, on the rate of ovulation could be detected.[52] Colchicine had no action on the weight of ovaries of mice similarly injected, or on the seminal vesicles of rats injected with testosterone.[52] Neither do results of experiments on silk-worms[33] justify the conclusion that colchicine is "hormone-mimetic." The only possibility is that through nonspecific action, this toxic drug could stimulate the secretion of hormones by endocrine glands, in particular the pituitary.

7.5–2: Liver and kidney damage. The mechanism of these changes is not clearly understood, but it certainly plays an important part in the general toxicity of the drug. Though bile secretion has been supposed to be increased, severe degenerative changes and necrosis have been described in the livers of mice,[56] especially after repeated injections.[40] In mice, the LD_{50} dose induces liver cell steatosis in one hour.[62] Steatosis of heart muscle cells and kidney tubules was also noted. Female mice appear to be more resistant to this damage than males.

Mitoses of liver cells have been described in human poisoning by colchicine. There are often arrested metaphases, even long after the drug has been administered, a fact which is explained by its slow excretion.[11] Three days after injection of colchicine in mice, normal mitoses also

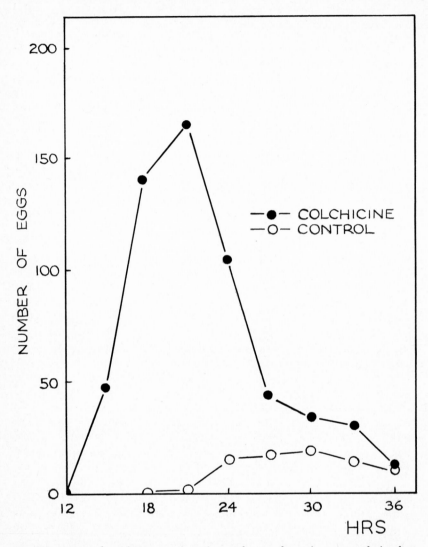

Fig. 7.8—Action of colchicine on the release of eggs from the ovary of the frog, treated **in vitro** with pituitary powder. (After McPhail and Wilbur[52])

have been observed in liver cells. These will be discussed in the next paragraph. After several injections of colchicine, many arrested mitoses are to be seen. The stages of recovery lead often to bizarre nuclei which may resemble those of megakaryocytes. Cellular damage may not be evident at all, and the cause of these divisions is not clear. A hormonal stimulation related to stress and the adaptation syndrome is possible.[53]

In chronic intoxication of mice, after daily injections of 12 to 15 μg. for 20 to 30 days a great number of liver nuclei are irregularly shaped. More than 40 per cent of these contain spherical bodies resembling huge nucleoli. These are diffusely stained by acid dyes. They persist 13 days after the end of the injections. No mitoses were seen, a rather surprising fact.[40] It may be suggested that these intranuclear bodies result from arrested mitoses, and represent spindle material, similar to the hyaline globules and pseudospindles (Chapter 3).

Kidney damage has been mentioned repeatedly,[19, 62] but has never been described in detail. It should be borne in mind while considering in Chapter 9 the use of colchicine in studies on the mitotic growth of kidney tubules.

7.5–3: The "late" mitoses. In many experiments on mitotic poisons, and in particular after the injection of trypaflavine (acriflavine), normal mitoses could be found in unusual locations several days after the mitotic poisoning itself.[73] Colchicine is also effective, and this is one of the observations that led to the belief that a true mitotic stimulation existed. Actually, things are probably far more complicated.

In adult mice,[47] divisions could be observed in many locations: liver cells and Kupffer cells, endothelial and epithelial cells of the pancreas, salivary cells, histiocytes, and renal epithelial cells. Some of these may be abnormal, but normal mitoses are usually found in liver, pancreas, kidney, and adrenals, from one to two days after an injection. While some of the divisions may be of a regenerative character, for instance in liver and kidney, the important fact is that this is not a phenomenon observed with colchicine alone. It obviously needs further investigation, because very few authors appear to have taken notice of it. In the light of all recent work on stress, the hypothesis that pituitary-adrenal stimulation of cellular division has taken place as a consequence of the general toxicity of colchicine, deserves notice.

7.5–4: Chemical changes of the blood. The idea of the alkaloid producing a stress effect may help to explain some unrelated facts mentioned in the pharmacological literature. The hyperglycemia following the intravenous injection of 1 gm/kg of glucose in the dog is increased 10 to 12 hours after colchicine.[49] The lethal dose of the drug in this species is 1 mg/kg. It decreases the blood sugar and also the body temperature.[64] The action on the glycemia does not appear to be related to pancreatic islet activity. The LD_{50} dose has the same effect. In pancreatectomized dogs, on the contrary, the glycemia again reaches its normal level within 6 to 14 hours.[65] The influence of the adrenal cortical hormones has not been studied in these experiments. Evidence has been presented that the adrenal plays an important part in controlling the temperature fall observed after colchicine poisoning (Fig. 7.2).

Considerable changes of blood-clotting time have also been reported in rabbits injected with large doses of colchicine. This may be five times too long.[48] It will be mentioned elsewhere that hemorrhage has been considered an important factor in the action of the drug on neoplastic growth.[7] One author has found that the direct action of colchicine, added *in vitro* to oxalated blood plasma containing thrombin, was to decrease the clotting time from 20 to 15 seconds.

Much remains to be learned about what happens when a complex organism is under the influence of such a poisonous chemical. It is evident that much of the reviewed work is incomplete, that even the exact chemical structure of the "colchicine" that is injected is not always known, and that we are confronted with a puzzle in which specific effects of colchicine are intermingled with general toxic reactions involving hormonal stimulation and metabolic changes. The importance of all these apparently unrelated facts emerges when one considers colchicine's action in gout, which will be discussed later. It is first necessary to have some idea of the metabolic changes, if any, of colchicine within the body. The study of this problem has recently received some new light.

7.6: Metabolism of Colchicine

Forensic medicine demonstrated long ago that colchicine could be detected, apparently unchanged, in the bodies of patients who had died of an overdose.[27] Experiments on cold-blooded animals, which can withstand considerable amounts of the alkaloid (Table 7.2), demonstrated that this remained unchanged. They also brought attention to the considerable variations in toxicity depending on body temperature.[27, 63, 75] For instance, a frog is able to withstand an injection of 50 mg. of colchicine. For several days the chemical may be detected unchanged in the urine. If such an animal, two to three weeks after the injection, is warmed to 32°C., a temperature in itself harmless, death supervenes in a few days. Progressive nervous paralysis is evident, a typical manifestation of colchicine poisoning. Similar facts are to be found in hibernating bats, which do not appear to be affected by colchicine.[31] Once the animals are warmed and awake, the characteristic nervous poisoning becomes visible.[31]

After injection in dogs and cats, colchicine is chemically detected in the feces and urine. Similarly in man, it is excreted unchanged in the urine. However, only a fraction of the initial dose can be recovered.[27] This suggested to early workers that the alkaloid was modified and metabolized in the animal and human body. The striking effect of temperature suggested that some of these changes may only be possible in warm-blooded animals, or in artificially warmed amphibians. Table 7.2 shows that the toxicity of colchicine is about the same in mammals and frogs when the latter are kept at 30–32°C.

It was also known that solutions of colchicine that had been left standing and have become brownish, probably as a result of oxidation, become far more toxic to frogs, even at low temperatures.[35] In 1890, an attempt was made to separate the toxic fraction of these oxidized

TABLE 7.2
RELATIVE TOXICITY OF COLCHICINE
(After Fuehner[28])

Species	Lethal Doses. After Subcutaneous Injection (*gm/kg of body weight*)
Rana esculenta, 15–20°C..........	1.200–2.000
Rana esculenta, 30–32°C..........	0.002–0.004
White mouse..................	0.003–0.010
Rabbit.......................	0.003–0.005
Dog.........................	0.001
Cat..........................	0.0005–0.001

preparations, and a substance tentatively named "oxydicolchicine" was isolated. This was believed to be made of two molecules of colchicine linked by an oxygen atom.[35] Artificial oxidation of colchicine with ozone yielded a similar substance. A further experiment attempted to prove that the kidney was the organ in which colchicine was oxidized to a more toxic product. About 330 mg. of amorphous colchicine were added to defibrinized hog's blood, and this was slowly perfused through the hog's kidney. From this organ 42 mg. of a brown substance were recovered. This, like "oxydicolchicine," displayed a rapid toxic action in the frog, where the symptoms were visible about one hour after the injection of 30 mg.

These experiments do not appear to have been checked by modern methods. This would be interesting now that the chemistry of the alkaloid has made such great progress (cf. Chapter 6). No substance of the structure assigned to "oxydicolchicine" has been described. On the other hand, experiments with mitotic poisoning are conflicting. In mice, solutions of colchicine lose about 20 per cent of their cytological activity after five weeks of standing.[47]

The fate of colchicine in the animal body has been studied by modern methods, chemical, biological, and physical. A colorimetric method of titration was checked by measuring the mitosis-arresting properties of solutions either by injecting them in mice or by studying their action on tissue cultures.[11] After a single injection the blood level in the adult rat decreased rapidly, and remained stable after a few minutes. The tissues contained less alkaloid than the blood. Elimination was by the bile and intestine, and within a few hours, 10 to 25 per cent of the dose injected was to be found in the intestine and its contents. Elimination by the urine only lasted a short time, while the blood concentration was at its highest. Within 16 hours, 50 per cent appeared to have been eliminated. There was neither evidence of a change into a more toxic substance, nor of any selective tissular fixation. The cumulative toxicity of repeated injections is a simple consequence of the slow excretion.

By growing *Colchicum* in an atmosphere containing radioactive carbon, C^{14}, in the form of CO_2, a biological synthesis of radioactive colchicine has been made possible.[76] The fate of this in the body of mice has been tested. One fact of importance is that four hours after the injection, no more colchicine could be detected in the central nervous system, muscle, heart, or blood. Most of the radioactive alkaloid was detected in the kidney, the spleen, and the intestine. Neoplastic tissue (sarcoma 180) did not contain more colchicine than the liver. An unexplained fact is that while the spleens of control animals were a site of active fixation, no more colchicine could be found in this location in tumor-bearing mice.[4] These observations appear to demonstrate that the alkaloid brings about quite rapidly some change in the brain without becoming fixed in this tissue.[4] Evidence will be presented elsewhere (Chapter 9) that colchicine may be retained for some time in tissues of cold-blooded animals (*Xenopus* tadpoles).

Further research is also necessary in this field, for there appears to be some contradiction between the stability of colchicine as evidenced from old and modern work, and the biological activity and specificity of this molecule. These problems will be discussed in the last chapter of this book.

7.7: The Treatment of Gout

Logically, colchicine pharmacology should be an introduction to its use in medicine and should enable us to understand why this plant alkaloid is effective in treating a disease of uric-acid metabolism. However, as will be noticed, actual data on pharmacology are of small help in understanding the curative properties of *Colchicum*. Many complicated side-effects have been described, many strange properties investigated, but modern medicine is apparently not much closer than the Ebers Papyrus in explaining the medical use of this plant.

Gout, which was still called a forgotten disease in 1946,[51] has regained much medical attention. New methods of treatment and new methods of study have brought this change. Also, the frequency of cases of gout may have increased in some countries. The principal and painful lesion that affects the joints of gouty patients results from deposits of uric acid. This chemical was believed to be mainly related to nucleoprotein metabolism. Studies with radioactive uric acid, marked with N^{15}, have helped to understand the origin of the so-called "miscible pool" of uric acid, which is considerably increased in some cases of gout. This has been demonstrated to originate from many pathways of metabolism. All proteins, carbon dioxide, ammonia, glycine, serine, and carbohydrates may be used as building blocks for uric acid. Methods for studying the changes of the "miscible pool" of uric acid have been developed.[28, 29, 70]

This has been mainly the consequence of the discovery that steroid hormones like cortisone,[6] and the adrenotropic hormone of the pituitary (ACTH) may play an important part in gout and may possibly be used for its treatment.[25, 28, 29] Now, the nonspecific toxic reactions of colchicine poisonings have been described. These would result in an increased secretion of ACTH and cortisone.[69, 57] Could colchicine possibly act in a nonspecific way in this disease?

The considerable amount of work, mainly clinical, which has been published these last years on this subject can only be rapidly reviewed here.[34, 45, 46, 60, 78, 79, 80] Current practice of handling gouty patients with colchicine has recently been summarized.[29]

The doses which elicit in animals the alarm-reaction and ACTH secretion are far larger than those effective in human therapeutics. The Thorn test of adrenal stimulation demostrates effectively that in patients with diseases other than gout, therapeutic doses of colchicine do not stimulate the pituitary and the adrenal. The urinary elimination of 17-cetosteroids is not modified either.[45, 46] A positive Thorn test is demonstrated by a rapid fall in the numbers of eosinophil leukocytes in the blood. In one case only was this positive, the eosinophils falling to 53/cmm. and later rising to the normal number of 269. This, however, was in a man who had taken 24 mg. of colchicine in 24 hours, that is to say more than six times the usual dose.

On the other hand, while ACTH and cortisone may be effective in the treatment of gout, they have by no means taken the place of colchicine. This is now used either at the same time or after the injections of hormones, and it is recognized that its action is unrelated to the alarm-reaction, and to put it shortly, "entirely unknown." [25]

Some workers believe that the acute crisis of gout, the origin of which is by no means clear, is related to allergy. Colchicine has been found to decrease the intensity of the anaphylactic shock in guinea pigs injected with ovalbumine.[1] In patients suffering from diverse types of allergy, such as serum sickness, Quinke's edema, or urticaria, colchicine has been used with results comparable to those of the antihistamine drugs.[54, 66] Colchicine, however, does not antagonize histamine, and this new use in therapeutics now presents further unsolved problems.

REFERENCES

1. ARLOING, F., AND LANGERON, L. Action de la colchicine dans les phénomènes expérimentaux de sensibilisation et de choc. C. R. Soc. Biol. Paris. 95:1321–22. 1926.
2. ARVY, L., AND CARIDROIT, F. Action de la colchicine sur les oiseaux. C. R. Soc. Biol. Paris. 134:499–500. 1940.
3. BACHMANN, H. Über die Freisetzung von Histamin bei Gewebesschädigungen durch Gifte. Arch. Exp. Path. Pharmak. 190:345–55. 1938.
4. BACK, A., WALASZEK, E., AND UYEKI, E. Distribution of radioactive colchicine in some organs of normal and tumor-bearing mice. Proc. Soc. Exp. Biol. and Med. 77:667–69. 1951.
5. BALDUINI, M., AND BERTOLOTTI, G. Sangue periferico e midollo osseo nella intossicazione sperimentale da colchicine. Haematologica. 31:65–80. 1948.
6. BISHOP, C., GARNER, W., AND TALBOTT, J. H. Effect of colchicine and cortisone on uric acid metabolism in gout. Fed. Proc. 9:151. 1950.
7. BOYLAND, E., AND BOYLAND, M. Studies in tissue metabolism. IX. The action of colchicine and B. typhosus extract. Biochem. Jour. 31:454–60. 1937.
8. BRETSCHNEIDER, L. H., AND DUYVENE DE WIT, J. J. Histophysiologische Analyse der sexuellendokrinen Organisation der Bitterlingweibchens (Rhodeus amarus). Z. Zellforsch. 31:1363–68. 1936.
9. BROWN, W. O. Effect of colchicine on human tissues. Arch. Path. 29:865–66. 1940.
10. BRUES, A. M., AND COHEN, A. Effects of colchicine and related substances on cell division. Biochem. Jour. 30:1363–68. 1936.
11. ——. The fate of colchicine in the body. Jour. Clin. Invest. 21:646–47. 1942. Discussion on "The mechanisms of cell division." Ann. N. Y. Acad. Sci. 51:1406–8. 1951.
12. BUSQUET, H. Sur l'activation des effets circulatories des substances sympathomimétiques par la colchicine. C. R. Soc. Biol. Paris. 130:870–72. 1939.
13. CARIDROIT, F., AND REGNIER, V. Influence du systéme nerveux sur la forme et la pigmentation du plumage de la poule domestique. Rev. Sci. 79:177–81. 1941.
14. CLARK, W. G., AND BARNES, R. H. Effects of salts and adrenal cortical extracts upon toxicity of drugs. Proc. Soc. Exp. Biol. and Med. 44:340–44. 1940.
15. COURTOIS-SUFFIT AND TRASTOUR. Sur un cas d'intoxication mortelle par la colchicine à dose thérapeutique. Bull. Mém. Soc. Hôp. Paris. 20:254–57. 1903.
16. DAS GUPTA, C. R. The action of leucopoietic drugs. Indian Jour. Med. Res. 26: 947–99. 1939.
17. DELCOURT, R. Réactions et lésions cellulaires provoquées par la colchicine chez les amphibiens. Arch. Int. Med. Exp. 13:499–515, 719–83. 1938.
18. DELIOUX AND SAVIGNAC. Colchique d'automne. In: Dictionnaire Encyclopédique des Sciences Médicales. Dir. A. Dechambre, P. Asselin et G. Masson, Edit. Paris. 1876.
19. DICKER, S. E. The renal effects of urethane and colchicine in adult rats. Brit. Jour. Pharmacol. 6:169–81. 1951.
20. DIXON, W. A manual of pharmacology. Arnold, Edit., London. 1906.
21. ——, AND MALDEN, W. Colchicine, with special reference to its mode of action and effect on bone-marrow. Jour. Physiol. 37:50–76. 1908.
22. DUSTIN, P., JR. Action de la colchicine sur le taux des réticulocytes du sang du lapin. Bull. Acad. Roy. Belg. Classe Sci. Ve Sér. 27:260–68. 1941. Intoxication mortelle par la colchicine. Étude histologique et hématologique. Bull. Acad. Roy. Méd. Belg. VIe Sér. 6:505–29. 1941.

23. FERGUSON, F. C. Colchicine. I. General pharmacology. Jour. Pharmacol. and Exp. Therap. 106:261–70. 1952. II. Metabolism of frog skeletal muscle. Jour. Pharmacol. and Exp. Therap. 108:186–200. 1953.

24. FREUD, J., AND UYDERT, I. E. The influence of colchicine upon mitoses in the intestine in normal and adrenalectomized rats. Acta Brev. Neerl. Physiol. 8:16–19. 1938.

25. FRIEDLANDER, R. D. Cortisone as an adjunct in the therapy of gout. Jour. Amer. Med. Assoc. 145:11–14. 1951.

26. FÜHNER, H., AND REHBEIN, M. Untersuchungen über die Darmwirkung des Colchicins. Arch. Exp. Path. Pharmak. 79:1–18. 1915.

27. ———. Die Colchicingruppe. Heffters Handbuch d. exper. Pharmakologie. Vol. II. Pp. 493–507. 1920.

28. GUTMAN, A. B. Some recent advances in the study of uric acid metabolism and gout. Bull. N. Y. Acad. Med. 27:144–64. 1951.

29. ———, AND YÜ, T. F. Current principles of management in gout. Amer. Jour. Med. 13:744–59. 1952.

30. HAAS, H. T. A. Über die Beeinflussung des Histamingehalts der Haut durch Reizstoffe. Arch. Exp. Path. 197:161–86. 1941.

31. HAUSMANN, W. Über den Einfluss der Temperatur auf die Inkubationszeit und Antitoxinbildung nach Versuchen an Winterschläfern. Pflügers Arch. Anat. Physiol. 113:317–26. 1906.

32. HAVAS, L. Influence of colchicine on the sexually induced colour change of *Rhodeus amarus*. Nature. 143:809. 1939. Some effects of colchicine in *Rhodeus* suggestive of hormonal influence. Arch. Int. Méd. Exp. 15:21–64. 1940. Effects of colchicine and other plant constituents on blood coagulation and of thrombokinetic agents and anticoagulants on plants. Experientia. 4:69–72. 1948.

33. ———, AND KAHAN, J. Hormone-mimetic and other responses of the silkworm (*Bombyx mori* L.) to some polyploidogenic agents. Nature. 161:570–71. 1948.

34. HELLMAN, L. Production of acute gouty arthritis by adreno-corticotrophin. Science. 109:280. 1949.

35. JACOBJ, C. Pharmakoligische Untersuchung über das Colchicum-gift. Arch. Exp. Path. 27:119–57. 1890.

36. JACOBSON, T. Action de la colchicine sur le coeur. C. R. Soc. Biol. Paris. 93:1178–81. 1925.

37. KEIBL, E., AND BICHLBAUER, U. Über die Wirkung des Colchicins auf die Thrombopoese. Klin. Med. 4:517–22. 1949.

38. KLEIN, H. Zur pathologische Anatomie der Alarmreaktion nach Kerngiften. Virchows Arch. 320:93–137. 1951.

39. LAYANI, F., ASCHKENASY, A., AND MOUZON, M. Intoxication aiguë par la colchicine: importantes altérations de la leucopoïèse. Bull. Mém. Soc. Hôp. Paris. 63:10–16. 1947.

40. LAMBERS, K. Über Organveränderungen bei chronischer Colchicin-vergiftung. Virchows Arch. 321:88–100. 1951.

41. LANDOLT, R. Über die Wirkung des Colchicins auf das normale und leukämische Blutbild und Knochenmark. Dtsch. Arch. Klin. Med. 191:378–98. 1943.

42. LEBLOND, C. P., AND SEGAL, G. Action de la colchicine sur la surrénale et les organes lymphatiques. C. R. Soc. Biol. Paris. 128:995–97. 1938.

43. LECOMTE, J. Action de la colchicine et des poisons radiomimétiques sur le muscle de grenouille. Arch. Int. Pharmacodyn. 78:440–44. 1949.

44. LEIBHOLZ. Ein Fall von Colchicin-Vergiftung und einige Bemerkungen über Gichtbehandlung. Med. Welt. 19:1669–70. 1923.

45. LEVIN, M. H., FRED, L., AND BASSETT, S. H. Metabolic studies in gout. Jour. Clin. Endocrin. 12:506–18. 1952.

46. LEVINE, H. The effect of colchicine on the adrenal cortex. Jour. Lab. Clin. Med. 38:921. 1951.

47. LITS, F. Contribution à l'étude des réactions cellulaires provoquées par la colchicine. C. R. Soc. Biol. Paris. 115:1421–22. 1934. Recherches sur les réactions et lesions cellulaires provoquées par la colchicine. Arch. Int. Méd. Exp. 11:811–901. 1936.

48. LOICQ, R. Recherches sur les effets de la colchicine sur la coagulabilité du sang. Arch. Int. Méd. Exp. 12:371. 1936.

49. LORTHIOIR, P. Hyperleucocytose expérimentale et glycorégulation. C. R. Soc. Biol. Paris. 113:401–3. 1933.

50. MANN, H. Die Einwirkung von Colchicin und Sexualhormonen auf den Sauerstoffverbrauch von Fischen. Zool. Anz. 127:315–18. 1939.

51. MCKRACKEN, J., OWEN, P., AND PRATT, J. Gout: still a forgotten disease. Jour. Amer. Med. Assoc. 131:367–72. 1946.

52. MCPHAIL, M. K., AND WILBUR, K. M. The stimulating action of colchicine on pituitary induced ovulation of the frog. Jour. Pharmacol. 78:304–13. 1943. Absence of potentiation of gonadotropin and steroid function in mammals by colchicine. Endocrinology. 35:196–97. 1944.

53. MISZURSKI, B., AND DOLJANSKI, L. Effect of colchicine on the rat liver. Amer. Jour. Anat. 85:523–45. 1949.

54. MUGLER, A. Action de la colchicine sur les accidents allergiques. Ann. Méd. 51:495–505. 1950.

55. ———, AND HAUSWALD, R. A propos de l'efficacité de la colchicine sur le prurit dans un cas d'ictère mécanique. Comparaison avec l'effet d'un anti-histaminique. Bull. Mém. Soc. Méd. Hôp. Paris. 1952.

56. MUSOTTO, G., AND DI QUATTRO, C. Sensibilità delle varie cellule dell, organismo verso differenti dosi di colchicina e sua stimolazione all'iperplasia cellulare. Sperimentale. 95:457–70. 1941. (Hyperplasia of histiocytes after repeated treatment with colchicine). Pathologica. 39:204–8. 1947.

57. PASCHKIS, K. E., CANTAROW, A., WALKLING, A. A., AND BOYLE, D. Adrenal cortical hormone levels in adrenal vein and peripheral blood. Endocrinology. 47: 338. 1950.

58. RAYMOND–HAMET. Sur une propriété physiologique nouvelle de la colchicine. C. R. Soc. Biol. Paris. 118:1292–95. 1935.

59. REHBEIN, M. Pharmakologische Untersuchungen über die Darmwirkung des Colchicins. Disser. Freiburg. i. B. 1917.

60. ROBINSON, W. D., CONN, J. W., BLOCK, W. D., LOUIS, L. H., AND KATZ, J. Role of the anterior pituitary and adrenal cortex in urate metabolism and in gout. Proc. 7th Internat. Congress on Rheumatic Diseases. Grune and Stratton, New York. 1949.

61. ROSSBACH, M. J. Die physiologischen Wirkungen des Colchicins. Arch. Ges. Physiol. 12:308–25. 1876.

62. ROSSI, S. Steatosi parenchimali da colchicina. Differenza di sensibilità dei due sessi animali intossicata. Experienta. 6:306. 1950.

63. SANNO, Y. Über den Einfluss der Temperatur auf die Giftempfindlichkeit des Frosches. Versuche mit Atoxyla und Colchicin. Arch. Exp. Path. 65:325–36. 1911.

64. SANTAVY, F. Les variations sanguines au cours de l'intoxication par la colchicine. Glucose du sang chez les chiens intoxiqués par la colchicine. C. R. Soc. Biol. Paris. 126:629–32; 633–34. 1937.

65. ———, AND KADLEC, K. Glucose du sang chez le chien intoxiqué par la colchicine. C. R. Soc. Biol. Paris. 129:105–6. 1938.

66. SCHMIDT, F., AND MUGLER, A. Action de la colchicine sur la tension artérielle dans le choc anaphylactique chez le lapin. Mise en évidence d'une action statique des doses sous-liminaires. C. R. Soc. Biol. Paris. 144:1392. 1950.

67. SCHROFF, K. D. V. Untersuchungen über die Zwiebel der Zeitlose und Versuche mit denselben an Thieren und Menschen. Z. k.-k. Ges Aertze. Vienna. 1:85–95. 1841.

68. SEED, L., SLAUGHTER, D. P., AND LIMARZI, L. R. Effect of colchicine on human carcinoma. Surgery. 7:696–709. 1940.

69. SELYE, H. Stress (The physiology and pathology of exposure to stress). Acta Inc. Montreal. 1950.

70. STETTEN, DE WITT, JR. The pool of miscible uric acid in normal and gouty man, studied with the aid of isotopic nitrogen. Jour. Mt. Sinai Hosp. 17:149. 1950.

71. TATSUMI, J. Effect of colchicine and epinephrine on the erythrocyte diameter. Mitt. Med. Akad. Kioto. 2:1070–80. 1940.
72. VACCARI, F., AND ROSSANDA, M. Blood glycosis during the alarm-reaction. Nature. 169:327–28. 1952.
73. VAN HEERSWYNGHELS, J. De l'action de la trypaflavine sur le thymus, les organes lymphoïdes, les mégacaryocytes de la rate, la surrénale et le pancréas. Arch. Int. Méd. Exp. 9:461–79. 1935.
74. VIBERT, C. Précis de toxicologie. Paris. 1907.
75. VOLLMER, H. Tiergrosse und Empfindlichkeit gegen Hydrochinon und colchicin. Arch. Exp. Path. 165:339–49. 1932.
76. WALASZEK, E. J., KELSEY, F. E., AND GEILING, E. M. K. Biosynthesis and isolation of radioactive colchicine. Science. 116:225–27. 1952.
77. WIDMANN, H. Ein Beitrag zum klinischen Bild der Colchicinvergiftung. Artzl. Forsch. 2:457–60. 1948. Leukopenie, eine Voraussetzung der Leukocytose? Tierexperimentelle Untersuchungen über die Wirkung kleiner Colchicindosen auf das weisse Blutbild. Artzl. Forsch. 3:86. 1949. Tierexperimentelle Untersuchungen über den Wirkungsmechanismus des Colchicins in letalen und subletalen Dose auf Blut und Knochenmark. Arch. Exp. Path. 207:218. 1949. Die Erzeugung leukämoider Veränderungen durch Colchicin bei der weissen Maus. Z. Ges. Exp. Med. 117:227–36. 1951.
78. WOLFSON, W. Q., COHN, C., AND LEVINE, R. Rapid treatment of acute gouty arthritis by concurrent administration of pituitary adrenocorticotrophic hormone (ACTH) and colchicine. Jour. Lab. Clin. Med. 34:1766. 1949.
79. ————, HUNT, H. D., COHN, C., ROBINSON, W. D., AND DUFF, I. F. ACTH and colchicine in the clinical treatment of acute gouty arthritis. Physiological considerations and review of therapeutic results in 51 attacks. Jour. Mich. Med. Soc. 49:1058. 1950.
80. ————, AND COHN, C. The role of the pituitary adrenocorticotrophic hormone (ACTH) and of adrenal cortical steroid hormones in the pathological physiology and experimental therapeutics of gout. Proc. First Clin. ACTH Conf. The Blakiston Co., Philadelphia. 1950.

CHAPTER 8

Embryonic Growth in Animals

8.1: Action on Gonads and Early Development

Eggs have often proved to be an excellent material for colchicine research, and in previous chapters results of work on various types of eggs have been mentioned. Nuclear structure is modified in *Tubifex*,[22, 23] the nuclear sap becomes granular in the *Anodonta* egg,[11] spindle changes are most evident in *Arbacia*,[4, 41] disturbances of cleavage are noted in *Sphaerechinus*,[6] while curious surface changes have been described in both *Tubifex*[44] and *Arbacia*.[26] The size of egg cells, their conspicuous spindle, and the possible induction of polyploidy were factors making them useful in some of the early colchicine research. It is remarkable, however, that the first paper on this subject was written by two botanists.[27]

We shall consider here only facts which have not been observed in ordinary cells, and which are related to the special physiology and cytology of eggs. Since there are few papers on modifications of spermatogenesis, it was thought natural to describe some of the results which may prove important for the possible induction of polyploidy in animals. This last problem will be discussed more thoroughly in Chapter 16. On the other hand, the disturbances of embryonic growth related to mitotic poisoning result in some quite peculiar malformations which will be considered later in this chapter.

8.1–1: The cleavage of eggs. All work in this field points towards the complexity of colchicine actions, which are not only related to the stage of maturation or growth reached by the eggs or the young embryo, but also to the concentrations of alkaloid used. For instance, in some of the early work on the egg of *Rana pipiens* the classification of cellular changes proved to be very difficult because of great differences of sensitivity.[18] A 1:1000 solution suppressed all cleavage and led to cellular disintegration; at 1:10,000, colchicine did not disturb the first cleavage, but the next ones were irregular and the grooves between the cells were only shallow; at 1:100,000, three cleavages proceed normally, but in many eggs the grooves faded away later. Even when the concentration was only 1:1,000,000 and when some apparently normal embryos grew, abnormal cleavages were visible, and on the third day all the embryos were found dead. It was evident that even when nuclear mitosis proceeded normally, cleavage could be inhibited. Gastrulation was made impossible, the eggs assuming a meroblastic type of growth.

It was soon discovered that in *Arbacia* the sensitivity of the eggs decreased rapidly after fecundation;[4] 40 minutes later, from 90 to 100 per cent of normal cleavages could be observed. In the sea urchin *Paracentrotus,* before fecundation, the eggs may live only in a 1:200,000 solution. Later, cleavage is quite abnormal. If colchicine is applied at fecundation, a 1:60,000 solution does no more than disturb gastrulation. A temperature effect was also observed. Inhibition of growth was nearly complete if colchicine had been allowed to act at 25°C., even if the eggs were kept at lower temperatures later. On the contrary, colchicine at 15°C. permitted growth to the morula stage, or, if the eggs were placed at 25°C. after colchicine, as far as the 16-celled stage. This temperature effect was tentatively related to permeability changes.[30]

The peculiar behavior of egg cells and the first stages of development of amphibia have been the subject of a thorough analysis, related in many papers of the French author, Sentein.[34, 35] Like other workers, he found that cleavage disturbances were not closely related to mitotic disturbances; precocious cleavage could, in some eggs, lead to anucleate blastomeres. The complexities of the action of colchicine are revealed by the various cytological anomalies described: polyploidy, plurinucleation, asymmetrical development, chromatin bridges between nuclei, pycnosis, and pluricentric mitoses. The last were found during recovery and are comparable to the multiple stars described in Chapter 3.

The variable reactions during development were analyzed in *Triturus, Pleurodeles, Bufo, Rana,* and *Amblystoma.*[34] After gastrulation, typical arrested mitoses of the star type are the rule, with clumped chromosomes that are progressively destroyed. In the earlier stages, however, nuclear changes are quite different. Rather concentrated, 1:500 and 1:1000, solutions of colchicine were used. However, the cytological changes were always delayed, as observed by the other authors mentioned above.[4, 18, 41] First of all, cleavage is inhibited, the nucleus completing its division. The result of this is the frequent observation of binucleate blastomeres. The spindle may be completely destroyed; large, probably polyploid nuclei are found later. However, the normal number of chromosomes is most often maintained because the spindle, even in these high concentrations of colchicine, recovers. This leads often to pluripolar spindles, which are considered to be an important factor counteracting the polyploidizing action of the alkaloid. Recovery is incomplete, and chromosome counts demonstrated a great variability from cell to cell.[16]

Another peculiarity of the spindle of amphibian eggs is its asymmetrical reactions towards the depolarization effects of colchicine. The hypothesis has been put forward that this may be related to a differential sensitivity of the centrosomes, whether of paternal or maternal origin.[34]

Similar disturbances of development have been described in *Rana agilis*[9] and *Bufo vulgaris,* where an apparent decrease of cellular respiration was observed.[37] The exact relation between mitotic changes and the abnormalities of later development, which will be related in the next section, are most difficult to understand. A detailed description of the action of colchicine on the cleavage and early development stages of the fish *Oryzias latipes* cannot possibly be summarized here, but should be consulted by embryologists interested in chemically induced abnormal growth.[39]

The changes described in the egg of *Tubifex,* an invertebrate, are remarkably similar to those reported in vertebrates. In 1:30,000 solutions of colchicine some eggs are able to divide twice. One of the main effects is on cytoplasmic limits, which may disappear after having been normally formed at telophase.[44]

A relative resistance towards colchicine, changes in sensitivity related to developmental stages, the absence of polyploidy in the embryos, and peculiar actions on cleavage are the main facts which at this time emerge from a great amount of observations.[29, 40] There is no doubt that cytologists and embryologists have many more problems to solve and probably new types of colchicine effects to discover.

8.1–2: Male gametes. There are surprisingly few data available on the action of colchicine on spermatogenesis. In mice, aged 22 days, some arrested mitoses (or meioses?) have been reported in early work.[24] In adult animals, colchicine brought evidence of nuclear and cytological destruction. Arrested mitoses of spermatogonia in rats injected with more than 1.4 mg/kg of the drug have been described. The spermatocytes did not appear to be altered, although 24 hours after the injection the number of metaphases was somewhat increased.[32]

Personal observations of the junior author (unpublished) are that in the testes of mice injected 1.25 mg/kg, most of the spermatocytes have no more spindle 24 hours later. Spermatogonia appear to be unaltered, and the stages of meiosis are normal, as long as no spindle activity is required. Many spermatids with vacuolated nuclei may be observed, but this phenomenon is a consequence of the general toxicity of colchicine, and has been described under various experimental conditions and with other mitotic poisons.[38] With less toxic colchicine derivatives, spindle inactivation is apparent in a few hours. Depending on the doses injected, recovery is possible, or considerable cellular damage may be found. Binucleated spermatids may result from the spermatogonial mitoses during recovery assuming the "distributed" type with two nearly equal groups of chromosomes (cf. Chapter 2).

In fowls also, colchicine may induce severe degenerative changes in testicular cells. These are followed by regeneration seven days later.[17]

No polyploid spermatozoa have been reported in vertebrates. On the contrary, in the insect *Triatoma infestans* (order: Hemiptera), colchicine not only inhibits the spindle function, but as a consequence, modifies considerably the size of the spermatids (Fig. 8.1). This is observed after nine days, when all spermatogenetic cells have disappeared. The simple numerical relations between nuclear sizes are a strong evidence in favor of polyploidy, although the exact interpretation of these facts awaits further research.[33]

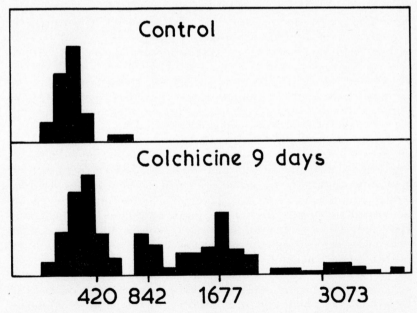

Fig. 8.1—Action of a prolonged treatment by colchicine on the nuclear diameters of the spermatids, expressed in conventional units, in **Triatoma infestans**. Several categories of polyploid nuclei with diameters in the relation 2,4,8,16. (After Schreiber and Pellegrino[33])

In Chapter 16, a technique of inducing polyploidy in vertebrates will be discussed. This involves using sperm treated with colchicine. It should be mentioned here that the alkaloid has not been reported to affect adult spermatozoa.[12, 13]

8.2: Colchicine-induced Malformations

The artificial production of embryonic monstrosities has received a great impetus from the work of Ancel and Lallemand.[1, 2, 21] This was initiated around 1937, and, together with the use of other chemicals, has opened a new field in developmental research. A detailed survey of this is to be found in Ancel's recent book, *La Chimiotératogenèse.*[1]

Through a small opening in a chick's egg, a minute quantity of a solution of colchicine in saline is introduced. The embryo is observed, to make sure that no abnormalities exist at the start of the experiment. The opening is closed and the egg hatched in an incubator.

One of the most striking results was the production of a malformation which had been described in calves by Gurtl (1832) and called *schistosomus reflexus.* This is a peculiar type of celosomy, that is, a total hernia of all the abdominal and thoracic viscera, resulting from an absence of the anterior body wall. Lesbre, in 1927, used the term *strophosomy,* or body-turned-inside-out, for the rachis and tail are strongly bent backwards, the hind limbs located close to the back of the head (Fig. 8.2). Such a malformation had never been seen in chicks, and naturally aroused great interest in colchicine. Further testing of more than fifty substances, several of which induced various abnormalities of development, demonstrated that only *ricine* and *abrine* could initiate strophosomy.

Figure 8.3 shows the difference between the formation of celosomy, which is much more frequent, and strophosomy; the posterior bending of the caudal part of the spine plays a great part in the second type of anomaly. The colchicine treatment of the eggs must be done within a quite definite period. The optimal period is after 48 hours of incubation; before this time, or after 68 hours, it is ineffective. Only 5 hours after the introduction of colchicine into the shell, the embryo demonstrates an exaggerated forward flexion of the infracardiac region. Many of the embryos die at this moment. Some also display a dorsal flexion of the caudal extremity of the rachis; these are the ones which will eventually become strophosomic. This malformation does not disturb the formation of the embryonic organs, and the chicks are capable of living nearly until hatching, the longest observed duration being 19 days. A similar condition had been

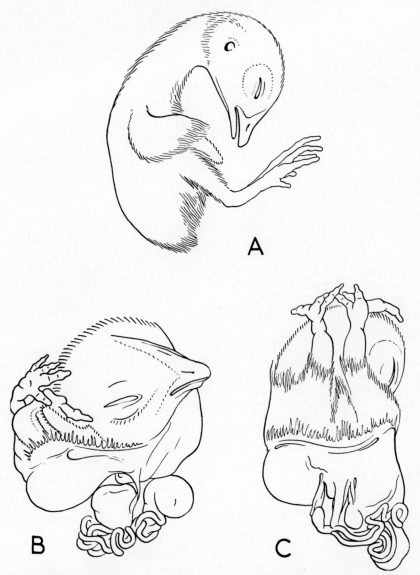

Fig. 8.2—Strophosomy induced by colchicine in the chick. **A.** Normal chick at 12 days of incubation. **B.** Strophosome at the same age. There is a total hernia of all viscera, no abdominal wall, and a backwards flexion of the hind limbs. **C.** Another strophosomic chick, after 13 days incubation. The animal is seen from the rear, the herniated viscera hang underneath, the legs here folded on the back. (After Lallemand[21])

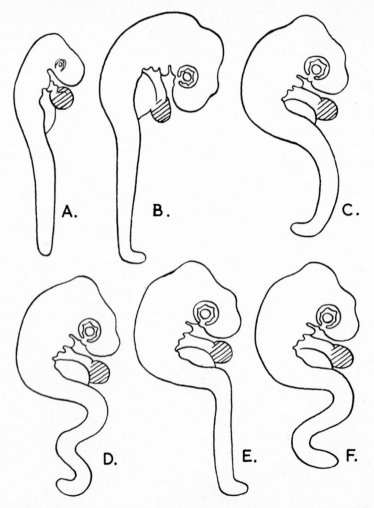

Fig. 8.3—Origin of strophosomy in chicks. Injection of colchicine in the eggs at 48 hours of incubation. **A.** Control at the time of injection. **B.** Control, incubated 72 hours. **C, D.** Colchicine-treated embryos, incubated 72 hours. These are future strophosomes, as indicated by the backward flexion of the tail. **E, F.** These chicks, similarly treated, will only develop celosomy. The tail is bent forward. (After Lallemand[21])

known to exist in calves, which may be born strophosomic after an intra-uterine growth of normal duration.

The caudal bending of the embryo appears quite important, and it is to be noted that pycnotic nuclei arising from arrested meta-phases are to be found in this region, mainly in the nervous system and the surrounding tissues. Neither the chorda nor the intestinal epithelium shows evidence of cellular destruction.

The problem of the determination of strophosomy has been further studied by local applications of colchicine in agar strips.[10] In embryos with 25–28 somites, the region between the omphalomesenteric vessels and the hind limb is the most sensitive in regard to this malformation. Absence of tail and hypophalangism and absence of tail were also observed; these phenomena led to a study of colchicine on the expression of the anomaly, polydactyly.[10] In other animals, colchicine is also a teratogenic agent,[8] but the changes mentioned are of very different types, ranging from exogastrulation[7] to variations in pigmentation, cyclopean eyes, abnormal blood formation, and disturbances of body flexures.[39] In the frog, many of the reported anomalies[42, 43] could also be initiated by X-rays, a fact strongly suggesting their relation to mitotic disturbances.

One other result is worth mentioning. Local application of a 1:7000 solution of colchicine on the posterior limb of *Xenopus* larvae resulted in a decrease in the number of toes.[5] With increasing effects all but the fourth toe disappeared during development. This is paralleled by no other type of regressive evolution of toes in vertebrates.

8.3: A Tool for the Study of Embryonic Growth

The use of colchicine for the detection of zones of maximal growth and of growth stimulation or inhibition will be discussed at length in Chapter 9. The "colchicine method" is fundamentally based on the observed increase in metaphases, arrested because of the absence of spindle, in growing tissues. Mitotic multiplication of cells is made more visible. Some of the difficulties of this method in adult animals will be discussed in Chapter 9. It is evident from all that has been written in this chapter, that in embryonic growth the complexity of the changes brought about by colchicine is considerable. Not only does the alkaloid inhibit mitoses, it may also completely alter the normal course of growth. Only a few experiments yield facts that are simple to interpret.

For instance, in chick embryos treated at the forty-second hour of development with dilute solutions of colchicine, there could be observed, 24 hours later, an "overproduction of cells." [28] The amount of neural tissue appeared to be increased, and several neural folds were to be seen, even in animals where the number of arrested mitoses did not appear to be great. These facts were considered as good evidence of mitotic stimulation and increased neuralization, that is to say, a colchicine-induced malformation. Chicks with spina bifida have been found in some experiments.[1] The number of mitoses seemed considerable to the author who observed for the first time these neural changes, but no accurate quantitative counting was done, nor, in fact, could have been properly done because of the malformation itself. It has also been suggested that the apparent increase in neural tissue was merely the consequence of abnormal cellular migrations, not of modified mitotic activity.[45]

Analysis of patterns of embryonic growth is made difficult by many facts. One is the varying sensitivity of tissues and stages of development. In *Molge palmata* Schneid., the zones of highest mitotic activity are the most sensitive to colchicine;[35] in other regions, the same concentration may yet enable mitosis to recover and to proceed to telophase through star and incomplete star metaphase. In *Discoglossus pictus* Orth., some periods of growth are very sensitive to the mitotic arresting activity of colchicine. The fifth day, corresponding to the "primary metamorphosis," when swimming is initiated, is one of these periods. In *Discoglossis, Rana,* and *Xenopus,* the metamorphosis is a period of increased sensitivity. The regions of the embryos where the mitoses are the most numerous are, rather naturally, the most rapidly altered by colchicine. Instances are the nervous system, the olfactory bud, and the germinative region of the eyes.[35]

These carefully studied facts do not leave much to say about papers which attempted to detect zones of growth by colchicine, especially in amphibia,[15, 25] for the complexities of the problem were not properly understood at the time of their publication. Some facts emerge, however, from the literature on this subject and are worth mentioning, for they may be starting points for further work. In young mice, colchicine demonstrated that liver and pancreatic cells cease to divide at about 20 days after birth;[31] the mechanism which prevents any further division, except in regeneration (Chapter 9), is unknown. In mice also, ganglionic nerve cells have been found, by the use of colchicine, to divide until three weeks after birth.[20] Colchicine has also been used to bring about the death of the litter of pregnant mice,[19] and to induce the formation of tetra- and octoploid cells in embryos of the fish *Coregonus* when the eggs had been treated three hours with a 0.5 per cent solution. Hastening of the metamorphosis of *Rana fusca* tadpoles is also reported.[14]

The publications which have been reviewed in the last paragraph would seem to indicate that colchicine is of little, if any, use in the study of embryonic growth. However, it must be recalled that most of these results have been published during the early phases of colchicine research, before the proper techniques could have been designed. Two recent papers show that important facts can be made clear by using colchicine as a tool in embryos.[3]

In the first one, the problem was to assess the comparative mitotic activities of the embryonic megaloblasts (young red blood cells) of the chick embryo, and of the megaloblasts of human Addison-Biermer anemia (cf. Chapter 9). These cells resemble closely the embryonic ones, though their existence is an evidence of pathological growth related to vitamin B_{12}, or folic acid, deficiency. A dose of 0.015 mg. of colchicine in saline solution was found to arrest all mitoses in the young chick embryo. The number of mitoses found after four and eight hours was counted. This gives a precise idea of the proliferative activity of these cells. In chicks at the sixtieth hour of growth, eight hours after colchicine, the number of megaloblastic mitoses is increased more than tenfold; while in controls, 38.6 cells per thousand are in division; in treated chicks, eight hours after colchicine, the figure reaches 457.9. This increase is markedly greater than that found in the bone marrow of Biermer anemia patients. However, the technique being different, the comparison is not quite valid. What is more interesting from the viewpoint of embryological growth, is that the megaloblasts are demonstrated to divide more than the undifferentiated connective cells from which they originate.

A detailed study of the relation between differentiation of the red blood cells and cell division in the chick embryo at different stages of growth has clearly indicated a decrease in mitotic activity as soon as hemoglobin is synthesized. Colchicine has been a remarkable tool for the precise study of this problem.[3] No doubt, it will not be the last contribution in a field open to many types of investigation (cf. Chapter 9).

REFERENCES

1. ANCEL, P. Sur la mise en évidence de différences individuelles dans la constitution des embryons par l'action associée de deux substances chimiques tératogènes. C. R. Soc. Biol. Paris. 141:208–9. 1947. La Chimiotératogenèse. Réalisation des monstruosités par des substances chimiques chez les vertébrés. G. Doin et Cie., Edit., Paris. 1950.
2. ———, AND LALLEMAND, S. Sur la tératogénie de la strophosomie expérimentale chez le poulet. C. R. Soc. Biol. Paris. 130:385–87. 1939. Sur le diagnostic précoce de la strophosomie d'origine colchicinique chez l'embryon de poulet. C. R. Soc. Biol. Paris. 130:1396–99. 1939. Sur la réalisation au moyen de la colchnicine d'embryons de poulets coelosomiens. C. R. Soc. Biol. Paris. 130:1399–1401. 1939. Sur la réalisation expérimentale de la coelosomie par divers mécanismes. C. R. Soc. Biol. Paris. 137:3–4. 1944.
3. ASTALDI, G., BERNARDELLI, E., AND RONDANELLI, E. La colchicine dans l'étude de la prolifération des cellules hémopoïétiques de l'embryon. Rev. Belge Path. 21:406–13. 1952. Study on the proliferation of embryonic erythroblasts. Rev. Belge Path. 22:172–78. 1952.
4. BEAMS, H. W., AND EVANS, T. C. Some effects of colchicine upon the first cleavage in *Arbacia punctulata*. Biol. Bull. 79:188–98. 1940.
5. BRETSCHER, A. Reduktion der Zehenzahl bei Xenopus-Larven nach lokaler Colchicin-behandlung. Rev. Suisse Zool. 54:273–79. 1947.
6. BROCK, N., DRUCKREY, H., AND HERKEN, H. Über Kerngifte und Cytoplasmagifte, Arch. Exp. Path. Pharm. 193:679–87. 1939.
7. BUSHNELL, R. J. Some effects of colchicine on the early development of the frog, *Rana pipiens*. Anat. Rec. 72:Suppl. p. 97. 1938.
8. CHANG, M. C. Artificial production of monstruosities in the rabbit. Nature. 154:150. 1944.
9. COLOMBO, G. L'azione della colchicina sulla sviluppo embrionale di *Rana agilis*. Boll. Soc. Ital. Biol. Sper. 20:657–58. 1945.
10. GABRIEL, M. L. Production of strophosomy in the chick embryo by local applications of colchicine. Jour. Exp. Zool. 101:35. 1946. The effect of local

applications of colchicine on Leghorn and polydactylous chick embryos. Jour. Exp. Zool. 101:339–50. 1946.

11. HAAS, H. T. A. Über die Beeinflussung des Zellkerns durch Pharmaka. Arch. Exp. Path. 197:284–91. 1941.

12. HAGGQVIST, G., AND BANE, A. Chemical induction of polyploid breeds of mammals. Kungl. Svenska Vetenskapakad. Handl. IV. Ser. 1:1–11. 1950. Kolchizininduzierte Heteroploidie beim Schwein. Kungl. Svenska Vetenskapakad. Handl. IV. Ser. 3:1–14. 1951.

13. HALL, T. S. Abnormalities of amphibian development following exposure of sperm to colchicine. Proc. Soc. Exp. Biol. and Med. 62:193–95. 1946.

14. HAVAS, L. J. L'action de la colchicine administrée seule ou en combinaison avec des hormones sur la croissance et sur le développement des embryons de la grenouille. Magyar Biol. Inst. Közl. 1942–43.

15. HUTCHINSON, C. The early development of the nervous system of *Amblystoma* studied by the colchicine technique. I. Medullary plate changes. Anat. Rec. 70:Suppl. 3:39. 1938.

16. JAHN, U. Induktion verschiedener Polyploidiegrade bei *Rana temporaria* mit Hilfe von Kolchizin und Sulfanilamid. Z. Mikr.-anat. Forsch. 58:36–99. 1952.

17. JENKINS, W. R., AND BOHREN, B. B. The effect of colchicine on the seminiferous tubules of fowl testis. Poultry Sci. 28:650–52. 1949.

18. KEPPEL, D., AND DAWSON, A. Effects of colchicine on the cleavage of the frog's egg (*Rana pipiens*). Biol. Bull. 76:153–61. 1939.

19. KERR, T. Mitotic activity in the female mouse pituitary. Jour. Exp. Biol. 20:74–78. 1943.

20. KJELLGREN, K. Studien-über die Entwicklung der Neuronen nach der Geburt. Acta Psych. et Neurol. Suppl. 29. 1944.

21. LALLEMAND, S. Réalisation expérimentale, à l'aide de la colchicine de poulets strophosomes. C. R. Acad. Sci. Paris. 207:1446–47. 1938. La strophosomie chez l'ambryon de poulet, réaction tératogène de la colchicine. Arch. Anat. Hist. Embryol. 28:217–53. 1939. Action de la colchicine sur l'embryon de poulet à divers stades du développement. C. R. Acad. Sci. Paris. 208:1048–49. 1939.

22. LEHMANN, F. E. Der Kernapparat tierischer Zellen und seine Erforschung mit Hilfe von Antimitotica. Schweiz. Zentralbl. Allg. Path. 14:487–508. 1951.

23. ———, AND HADORN, H. Vergleichende Wirkungsanalyse von zwei antimitotischen Stoffen, Colchicin und Benzoquinon, am Tubifex-Ei. Helv. Physiol. et Pharm. Acta. 4:11–42. 1946.

24. LITS, F. (*see* Ref. No. 61, Chap. 2).

25. MILLS, K. O. Variations in the rate of mitosis in normal and colchicine-treated tadpoles of *Rana pipiens* and *Amblystoma jeffersonianum.* Jour. Morph. 64:89–113. 1939.

26. MONROY, A., AND MONTALENT, G. Cyclic variations of the submicroscopic structure of the cortical layer of fertilized and parthenogenetic sea urchin eggs. Nature. 158:239. 1946.

27. NEBEL, B. R., AND RUTTLE, M. L. The cytological and genetical significance of colchicine. Jour. Hered. 29:3–9. 1938.

28. PAFF, G. The action of colchicine upon 48-hour chick embryo. Amer. Jour. Anat. 64:331–40. 1939.

29. PINCUS, G., AND WADDINGTON, C. H. The effect of mitosis-inhibiting treatments on normally fertilized pre-cleavage rabbit eggs. The comparative behaviour of mammalian eggs *in vivo* and *in vitro.* Jour. Hered. 30:514–18. 1939.

30. POUSSEL, H. Influence de la colchicine sur le développement de l'oeuf d'oursin: remarques sur quelques conditions d'action. C. R. Soc. Biol. Paris. 136:240–42. 1942.

31. RIES, E. Wann erlischt die mitotische Vermehrungsfähigkeit der Gewebe? Z. Mikr.-anat. Forsch. 43:558–66. 1938.

32. ROOSEN-RUNGE, E. C. Quantitative studies on spermatogenesis in the albino rat. II. The duration of spermatogenesis and some effects of colchicine. Amer. Jour. Anat. 88:163–76. 1951.

33. SCHREIBER, G., AND PELLEGRINO, J. Analise citologica e cariometrica da ação da colchicina sôbre a espermatogênese dos Hemipteros. Mem. Inst. Oswaldo Cruz. Rio de Janeiro. 49:513–42. 1951.

34. SENTEIN, P. Mode d'action de la colchicine sur la caryocinèse de *Molge palmata* Schneid. C. R. Soc. Biol. Paris. 137:133–34. 1943. Action de la colchicine sur les mitoses de maturation chez le triton. C. R. Soc. Biol. Paris. 137:132–33. 1943. Relation entre la mito-inhibition et les troubles de l'ontogénèse chez les oeufs et les larves d'anoures et d'urodèles. Bull. Acad. Sci. Montpellier. 76:51–53. 1946. Action de la colchicine et de l'hydrate de chloral sur l'oeuf de *Triturus helveticus* L. en développement. Acta Anat. 4:256–67. 1947. Action de substances mitoinhibitrices sur la segmentation et la gastrulation de l'oeuf de triton. C. R. Soc. Biol. Paris. 142:208–10. 1948. Action comparée des substances antimitotiques sur la segmentation et la gastrulation chez les anoures. C. R. Soc. Biol. Paris. 142:206–8. 1948. Analyse du mécanisme de la caryocinèse par l'action de substances antimitotiques sur l'oeuf en segmentation. Jour. Physiol. Paris. 41:269–70. 1949. Nouvelles observations sur l'action des substances antimitotiques: effets de la colchicine, du chloral et du carbamate d'éthyle (uréthane) sur la segmentation de l'oeuf d'amphibien. C. R. Assoc. des Anat. 35:355–63. 1949. Structure des noyaux géants polymorphes obtenus par transformation télophasique des chromosomes dans les cinèses bloquées de l'oeuf. Rapports entre polyploidie, amitose et pluripolarité. C. R. Assoc. des Anat. 36:613–20. 1950. Sur les déviations de l'axe mitotique au cours de la segmentation de l'oeuf traité par la colchicine, et leur signification. C. R. Soc. Biol. Paris. 145:87–89. 1951. Les transformations de l'appareil achromatique et des chromosomes dans les mitoses normales et les mitoses bloquées de l'oeuf en segmentation. Arch. Anat. Strasbourg. 34:377–94. 1952.

35. ———. Mise en évidence des zones germinatives de l'oeil par le blocage des mitoses chez les larves d'amphibiens. C. R. Soc. Biol. Paris. 140:185–87. 1945. Action expérimentale de la colchicine sur la mitose chez quelques batraciens anoures à l'état adulte et au cours du développement. Montpellier Méd. 21–22:494–95. 1942. Les différences de sensibilité à l'action de la colchicine chez les larves de batraciens. Bull. Acad. Sci. Montpellier. 76:61–62. 1946. Sur l'action comparée de la colchicine et du chloral sur les cellules épithéliales et nerveuses des larves d'amphibiens. C. R. Assoc. des Anat. 34:440–51. 1947.

36. SVARDSON, ... Chromosomes studies on Salmonidae. I. Haeggströms (Stockholm). 1945.

37. URBANI, E. L'assunzione di ossigeno in uova di anfibi trattate con colchicina. Boll. Soc. Ital. Biol. Sper. 23:637. 1947.

38. VAN ROS, G. Recherches expérimentales sur la vacuolisation nucléaire des spermatides de la souris. C. R. Soc. Biol. Paris. 147:547. 1953.

39. WATERMAN, A. J. Effect of colchicine on the development of the fish embryo, *Oryzias latipes*. Biol. Bull. 78:29–34. 1940.

40. WELDS, C. M., AND WIMSATT, W. A. The effect of colchicine on early cleavage of mouse ova. Anat. Rec. 93:363–76. 1945.

41. WILBUR, K. M. Effect of colchicine on the viscosity of the *Arbacia* egg. Proc. Soc. Exp. Biol. 45:696–700. 1940.

42. WOLSKY, A. Untersuchungen über die Wirkung des Colchicins bei Amphibien. Arb. Ung. Biol. Forsch. Inst. (Tihany). 12:352–58. 1940.

43. ———, AND ALLODIATORIS, I. II. Histologische Befunde an Colchicinbehandelten Froschkeimen. Arb. Ung. Biol. Forsch. Inst. (Tihany). 13:546–58. 1941.

44. WOKER, H. Phasenspezifische Wirkung des Colchicins auf die ersten Furchungssteilungen von Tubifex. Rev. Suisse Zool. 50:237–43. 1943. Die Wirkung des Colchicins auf Furchungsmitosen und Entwicklungleistungen des Tubifex-Eies. Rev. Suisse Zool. 51:109–71. 1944.

45. WOODWARD, T. M., AND ESTES, S. B. The mitotic index in the neural tube of the 48-hour chick as determined by the use of colchicine. Anat. Rec. 84:501. 1942. Effect of colchicine on mitosis in the neural tube of the 48-hour chick embryo. Anat. Rec. 90:51–54. 1944.

CHAPTER 9

Experimental Growth in Animals

9.1: Endocrinological Research

One of the most striking features of colchicine, whether injected into animals or acting upon tissue cultures,[23] is the accumulation of mitoses arrested at metaphase (Fig. 9.1). This is a consequence of the absence of spindle (cf. Chapter 3). The increase in the number of mitotic cells was soon understood to be most useful for the analysis of growth by cellular multiplication. Several lines of research were started in the years 1934–36. At this time, the isolation and the synthesis of hormones were proceeding rapidly, in particular, the steroid hormones of the sexual glands. These substances have most powerful physiological effects, the principal being to stimulate cells to increase the rate of appearance of new mitoses. Now, ordinary histological techniques give only an instantaneous picture of the state of the tissues at one given moment. If the cell divisions proceed very rapidly, there will be small chance of observing them in a microscopic slide. Colchicine, by arresting all these rapid cellular changes, would be able to let the mitoses progressively accumulate in a given tissue. Counting would be easier, and easier also the localization of regions of maximal growth.

While several authors understood the usefulness of colchicine as a tool for the study of growth, the largest amount of work was done in the field of endocrinology. Allen, Smith, and Gardner[2] are to be credited with the publication, in 1937, of an excellent paper with splendid photomicrographs that gave added impetus to research with this new technique. They were studying the action of estrogens in the mouse. After injecting the still chemically impure hormone of that type at their disposal, "theelin," they observed that colchicine increased tremendously the visible mitotic action in tissue sections. In the vaginal epithelium, they mention "a most incredible number of mitoses." * In a single transverse section of the vagina, controls in-

---

* E. Allen, M. Smith, and W. V. Gardner, "Accentuation of the Growth Effect of Theelin on Genital Tissues of the Ovariectomized Mouse by Arrest of Mitosis With Colchicine," *Amer. Jour. Anat.*, 61 (1937), p. 324.

jected with "theelin" alone showed 20 to 30 dividing cells. After colchicine, this was increased to more than 1500 in about 10 hours. In one experiment in which "theelin" and colchicine were injected simultaneously, the authors wrote that "the general impression is that approximately every other cell is in mitosis."* These results aroused great interest, and marked one of the starting points for

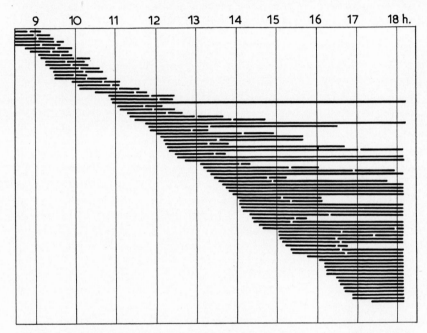

Fig. 9.1—Graphical representation of the course of cell division in a fibroblast culture treated by colchicine (1/20,000,000). During the two first hours, no notable changes. Later, progressive accumulation of arrested mitoses. Each horizontal line represents one mitosis; it is interrupted at the end of metaphase. Any vertical line indicates the number of visible mitoses at one moment, that is to say, the mitoses which should be seen in a fixed preparation. This number progressively increases under the influence of colchicine. The rate of apparition of new prophases is not disturbed with this concentration. There is no mitotic stimulation. (From a cine-micrographic recording. After Bucher, 1939)

colchicine research outside of the Brussels laboratory. Together with the discovery of colchicine polyploidy in 1937, this study initiated the publication of a great number of papers in which colchicine was mainly considered as a *tool* for making mitotic growth more visible and easier to analyze.

However, any tool has its advantages and its shortcomings. Many workers do not appear to have considered carefully the fundamental problems involved in what Allen called the "freezing" of mitoses.

---

* *Ibid.*, p. 325.

Some of the complexities have already been scrutinized in the first chapters of this book. A few more considerations about this particular problem of multiplying the numbers of mitoses by destroying their spindle will be useful for future workers in this field. While the number of papers published about the colchicine method appears to be on the decrease, so far as can be assessed, for colchicine is not always mentioned in the titles, much work remains to be done. This chapter will point out several unexplored fields.

9.2: Theoretical Considerations

Most of the American authors, following the first papers of Allen, those of Brues[19, 20, 21, 22] on liver regeneration, and the tissue culture work of Bucher[23] and Ludford,[62] considered colchicine simply as a means of stopping any mitosis at metaphase. The complexities of colchicine pharmacology (Chapter 7) should alone call for more caution.

A. P. Dustin, Sr., in a paper published in 1936, but which could not have received much publicity, demonstrated the utility of colchicine as a tool.[41] He had noticed the increased number of divisions in the wall of a parasitic cyst in a mouse, a fact which was the starting point for experiments on the healing of wounds, reviewed further on in this chapter. In his own words, "colchicine enables the detection of the otherwise invisible state of preparedness to mitosis." * It throws into an abortive division all the cells which are ready to divide, or had been prepared for mitosis, for instance, under the influence of endocrine or other stimuli. This was in agreement with the line of thought which had led to the discovery of colchicine's action in 1934, and which was the study of the regulation of mitotic growth.

The theories of "mitotic arrest" or "arrest after mitotic stimulation" are conflicting. In work where the location of mitoses is the main purpose and where no quantitative data are required, colchicine is useful whatever the opinion one has about a possible stimulation of mitosis. This problem, however, should not be overlooked. For instance, several authors have thought it possible to calculate from the number of mitoses found after colchicine, the average duration of these mitoses, had they not been arrested. This duration is, of course, an indication of the rapidity of cellular growth in the tissues studied. It should be clearly realized that such calculations imply several unknown factors, and they have a precise signification only if the following conditions are fulfilled:

1. Colchicine arrests all mitoses, shortly after it has been injected and until the end of the experimental period.

---

* A. P. Dustin, "La Colchicine, Réactif de l'Imminence Caryocinétique," *Arch. Portugaises Sci. Biol.*, 5 (1936), p. 41.

2. The intermitotic period is much longer than the duration of the experiment, and is not modified by the experiment.
3. The arrested mitoses are not destroyed before the moment the tissues are fixed and examined.
4. The tissue is homogeneous from the point of view of mitosis, that is to say, mitotic rates and intermitotic periods do not vary from one region of the tissue to another.
5. The mitotic rate does not vary during the experimental period, in control animals.

Such conditions are not often fulfilled. One type of experiment in which they are is liver regeneration; this will be considered further. In mammals, cellular destruction is a factor which cannot be ignored. If, however, the above-mentioned causes of error do not exist, the average duration of mitosis can be found by the formula $A = Mt/X$, in which M is the mitotic index before colchicine, and X the index found t hours after the injection of the alkaloid.

If this formula is applied to the results obtained in the experiments referred to in the previous paragraph,[2] it is found that after "theelin" stimulation, the average duration of mitoses would be 10 minutes. This is a remarkably short period, and it may be questioned whether mitoses can be completed so rapidly. However, results obtained by A. P. Dustin, Sr., in the uterus of the rabbit after stimulation by chorionic gonadotropic hormones, are rather similar.[41] The increase in the number of mitoses was observed in repeated biopsies. Figure 9.2 shows that it was considerable, and that in one animal, the calculated duration of each mitosis, had it not been arrested by colchicine, would be 12 minutes. These results bring some evidence for mitotic stimulation, for the prophase mitotic index increased also. This indicates that more cells were undergoing prophase than expected; that is to say, a true stimulation took place. This index rose from 7.56 to 14.8 in 2 hours, and from 4.8 to 24.4 in 7 hours. It must, of course, be supposed here that the duration of each prophase was not affected by colchicine.

Such results are rather complex, for the mitotic index could have been modified by the traumatisms of the biopsies themselves, and also by the continued action of the hormone. The possibility of a synergic action of hormones and colchicine cannot be ruled out[66] (cf. Chapter 7).

The following results[29] are all the more interesting, for while they apparently could demonstrate such a synergism, a much simpler explanation is possible. Table 9.1 gives the results of mitotic counts in the seminal vesicles, after stimulation by a single large dose of testosterone. There appears to be a veritable "explosion" of mitoses, to use the expression coined by A. P. Dustin, Sr. Does this give evidence of mitotic stimulation by the alkaloid? The counts of the control animals demonstrate that it does not, for it can be seen that between the thirtieth and thirty-fifth hours after the hormone injection the mitotic index rises sharply. If colchicine had been injected at the thirty-first hour, a mitotic increase from 2.92 to 108.60 would have been observed, and this could not be explained by the theory of metaphase arrest. This increase is, however, not only the result of mitotic

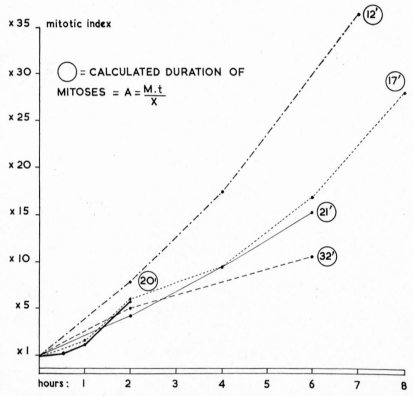

Fig. 9.2—Progressive increase of the numbers of mitoses, in repeated biopsies from the rabbit's uterus, after stimulation by chorionic gonadotropins and injection of colchicine. Calculated duration of mitoses on the assumption that colchicine does nothing more than arrest them at metaphase. (From original data of A. P. Dustin, 1943[41])

stasis, but also of the progressive action of testosterone, demonstrated by the fact that in untreated animals the mitotic count rises about threefold. Therefore, colchicine alone has increased the mitoses only from about 10 (2.92 × 3) to 108.60 within 4 hours, which means that the average mitotic duration must be about 25 minutes or less. This agrees with knowledge of mitotic duration in mammals.

Such an example demonstrates the intricacies of quantitative work with colchicine. Others will be found in this chapter. Here, as in other fields of colchicine work, problems must not be over-simplified, and here especially, the greatest care should be taken in all quantitative estimations. It is striking that it is when colchicine is considered as a tool that the need for fundamental knowledge is the most apparent.

9.3: Cellular Multiplication in Normal Growth

Growth patterns in the organs of adult animals can be revealed far better after colchicine than with ordinary tissue sections. The alkaloid may do more than simply locate the germinative zones of organs; under strict experimental conditions, it may solve some quantitative problems of growth. Another method, which has brought excellent results, is to study the growth of explanted tissues. This has been done by the ordinary methods of tissue culture,[23, 62, 88] or

TABLE 9.1

Mitotic Activity in the Seminal Vesicles of Castrated 80-day-old Rats Treated With 0.3 mg. of
Testosterone Propionate

(Abridged from Burkhart[29])

Time After Treatment (*hours*)	Control	Colchicine
15..........	0	0.04
19..........	0	0.24
23..........	0.28	0.20
27..........	5.00	2.04
31..........	2.92	7.60
35..........	10.68	*108.60*

by a modified technique in which cellular multiplication was observed only for a few hours after explantation.[5-8, 24-27] Some of the results demonstrating how useful colchicine may be as a tool in such work will be summarized here.

9.3–1: Studies in vivo. Some of the early work in this field was done on the ovary. Colchicine, by increasing from 11 to 35 times the number of mitoses that could be observed in the germinal epithelium of the ovary of mice, demonstrated that this was a region of active growth.[1, 38, 14, 80] Similar facts were observed in guinea pigs. [76, 77] The relation between the mitotic activity in the ovarian follicles and the estrus cycle were carefully analyzed (Fig. 9.3). In the endothelial cells of the theca interna of the ovarian follicles, immediately before ovulation, the karyokineses were found to increase about sixtyfold. Arrested mitoses of follicular cells in the rat can be found around eggs after they have reached the uterus (Fig. 9.4).[4] Some follicles are found to be growing rapidly while others are quiescent.

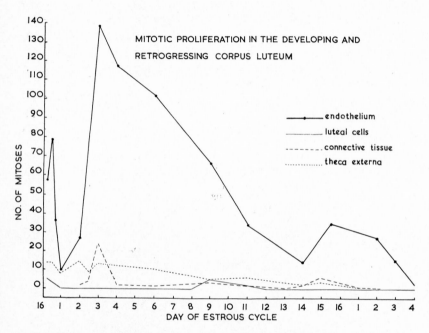

Fig. 9.3—Mitoses in the corpus luteum of the ovary of a normal mature guinea pig, studied by the colchicine method. (After Schmidt[77])

This fact is not evident in control animals, because the number of mitoses is too small.

In the pituitary glands of mice, colchicine increases the number of mitoses about threefold. This is an indication that these mitoses are normally of long duration. Many data have been gathered about the mitotic activity in this organ in various physiological conditions. [9, 52] Table 9.2 shows how evident is the action of age on mitotic activity when the number of metaphases has been artificially increased by spindle poisoning.[52]

A quantitative study of cell regeneration in the mucosa of the intestine in rats has been made possible by colchicine. It was known that the intestinal cells are continuously shed, but how long it took for the whole epithelial lining to be replaced was not known. Table

9.3 gives the results, with the percentages of dividing cells and of mitotic stages in control and colchicinized animals.[60] From these results, it is apparent that mitotic arrest at metaphase has increased in six hours the number of cell divisions by 17.63/3.32. The mitotic duration, calculated as indicated in Section 9.2, is 3.32 × 6.0/17.63 = 1.13 = 1 hr. 8 min. It can be calculated from this result that in 37.7 hours (1.57 days), 100 per cent of the cells will have divided; that is to say, a complete renewal of the epithelium will have taken place. This is, of course, only statistically correct, for there must remain a certain number of stem cells so that growth may persist. These cells will divide into one differentiating cell and one stem cell identical to the first. A great discrepancy between results obtained with radio-phosphorus on the nucleic acid turnover and the figures given by the colchicine method as used by the same authors has been discovered.[81] This may throw more light on the complex problems of growth in differentiating tissues.

The skin of small rodents has been excellent testing material for the study of growth as analyzed by colchicine. A very extensive series

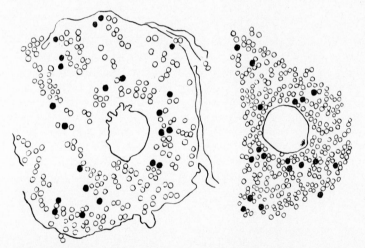

Fig. 9.4—Colchicine-mitoses (black dots) in an ovarian follicle **(left)**, and in follicular cells surrounding an egg found in the uterus in the rat. (After Allen et al.[4])

of experiments has been carried on, especially by Bullough.[24-27] This has provided ample material for a precise analysis of growth and the fundamental mechanisms of mitosis. Further reference will be made to some of these papers in the section on hormonal stimulation of mitosis. Diurnal variations, the action of sleep, the effects of blood-sugar level and of injections of starch, have led to the most important conclusion that carbohydrate metabolism is indispensable for mitosis in epidermal cells, and that it provides the energy necessary for a cell to initiate division. Once prophase has started, no further energy requirements are apparent, and mitosis proceeds as if it were an all-or-none reaction.[24, 26] These experiments have also shown that the mitotic increase after colchicine corresponds to a

TABLE 9.2

EFFECT OF AGE ON MITOTIC ACTIVITY IN THE PITUITARY GLANDS OF FEMALE RATS
(After Hunt[52])

Age (days)	Pituitary Mitoses (per sq. mm.)
96	77.5
148	45
188	32
220	15
300	5

normal duration of about three hours. This is very long compared to that of ten minutes mentioned in Section 9.1. The difference may be partly explained by the action of hormonal stimulation, which not only increases the number of new cells starting to divide but also apparently shortens the duration of mitosis. This will be considered in a subsequent paragraph. Some other complexities of the study of epidermal growth and of the action of colchicine can be understood by the fact that the alkaloid may decrease the number of new mitoses,[24] and that unless observations are made within six hours after the injection of the alkaloid, some arrested metaphases may proceed to telophase.

TABLE 9.3

DIVIDING CELLS (PER CENT) IN THE ILEAL EPITHELIUM OF MALE RATS
(After Leblond and Stevens[60])

	Per Cent Nuclei Undergoing Mitosis (Normal and Abnormal)	Stages (per cent)				
		Prophase	Metaphase (Normal)	Metaphase (Degenerating)	Anaphase	Telophase
Controls	3.32 ± 0.35	24	36	0	5	35
Colchicine	17.63 ± 0.82	2	57	41	0	0

These studies of the epithelial growth in mice lead to a most interesting development which will now be considered: the study of growth in explanted tissues.

9.3–2: Growth in vitro. Many of the fundamental discoveries related to colchicine-mitosis were made on tissue cultures.[6, 23, 61, 62, 84, 88, 90] The importance of metaphase arrest in increasing the number of visible mitoses without modifying the mitotic rate has been illustrated by Figure 9.1. Other results on the action of colchicine on neoplastic cells in tissue culture, and on the mitosis-arresting properties of colchicine derivatives and other mitotic poisons will be related in Chapters 10 and 17. Tissue culture work offers definite potentialities for further investigation. The utilization of synthetic or semi-synthetic media and the roller-tube technique are some of the modern aspects of tissue culture which could benefit from colchicine.

On the other hand, most important results have been obtained by simplified methods in which surviving tissues are utilized. Within the short duration of the experiments, mitoses proceed normally, and problems of bacterial contamination, transplantation, and dedifferentiation do not arise. These methods have been used in the study of the skin and bone marrow of mammals, including man.

As a consequence of previously mentioned work on the skin of the ears of mice, Bullough[24] developed a technique of *in vitro* study of the mitotic activity. *In vivo* experiments had demonstrated that glucose[26] and oxygen[27] were indispensable for providing the energy required for cell division. Glutamate was further demonstrated to increase the rate of cell division. The *in vitro* method should eventually bring forth important new data on the metabolic requirement of epidermal cells. Colchicine increases the amount of visible mitoses and makes counts simpler. However, because of the long duration of cell division in this type of tissue, colchicine does not produce any of the spectacular increases which have been seen in other organs. An important result was to establish that a linear relation existed between the number of arrested mitoses and the oxygen tension. While only 0.4 mitoses could be seen in pure nitrogen, the figures were 3.9 for 60 per cent nitrogen and 40 per cent oxygen, and 8.3 in pure oxygen.[27] The general significance of these results is made clear by nearly identical findings with bone marrow cells.[5] This work has been done mainly in Italy. Astaldi and a group of collaborators first studied the colchicine response of human bone marrow.[6] This is readily available by sternal puncture, and colchicine has provided a new insight on the growth of this tissue. This growth is far more rapid than that of skin; in mammals, bone marrow and intestinal mucosa are the tissues which have the highest mitotic index. After explantation, small fragments were kept at 37°C. in human serum, and their growth could be studied for as long as 36 hours. The number of mitoses was considerably increased by colchicine, and the authors have indicated that this "stathmokinetic index," as it has been called, may throw considerable light on many problems of normal and neoplastic cellular division. Some of these will be mentioned in Chapter 10.

Very small amounts of colchicine are effective; dilutions of 1:1,000,000 were used. The alkaloid may disturb slightly the normal maturation of cells of the erythroblastic series. This is only visible after 12 hours *in vitro,* and for most experiments, important data can be recorded from 4 to 8 hours after colchicine. The action of embryonic extracts[7] and that of irradiation with X-rays[8] have been studied on normal marrow. This has also been compared with marrow from patients suffering from Addison-Biermer anemia (cf. Chapter 8), polycythemia and leukemia (Chapter 10), and thalassemia (Cooley's anemia) .[7]

Figure 9.5 demonstrates that the mitotic activity of erythroblasts (young red blood cells) is depressed by absence of oxygen. This experiment was carried on in a vessel in which a partial vacuum could be maintained. It is made clear by colchicine that the younger cells, the basophil erythroblasts, are more depressed than the more differentiated ones, which have already some hemoglobin. These important results are to be compared to those mentioned above, on the importance of oxygen for mitosis in the epithelial cells of the mouse's ear.[27] This might have passed entirely unnoticed if a tool had not existed to increase the number of visible mitoses and make counting a simple proposition. It must, however, always be kept in mind that control experiments should be made, for it remains to be proved that colchicine, which has such a wide variety of pharmacological effects (Chapter 7), does not disturb some mitoses more than others. These experiments are, of course, entirely based on the assumption that the alkaloid does no more than "freeze" the mitoses at metaphase.[2, 23, 62]

9.4: Hormone-stimulated Growth

A considerable number of papers have been published following the contributions of Allen, Smith, and Gardner.[2] It is not contemplated to review them all here, even if such a task were possible, for many papers of endocrinological interest do not mention in their titles that colchicine has been used, and it has become impossible to keep up a complete set of references. Table 9.4 gives a summary of some of the work which has been published. It is evident that the sex hormones have been the most studied, partly because their isolation and chemical identification took place in the period im-

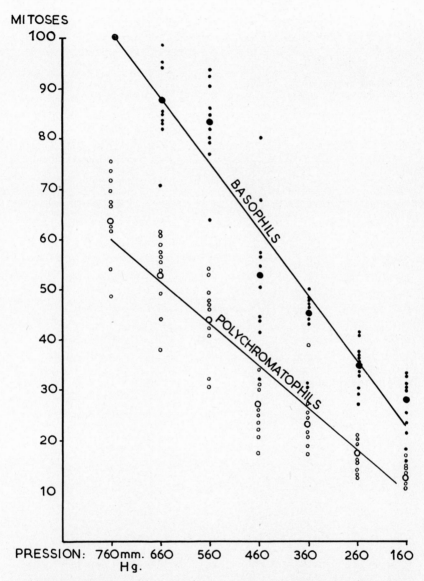

Fig. 9.5—Linear relation between pressure of atmospheric air and mitoses in bone-marrow erythroblasts studied by culture **in vitro**. The results are expressed as percentages of the maximum mitotic rate, i.e., that of basophil erythroblasts at atmospheric pressure. (After Astaldi et al.[8])

TABLE 9.4

EXPERIMENTS ON HORMONE-INFLUENCED GROWTH

Hormones	Animal	Receptor Tissue and References
1. *Pituitary hormones*		
gonadotropins	mouse	uterus (muscle)[3]
	rabbit	uterus[30]
	guinea pig	hypophysis[78]
		parathyroid[78]
		adrenals[78]
		testis (interstitial cells)[78]
		seminal vesicles; uterus[12]
	Molge marmorata	prostate[78]
		cloacal epithelium[78]
chorionic gonadotropins	mouse	uterus (glands and muscle)[3]
	guinea pig	testis (interstitial cells)[53]
	rabbit	uterus[30,41]
prolactin	pigeon	crop-sac[58,59,56]
adrenocorticotropic hormone (ACTH) *	rat	adrenal cortex[92]
thyrotropic hormone	rat	thyroid[50]
	guinea pig	thyroid[12,11] †,[44]
anterior lobe extract	rat	Langerhans' islets[50,92]
2. *Ovarian hormones*		
a. estrogens ("theelin," estradiol, estrone, etc.)	mouse	vagina[2,91]
		uterus: glands,[91] muscle[2]
		mammary gland[2]
		hypophysis ‡[9,54]
		rectum[91]
		ovary[91]
		skin[24]
		seminal vesicles[40]
		various tissues[24]
	rat	uterus (muscle)[3]
		vagina[73,32]
		hypophysis[55]
		parathyroid[12]
		seminal vesicles[44,67]
		ventral prostate[67,29]
	guinea pig	nipple[89]
		uterus (muscle)[15]
	woman	vagina[79,72]
	Rhodeus amarus	ovipositor[18]
	rabbit	uterus (glands)[28]
		(muscle)[28]
b. progesterone	rat	parathyroid§[12]
		vagina[32]
		prostate[37]

TABLE 9.4 (*continued*)

Hormones	Animal	Receptor Tissue and References
c. pregnane	woman *Rhodeus amarus*	seminal vesicles[37] vagina[79,72] ovipositor[18]
3. *Testicular hormones* (androgens) testosterone, androsterone, androstenediol	mouse rat guinea pig *Rhodeus amarus*	seminal vesicles[65,85,87,39,40] *Id.* transplanted to female[82] prostate[85] seminal vesicles[12,85,44,67,29] prostate[85,29] thyroid (in female)[68] parathyroid (*id.*)[68] adrenal[69] skin epoophoron[48] ovipositor[18]
androstane	*Molge marmorata*	prostate[78] cloacal epithelium[78]
4. *Adrenal cortical hormones* a. desoxycorticosterone	rabbit	uterus[67]
b. cortisone	mouse	skin[27]
c. corticosterone, total extract of cortex	*Rhodeus amarus*	ovipositor[18]
5. *Other hormones* thyroxine	mouse rat	adrenal[47] regenerating kidney[51]
tachysterine	rat	parathyroid[12]
insulin	rat	Langerhans' islets[33]

* Non-purified extract of pituitary.
† Extracted from human urine.
‡ Also experiments with stilbestrol.
§ With estradiol benzoate.

mediately following 1937, when colchicine was taken up as a "fad." Endocrinologists appear to have lost some of their interest in this tool, and this may explain how such important substances as cortisone and ACTH have hardly been tested by colchicine methods. Most of the work was on hormones which stimulated mitosis; cortisone, on the contrary, appears to have an inhibitory action.[24] The usefulness of colchicine in the study of mitotic inhibitors has not yet been fully understood, and further work will undoubtedly demonstrate that this is a tool for the study of mitotic activity, whether stimulated or depressed. Results reported in Chapter 10 support this opinion.

9.4–1: Pituitary hormones. Prolactine, the hormone stimulating secretion of the mammary gland in mammals, was used in one of the first and most spectacular experiments of this type. In birds, this hormone stimulates the crop-sac. This organ secretes "milk" by a

TABLE 9.5

Mitosis in the Crop-Sac of the Pigeon After Prolactin Stimulation

(Colchicine is injected 9 to 11 hours before the animal is killed.)

(After Leblond and Allen[59])

	Number of Animals	Colchicine (*mg.*)	Pro-lactin (*bird units*)	Mitoses per 2000 Cells (Average, Smallest, and Greatest Figures)	Average Mitotic Index
Colchicine controls..	2	0.10–0.25	....	12 (9–15)	1
	6	0.40–0.50	....	46 (8–173)	2
Prolactin controls...	2	....	40	15 (9–21)	1
Prolactin-colchicine..	6	0.10–0.35	40	' 27 (11–48)	1
	5	0.50	40	534 (210–1075)	26

process which has no relation to that observed in mammals. The bird's "milk" is made of fat-laden cells desquamating from the thickened epithelium of the crop-sac. Table 9.5 shows the increase of the mitotic index for this epithelium in pigeons injected with prolactine and colchicine.[58, 59] In one animal, 53 per cent of all epithelial crop-sac nuclei were found to be in a condition of arrested mitosis. The average increase of the mitotic index is 37-fold, and calculation based on the assumption of arrest only, leads to the result that the pro-lactine-stimulated cells must divide in about 16 minutes. It is not certain that such a calculation is correct, because many factors, for instance cellular differentiation, are involved. Also, from the published photomicrographs[59] it is not evident that the thickness of the control and the colchicinized epithelia are comparable. Whatever the significance of these quantitative estimations may be, colchicine demonstrated clearly that connective tissue cells, and muscular cells of the crop-sac wall also divided under the influence of prolactine. This fact had never been observed.[56, 57]

The thyroid-stimulating hormone, thyrotropin, also increases the cell divisions in the thyroid. This is made much more evident by spindle poisoning. In controls 6.3 mitoses were found per 100 thyroid vesicles in the guinea pig. This figure was increased to 16.8 by the hormone alone, and to 119 by hormone + colchicine.[12] A method for the detection of increased amounts of this hormone in the urine of patients has been proposed[11] (Table 9.6). A response is positive when more than 4 mitoses per 100 vesicles are detected.[11] Other authors have confirmed these results, but some abnormal responses were attributed to a rhythmic growth response of the thyroid.[50]

The gonadotropic hormones stimulate mitotic growth in many tissues, and this was studied by means of colchicine as early as 1937.[12] In the uterine glands of guinea pigs, colchicine made clear the location of the zones of maximal growth. Action of pituitary hormones on endocrine glands will be considered later. Results of work on pregnant guinea pigs may be mentioned however, because they bring evidence of many, often unsuspected stimulations of mitosis by the increased amount of gonadotropic and other steroid sex hormones during pregnancy.[33] Especially notable is the stimulation

TABLE 9.6

MITOSES IN ONE MICROSCOPIC FIELD IN THE THYROID OF THE GUINEA PIG

(After Bastenie[11])

Substance Injected	Number of Cases	Mitoses
Colchicine alone		0.5–1
Anterior lobe extract + colchicine		.35
Extracts of urine + colchicine:		
myxedema	5	*1–7*
myxedema after treatment	3	0.1–0.5
hyperthyroidy	3	0.15–0.25
hypothyroidy of pituitary origin	3	0.05–0.4
Froelich's syndrome	2	0.05–0.1
Acromegaly	1	0.2
Other diseases, without thyroid disturbances	3	0.2–0.4

of the parathyroids, exocrine glands of the pancreas, and kidney tubules — changes which would have been unnoticed without colchicine. This important work does not seem to have been pursued so far as colchicine is concerned (Table 9.7).

The absence of publications on the adrenocorticotropic hormone (ACTH) and colchicine has already been mentioned.[24] It is still

TABLE 9.7

Mᴛᴏᴛɪᴄ Iɴᴅᴇx ɪɴ Oʀɢᴀɴs ᴏғ Pʀᴇɢɴᴀɴᴛ Gᴜɪɴᴇᴀ Pɪɢ

I: without colchicine
II: 9 hours after 0.625 mg./100 g. colchicine
A: embryos less than 5 mm. long
B: embryos from 5 to 15 mm.
C: embryos longer than 15 mm.

(After Cavallero[33])

	Controls		A		B		C	
	I	II	I	II	I	II	I	II
Hypophysis (anterior lobe)	0	2	5	*17*	1	7	0	6
Thyroid	0.2	0.3	2	7	1	5	0	3
Parathyroids	0	1	1	*14*	0	7	0	2
Adrenal cortex	0	0	2	4	0	4	0	1
Adrenal medulla	0	0	0	0	0	0	0	0
Langerhans' islets	0	1	0.3	*5*	0	0	0	0
Corpus luteum	0	. . .	1	1	6	6	. . *	5
Kidney	0	2	2	8	9.5	5	0.5	*18*
Pancreas (exocrine) . . .	0	0.5	1	4	0	*10*	0	5
Liver	0	0	0	0	0	0	0	0

* The figure given in the original paper has been omitted because of a typographical error which it has not been possible to correct (Cavallero, personal communication).

more remarkable that the growth hormone, somatotropin (STH), has only been studied with the colchicine method in a single paper, which pointed to stimulation of hemopoiesis.[74] This shows that many pathways remain open. The results obtained with other hormones are good evidence that important and unsuspected findings still remain before us.

9.4–2: Sex hormones. These are powerful stimulants of mitotic growth. Some of the results with estrogens have been reported in the first paragraph of this chapter.[2, 93] It was not always realized that estrogens may stimulate growth in other epithelia than those of the genital tract. In his observations on mice, Bullough, using colchicine to detect the increased mitotic activity, demonstrated stimulation in most tissues, including connective tissue.[24] In further experiments, this author has called attention to a remarkable effect of estrogens. Figure 9.6 shows that colchicine increases the mitotic index of the

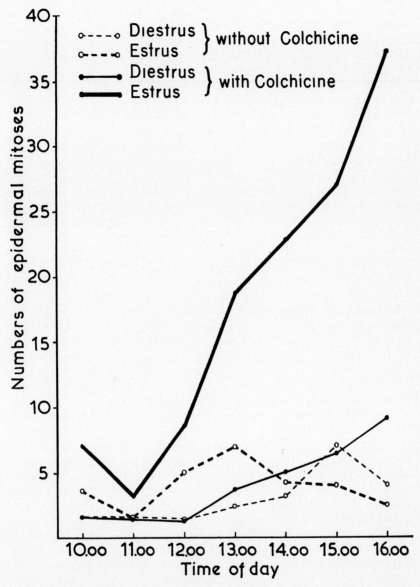

Fig. 9.6—Mitotic activity, as demonstrated by colchicine, in the epidermis of the ear of female mice, in estrus and diestrus. Controls: dotted lines. The far greater increase observed after colchicine during estrus is considered to be an indication that normally epidermal mitoses last longer in diestrus. (Modified, after Bullough, 1950[24])

epidermis of the ear considerably more during estrus than during diestrus. The mitoses were counted hour by hour by clipping small fragments of the ear. This difference can be explained by a shortening of the time taken for one division, from about 2 hours in diestrus to 3/4 hour in estrus. This significant result is not discussed; other possible hypotheses are, for instance, synergic action of colchicine and hormone, or changes in the duration of interphase. The alkaloid is simply considered to stop metaphases.[2, 23, 62]

Androgenic hormones, also, stimulate mitotic growth, and the use of colchicine was advocated in 1937 for the study of the changes in the seminal vesicles[85, 65, 12] (Fig. 9.7). The accumulation of arrested mitoses in the prostate or seminal vesicles of castrated mice or rats has been proposed as a test for androgens.[85] In mice, colchicine helped to prove that the prostate is a more sensitive reactor than the seminal vesicles to testosterone.[44] Data about the "explosive" aspect of mitotic stimulation when studied with colchicine in these tissues has been discussed already and presented in Table 9.1.

The quantitative aspects of the seminal vesicle reaction to various androgens and related hormones have been carefully investigated.[39, 40] Figure 9.8 demonstrates how the increased number of mitoses helps to establish the linear relations between the doses of androgen injected and the intensity of the reaction. With other hormones, such as progesterone and estrogens, though the mitotic index may increase, no such relation is found[40] (Fig. 9.9).

Colchicine also brought further evidence that in the female guinea pig, the epoophoron reacted to colchicine like the male epididymis, of which it is the anatomical homolog.[48]

9.4–3: Mitotic stimulation of endocrine glands. Though pituitary hormones play a great part in mitotic stimulation in various organs, the cells of the pituitary may also undergo mitosis under the influence of hormonal stimuli.[9, 55, 71] Colchicine helped to demonstrate that in virgin female rats, ovariectomy did not promote pituitary mitoses.[55] On the contrary, injections of estrogens, natural or synthetic, enlarge the pituitary as a consequence of mitotic growth made evident with colchicine.[55] It has, however, been shown that castration could influence the numbers of c-mitoses of the basophil cells of the anterior lobe of the pituitary.[71] There are no data about the posterior lobe of the organ, which may be an interesting object for future colchicine work.

Several papers deal with mitotic stimulation in the cortical region of the adrenals.[92, 78, 68, 69, 47] In immature female rats, colchicine reveals a stimulation which reaches its maximum 96 hours after an injection of testosterone. At the same time, however, mitotic activity is increased in thyroid, parathyroid, and ovary. This may be evi-

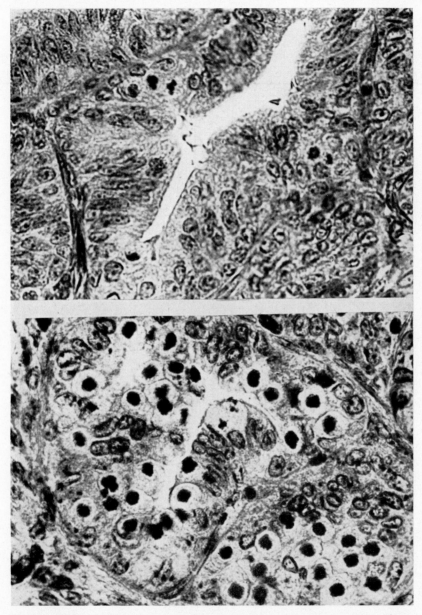

Fig. 9.7—Mitotic stimulation by testosterone propionate in the seminal vesicles. **Above.** Hormone alone. **Below.** Hormone + colchicine. (Original photomicrographs from Bastenie and Zylberszac[12])

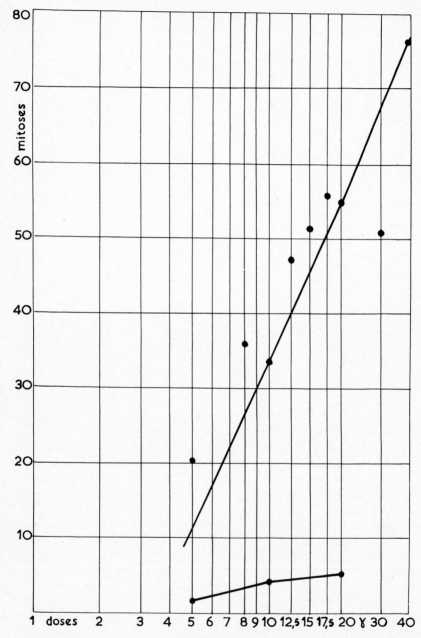

Fig. 9.8—Seminal vesicle test with testosterone propionate. The line (**below**), without colchicine, does not make clear the correlation between number of mitoses and dose. With colchicine, a linear relation is evident (**above**). (After Dirschel et al.[40])

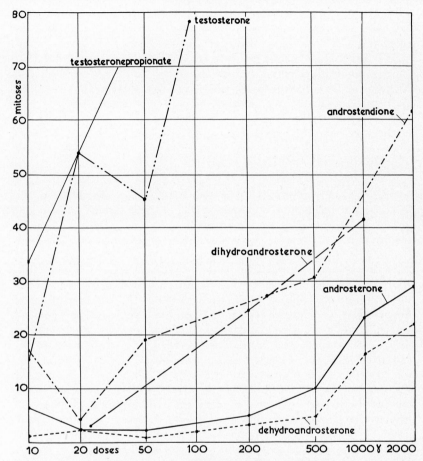

Fig. 9.9—Seminal vesicle test with various androgens. Amplification of the number of visible mitoses by colchicine. (After Dirschel *et al.*[40])

dence of an indirect action via pituitary stimulation.[68] The same applies probably for the increased mitotic activity detected in the thyroid of female rats injected with testosterone.[69]

The mitotic activity of the parathyroid glands of mammals is usually very low, and is difficult to study; hence, the utility of colchicine. *Folliculin* (estradiol) and progesterone injections in the rat result in the appearance of many mitoses.[12] This effect may be the consequence of hypocalcemia. The contrary, hypercalcemia, probably explains why irradiated tachysterin (Holtz's A.T.10) decreases the parathyroid mitotic activity. Testosterone injections increase mitoses in this organ; this may be an indirect effect mediated by the pituitary.[69]

In the Langerhans' islets of the pancreas, pituitary stimulation [92, 50] and pregnancy increase the number of mitoses, as detected by colchicine.

It is surprising to find no paper dealing with mitotic stimulation in the interstitial (Leydig) cells of the testes. In guinea pigs injected with chorionic gonadotropins, these cells increase in number, but colchicine failed to detect mitoses. It was concluded that the hormone-secreting cells originated from ordinary connective cells.[53] Further work on this tissue is obviously needed.[46]

9.5: Regeneration and Hypertrophy

The problem which was under study in the laboratory of A. P. Dustin, Sr., since about 1920 and which led to the discovery of the properties of colchicine was that of the regulation of growth and mitotic activity in pluricellular animals. In vertebrates, for instance, cell division takes place only in some tissues, and then in an orderly way. While in the adult, nerve cells become incapable of any mitosis, other organs, such as the liver and the kidney, while nearly devoid of any mitotic activity in normal conditions, may grow rapidly by cellular multiplication after surgical excision. In the rodents, and in particular the rat, large portions of the liver may be removed surgically. The remaining cells start to divide at once, and regeneration of the normal liver mass is remarkably rapid.[21] The exact determinism of this cellular growth is unknown. This was one of the first subjects to be studied with the help of colchicine as a tool for a better analysis of mitotic activity.[19, 20, 21, 22] Hence, the work which had been initiated in order to understand better such problems as regenerative growth led indirectly to the discovery of a new tool, colchicine, which was rapidly put to use in several countries.[19, 31, 41, 43] The problems of cellular division in wound healing, which is closely related to regeneration, will be considered in the next section of this chapter. This work deserves special attention, for important results appear to have been often overlooked. Once again, colchicine was taken up with enthusiasm as a new tool; new discoveries were made possible, but only in a few instances was the study pursued long enough to come near a solution of the problems.[51] This field appears today as one of the most promising for future research.

9.5–1: Liver. In the rat, as much as 68 per cent of the liver parenchyma may be removed surgically. After an initial period of edematous swelling lasting about 24 hours, cell division takes place. This type of growth has been extensively studied, for it lends itself to quantitative estimations of the numbers of new cells formed each day.[2] The duration of mitosis was found to be between 48 and 53 minutes. After colchicine, many arrested mitoses are visible. Their number can be explained on the basis of mitotic arrest.[19, 20, 21] Some show only slight abnormalities, but most are of the exploded type (Fig. 2.5). When up to one-fifth of all the liver cells are in this condition, swollen and their chromosomes dispersed, the liver becomes extremely friable.[22] The various stages of restitution after the injection of colchicine have been described and illustrated in Chapter 2. It is surprising that the regeneration is only slightly slowed down by several injections of the sublethal dose of 50 mg. This has been explained by the fact that the exploded metaphases, after building cells with many micronuclei, regained normal nuclei by the fusion of the micronuclei (Figs. 2.7, 2.8, 2.9). These facts remain rather difficult to understand from a quantitative point of view.

Apart from this work, liver regeneration studied with colchicine has provided some material for counting the chromosomes. This is done readily in the exploded metaphases. Diploid, tetraploid, and octoploid nuclei were observed, a fact which agrees with karyometric data.[35] About the analysis of the differential growth of various liver constituents — liver cells, Kupffer cells, bile canaliculi, blood vessels — hardly anything is known, and there remain ample opportunities for further colchicine research.[83, 64, 75] The biochemical stimulus to mitotic growth after hepatectomy is also unknown; some unpublished results obtained at Brussels indicate that the ligature of bile ducts may increase mitoses, as observed in the liver by the colchicine method.

9.5–2: Kidney. The increase of the volume of one kidney after removal of the other is closely related to regeneration. It proceeds by mitotic growth. This is particularly difficult to analyze in such a complex organ as the kidney, and any tool increasing the number of visible mitoses is most helpful.[41, 43, 31] The great number of mitoses observed in rats injected with 2.5 mg/kg after unilateral nephrectomy and killed 10 hours later is apparent from Table 9.8.

The problems of kidney mitoses in this condition and in other experiments carried on to throw light on the causal factors have been the object of several publications from the Brussels school. After unilateral nephrectomy, the maximal number of mitoses is found during the first four days in the convoluted tubules, then in the glomeruli, and on the seventh day in Henle's loops and the Schweiger-Seidel tubules.[41, 43] No mitoses are to be found in the epithelium of the renal pelvis. Exploded c-mitoses are the most frequent in the convoluted tubes. If a partial nephrectomy is added to the ablation of the other kidney, the remaining tissue shows mitoses in all locations, including the pelvis. Ligation of the ureter, without nephrectomy, also stimulates kidney cells to divide, a fact which may prove of great experimental importance[51] (Fig. 9.10). Another remarkable result is found when colchicine is injected into animals after one renal artery has been ligated.[43] The ischemic kidney shows a considerable number of mitoses, mainly in the excretory (Schweiger-Seidel) tubules and the pelvis (Fig. 9.11). Similar facts have been observed in kidneys made partly ischemic by the endocrine kidney operation of Selye.[33] The following experiments were aimed

TABLE 9.8

MITOTIC INDEX IN THE REMAINING KIDNEY OF ADULT RATS INJECTED WITH COLCHICINE
(After Carnot and May[31])

Days After Unilateral Nephrectomy	Cortex	Medulla		Total
		External Zone	Internal Zone	
Controls...............	3	1.5	0	4.5
3......................	43.5	13.5	0.5	57.5
8......................	43	9	1.5	53.5
14.....................	18	4	0	22
21.....................	18	0	0	18

at finding the possible nature of the mitotic stimulus.[51] The number of renal mitoses after nephrectomy was decreased by injections of thiouracil, a drug which depresses thyroid function. Thyroidectomy, however, did not prevent or retard the increase of size of the remaining kidney in the rat.[51] Thyroxin was nevertheless found to stimulate renal mitoses as much as would a nephrectomy. When this was carried on and thyroxin injected afterwards, the mitotic increase was greater than expected. This may indicate a truly synergic action of the two stimuli. The differences in body weight between controls (nephrectomy alone) and the other rats, and the fact that the mitotic counts were corrected for 100 g. of body weight, make these results difficult to interpret and suggests the need for further research (Table 9.9).

The hypothesis which was put forward following these data was that thyroxin did not act directly on renal tissue, but that the increased protein catabolism resulting from the action of the hormone provided the factor responsible for mitosis.[51] Some substance present in the urine may be suspected since, as mentioned above, ligature of the ureter promotes cell division (Fig. 9.10). However, such mitotic activity is mainly located in the connective tissue of the kidney. An important fact is that unilateral ureter ligation promotes mitosis in

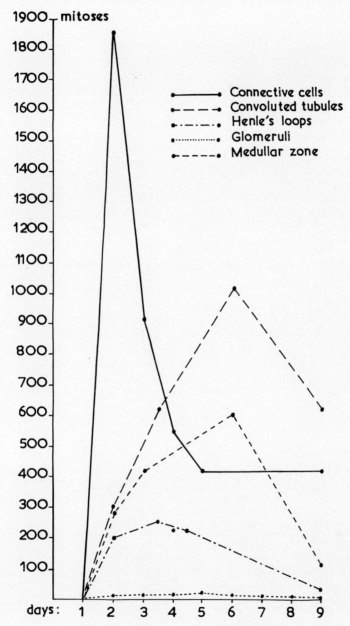

Fig. 9.10—Mitotic activity in the kidney of the rat after ligature of the ureter, studied with the colchicine-technique. (After Herlant[51])

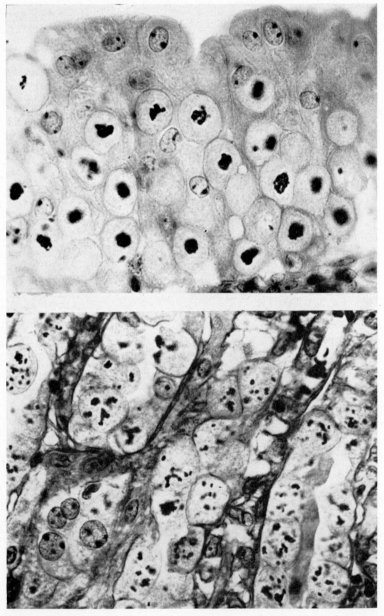

Fig. 9.11—Colchicine-mitoses in the kidney of the rat, 72 hours after ligature of the renal artery. **Above.** Star and ball metaphases with clumped chromosomes in the renal pelvis. **Below.** Exploded metaphases in the tubuli contorti. (A. P. Dustin and Zylberszac[41, 48])

the other kidney also; this resembles closely the changes of compensatory hypertrophy (Fig. 9.12). Substances reabsorbed from the urine may promote division first in the ligated kidney and later in the other one. Research by other workers has suggested that xanthopterin or substances of that chemical constitution may initiate the kidney hypertrophy. The problems are far from being solved, but the utility of colchicine for the observation of mitotic growth has been amply demonstrated.

9.5–3: Other organs. The following results give an indication of the multiple uses of colchicine as a tool. In the Langerhans' islets of the pancreas, alloxan brings about a selective destruction of the so-called β-cells, which secrete insulin. Regeneration and mitoses of these cells are prevented if the animals receive insulin. This probably acts through a pituitary mechanism, for extracts of the pituitary gland increase considerably the number of cell divisions in islet regeneration. Colchicine-mitoses are also observed in the anterior lobe of the pituitary[33] (Table 9.10). The regeneration of the adrenal cortex after unilateral adrenalectomy in rats has also benefited from the use of mitosis arrest.[10] In rats also, colchicine helped to demonstrate that compensatory hypertrophy of parathyroids after partial parathyroidectomy does not take place in hypophysectomized animals[37] and that testosterone inhibited the epithelial mitoses in thymic regeneration following X-irradiation.[49]

TABLE 9.9

ACTION OF THYROXIN ON RENAL HYPERTROPHY AFTER UNILATERAL NEPHRECTOMY NUMBER OF MITOSES IN A MEDIAN SECTION OF THE WHOLE KIDNEY, 9 HOURS AFTER COLCHICINE

(Abridged from Herlant[51])

Experiment	Mitoses					
	Convoluted Tubules	Henle's Loops	Glomeruli	Medulla	Connective Tissue	Total
1. Unilateral nephrectomy (4 rats)*	61–125	8–19	0–3	26–87	44-62	163–210
2. Thyroxin alone (4 rats)†	173–252	3–5	0–2	2–5	3–7	186–250
3. Unilateral nephrectomy + thyroxin (7 rats)†	315–589	35–65	2–15	25–152	31–132	523–722

* Animals weighing 260–360 gm.
† Six daily doses of 0.25 mg. thyroxin; killed the seventh day after 2 mg/kg colchicine. Animals weighing 120–220 gm.

9.5–4: Regeneration in developing animals. The complex actions of the *Colchicum* alkaloid in embryonic development and larval growth have already been reviewed. It is not surprising that in some conditions colchicine may actually inhibit regenerative growth; thus, it could not properly be used as a tool. In *Amblystoma opacum* and *A. punctatum*, 18 to 25 mm. long, limb regeneration was studied

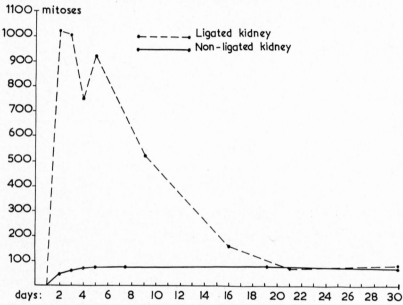

Fig. 9.12—Unilateral ligature of the ureter in a rat. Mitoses in ligated and non-ligated kidney, detected by the colchicine-method. (After Herlant[51])

when the larvae were placed in 1:1000 or 1:5000 solutions of colchicine. If this was done at the moment of amputation, all regeneration was suppressed. Various degrees of inhibition of the limb-blastema formation and of further differentiation, according to the length of the colchicine treatment, were described.[86]

The regenerating tail of tadpoles of *Xenopus laevis* reacts similarly.[63] In very dilute solutions of colchicine, this material provided some results which appeared to indicate not only that mitoses were arrested at metaphase but that a true mitotic stimulation existed. Figure 9.13 shows that in control animals the number of mitoses is quite small. If colchicine is assumed to have only a metaphasic arresting action, it is possible to calculate the number of mitoses which should be observed at various intervals, for the duration of mitosis has been observed and calculated in *Xenopus* (Chapter 3). Figure 9.13 indicates that many more mitoses are found than expected, and

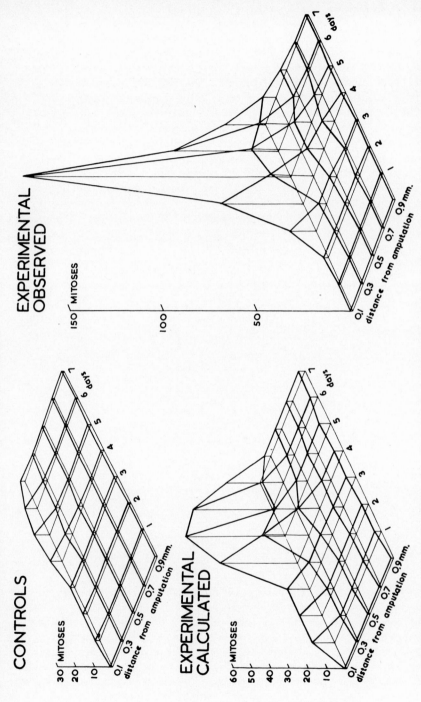

Fig. 9.13—Analysis of the mitotic increase in the regenerating tail of **Xenopus laevis**, in relation to time after amputation and distance from wound. The "calculated" number of mitosis is based on data about the duration of one cell-division in this material, and on the theory that colchicine does no more than "arrest" metaphases. The observed data bring evidence of a considerable increase, close to the wound, on the fifth day. (Slightly modified, from Lüscher[08])

that instead of a gradual rise, there is a steep increase on the fifth day. However, the experimental conditions are complex and stimuli from other growth-promoting substances cannot be excluded. These data with those given in Section 9.2 comprise the best evidence to date of possible mitotic stimulation of animal cells by colchicine.

In *Xenopus,* a short treatment, one hour in a 1:2000 solution, may completely inhibit growth. However, regeneration often proceeds normally during the first three days after this "colchicine shock" because cellular migration is not disturbed. On the fifth day, on the contrary, when divisions should be taking place, regeneration was completely inhibited (Fig. 9.14). Some pharmacological conclusions are important to mention; they are the results of an extensive series of experiments on this favorable material. Colchicine was demon-

TABLE 9.10

INFLUENCE OF ALLOXAN DIABETES ON PANCREATIC, PITUITARY, AND SUPRARENAL
MITOSES; INHIBITION BY INSULIN; STIMULATION BY PITUITARY EXTRACTS

I: rats injected with 150 mg/kg alloxan
II: *id.* + 10 to 20 units insulin per day
III: *id.* + pituitary extract (about 32 mg. dry powder per day)

(After Cavallero[33])

	Mitoses								
	Langerhans' Islets			Anterior Lobe of Hypophysis			Adrenal Medulla		
Days	I	II	III	I	II	III	I	II	III
1....	8	0	3	15	15	24	2	4	1
2....	7	1	24	24	19	16	2	7	3
3....	44	2	132	54	2	64	1	0	0
4....	81	0	185	81	9	164	3	2	0
5....	31	1	86	15	14	12	0	9	0
9....	2	0	8	27	8	10	0	0	0
12....	7	1	7	27	22	8	0	7	2

strated to act locally, for no inhibition was observed when only the anterior part of the larva was immersed in the solution. This is also evidenced by the absence of inhibition if colchicine is applied to another wound close to the amputation. Experiments in which the tail blastema was amputated and growth resumed, demonstrated that colchicine did not penetrate more than 2 mm. from the wound. These also showed that colchicine was fixed in the tissues of the wound for at least three days. Such a fixation of the alkaloid in tissues has not been described in pharmacological work (Chapter 7). The inhibition of regeneration was clearly the consequence of a great number of the mitoses, sometimes up to 70 per cent, being destroyed after a prolonged period of metaphase arrest (cf. Chapter 3).[63] Similar results have been reported in *Rana temporaria* tadpoles. The local

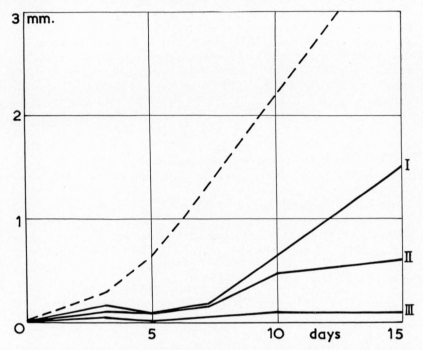

Fig. 9.14—Inhibition of the regeneration in the tail of **Xenopus laevis** after a short treatment with colchicine. Dotted line: normal growth curve. I. Inhibition of regeneration for more than 5 days, then resumed growth. II, III. Strong and persistent inhibition of growth. (After Lehmann et al. 1945, and Lüscher[63])

application of a 1:500 *M* solution of colchicine for only 20 minutes inhibits the regenerative growth of the tail, but has no influence on the growth of the tadpole.[13]

These facts, apart from the conclusion that colchicine is not always a harmless "tool," indicate a remarkable property of the alkaloid of becoming fixed in some tissues. This is surprising for a substance soluble both in water and in lipids. Pharmacologists should pay attention to this possibility, for instance in the analysis of the action of colchicine on muscle and brain. Nearly all data available on colchicine metabolism in warm-blooded animals contradict this idea of a fixation of the alkaloid. One of the purposes of this book is being fulfilled whenever similar contradictions between work done in widely separated fields of research are brought to light.

9.6: Wound Healing

The histological changes found in wounds after injections of colchicine were some of the most surprising observed by A. P. Dustin, Sr.[42] They appeared to give good support to the theory that a true mitotic excitation followed the injection of the alkaloid. Experiments were performed in rats. Two parallel incisions were made in the dorsal skin, and aleurone grains inserted as an irritant in the wounds before suturing. One of the scars was removed as a control at the time colchicine was injected. The dose was 1.25 mg/kg and the animals were killed 9 hours later. This method made available some new facts about wound healing and the formation of granulation tissue near the aleurone grains. The endothelial cells are the first to divide. Extraordinary pictures of capillaries with up to 10 c-mitoses in a single section were observed. These cells appeared swollen. The rapid mitotic growth was not noticeable without the use of the colchicine tool.[42]

In nerve regeneration, the alkaloid, by increasing the numbers of mitoses, makes clear that their repartition is different on both sides of a section. This may result from the influence of the disintegration products of myelin on the division of the Schwann cells (Fig. 9.15).[36]

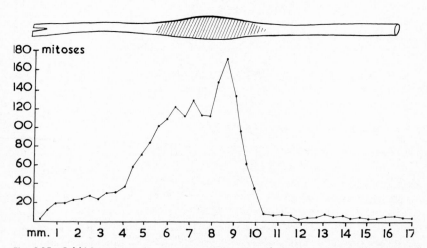

Fig. 9.15—Colchicine-mitoses in a regenerating nerve of the rat. The shaded zone is that of cicatrisation following sectioning. There are more mitoses in the Schwann cells in the peripheric end, at left, than in the central part of the nerve. (After Delcourt[36])

Bone repair has been studied in rabbits.[17] The tibia was cut transversely, without damaging the periosteum otherwise than locally. Mitoses were counted from day to day, the animals being killed 9 to 10 hours after 0.625 mg/kg of colchicine. The amplification of the mitotic changes made estimations of relative growth far easier than in control animals (Fig. 9.16).

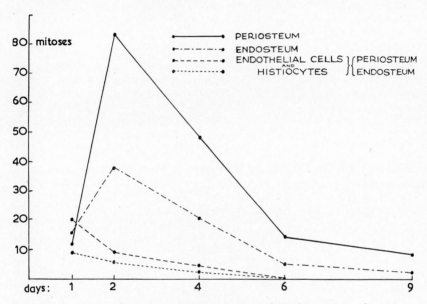

Fig. 9.16—Repartition of mitoses during bone repair, studied after injection of colchicine. (After Borghetti and Parini[17])

These few papers have studied only some limited aspects of healing and inflammatory reactions. Here again, large fields remain open for investigation, and it is surprising that more work has not been completed.

9.7: The Action of Chemicals on Mitotic Growth

Few papers have been published in this section, a surprising fact, for colchicine could no doubt help in the study of many substances affecting growth. In work on vitamins, for instance, many experiments could be imagined. Some results with folic acid antagonists will be mentioned in Chapter 10.

The possibilities of finding new facts is illustrated by the following experiments: Young rats were intoxicated with carbon tetrachloride and studied at various intervals by a routine colchicine technique (Fig. 9.17). Arrested mitoses were observed in the liver cells and in

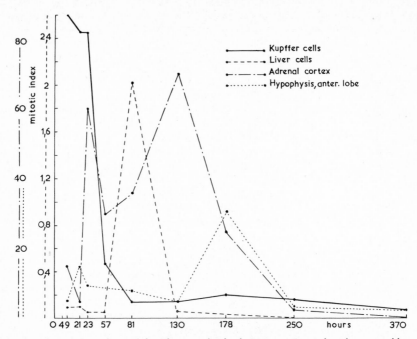

Fig. 9.17—Mitoses in liver and endocrine glands during experimental carbon tetrachloride poisoning, detected by the colchicine-method. (After Cavallero[33])

the Kupffer cells in relation with the progressive cirrhotic changes on the liver. No mitoses were observed in bile ducts, though the number of these apparently increased.[33] After 15 inhalations of carbon tetrachloride, an increased number of reticulo-endothelial mitoses could be observed in the spleen. A systematic study of the endocrine glands revealed evidence of mitotic stimulation in the adrenal cortex, the pituitary, and later, the adrenal medullary zone. These divisions do not appear to be related to local damage, and may be an evidence of a pituitary stimulus arising from "stress" (cf. Chapter 7).

Some work on the mitotic stimulation in the thyroid of rats injected with thiouracil may be mentioned here.[70, 45] The stimulus for cell division is not, however, the chemical itself, but the secretion of the thyrotropic hormone by the pituitary, as mentioned in Subsection 9.4–1. Colchicine has also helped to study, in experiments of this type, the mitotic changes which take place in the pituitary.[16]

Results obtained in young rabbits on the influence of thyroidectomy and thiouracil on healing of cornea wounds are important to consider under this heading, for they throw light on some difficulties of interpretation.[45] Doses of 5 mg/kg of colchicine were injected 4 hours before killing the animals. The results are summarized in

Table 9.11. It is evident that the mitotic index is more depressed by thiouracil than by thyroidectomy, but it seems surprising that this fact is not at all noticeable without colchicine, thiouracil-injected animals having a slightly higher mitotic count than the controls. The authors think that the count after thiouracil results from a double effect, i.e., a decrease of the mitotic rate, which would decrease the mitotic index, and a simultaneous lengthening of the duration of mitosis, which would have the opposite effect.

TABLE 9.11
CORNEAL MITOTIC COUNTS IN A RABBIT
(After Fleischmann and Breckler[45])

	Without Colchicine	With Colchicine
Controls..................	92 ± 35	393 ± 59
Thiouracil-treated..........	100 ± 17	168 ± 42
Thyroidectomized.........		228 ± 41

REFERENCES

1. ALLEN, E., AND GREADICK, R. N. Ovogenesis during sexual maturity. The first stage of mitosis in the germinal epithelium, as shown by the colchicine technique. Anat. Rec. 69:191–95. 1937.
2. ——, SMITH, M., AND GARDNER, W. U. Accentuation of the growth effect of theelin on genital tissues by arrest of mitosis with colchicine. Anat. Rec. 67: Suppl. 1:49. 1936. Accentuation of the growth effect of theelin on genital tissues of the ovariectomized mouse by arrest of mitosis with colchicine. Amer. Jour. Anat. 61:321–42. 1937. A short test for ovarian follicular hormone and other estrogens. Endocrinology. 21:412–13. 1937.
3. ——, ——, AND REYNOLDS, S. R. M. Hyperplasia of uterine muscle, as studied by the colchicine method. Proc. Soc. Exp. Biol. and Med. 37:257–59. 1937.
4. ——, THOMAS, T. B., WILSON, J. G., AND HESSION, D. Differential growth in the ovaries and genital tract near the time of ovulation in rats treated with colchicine. Amer. Jour. Anat. 72:291–337. 1943.
5. ASTALDI, G., BERNARDELLI, E., AND REBAUDO, G. Research on the proliferation activity of erythroblasts at low atmospheric pressure. Experientia. 8:117–19. 1952. La prolifération de l'érythroblaste en dépression. Le Sang. 23:293–310. 1952.
6. ——, AND MAURI, C. La valutazione dell'attività proliferativa delle cellule midollari. Studio di un "test statmocinetico." Haematologica. 33:1–46. 1949.
7. ——, AND ——. New criteria for the evaluation of the bone-marrow cells mitotic activity. Le Sang. 21:378–82. 1950.
8. ——, ——, AND DI GUGLIELMO, L. L'effetto dei raghi roentgen sull'attività proliferativa degli eritroblasti studiati nel midollo osseo umano in cultura. Haematologica. 35:867. 1950.
9. BAER, F. Über das Vorkommen von Mitosen im vorder- und zwischenlappen der Hypophyse. Acta Neerl. Morph. 3:97–128. 1939.
10. BAKER, D. D., AND BAILLIF, R. N. Role of capsule in surrenal regeneration studied with aid of colchicine. Proc. Soc. Exp. Biol. and Med. 40:117–21. 1939.

11. BASTENIE, P. Détection de l'hormone thyréotrope dans les urines. Méthode et résultats. Arch. Int. Méd. Exp. 14:111–22. 1939.

12. ——, AND ZYLBERSZAC, C. Mise en évidence des stimulations hormonales par la colchicine. I. Détection de stimulation thyroïdienne par l'extrait anté-hypophysaire. C. R. Soc. Biol. Paris. 126:446. 1937. II. Détection de l'action stimulatrice du propionate de testostérone sur les vésicules séminales. C. R. Soc. Biol. Paris. 126:891. 1937. III. Action de l'extrait anté-hypophysaire sur l'appareil génital du cobaye impubère. C. R. Soc. Biol. Paris. 126:1282. 1937. IV. Doses croissantes de propionate de testostérone sur l'appareil génital du cobaye impubère. C. R. Soc. Biol. Paris. 126:1283. 1937. V. Stimulation de la parathyroïde. C. R. Soc. Biol. Paris. 127:882. 1938. Mise en évidence de stimulations hormonales par la méthode colchicinique de Dustin. Arch. Int. Méd. Exp. 13:183–203. 1938. Influence de la tachystérine irradiée. (AT 10 de Holtz) sur la parathyroïde de la rate. C. R. Soc. Biol. Paris. 132:95–96. 1939.

13. BERNHARD, W. Regenerationshemmung und Auslösung epithelialer Wucherungen durch Colchicin am Schwanz von Rana-Larven. Rev. Suisse Zool. 54:713–57. 1947.

14. BERRIAN, J. H., AND DORNFELD, E. J. Cellular proliferation in the germinal epithelium of immature rat ovaries. An *in vitro* method for the study of mitotic rate. Jour. Exp. Zool. 115:493–512. 1950. The effects of ribonucleotides on mitosis in the germinal epithelium of immature rat ovaries cultured *in vitro*. Jour. Exp. Zool. 115:513–20. 1950.

15. BIMES, C. Mitoses dans le myomètre chez la femelle du cobaye hyperfolliculinisée. C. R. Assoc. Anat. 34:48–55. 1947.

16. BORDONARO, F. La correlazione ipofiso-tiroidea nel ratto a trattamento tiouracilo. Studio citofunzionale a mezzo del metodo colchicinico. Rev. "L'Ospedale Magg." 35 (6) Giugno, 1947.

17. BORGHETTI, U., AND PARINI, F. Fratture sperimentale studiate con l'aiuto de un metodo colchicinico. Med. Sper. Arch. Ital. 8:665–84. 1941.

18. BRETSCHNEIDER, L. H., AND DUYVENE DE WIT, J. J. Histophysiologische Analyse der sexuallendokrinen Organisation des Bitterlingweibchens. (*Rhodeus amarus*). Z. Zellforsch. 31:227–334. 1941.

19. BRUES, A. M. The effect of colchicine on regenerating liver. (Proc. Physiol. Soc.) Jour. Physiol. 86:63–64. 1936.

20. ——, AND COHEN, A. Effects of colchicine and related substances on cell division. Biochem. Jour. 30:1363–68. 1936.

21. ——, AND MARBLE, B. B. An analysis of mitosis in liver restoration. Jour. Exp. Med. 65:15. 1937.

22. ——, AND JACKSON, E. B. Nuclear abnormalities resulting from inhibition of mitosis by colchicine and other substances. Amer. Jour. Cancer. 30:504–11. 1937.

23. BUCHER, O. Zur Wirkung einiger Mitosegifte auf die Gewebekultur. Le Sang. 21:382–89. 1950. Le rôle de la culture des tissus *in vitro* dans l'étude des poisons de la mitose. Mém. Soc. Vaudoise Sci. Nat. 10:245–70. 1951.

24. BULLOUGH, W. S. Mitotic activity in the adult female mouse *Mus musculus* L. A study of its relation to the oestrus cycle in normal and abnormal conditions. Phil. Trans. Roy. Soc. B 231:435. 1946. Epidermal thickness following oestrone injections in the mouse. Nature. 159:101–2. 1947. The action of colchicine in arresting epidermal mitosis. Jour. Exp. Biol. 26:287–91. 1949. The mitogenic actions of starch and oestrone on the epidermis of the adult mouse. Jour. Endocrin. 6:350–61. 1950. Epidermal mitotic activity in the adult female mouse. Jour. Endocrin. 6:340–49. 1950. Stress and epidermal mitotic activity. I. The effects of the adrenal hormones. Jour. Endocrin. 8:265–74. 1952.

25. ——, AND VAN OORDT, J. The mitogenic actions of testosterone propionate and of oestrone on the epidermis of the adult male mouse. Acta Endocrin. Copenhague. 4:291–305. 1950.

26. ——, AND EISA, E. A. The effect of a graded series of restricted diets on epidermal mitotic activity in the mouse. Brit. Jour. Cancer. 4:321–28. 1950.

27. ——, AND JOHNSON, M. Epidermal mitotic activity and oxygen tension. Nature. 167:488. 1951.

28. Bureau, V. L'action de l'oestrone et de la progestérone sur la corne utérine de la lapine, étudiée par la méthode à la colchicine. C. R. Soc. Biol. Paris. 130:933–36. 1939.

29. Burkhart, Z. E. Colchicine reactions in ventral prostate of castrated male rats following androgenic treatment. Proc. Soc. Exp. Biol. 40:137–39. 1939. A study of the effects of androgenic substances in the rat by the aid of colchicine. Doctoral Dissertation. University of Chicago Library. 1940. A study of the early effects of androgenous substances in the rat by the aid of colchicine. Jour. Exp. Zool. 89:135–66. 1942.

30. Burrill, M. W., and Greene, R. R. Androgen production during pregnancy and lactation in the rat. Anat. Rec. 83:209–28. 1942.

31. Carnot, P., and May, R. M. La régénération du rein chez le rat étudiée au moyen de la colchicine. C. R. Soc. Biol. Paris. 128:641–43. 1938.

32. Castelnuovo, G., and Freud, J. Mitogénèse dans l'épithélium vaginal des rats. Arch. Int. Pharm. Ther. 61:491–93. 1939.

33. Cavallero, C. Étude de la cirrhose expérimentale par le tétrachlorure de carbone à l'aide de la réaction stathmocinétique (colchicinique) de Dustin. Arch. Int. Méd. Exp. 14:1–14. 1939. Réactions hormonales au cours de l'intoxication par le tétrachlorure de carbone, poison cirrhogène, mises en évidence par la méthode stathmocinétique (colchicinique) de Dustin. Arch. Int. Méd. Exp. 14:15–22. 1939. Les glandes endocrines au cours de la grossesse. Étude cyto-physiologique faite à l'aide de la réaction colchicinique (stathmocinétique) de Dustin. Arch. Int. Méd. Exp. 14:125–35. 1939. Application de la méthode colchicinque à l'étude du diabète alloxanique chez le rat. Rev. Belge Path. 18:323–32. 1947.

34. ———, and Pellegrini, G. F. L'effetto colchicinico nel "rene endocrino" di Selye. Atti. Soc. Ital. Path. 1:408. 1949.

35. D'Ancona, U. Verifica del poliploidismo delle cellule epatiche dei mammiferi nelle cariocinesi provocate sperimentalmente. Arch. Ital. Anat. Embryol. 47: 253–86. 1942.

36. Delcourt, R. Étude de la régénération des nerfs périphériques par la réaction stathmocinétique. Acta Brev. Neerl. Physiol. 9:241. 1938. Contribution à l'étude de la formation des bandes de Bungner-Ranvier par la réaction stathmocinétique de Dustin. Arch. Int. Méd. Exp. 15:1–13. 1940.

37. Desclin, L. A propos de l'action androgénique de la progestérone. C. R. Soc. Biol. Paris. 132:43–45. 1939. Hypophyse et parathyroïdes. Les parathyroïdes après hypophysectomie chez le rat blanc. Bull. Acad. Roy. Méd. Belg. VIe. Sér. 8:427–38. 1943.

38. Dornfeld, E. J., and Berrian, J. H. Stimulation of mitoses in the germinal epithelium of rat ovaries by intracapsular injections. Anat. Rec. 109:129–38. 1951.

39. Dirschel, W., and Kropp, K. Vitamine und Hormone. 5:280. 1944.

40. ———, Zilliken, F. W., and Kropp, K. Colchicin-Mitosen Test an den Vesiculardrüsen der kastrierte Maus. II. Die Spezifität des Testes. Biochem. Z. 318:454–61. 1948.

41. Dustin, A. P. La colchicine, réactif de l'imminence caryocinétique. Arch. Portugaises Sci. Biol. 5:38–43. 1936. Étude de l'hypertrophie compensatrice du rein par la réaction stathmocinétique. Acta Unio Internat. Cancrum. 4:679–83. 1939. Recherches sur le mode d'action des poisons stathmocinétiques. Action de la colchicine sur l'utérus de lapine impubère sensibilisé par injection préalable d'urine de femme enceinte. Arch. Biol. 54:111–87. 1943.

42. ———, and Chodkowski, K. Étude de la cicatrisation par la réaction colchicinique. Arch. Int. Méd. Exp. 13:641–62. 1938.

43. ———, and Zylberszac, S. Étude de l'hypertrophie compensatrice du rein par la réaction stathmocinétique. Bull. Acad. Méd. Belg. VIe. Sér. 4:315–20. 1939.

44. Fleischmann, W., and Kahn, S. Über das Colchicin als Hilfsmittel beim Studium hormonal bedingter Wachstumsvorgänge. Biochem. Z. 296:374–82. 1938. The use of colchicine in the assay of androgens. Endocrinology. 25: 798–800. 1939.

45. FLEISCHMANN, W., AND BRECKLER, I. A. Mitotic and wound-healing activities of the corneal epithelium in thiouracil treated and thyroidectomized rats. Endocrinology. 41:266–68. 1947.

46. GATZ, A. J. The cellular changes induced in the testes of the albino rat by artificial cryptorchidism aided by the arrest of mitosis with colchicin. Anat. Rec. 70:Suppl. 1:87. 1937.

47. GINESTE, D. J. Recherches sur la régénération des éléments de la glande cortico-surrénale par la méthode colchicinique. Action de divers facteurs. C. R. Soc. Biol. Paris. 140:221–22. 1946.

48. GRANEL, F. La sensibilité de l'époophore à la testostérone. Réaction colchicinique. C. R. Soc. Biol. Paris. 131:1255–56. 1939.

49. GRÉGOIRE, C. Recherches sur les relations entre thymus et surrénales. II. Les réactions des cellules du réticulum épithélial thymique à l'ablation des surrénales. Arch. Int. Pharmacodyn. 67:446–63. 1942. Sur le mécanisme de l'atrophie thymique déclanchée par des hormones sexuelles. Arch. Int. Pharmacodyn. 70:45–77. 1945.

50. GÜTHERT, H. Der Einfluss von Hypophysenvorderlappenextracten und Colchicin auf Kerngrösse und Kernteilung in der Schilddrüse. Virchows Arch. 307:37–70. 1940. Die Einfluss von Hypophysenvorderlappenextracten und Colchicin auf die Langerhanschen Inseln des Pankreas. Virchows Arch. 307: 175–99. 1940.

51. HERLANT, M. Influence du thiouracyl sur l'hypertrophie compensatrice du rein. Bull. Acad. Roy. Belg. Classe. Sci. 5e Sér. 33:567–76. 1947. Activité mitotique des cellules rénales au cours de l'hydronéphrose unilatérale. Bull. Acad. Roy. Méd. Belg. 6e Sér. 13:315–30. 1948. Experimental hydronephrosis studied by the colchicine method. Nature. 162:251–52. 1948.

52. HUNT, T. E. Mitotic activity in the anterior hypophysis of female rats of different age groups and at different periods of the day. Endocrinology. 32:334–39. 1943.

53. JAILER, J. W. Mitotic index of hyperplastic interstitial cells of the guinea-pig. Proc. Soc. Exp. Biol. and Med. 39:281–83. 1938.

54. KERR, T. Mitotic activity in the female mouse pituitary. Jour. Exp. Biol. 20:74–78. 1943.

55. KUZELL, W. C., AND CUTTING, W. C. Pituitary mitotic changes after the administration of oestrogen and after ovariectomy. Endocrinology. 26:537–38. 1940.

56. LAHR, E. L., AND RIDDLE, O. Proliferation of crop-sac epithelium in incubating and in prolactin-injected pigeons studied with the colchicine-method. Amer. Jour. Physiol. 123:614–19. 1938.

57. ―――, ALWELL, L. H., AND RIDDLE, O. Mitosis observed under colchicine in crop-sac tissue after subcutaneous and intramuscular injection of prolactin. Arch. Int. Pharmacodyn. 65:278–82. 1941.

58. LEBLOND, C. P. Action de la prolactine sur le jabot du pigeon mise en évidence par l'arrêt des mitoses à l'aide de la colchicine. C. R. Assoc. des Anat. 32:241–47. 1937.

59. ―――, AND ALLEN, E. Emphasis of the growth effect of prolactin on the crop gland of the pigeon by arrest of mitoses with colchicin. Endocrinology. 21: 455–60. 1937.

60. ―――, AND STEVENS, C. E. The constant renewal of the intestinal epithelium in the albino rat. Anat. Rec. 100:357–78. 1948.

61. LETTRÉ, H. Über Mitosegifte. Ergebn. Physiol. 46:379–452. 1950.

62. LUDFORD, R. J. The action of toxic substances upon the division of normal and malignant cells *in vitro* and *in vivo*. Arch. Exp. Zellforsch. 18:411–41. 1936.

63. LÜSCHER, M. Hemmt oder fördert Colchicin die Zellteilung im regenerierenden Schwanz Xenopus-Larve? Rev. Suisse Zool. 53:481–86. 1946. Die Hemmung den Regeneration durch Colchicin beim Schwanz der Xenopus-Larve und ihre entwicklungsphysiologische Wirkungsanalyse. Helv. Physiol. et Pharm. Acta. 4:465–94. 1946.

64. MALINSKY, J., AND LANG, B. Hyperplasie du foie de rat après hépatectomie partielle et influence des corps colchicinés sur celle-ci. C. R. Soc. Biol. Paris. 145:609–12. 1951.

65. MANUS, M. B. C. Zaadblaastest met behulp van colchicine. Nederl. Tijdschr. Geneesk. 81:4128–29. Samenblasentest mit colchicin. Acta Brev. Neerl. Physiol. 7:175. 1937.

66. McPHAIL, M. K., AND WILBUR, K. M. Absence of potentiation of gonadotropin and steroid function in mammals by colchicine. Endocrinology. 35:196–97. 1944.

67. MORATO-MANARO, J. Accion del acetato de desoxycorticosterone sobre el utero de la coneja infantil estudiato por el método colchicinico. Arch. Soc. Biol. Montevideo. 10:110–14. 1940. Accion de los androgenos sobre la vesicula seminal de la rata, estudiata por el método colchicinico. Arch. Soc. Biol. Montevideo. 10:193–201. 1941.

68. NATHANSON, I. T., BRUES, A. M., AND RAWSON, R. W. Effect of testosterone propionate upon thyroid and parathyroid glands in intact immature female rat. Proc. Soc. Exp. Biol. and Med. 43:737–40. 1940.

69. ———, AND ———. Effect of testosterone propionate upon the mitotic activity of the adrenals in the intact immature female rat. Endocrinology. 29:397–401. 1941.

70. PASCHKIS, K. E., CANTAROW, A., RAKOFF, A. E., AND ROTHENBERG, M. S. Mitosis stimulation in the thyroid gland induced by thiouracil. Endocrinology. 37: 133–35. 1945.

71. POMERAT, G. R. Mitotic activity in the pituitary of the white rat following castration. Amer. Jour. Anat. 69:89–121. 1941.

72. PUNDEL, M. P. Étude des réactions vaginales hormonales chez la femme par la méthode colchicinique. Ann. Endocrin. 2:659–64. 1950.

73. ROGERS, P. V., AND ALLEN, E. Epithelial growth caused by stimulation with various smear methods as demonstrated by mitotic stasis with colchicine. Endocrinology. 21:629–32. 1937.

74. SACCHETI, C., AND BIANCHINI, E. Action directe de la S. T. H. sur les activités de la moëlle osseuse humaine normale. Le Sang. 24:344–54. 1953.

75. SCHEIBLEY, C. H., AND HIGGINS, G. M. Effect of administration of colchicine after partial removal of the liver. Proc. Mayo Clin. 15:536. 1940.

76. SCHMIDT, I. G., AND HOFFMAN, F. G. Proliferation and ovogenesis in the germinal epithelium of the normal mature guinea-pig ovary, as shown by the colchicine technique. Amer. Jour. Anat. 68:263–72. 1941.

77. SCHMIDT, I. G. Mitotic proliferation in the ovary of the normal mature guinea-pig treated with colchicine. Amer. Jour. Anat. 71:245–70. 1942.

78. SENTEIN, P., AND TUCHMANN-DUPLESSIS, H. Mise en évidence de mitoses dans l'hypophyse du cobaye par l'action de la colchicine. Variation de l'activité divisionnelle à l'état normal et après injections d'hormone gonadotrope. Montpellier Méd. 23–24:163–64. 1943. Sur la présence des mitoses colchiciniques dans le cloaque et la prostate du Triton marbré (*Molge marmorata* Latr.) soumis à l'action des hormones sexuelles et hypophysaires. Montpellier Méd. 23–24:240–42. 1943. Sur quelques particularités d'action de la colchicine sur les glandes endocrines du cobaye injecté d'hormone gonadotrope. Montpellier Méd. 29–30:133–35. 1945.

79. SHORR, E., AND COHEN, E. Use of colchicine in detecting hormonal effects on vaginal epithelium of menstruating and castrate women. Proc. Soc. Exp. Biol. and Med. 46:330–35. 1941.

80. STEIN, K. F., AND FOREMAN, D. Effect of thyroid substances in the ovarian capsule upon mitosis in the germinal epithelium. Anat. Rec. 105:643–56. 1949.

81. STEVENS, C. E., DAOUST, R., AND LEBLOND, C. P. Rate of synthesis of desoxyribonucleic acid and mitotic rate in liver and intestine. Jour. Biol. Chem. 202: 177–86. 1953.

82. TAKEWAKI, K. Mitotic activity in seminal vesicle cells transplanted to female mice. Jour. Fac. Sci. Tokyo Univ. 5:291. 1941.

83. TEIR, H. Colchicine-tests for the purpose of ascertaining cell-division regenerative conditions in the liver of the rat. Acat. Path. Microb. Scand. 25:45–51. 1948.

84. TENNANT, R., AND LIEBOW, A. A. The actions of colchicine and ethylcarbylamine on tissue cultures. Yale Jour. Biol. and Med. 13:39–49. 1940.

85. THALES-MARTINS. Test rapido para o hormonio masculino: mitoses na genitalia accessoria. Brasil Med. 51:717–19. 1937. Test rapide de l'hormone masculine: mitoses dans les genitalia accessoires de mâles castrés. C. S. Soc. Biol. Paris. 126:131–34. 1937.
86. THORNTON, C. S. The effect of colchicine on limb regeneration in larval *Amblystoma*. Jour. Exp. Zool. 92:281–93. 1943. Colchicine and limb regeneration in larval *Amblystoma*. Anat. Rec. 84:512. 1942.
87. TISLOWITZ, R. Über die Latenzperiode von Testosterone und Testosterone-propionat. Kongressber. 16. Internat. Physiol. Kongr. 1938. The colchicine test as a method for determining the time of onset and the duration of action of male substances. Endocrinology. 25:749–53. 1939. The action of estrogens in inducing mitoses in the muscle, connective tissue, and epithelium of the prostate and seminal vesicle as determined by the colchicine technique. Anat. Rec. 75:265–74. 1939.
88. TÖRÖ, E., AND VADASZ, J. Untersuchungen über die Wirkung von Colchicin und Corhormon in Gewebekulturen mit Hilfe von Filmaufnahmen. Arch. Exp. Zellforsch. 23:277–98. 1939.
89. UELINGER, E., JADASSOHN, W., AND FIERZ, H. E. Mitoses occurring in the acanthosis produced by hormones. Jour. Invest. Derm. 4:331–35. 1941.
90. VERNE, J., AND VILTER, V. Étude de l'action de la colchicine sur les mitoses des fibroblastes cultivés *in vitro*. Concentrations dites fortes. C. R. Soc. Biol. Paris. 133:618–21. 1940. Mécanisme d'action de la colchicine, employée en concentrations faibles, sur l'évolution de la mitose dans les cultures de fibroblastes *in vitro*. C. R. Soc. Biol. Paris. 133:621–24. 1940.
91. WILLIAMS, W. L., STEIN, K. F., AND ALLEN, E. Reaction of genital tissues of the female mouse to the local application of colchicine. Yale Jour. Biol. and Med. 13:841–46. 1941.
92. WOLF, O. Mitotic activity of stimulated rat adrenals and spleen measured by colchicin technic. Anat. Rec. 70:Suppl. 1:86. 1937. Mitotic activity of the islands of Langerhans and parathyroids of rats following pituitary extract and colchicine injections. Biol. Bull. 75:377–78. 1938.
93. WORTHINGTON, R. V., AND ALLEN, E. Growth of genital tissues in response to estrone as studied by the colchicine technique. Yale Jour. Biol. and Med. 12:137–53. 1939.

CHAPTER 10

Neoplastic Growths

– In Animals and Plants

10.1: Colchicine in Cancer Research

Mitotic changes induced by colchicine in a Crocker sarcoma of the mouse were described by Professor A. P. Dustin, Sr., in 1934[24] (Fig. 10.1). This now recognized classic research marked a new trend in the study of cancer. At that time, the toll of life from bacterial diseases was declining as a result of the use of the sulfa drugs, and the relative incidence of cancer was gaining the impressive figure it has reached today in civilized countries. It is not surprising that the discovery of a specific action upon mitosis, the metaphase arrest, attracted wide attention. This research made clear for the first time the possibility of arresting cell division with chemicals acting specifically. Such a relation had, it is true, been demonstrated several years earlier in the Brussels laboratory,[24, 25] but colchicine, being such a unique chemical, helped greatly in convincing research men of the possibility of cancer chemotherapy. A. P. Dustin, Sr., grasped immediately the potentiality of this new approach.[24] His 1934 publication and the demonstration given by his school at the Second International Cancer Congress, held in Brussels in 1936, marked a turning point and led many people to work on neoplastic growth.

It is quite remarkable that colchicine, like other plant substances used in popular medicine, such as chelidonine,[20] may have been utilized in cancer treatment long before that date. At least two French textbooks of pharmacology[46, 50] mention that Dominici, the great French hematologist and radiotherapist who died in 1919, had observed favorable effects of colchicine in cancerous patients who had received X-ray while under treatment for gout. We have been unable so far to discover the original text of Dominici's observation and his publication. The idea of some interrelation between gout and cancer was mentioned in 1920 in Belgium by A. P. Dustin, Sr.[24] Again,

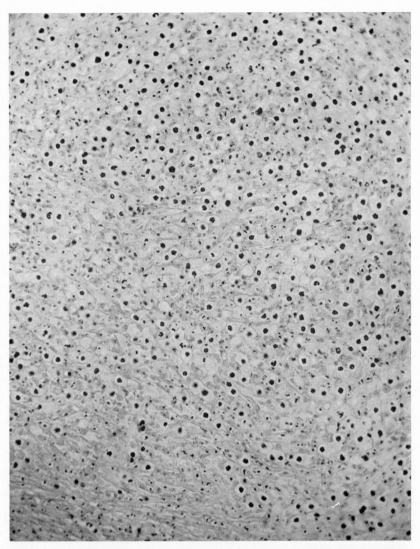

Fig. 10.1—Action of colchicine on the Crocker sarcoma in a mouse. All the nuclei which appear as black dots are in a condition of arrested metaphase of the "ball" type, with clumping and progressive fusion of chromosomes. There is no hemorrhagic effect in this area. Nuclear staining: iron-hematoxylin. (From an original preparation from the collections of the Department of Pathology, Brussels University. A. P. Dustin, 1934[24])

in the first report of favorable effects of colchicine on tumors in mice and in one epithelial cancer in a dog,[1] made in 1935, the author, E. C. Amoroso, did not mention any of the work done in Brussels, but writes:

Following on some earlier observations (unpublished, 1927) which I made with the late Prof. M. R. J. Hayes on the beneficial effects of deep X-ray therapy on neoplasms in patients suffering from acute attacks of gout, which were being treated with colchicum, a series of experiments was . . . planned. *

These results are only known in a preliminary form, and no detailed paper appeared later. They may have influenced one report on favorable results of the treatment by colchicine of a malignant growth in a mare.[76] The first report in English on the action of colchicine on normal and malignant cells in tissue cultures, which was published in 1936,[47] acknowledges these references and claims not to have been influenced by the work done in Brussels.[24, 44] It is, however, surprising that this paper also describes the effects of arsenical derivatives on the spindle, for this was discovered in Belgium in 1929 and had only received scant attention.[60, 25]

Many experiments and also practical applications of colchicine in experimental and human tumors were made; this subject has been reviewed recently.[47] The conclusion was reached that colchicine is no cure for cancer. However, much work is now in progress[10, 22] in the search for chemicals, more or less related to colchicine, with a lower general toxicity and a more specific action against malignant cells. The study of these will be described in the last chapter of this book.

The discovery of colchicine heralded a greater search for mitotic poisons, i.e., substances specifically harmful to dividing cells. This subject has become so extensive that is more and more difficult, even for specialized workers, to review it all.

It has been shown in previous chapters what a unique substance colchicine is as a tool for detecting cellular proliferation. It could be used as such for the study of carcinogenesis, on the one hand, and malignant growth on the other. A surprisingly limited amount of research has been conducted in this direction.[54, 62, 68] However, interesting results have been obtained recently with the use of colchicine *in vitro*. This work demonstrates the quite unexpected fact that, apparently, cells from acute leukemia, a disease in which cellular proliferation was always believed to be extremely rapid, grow much more slowly than the normal constituents of the human bone marrow.[3]

A section related to the problem of plant overgrowths and tumors is included in this chapter because some careful work has been done

---

* E. C. Amoroso, "Colchicine and Tumour Growth," *Nature,* 135 (1935) , p. 266.

in this field. The basic relationship between the action of colchicine and abnormally proliferating plant cells remains unsolved. An induced vascularization similar to that referred to in Chapter 4 may be related to this problem, and would provide a promising new approach.

The combined action of colchicine and X-irradiation on animal and plant materials has been studied in several laboratories. No decisive results appear to have been obtained. However, some recent research indicating the action of irradiation on metaphasic chromosomes, shows that this work is well worth reviewing.

All the studies on neoplastic cells point towards the same inescapable fact: Whereas colchicine, as a treatment for gout, may well have been observed prior to 1934 to have some favorable action against cancer, all the papers which connect both have been published since 1934. This clearly indicates the significance of the cytological work published at that time by A. P. Dustin[24] and demonstrated at the 1936 Cancer Congress.

10.2: Experimental Study of Neoplastic Cells

Malignant cells, especially in animal tumors, often display "spontaneous" mitotic abnormalities. These have been compared to those induced by colchicine, and it has been suggested that the cells were under the influence of some mitotic poison acting like colchicine.[29] It has been suggested that this may be lactic acid.[74] However, these spindle disturbances often appear to be the consequence of more deep-seated nuclear changes, closely related to the cause of malignancy itself, and leading to chromosome breakages and rearrangements. In early human carcinomas, however, it has been pointed out that the spindle changes appeared first.[55] The behavior of such cells when brought under the influence of colchicine is of great importance, for it would be of value to determine whether a specific destruction of malignant cells by a spindle poison is possible.

The effect of colchicine on cancerous growths has been studied either by injecting the animals with the drug, or by explanting the abnormal cells *in vitro* and using the methods of tissue culture. This last procedure has been followed with a mammary carcinoma[73] and a sarcoma[18] of the mouse, and with Ehrlich mouse carcinoma growing as an "ascites tumor" in the abdominal cavity.[40, 63] Concentrations of $100 \times 10^{-6} M$ to $1.25 \times 10^{-6} M$ inhibit outgrowth from the explants and arrest cell divisions. This effect is still evident on carcinoma cells at a concentration of $0.5 \times 10^{-6} M$. In culture containing explants of both tumor and embryonic kidney, the latter showed the greatest cellular destruction following the mitotic arrest. Differences of sensitivity between various strains of carcinomas were found, while the Crocker sarcoma showed fewer arrested metaphases.[47]

The ascites tumor enables colchicine to be brought in direct contact with the malignant cells *in vivo*. The tumor cells float freely in the fluid which gradually fills the abdominal cavity. It is possible, simply by pipetting cells from the abdomen, to examine all the changes brought about by the injection of colchicine.[11, 40, 63] Growth curves of the tumor indicate that on the average each cell divides every 2 to 2½ days. After an injection of colchicine, the percentage of mitotic cells rises in 9½ hours from 1.2 to 14.2. Thirteen hours after injection, it reaches 18.2, and falls to 2.0 after 48 hours. From these figures, the normal average duration of mitosis can be calculated as follows: $1.2 \times 9.5/14.2 \cong 1.2 \times 13/18.2 \cong 0.8$ hours, or 48 minutes.

Scattered groups of chromosomes and micronuclei are observed in the colchicine-treated tumor cells.[11, 37] Resting (intermitotic) nuclei are also affected; their chromatin network becomes coarser.[11] In sarcoma-bearing mice, a series of experiments was carried out to determine whether administration of colchicine had any effect upon subsequent growth of the tumor cultivated *in vitro*.[18] Colchicine (0.004 to 0.06 mg.) was administered by subcutaneous or intravenous injection, and fragments of sarcoma were removed for cultivation at various intervals after treatment. The growth of tumor tissue *in vitro*, obtained from an animal treated with colchicine, was inhibited to a large extent. Colchicine arrested mitoses, both normal and neoplastic.

In human malignant growth, colchicine has been found useful for the study of cellular multiplication. In 11 patients injected with 1.5 to 4 mg. subcutaneously or intramuscularly, modification of tumor mitoses were observed.[53] Four other patients did not show any response, a fact which is not surprising, the dose being kept relatively small by comparison with doses administered in animal work, because of the great toxicity of colchicine in man. In one case of adenocarcinoma of the bowel, the progressive increase of the mitotic index could be followed by repeated biopsies. The control specimens had an index of 2.6, which rose to 7.3 five hours after colchicine and reached 19.6 after 12 hours. This last biopsy demonstrated a considerable increase of arrested mitoses. It is regrettable that, owing partly to the too great danger of colchicine poisoning (cf. Chapter 7), no further research of this type has been conducted. Now that new and less toxic colchicine derivatives are available[10] (Chapter 17), a more thorough study of the rate of growth of human neoplasms may be possible. This could then be compared with data on normal tissues obtained by the same method.

Colchicine may yet be used on explanted human tissues, and it is surprising that only two papers on that subject can be recorded up to now. In polycythemia vera, a disease in which the abnormal number of red blood cells has often been considered closely related to malignant growth, and which may end in leukemia, the increase of metaphases of bone-marrow cells explanted *in vitro* in a solution of colchicine was found not to differ from normal.[5] The striking results obtained with marrow of patients with acute leukemia have been mentioned in Section 10.1.[3]

10.3: Cancer Chemotherapy

It is evident that the data on the growth of neoplastic cells treated with colchicine are meagre. Workers were quickly attracted by the false idea of finding a cancer cure, and they injected colchicine into animals bearing various tumors. Botanists, also, painted plant tumors with colchicine. Neither were much interested in the fundamental changes taking place. As a result, the cytological data are often incomplete and only mention "cellular destruction," "nuclear fragmentation," or "tumor necrosis and hemorrhage." This emphasis on the gross changes in animal tumors has led to a neglect of the fundamental problem which is at the base of any cancer chemotherapy: Are malignant cells more severely damaged than normal ones? This is of great importance with a chemical like colchicine which affects all types of mitoses. The appearance of large zones of hemorrhage in tumors treated with colchicine has led some workers[9, 47, 70] to the conclusion that this is the main action of the drug and the only possibility of obtaining a destruction of the neoplastic growth. This problem will be discussed first, though it is quite evident to all engaged in cancer chemotherapy that a drug the main action of which would be hemorrhagic destruction, is of no use in medicine.

10.3–1: The hemorrhagic effect and metabolic changes. Many reports on experimental tumors in mammals, whether induced by carcinogens or grafted, showed that colchicine was unable to prevent the neoplastic growth.[62, 66, 18, 65] In the sarcoma 180 of the rat even the largest tolerated doses were unable to arrest all mitoses at metaphase.[14] From the unaffected ana- and telophases the malignant growth resumed its activity once colchicine was discontinued.

On the other hand, the metabolic changes in tumors treated by colchicine were being investigated. In grafted tumors in rats the metabolism, measured *in vitro*, was found to decrease. At the same time, the ascorbic acid content of the tumors was considerably lowered, and large zones of hemorrhage were seen.[9] This last change was believed to play a great part in the regression of the tumors. Similar changes could be observed after the injection of *Bacillus typhosus* extracts. It was not reported that these bacterial products induced any nuclear or mitotic change.[9] Similar hemorrhages were also noticed in other grafted carcinomas, in spontaneous mammary tumors, and in methylcholanthrene-induced tumors of mice. They were most apparent 18 to 20 hours after colchicine. The spontaneous tumors appeared the most resistant towards this new "colchicine-effect." A parallel decrease in ascorbic acid content, respiration, and glycolysis was observed.[9]

The significance of these hemorrhages, which appear only with sublethal doses,[2] is not clear. It has been suggested that mitotic poisoning of the endothelial cells of the tumor capillary bed (cf. Chapter 9) may play an important part.[47] *Escherichia coli* filtrates have similar hemorrhagic properties, and add their effect to those of colchicine, but the over-all toxicity is also increased. The polysaccharide extracted from *Serratia marcescens* is interesting, for it also produces hemorrhages in tumors and has been shown to interfere with cell division.[70]

Tumors treated with colchicine become quite fragile. In the Flexner-Jobling carcinoma of rats the injection of distilled water in the tumor has a destructive action 15 hours after colchicine. These experiments, which were done on a great number of animals, have been reported only in a short note.[30]

In a recent review,[47] the effects of colchicine on 17 different strains of tumors and 49 spontaneous mammary carcinomas in mice have been summarized. While the effects vary according to age, genetic constitution, rate of tumor growth, toxicity of colchicine, and histological structure, the hemorrhagic effect was considered to be the main factor in tumor regression. In highly cellular and soft tumors growing on RIII mice, complete cures were reported. Regression is obtained only by doses very close to the lethal one and far above those that simply arrest mitosis. Soft and rapidly growing tumors respond well, while slowly growing and fibrous tumors are resistant.

This conclusion applies only to the experience of one group of authors, and instances can be found of malignant growths which respond to colchicine without any hemorrhage. Such is the case of a benzopyrene-induced sarcoma (HL tumor) in albino rats.[7] The regression appeared here to bear some relation to a decrease in the pyrophosphatase of the neoplasm, while liver and kidney pyrophosphatase were not affected.

Further examples will be given of favorable effects unrelated to hemorrhage, which is clearly related to very toxic doses and is of no practical interest in chemotherapy. The hemorrhagic effect is one more of the riddles of colchicine, but to insist too much on it as the main mode of action of the drug on tumors is to discourage any further work on nontoxic derivatives with mitosis-arresting properties.

10.3–2: Animal tumors. One of the most striking effects of colchicine noticed in the first experiments on animals[44] was the destruction of lymphoid and thymic cells following the metaphase arrest of their mitoses. This action is certainly related to the general toxicity of colchicine and to a "stress" releasing cortisone and other lymphocyte-damaging hormones from the adrenals (Chapter 7). It led to the idea of treating lymphoid tumors in C3H strain mice with colchicine.[45] The malignant lymphocytes, like those of thymus and spleen, underwent a pycnotic destruction after injections of 0.025 mg. repeated every third day. The average duration of life of the animals after the tumors had been grafted was significantly prolonged. In controls it was 31.5 days; in those injected with colchicine, 50.5 days. Histological study showed that the reticulum cells and some of the neoplastic lymphocytes escaped destruction, and resumed growth when the injections were interrupted. In another series of experiments[4] a permanent regression of the 6C3HED lymphosarcoma (in C3H mice) was obtained by daily injections of 0.5 to 0.75 mg/kg after the tumor had reached a diameter of about 1 cm. The animals cured from the grafted neoplasm became immune to further graftings of the same tumor. No similar effects were observed after cortisone. This appears to rule out the possibility of colchicine acting on tumor growth by the indirect pathway of the pituitary-adrenal system. In these lymphoid tumors, colchicine destroyed the cells and their mitoses, and no mention is made of hemorrhage playing any part in the chemotherapeutic action.[45, 4]

In epithelial tumors the results vary considerably. For instance, the Brown-Pearce carcinoma of the rabbit showed some increase in the percentage of metaphases after 1 mg/kg of colchicine. The response was, however, so unpredictable as not to warrant further study.[23] Some authors have reported an important prolongation of life in mice bearing the Ehrlich carcinoma,[40] while in various other tumors of mice and rats no such prolongation could be claimed.[52, 61, 66]

Studies on virus-induced malignant growths in fowl are of interest. In animals grafted with the Rous sarcoma, doses capable of arresting the testicular mitoses did not modify the tumor growth. Larger doses killed the birds.[16] In avian erythroblastosis, a dose of 1 mg/kg injected over a period of five days did not alter the evolution of the malignant growth of blood cells.[62] Some inhibition of the growth of the Rous virus has, however, been observed,[21] especially when this is cultivated on the chorio-allantoic membrane of eggs.

It appears that considerable variations in sensitivity towards colchicine exist from one tumor to another,[41, 48] and that the toxicity of the drug has often limited its use. Further work should clearly be aimed at many different tumors and at the use of the new colchicine derivatives, which are discussed in Chapter 17.

10.3–3: The Shope papilloma in rabbits. This is a virus-induced tumor, which is very widespread in this species. A closely related virus, myxomatosis, has even been advocated as a tool for the extermination of rabbits in Australia and other countries. This tumor is benignant, but under the influence of carcinogens it may become malignant. A series of papers has been devoted to its possible cure by colchicine.[57, 58, 59] This may be obtained after injections of colchicine in the animal.[57] While one is always limited by the toxicity reactions, it was found that the local application of a colchicine ointment to the skin tumors could definitly cure a great number of animals. A remarkable and rather perturbing fact was noticed.[59] If both ears of a rabbit are inoculated with the Shope virus, and a cure is obtained on one side with the colchicine ointment, the tumors of the other ear become more liable to undergo a malignant change înto carcinomas. The conclusions of these papers are most important for they opened a new pathway for the use of colchicine in human pathology.[59] To quote: ". . . these experimental data suggest the possibility of using colchicine in human therapeutics . . . by local applications, to precancerous lesions or benignant skin tumors." * The results obtained in tumor-bearing patients will now be discussed.

10.4: Chemotherapy of Human Neoplasms

The suggestion of a local application of colchicine, enabling a strong concentration to act upon abnormal cells without general toxicity symptoms, was taken up in 1941. Colchicine, either in a paste or an injection as an oily solution, was applied to metastatic nodules of epithelial cancers.[67] The volume of the treated metastases clearly decreased.

However, it appeared more logical to begin with benign growths of the skin. Some of these, such as the venereal papillomas or warts, may be very extensive, and their treatment by usual methods involves large surgical excisions. These are virus-induced growths, comparable to the papillomas of the rabbit. A colchicine-lanoline paste (0.05 per cent) was applied twice daily to six of such cases.[11] Remarkable regressions were observed after several weeks of treatment. The tumor became more and more resistant to colchicine, and in the last stages, had to be removed surgically. This was facilitated considerably by the regression of the size and extension of the tumor. Colchicine-mitoses can be found in great numbers in biopsies of treated papillomas.[8] It is quite evident that the regression of the neoplastic growth is a simple consequence of the arrest of its cell divisions. No hemorrhage is to be seen. It appears also that the mitoses of normal skin are less modified by the treatment, for there is no skin ulceration, and after the tumor has disappeared, the skin has a normal aspect.[11, 8]

---

* A. Peyron, G. Poumeau-Delille, and B. LaFay. La tumeur de Shope du lapin et sa sterilisation par la colchicine. Bull. Assoc. Franc. Étude Cancer 26:633. 1937.

Colchicine has now been replaced in the treatment of such warts and papillomas by another substance of plant origin, podophyllin, a resin extracted from *Podophyllum* sp.[36] This substance is a complex mixture of chemicals, the most active being podophyllotoxin and the peltatins. These are, quite like colchicine, mitotic poisons, and they interfere mainly with the spindle formation.[36] The use of the resin of podophyll was known in the United States as a popular medical remedy; it is remarkable that another plant, known in Europe to have good effect on warts, *Chelidonium majus,* contains an alkaloid, chelidonine, which has also been demonstrated to inhibit spindle formation in tissue cultures.[40] Chelidonine was advocated for the treatment of cancer at the end of the nineteenth century.[20]

These empirical remedies, probably centuries old, are most interesting, and it may be recalled that Dioscorides recommended the use of *Ephemeron,* a species containing colchicine, in the treatment of some tumors. Colchicine-paste has also proved to be successful in the treatment of some skin cancers of the basal-cell type.[11, 17] In ulcerating mammary tumors, interesting results have been obtained. A striking fact is that here again the growth of normal skin appears to be less altered than that of the neoplasm.[11]

In human malignant tumors, the effect of colchicine has so far proved quite disappointing, and from the reports available, it is difficult to understand how it could have been observed to be of any benefit to cancerous patients.[1] It may arrest tumor mitoses in man,[53] but this effect is never powerful enough to stop the malignant growth. The toxicity of colchicine is redoubtable. Even in a series of four patients, where some favorable effects were noticed, one case of severe leukopenia was noted, and another patient lost almost all his hair.[65] In another series, two out of three patients died of agranulocytosis, which was probably the consequence of mitotic inhibition in the bone marrow.[12]

In severe neoplastic blood diseases, colchicine has also been tried by a few investigators. In lymphoid tumors the results were of no practical interest,[39] and intramedullary injections did not change the fatal course of acute leukemia.[28] In chronic myeloid leukemia, a disease which is known to respond favorably to many mitotic poisons, more promising results have been recorded. In one patient, who received 0.5 mg. of colchicine three times and later twice daily, the leukocyte count was found to fall from 110,000 to 2400. This improvement was only of short duration.[38, 56]

These data, which are very sketchy, may seem to rule out colchicine for the treatment of cancer in man. However, recent developments are more promising, though still in an experimental stage. In Hodgkin's disease, a neoplastic condition affecting mainly the lymphoid tissue, excellent effects have been described. Colchicine administered intravenously produced a sharp fall in temperature, which in these patients is often very high.[35] Substances chemically close to colchicine but less toxic are being tested; "methyl-colchicine" has quite recently proved to be of value in the management of cases of chronic myeloid leukemia.[51] It is quite evident that it is too early to draw a conclusion about the future of colchicine in cancer therapy, and that far more work remains to be done.

10.5: A Tool for the Study of Cancer Chemotherapy

The mitotic stasis resulting from spindle destruction can make visible small changes in the mitotic rate which would pass unnoticed in microscopic sections (cf. Chapter 9). Some promising work has been initiated in this field. Urethane, at a dose of 0.5 gm/day, has been demonstrated not to modify the number of mitoses, studied with the colchicine method, in the Walker rat carcinoma 256.[27] Azaguanine,[69, 77] on the other hand, has been proved to be one of the most remarkable chemotherapeutic substances. This antagonist of guanine and adenine can be demonstrated not to affect normal mitoses, while strongly decreasing those of the Brown-Pearce carcinoma. This tumor was studied while grafted in the anterior chamber of the guinea pig's eye.[69] This type of mitotic depression is made more evident by the use of colchicine.

Another type of experiment was planned for the study of an antifolic drug, aminopterine. This substance is widely used in the treatment of acute leukemia. When large doses are injected into mice, the cell divisions in the intestine do not take place any more for about 48 hours. During this period of mitotic inhibition, cellular and nuclear growth are not impaired, and very large nuclei are formed. When these divide again, the mitoses are of exceptional size. Colchicine was used as a tool to arrest these mitoses and to provide a greater number for study, as a consequence of the mitotic stasis. Also, the shortening of the chromosomes made their counting easier, and ball metaphases provided excellent material for photometric measurements. These experiments indicated that the increase in nuclear size was neither the result of polyploidy nor of polyteny.[26]

10.6: Plant Tumors

Whatever may be the exact relation between tumors in animals — and, in particular, cancerous growths — and the various types of gall formations induced in plants by *Bacillus tumefaciens*, insects, etc., it is interesting to compare the effects obtained with colchicine with those described for animal neoplasms. In a series of experiments on *Lycopersicum esculentum* inoculated with *B. tumefaciens*, a 1:10,000 solution of colchicine, locally applied, decreased the number and the volume of the induced tumors without disturbing the growth of the plant itself.[31] An extensive series of experiments was started shortly after on seven species.[19] By injecting colchicine in plants at the time of infection by *B. tumefaciens,* tumor growth was only prevented in 9 out of 61 plants. On the contrary, to arrest the growth of tumors and to destroy them later were possible in most cases by several techniques of application of the alkaloid. In *Tagetes patula,* these tumors, after daily paintings with a 1 per cent colchicine solution, stop growing after 7 days and then progressively decrease and die. The principal microscopic effect is a great enlargement of the tumor cells, four or five of the colchicinized ones occupying the area of 30 normal ones. This enlargement is the most visible with rather concentrated solutions of colchicine (up to 0.1 per cent). The smallest cells are 64-ploid (1536 chromosomes), the larger 1014-ploid (24,500 chromosomes). Some nuclei have irregular shapes and some cells are multinucleated. Cellular death is a direct consequence of the extreme degree of polyploidy which is reached, the giant cells becoming at some stage quite unable to divide any further. There is no effect on the bacterial growth.[19] Similar results have been obtained in *Pelargonium* and *Ricinus.*[72] It was supposed that the death of the tumor was the consequence of its isolation by a layer of cork.[72]

Though animal cells, through failure of centromere division, cannot usually go through repeated colchicine mitoses, it is thought-provoking, however, to compare these effects with those of X-rays in animal tumors. Cellular proliferation after X-ray therapy is also stopped when cells become gigantic and highly polyploid through repeated abnormal mitoses.

10.7: Colchicine and X-rays Associated

When the first work on colchicine and tumors was done in 1934, ionizing radiations were supposed to have the most harmful effects on mitotic chromosomes, and it was expected that accumulating such a great number of divisions, as seen in sarcomas for instance, would increase the radiosensitivity of the tumors (Fig. 10.1). Most recent work, however, shows that the sensitive period of the mitotic cycle is before prophase, and thus, accumulating metaphases could not be expected to increase radiosensitivity since the rate of prophases is not disturbed.[64] This is confirmed by most work on colchicine and tumors, whether in animals or in plants.

10.7–1: Animal tumors. X-rays were observed to be considerably more efficient in killing *in vitro* tumor cells when these had been previously treated by colchicine (Flexner-Jobling grafted carcinoma of the rat).[30] Here the test used was the grafting of fragments of tumor, the number of "takes" being decreased. Colchicine (1 mg/kg) administered 15 hours before irradiation (188 r. twice weekly) increased also the effects of X-rays as measured by the size of tumors in surviving animals. No similar increase in mice and rats, even with large doses of colchicine, was found.[12] In the Yale carcinoma of the mouse, 2 mg/kg produced extensive necrosis and hemorrhage, but a border of viable tissue was always seen to persist.[14] The addition of 2500 r. produced only a slightly higher rate of curability "not significant to warrant further investigation." [32] In the Ehrlich carcinoma, colchicine was injected every day (5 mg.) and 260 to 300 r. delivered.[11] Some results seemed to indicate an improvement of the colchicine action by X-rays, which alone are not effective. However, if the dose of irradiation was increased, the life span of the colchicinized mice became shorter than the nontreated controls. From Table 9.2, it is clear that no significant improvement is obtained by combining the two treatments. It must, however, be pointed out that this is a radio-resistant tumor, not well suited for such studies.

One paper mentions that in a case of gastric carcinoma, two metastases were irradiated with the same dose of X-rays, while one was injected with colchicine; the post-mortem disclosed that the latter was severely necrotic, a fact which is not surprising in view of a large local injection of colchicine and which does not demonstrate a true synergism between the two agents.[13]

The action of colchicine on human tumors has been followed by multiple biopsies.[43] The patients were injected intramuscularly with 2 mg. of colchicine. An increase of the metaphase percentage was noted, as well as some hemorrhage and cells with highly polyploid nuclei. These data, which are supposed to open the way towards a treatment with colchicine and X-ray combined, were not examined critically, and the variations observed may be entirely fortuitous.

A series of clinical reports have been published[33, 49, 43] about colchicine increasing the effectiveness of X-rays, but these results are not statistically valid and cannot be accepted without further research. Colchicine was used for some time as a routine in irradiated cancerous patients at the Cancer Hospital, Brussels, with no convincing results (unpublished).

10.7–2: Plant overgrowths. In plants, experimental work[75] brings some significant detailed cytological data on the action of irradiation on mitoses previously arrested by colchicine, which appear to be abnormally fragile. Root tips of *Pisum sativum* and *Allium cepa* were dipped into a 1:2000 solution of the alkaloid, and irradiated (3500 r. in one minute) at various intervals later. Prophases were observed to be quite resistant, but the c-metaphases were very rapidly modified, the chromosomes clumping together and later undergoing katachromatic changes into apparently normal restitution nuclei (6 hours after irradiation). The nuclear membrane may give some protection to the prophasic chromosomes.

The results of these changes on the growth of the root tips and of the leaves of bulbs of *Allium cepa* have been studied.[42] Exposure to 0.01 per cent solutions of colchicine induces the well-known root tip swelling, the so-called c-tumors, and when the plants are replaced in water, growth is resumed. If the root tips are irradiated with 900 or 1500 r. after 48 hours of colchicine, growth is arrested and leaf development is strongly impaired. These effects are greater than those obtained by irradiation alone. The action of X-rays appears to be independent of the nuclear division stage. After 48 hours of colchicine, "some non-recognizable toxic effects in the cell . . . sensitize it to irradiation." * The same author has published detailed results of investigations on the combined action of colchicine and X-irradiation on onion root tips.[43] It appears evident that the two actions add their effects, but the mechanism is not clear, and does not seem to be related to an increase of mitotic cells at the time of irradiation. For instance, the 48-hour colchicine bulbs are more vulnerable to X-treatment, "even though the time of exposure occurred when the number of dividing cells had passed the peak of metaphase arrest."† Irradiation by 900 r., which has only a temporary retarding effect on growth, inhibits completely cellular multiplication and growth without any immediate death of the tissues when the roots have been previously treated for 48 hours with a 0.01 per cent solution of colchicine. A long exposure to the alkaloid seems necessary, for, "while colchicine causes analogous cytological changes at 6, 12, 18, 24 and 48 hours, the larger exposures induce some microscopically unrecognizable alterations. This . . . arrests growth permanently and completely [with 1500 r.]"‡ The optimum growth-inhibition effects were observed after 1500 r. and a more than 36 hours' exposure to colchicine.

On the other hand, onion bulbs treated for 45 minutes in a 0.05 per cent solution of colchicine, then irradiated with 300 r. and replaced in the solution, showed less chromosome rearrangements than controls, while the number of breakages was not appreciably altered. It is supposed that the short colchicine treatment could not have increased the metaphases, but impairment of the spindle function may slow the movements of chromosomes. This would leave less opportunity for the broken ends to reunite into abnormal structures.[15]

---

* M. Levine, "The Action of Colchicine on Cell Division in Human Cancer, Animal and Plant Tissues." *Ann. N. Y. Acad. Sci.*, 51 (1951), p. 1400.
† *Ibid.*, p. 1397.
‡ *Ibid.*, p. 1399.

It is evident that work in this field is particularly difficult, because the interpretation of the results depends on the action of two agents, each having a complex nature. It has recently been shown that metaphase chromosomes could be singled out and destroyed in a beam of neutrons.[78] Modern cytological and radiobiological methods should enable similar experiments to be performed with arrested metaphases. The exploded type would be an excellent test object for a study of the action of irradiation on isolated chromosomes.

10.8: The Study of Carcinogenesis

Chapter 9 has shown how useful colchicine could be in the analysis of growth. It is regrettable that more studies have not been done on the first stages of malignant change under the effect of various carcinogens. For instance, the action of azo-dyes on the liver, and the various factors which are known to influence the origin of liver carcinomas have never been subjected to the colchicine method. From the few instances which will be quoted here, there is little doubt that the early changes in mitotic activity in the liver would be fascinating to study with the colchicine tool.

In one of the first modern papers on colchicine, this was described as a tool for the detection of the increased mitotic rate in the skin of animals painted with the methylcholanthrene.[24] Shortly after, in the 39th Annual Report of the Imperial Cancer Research Fund, similar findings were described in mice painted with benzopyrene. This British work does not appear to have ever been published *in extenso*. These early results, demonstrating for the first time that mitotic activity is increased shortly after the application of carcinogens, is in agreement with later findings.[6] These confirm the idea that some subtle cellular change takes place soon after the first painting with a carcinogen even when no malignant growth will develop for several weeks. Colchicine could evidently be used for studying all the intermediate stages between benignancy and cancerous growth.

Another observation published in 1934 is remarkable.[24] In methylcholanthrene-treated mice a great increase in the numbers of mitoses, as detected by colchicine, was found in the thyroid, in the salivary glands, and in histiocytes. The meaning of this remains unknown.

A single paper gives a detailed cytological study of the hair follicles of mice,[54] in normal skin, in embryos, and in skin painted with methylcholanthrene. Ultracentrifugation studies were carried out to study the cellular viscosity. This was not found to be modified, even in arrested mitoses.

There is also a possibility that colchicine may act as an anticarcinogen. In mice implanted with methylcholanthrene and injected with colchicine, no skin tumors appeared.[62] This result is contradicted by experiments demonstrating that methylcholanthrene tumors appeared in 30 days in mice injected with colchicine.[68] The time for the controls was 100 days. There is no evidence from the data of the literature that colchicine may be itself a carcinogen.

REFERENCES

1. AMOROSO, E. C. Colchicine and tumour growth. Nature. 135:266–67. 1935.
2. ANDERVONT, H. B. Effect of colchicine and bacterial products on transplantable and spontaneous tumors in mice. Jour. Nat. Cancer Inst. 1:361–63. 1940.
3. ASTALDI, G., AND MAURI, C. Recherche sur l'activité proliférative de l'hémocytoblaste de la leucémie aiguë. Rev. Belge Path. 23:69–82. 1953.
4. BASS, A. D., AND PROBERT, C. Response of a transplantable lymphosarcoma to colchicine. Cancer Res. 10:420–22. 1950.
5. BERNARDELLI, E., RONDANELLI, E. G., AND GORINI, P. Ricerca sull'attività proliferativa e differenziativa dell'eritroblasto della policitemia vera. Haematologica. 36:891–906. 1952.
6. BERNELLI-ZAZZERA, A. Contributo alla conoscenza dei fattori co-cancerogeni e del loro mecanism d'azione sulla cute del topo. Tumori. 38:339–50. 1952.
7. BLOCH-FRANKENTHAL, L., AND BLACK, A. Effect of colchicine on tumor growth and tumor pyrophosphatase. Proc. Soc. Exp. Biol. and Med. 76:105–9. 1951.
8. BOURG, R., AND DUSTIN, P., JR. Le traitement des papillomes vulvaires par l'application locale de colchicine. Presse Méd. 43:578. 1945.
9. BOYLAND, E., AND BOYLAND, M. E. Studies on tissue metabolism. IX. The action of colchicine and *B. typhosus* extract. Biochem. Jour. 31:454–60. 1937. Studies on tissue metabolism. XII. The action of colchicine on transplanted, induced and spontaneous mouse tumors. Biochem. Jour. 34:280–84. 1940.
10. BRANCH, C. F., FOGG, L. C., AND ULLYOTT, G. E. Colchicine and colchicine-like compounds as chemotherapeutic agents. Acta Unio Internat. Cancrum. 6: 439–47. 1949.
11. BRODERSEN, H. Mitosegifte und ionisierende Strahlung. Strahlenther. 73: 196–254. 1943.
12. BROWN, W. O. Effect of colchicine on human tissues. Arch. Path. 29:865–66. 1940.
13. BRÜCKE, E. T. V., AND HÜBER, E. V. Über die erfolgreiche Behandlung einer Krebsmetastase mit Colchicin und Röntgenbestrahlung. Klin. Wschr. 18: 1160–61. 1939.
14. BRUES, A. M., MARBLE, B. B., AND JACKSON, E. B. Effects of colchicine on growth of normal tissues and tumors. Amer. Jour. Cancer. 38:159–68. 1940.
15. BRUMFIELD, R. T. Effect of colchicine pre-treatment on the frequency of chromosomal aberrations induced by X-radiation. Proc. Nat. Acad. Sci. 29: 190–93. 1943.
16. CARR, J. G. The effect of some substances influencing cell activity upon the growth of the Rous n° 1 sarcoma. Brit. Jour. Exp. Path. 23:221–28. 1942.
17. CHEVALLIER, P., AND COLIN, M. Vaste epithelioma basocellulaire traité localement par la colchicine. Ann. Soc. Franç. Dermat. Syph. 6:297–98. 1946.
18. CLEARKIN, P. A. The effect of colchicine on normal and neoplastic tissues in mice. Jour. Path. Bact. 44:469. 1937.
19. DERMEN, H., AND BROWN, N. A. A cytological study of the effect of colchicine on plant tumors. Amer. Jour. Cancer. 38:169–90. 1940.
20. DENISSENKO, P. Traitement de la carcinose par l'usage interne et les applications locales d'extrait de chélidoine. Semaine Méd. (quoted in Ménétrier, *see* Ref. 50.) 1896.
21. DICKINSON, L., AND THOMPSON, M. J. Chemotherapeutic investigations with Rous sarcoma virus. Brit. Jour. Pharmacol. 7:277–86. 1952.
22. DOWNING, V., HARTWELL, J. L., LEITER, J., AND SHEAR, M. J. Effect of a single injection of colchicine, colchicine derivatives and related compounds on mouse tumors. Cancer. Res. 9:598. 1949.

23. Du Bilier, B., and Warren, S. L. The effect of colchicine on the mitotic activity of the Brown-Pearce rabbit epithelioma. Cancer Res. 1:966–69. 1941.

24. Dustin, A. P. Recherches d'histologie normale et expérimentale sur le thymus des amphibiens anoures. Arch. Biol. 30:601–83. 1920. Contribution à l'étude de l'action des poisons caryoclasiques sur les tumeurs animales. II. Action de la colchicine sur le sarcome greffé, type Crocker, de la souris. Bull. Acad. Roy. Méd. Belg. 14:487–502. 1934. L'action de la colchicine sur les tumeurs malignes. Leeuwenhoeck Ver. 55e Conf. Colchicine et cancer. Gaz. Hôp. Paris. 41:10 pp. 1938.

25. ————, and Grégoire, C. Contribution à l'étude des poisons caryoclasiques sur les tumeurs animales. I. Action du cacodylate de Na et de la trypaflavine sur le sarcome greffé, type Crocker, de la souris. Bull. Acad. Roy. Méd. Belg. 13:585–92. 1933.

26. Grampa, G., and Dustin, P., Jr. Analyse, par la colchicine, des effets radiomimétiques de l'acide 4-amino-pteroylglutamique (aminoptérine). Rev. Belge Path. 22:115–25. 1952. Impiego associato di aminopterina e colchicina e anomalie nucleari: ricerche sperimentali sull'intestino del topo. Tumori. 39:63–71. 1953.

27. Green, W. J., Jr., and Lushbaugh, C. C. Histopathologic study of the mode of inhibition of cellular proliferation by urethane. Effect of urethane on Walker rat carcinoma 256. Cancer Res. 9:199–209. 1949.

28. Guichard, A., Brette, R., and Philippe, L. P. Essai de traitement de deux cas de leucémie aiguë par la colchicine intramédullaire. Le Sang. 17:247–49. 1946.

29. Garrigues, R. Sur certaines anomalies de la mitose observées dans du cancer humain. C. R. Acad. Sci. Paris. 216:822–24. 1943.

30. Guyer, M. F., and Claus, P. E. Irradiation of cancer following colchicine. Proc. Soc. Exp. Biol. and Med. 42:565–68. 1939. Destructive effects on carcinoma of colchicine followed by distilled water. Proc. Soc. Exp. Biol. and Med. 43:272–74. 1940.

31. Havas, L. J. L'action de la colchicine sur le développement du "phytocarcinome" de la tomate. Bull. Assoc. Franç. Cancer. 26:635–62. 1937. Colchicine, "phytocarcinomata" and plant hormones. Nature. 140:191–92. 1937.

32. Hirschfeld, J. W., Tennant, R., and Oughterson, A. W. The effect of colchicine and X-ray on transplantable mammary carcinoma in mice. Yale Jour. Biol. and Med. 13:51–59. 1940.

33. Huant, E. Action de la colchicine sur la radiosensibilité des tumeurs malignes. Gaz. Hôp. Paris. 15. 1944. Nouvelles considérations quant à l'action de la colchicine sur la radiosensibilité des tumeurs. Gaz. Hôp. Paris. 15:230. 1944.

34. ————. Action de la colchicine associée à la radiothérapie dans le traitement des tumeurs malignes. Acta Unio Internat. Cancrum. 9:83–93. 1953.

35. Isch-Wall, P. Quatre cas de maladie de Hodgkin traités par la colchicine. Le Sang. 23:689–93. 1952.

36. King, L. S., and Sullivan, M. Effects of podophyllin and colchicine on normal skin, on condyloma acuminatum and on verruca vulgaris. Arch. Path. 43:374–86. 1947.

37. Klein, G., E., and E. The viability and the average desoxypentose-nucleic acid content of micronuclei-containing cells produced by colchicine treatment in the Ehrlich ascites tumor. Cancer Res. 12:484–89. 1952.

38. Kneedler, W. H. Colchicine in acute myelogenous leukemia. Jour. Amer. Med. Assoc. 129:272–73. 1945.

39. Lenegre, J., and Soulier, J. P. De l'action de la colchicine sur certaines tumeurs ganglionnaires. Bull. Mém. Soc. Méd. Hôp. Paris. 58:402–4. 1942.

40. Lettré, H. Einige Beobachtungen über das Wachstum des Mäuse-Ascites-Tumors und seine Beeinflussung. Hoppe-Seyl. Z. 268:59–75. 1941. Ergebnisse und Probleme der Mitosegiftforschung. Naturwiss. 3:75–86. 1946. Über Mitosegifte. Ergebn. Physiol. 46:379–452. 1950.

41. ————, and Kramer, W. Eine gegen Colchicin resistente Abart des Mäuse-Ascitestumors. Naturwiss. 39:117. 1952.

42. Levine, M. Colchicine and X-rays in the treatment of plant and animal overgrowths. Bot. Rev. 11:145–80. 1945.

43. LEVINE, M. The action of colchicine on cell division in human cancer, animal and plant tissues. Ann. N. Y. Acad. Sci. 51:1365–1408. 1951.

44. LITS, F. Contribution à l'étude des réactions cellulaires provoquées par la colchicine. C. R. Soc. Biol. Paris. 115:1421–23. 1934. Recherches sur les réactions et lésions cellulaires provoquées par la colchicine. Arch. Int. Méd. Exp. 11:811–901. 1936.

45. ――――, KIRSCHBAUM, A., AND STRONG, L. C. Action of colchicine on a transplanted malignant lymphoid neoplasm in mice of the C3H strain. Amer. Jour. Cancer. 34:196–213. 1938.

46. LOEPER, M., et al. Thérapeutique médicale. V. Peau; syphilis, cancer. Masson et Cie. Paris. P. 358. 1932.

47. LUDFORD, R. J. Colchicine in the experimental chemotherapy of cancer. Jour. Nat. Cancer Inst. 6:89–101. 1945.

48. ――――. Factors determining the action of colchicine on tumour growth. Brit. Jour. Cancer. 2:75–86. 1948.

49. MALLET, L., AND LE CAMUS, H. Poisons caryoclasiques et radiothérapie dans le traitement du cancer. Presse Méd. 52:230–31. 1944.

50. MÉNÉTRIER, P. Cancer. Formes et variétés des cancers et leur traitement. In: Nouveau Traité de Médecine et de Thérapeutique (P. Carnot et P. Lereboullet). Librairie J. B. Baillière et Fils. Paris. 1927.

51. MOESCHLIN. Personal communications. 1953.

52. NICOD, J. L. La colchicine dans le traitement du cancer de la souris. Schweiz. Med. Wschr. 72:1074–77. 1942.

53. OUGHTERSON, A. W., TENNANT, R., AND HIRSCHFELD, J. W. Effect of colchicine on human tumors. Proc. Soc. Exp. Biol. 36:661–64. 1937.

54. PALETTA, F. X., AND COWDRY, E. V. Influence of colchicine during methylcholanthrene epidermal carcinogenesis in mice. Amer. Jour. Path. 18:291–311. 1942.

55. PARMENTIER, R., AND DUSTIN, P., JR. Reproduction expérimentale d'une anomalie particulière de la métaphase des cellules malignes (métaphase "à trois groupes"). Caryologia. 4:98–109. 1951. On the mechanism of the mitotic abnormalities induced by hydroquinone in animal tissues. Rev. Belge Path. 23:1–11. 1953.

56. PAUL, J. T., BROWN, W. O., AND LIMARZI, L. C. Effect of colchicine on myeloid leukemia. Amer. Jour. Clin. Med. 11:210. 1941.

57. PEYRON, A., LAFAY, B., AND KOBOZIEFF, N. Sur la régression de la tumeur de Shope du lapin sous l'action de la colchicine. Bull. Assoc. Franç. Cancer. 25:874–75. 1936. Sur la régression du papillo-épithélioma du lapin sous l'action de la colchicine. C. R. Acad. Sci. Paris. 205:378–80. 1937.

58. ――――, POUMEAU-DELILLE, G., AND LAFAY, B. La tumeur de Shope du lapin et sa stérilisation par la colchicine. Bull. Assoc. Franç. Cancer. 26:625–34. 1937.

59. ――――, AND ――――. Sur l'évolution maligne du papillo-épithélioma du lapin et son mode de régression sous l'action de la colchicine. C. R. Soc. Biol. Paris. 126:625–28. 1937. L'histopathologie et les modalités évolutives de la tumeur cutanée de Shope chez le lapin. Bull. Assoc. Franç. Cancer. 28:180–94. 1939.

60. PITON, R. Recherches sur les actions caryoclasiques et caryocinétiques des composés arsenicaux. Arch. Int. Méd. Exp. 5:355–411. 1929.

61. POULSSON, K. T. Colchicinbehnadling av maligne soulster hosmus. Norsk. Mad. Laegevidensk. 96:735–36. 1935.

62. RUFFILLI, D. Azione di un veleno statmocinetico sull'eritroblastosis dei polli. Boll. Soc. Ital. Biol. Sper. 16:140–41. 1941. Azione della colchicina sulla cancerogenesi da metilcolantrene. Nota preventiva. Boll. Soc. Ital. Biol. Sper. 17:75–77. 1942.

63. SCHAIRER, E. Der Einfluss des Colchicins auf den Mausasciteskrebs. Z. Krebsforsch. 50:143–54. 1940.

64. SCHJEIDE, O. A., AND ALLEN, B. M. The relation of mitosis to the manifestation of X-ray damage in hematopoietic cells of tad-poles. Jour. Cell Comp. Physiol. 38:51–67. 1951.

65. SEED, L., SLAUGHTER, P. P., AND LIMARZI, L. R. Effect of colchicine on human carcinoma. Surgery. 7:696–709. 1940.

66. SELDAM, B. E. J., AND SOETARSO, B. De werking van colchicine of enkele experimenteele Rattensarcome. Geneesk. Tijdschr. Ned.-Ind. 78:3187–96. 1938.
67. SENTEIN, P. L'action des toxiques sur la cellule en divison. Effets de la colchicine et du chloral sur les mitoses et tissus normaux et sur quelques tumeurs malignes. Thèse. Montpellier. 1941.
68. SETALA, K. Colchicine as carcinogenic agent in skin carcinogenesis in mice. Ann. Med. Biol. Fenniae. 26:126–30. 1948.
69. SHAPIRO, D. M., WEISS, R., AND GELLHORN, A. The effect of azaguanine on mitosis in normal and neoplastic tissues. Cancer. 3:896–902. 1950.
70. SHEAR, M. J. Chemical treatment of tumors. IX. Reactions of mice with primary subcutaneous tumors to injection of a hemorrhage-producing bacterial polysaccharide. Jour. Nat. Cancer Inst. 4:461–76. 1944.
71. SKIPPER, H. E., CHAPMAN, J. B., AND BELL, M. The antileukemic action of combinations of certain known antileukemic agents. Cancer Res. 11:109–12. 1951.
72. SOLACOLU, T., AND CONSTANTINESCO, M., AND D. Action de la colchicine sur les tumeurs végétales provoquées par le *Bacillus tumefaciens*. C. R. Soc. Biol. Paris. 130:1148–50. 1939.
73. TENNANT, R., AND LIEBOW, A. Actions of colchicine and ethylcarbylamine on tissue-cultures. Yale Jour. Biol. Med. 13:39–49. 1940.
74. THOMAS, P. T. Experimental imitation of tumour conditions. Nature. 156: 738–40. 1945.
75. VILLARS, R. Étude cytologique de l'action des rayons X sur les racines colchicinées. C. R. Soc. Biol. Paris. 133:424–26. 1940.
76. WILLIAMSON, G. The treatment of tumours by the injection of colchicine. Jour. Roy. Army Vet. Corps. 8:23–25. 1936.
77. WOODSIDE, G. L., KIDDER, G. W., DEWEY, V. C., AND PARKS, F. E., JR. The influence of 8-azaguanine on the mitotic rate and histological appearance of certain normal and neoplastic tissues. Cancer. Res. 13:289–91. 1953.
78. ZIRKLE, R. E., AND BLOOM, W. Irradiation of parts of individual cells. Science. 117:487–93. 1953.

CHAPTER 11

The Experimental Polyploids

11.1: 1937 — Beginning of a New Era in Polyploidy

Colchicine replaced practically all the techniques used to double the number of chromosomes in plants. The procedure was new and could easily be fitted to many different kinds of plants. Within a short time geneticists became convinced that a very useful tool had been discovered, because colchicine methods were more effective and more suitable for making polyploids, plants with additional sets of chromosomes, than any formerly used.

Immediate and wide universal interest in colchicine developed among botanists, as shown by the rapid rise in popularity that followed closely upon the announcements of chemical induction of chromosomal doubling.[11, 12, 52, 53, 62] A new era in polyploidy investigations began in 1937, the year the colchicine method was discovered.[36, 72]

Soon the advantages of colchicine became clear. One out of 600 cotton plants treated by "heat-shock" became polyploid (1:600), but colchicine procedures applied to a comparable group yielded 50 polyploids from among 100 (1:2) of the cotton plants surviving the chemical treatment.[8] Similarly the superiority of colchicine was discovered by workers at the chromosome laboratory, Svalof, Sweden, where up to the time colchicine was introduced, elaborate heat-shock machinery, with refrigeration controls, had been used to double the number of chromosomes.[46] Swedish botanists soon discovered that such complicated equipment was no longer necessary.[46] A rapid change-over to colchicine took place.[44, 3, 8, 14, 16, 20, 21, 23, 25, 26, 30, 32, 41, 43, 46, 51, 50, 54, 56, 57, 58, 59, 63, 64, 65, 66, 69, 70, 73, 74] The switch to colchicine in Sweden and elsewhere was so fast that it appeared that the colchicine "fad" in research had arrived.[72, 28]

As we mentioned in Chapter 2, colchicine was not the first chemical to be tried and used for doubling of chromosomes. Other chemicals, heat-shock methods,[10] production of callus tissue,[40] and other techniques yielded polyploid types.[60] The reason these methods were replaced is found in the two specific advantages demonstrated by colchicine: First, colchicine was very effective for making polyploids with many different species; and second, the drug was applied easily to young growing plants with very little damage being done to them.

There are several noteworthy features of colchicine that account for its effectiveness as a polyploidizing agent. Briefly, colchicine is highly soluble in water; colchicine is not toxic to plant cells even in strong dosages; colchicine is effective in concentrations ranging from 1.0 to 0.01 per cent (1:100 to 1:10,000); and finally, it is soluble in lipoids. Furthermore, the effect obtained during a treatment is wholly reversible. Thus the drug is almost "made to order" for changing diploids into polyploids.

After recovery from treatment the new tissue from treated generations (C_0 = generation) and the progeny of succeeding generations (C_1 = first, C_2 = second, etc.) do not show damage of a hereditary nature. The usual changes associated with multiplication of chromosomes, gigantic characters in leaf, flower, fruit, and seed, are transmitted to the next generations; there is no evidence that "deterioration"[47] sets in after colchicine reaches the protoplasm. While the treated plants may perhaps have wrinkled leaves, distorted stems, and various anatomical malformations, such temporary changes disappear in C_1, C_2, and later cycles.

Gene changes or chromosome repatterning have not been proved, [33, 71] although preliminary tests led to these suggestions. This much is certain: Changes comparable to those produced by X-ray have not been found, and if we choose to use the word *mutation,* it must be clearly stated that colchicine does not cause gene mutations. Only in the broad sense of *mutation,* which includes chromosomal doubling, may we use the term in connection with colchicine as a producer of mutations.[24] If the definition is limited to *gene changes* and *chromosome repatterning* (inversions and translocations), colchicine does not cause mutations. Hence it is incorrect to classify colchicine with *mutagens,* such as p-acetamidotropolone, a 7-carbon compound which appears to cause chromosomal breakage.[71]

More knowledge about the meaning and use of chromosome numbers in relation to species relationship formation is desirable. Every experimenter before commencing a project with colchicine should know the drug is not a chemical fertilizer; it is not a phytohormone; it is not a weed killer; it is not a vitamin; it is not a mutagen; and finally, colchicine is not merely one more organic substance on the present long list now at the disposal of many persons interested in plants.[29] The drug has specific and limited uses; therefore, reports giving directions to spray a field with colchicine or to soak the soil as one would with fertilizing agents, are completely erroneous.

In this chapter and the next four chapters the future possibilities,[70] limitations, and accomplishments are given. Miracles were predicted in the numerous writings in praise of colchicine, but there often followed a serious disillusionment for those not informed in polyploidy and cytogenetics.[27] A wave of great enthusiasm for colchicine in some quarters was succeeded by a loss of interest. Totally discounting colchicine, however, is quite wrong.

11.2: Terminology

In the rapidly expanding field of cytogenetics, new terms are constantly being added, while others are modified as more information is acquired. The two terms, *auto-syndesis* and *allo-syndesis,* have been used with exactly opposite meanings by two groups. Now each time the terms are used, an explanation must accompany the usage. When autopolyploidy and allopolyploidy were first pointed out by Kihara and Ono in 1926,[43] the distinctions were based on materials at hand. When many more examples came into consideration, the differences were not as specific as one might desire for a classification. Terms and their meanings often introduce added confusion. The terminology and definitions used here have in large part been adapted from Clausen, Keck, and Heisey.[18] Extensive work on terminology has been done by Stebbins.[66]

Ploidy, in recent usage, means *fold* (from the Greek *ploos*) and a combining form *like* (*oid*). Thus the prefixed word *polyploidy* means *many-fold*. This refers to the number of sets of chromosomes for a particular plant or animal. *Monoploid* refers to those cells or individuals with one set; *diploid,* twofold; *triploid,* threefold; *tetraploid,* fourfold. Then *autoploid* means self-fold; *amphiploid,* both-fold.

Polyploidy describes a serial relation of numbers in multiples starting from some basic number. If the number is 7, then the polyploid series would read 21, 28, 42, for triploid, tetraploid, and hexaploid, respectively.

Autoploidy is an abbreviated form of the term *autopolyploidy* and will be used for those polyploids formed by multiplication of sets of chromosomes within the limits of a species. Admittedly, the range is wide, and complications arise in classification because the autoploid with four homologous sets will differ from the one derived from two subspecies, that is, the doubled intraspecific hybrid.

Amphiploidy embraces the polyploids derived from the additions of two distinct species. A sterile hybrid *AB* upon doubling becomes the amphiploid *AABB*. If the number of species included increases beyond two, a polyploid-amphiploid condition obtains.

Segmental allopolyploid is an amphiploid which shows characteristics of autoploids with respect to pairing of chromosomes, resemblance to parents, and fertility; yet the amphiploid exhibits enough difference between the genomes contributed by the parents to fall within the scope of amphiploids. Segmental types are important for practical and theoretical reasons. Our discussion of the segmental allopolyploid will be included in Chapter 12 (The Amphiploids).

Genome designates the set of chromosomes derived from a species; the term may be used to express a relationship between species. Extensive use has been made of genomes since many interspecific hybrids have been made and doubled with colchicine. Among species of *Gossypium* the genome concept is related to geographical distribution of species. The genomes of *Triticum* refer to generic contributions. The original term was introduced by Winkler in 1920.

Dysploidy refers to a series of polyploids in nature whose basic numbers are not multiples. A dysploidy is superimposed upon an amphiploid series. A good example is found among the Cruciferae, where basic numbers 5, 6, 7, 9, 11 fall at levels of diploid, tetraploid, and hexaploid status.

Aneuploidy is a condition in which chromosomes are added or lost from the diploid set of chromosomes. Aneuploids may or may not represent balanced genotypes. The loss or addition may be found at polyploid levels. For example, the nullisomic is essentially aneuploid.

Cryptic structural hybridity[66] designates a chromosomal differentiation in very small segments that does not readily find expression in configuration at metaphase of meiosis. Pairing of chromosomes may be bivalent and apparently normal, for the segments that are differentiated are so small that no opportunity is afforded for abnormal configurations during synapsis. For these reasons a structural hybridity of this nature may be indistinguishable from the genetic hybridity.

11.3: Cataclysmic Origin of Species

The origin of a new species by gene mutation or chromosomal repatterning (inversions or translocations) is a slow process and requires a long time. Surprisingly, there exists in nature, alongside these slower processes, a very rapid method that can catapult a new species into existence within a generation or two.[7] This sudden origin is called "cataclysmic evolution." [24] By this process a new plant is separated at once from its immediate parents and is destined to occupy new environments different from either, or both, of its progenitors (Fig. 11.1).[73]

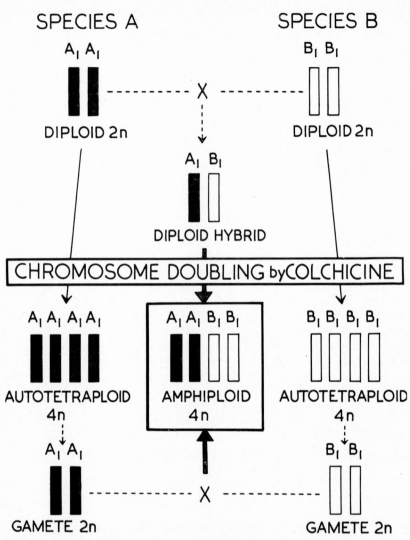

Fig. 11.1—Use of colchicine to make autotetraploids. Doubling the chromosomes of interspecific diploid hybrid. Amphiploids made by hybridizing two autotetraploid species. (After Wexelsen)

This kind of evolution was formulated as the $A \times B$ hypothesis by Winge in 1917 before any examples were well known, although the doubling of *Primula kewensis* was on record.[66] According to the $A \times B$ hypothesis, a polyploid series with a basic number of 7 would read 21, 28, and 42; or triploid, tetraploid, and hexaploid, respectively. These can originate as follows: A triploid, sterile hybrid arises from the hybridization between the diploid, $2n = 14$, and a tetraploid, $4n = 28$; upon doubling of the 21-chromosome triploid, a hexaploid (42-chromosome) species originates.[49] In this way species hybridization, followed by doubling of the chromosomes, fulfils the principle of the Winge hypothesis. Among the wheats (Triticinae) there is an excellent chance to show how this mode of evolution accounts for speciation as well as the production of mankind's most valuable economic crop species, hexaploid wheat, (42-chromosome *Triticum aestivum* L.).[49] However, on a purely numerical basis and without a knowledge of the only known case to support his assumption, the $A \times B$ hypothesis was outlined to explain the origin of species with high chromosomal numbers. The data which Winge needed were published by Digby for *Primula kewensis.*[66]

The facts of cataclysmic evolution became clearer, for new tetraploids were discovered[34] or synthesized continuously from 1926. These include Müntzing's synthetic *Galeopsis tetrahit;*[51] *Primula kewensis,* arising under culture at Kew Gardens;[66] Karpechenko's *Raphanobrassica,*[24] a doubled intergeneric hybrid between radish and cabbage. Finally *Spartina townsendii,*[18] a new polyploid of recent historic times, is a new species which invaded a habitat not previously occupied. The mud flats along the channel coastline of England abound with this new species, but records show that prior to 1870 no plants were present in this area.[18]

Two important conclusions emerge from the numerous studies dealing with polyploidy and evolution. (1) Polyploid species are abundant in nature; by one estimate as many as 50 per cent of the flowering plants are in some duplicated form. (2) Valuable economic crop species (food, fiber, and others) are polyploid, e.g., bread wheat, cotton, oats, sugar cane, tobacco, grapes, berries, nuts, and many other horticultural and floricultural species. In the first instance our problem may be called cataclysmic evolution in nature; in the second, evolution under domestication.[48]

Polyploid agricultural species originated through the years in nature without man's guidance, but under his hand and through his selection they may have become quite different species than if left to natural processes of selection. When man eliminates certain types and nurtures the environment for his choice plants, the situation is not comparable to nature's elimination process and selection that goes on competitively without cultivation. Nevertheless, the problems of evolution in nature and under domestication[48] are very closely interrelated. That is why closer integration of theoretical and practical work seems advisable in polyploidy research. Increasing the information about the origin of polyploids in nature improves our position in the planning of a new hybridization program.[66] Furthermore, the data from countless selections by the practical breeder could be valuable for analysis with purely theoretical objectives in mind.[67]

When colchicine was discovered as a tool for doubling the chromosomes, it was believed by many that evolution was about to be speeded up out of proportion to anything known. The tool, colchicine, did in fact remove a serious bottleneck[66] in permitting a doubling of the species hybrid by a new and more efficient method than ever before available. Many newcomers to the ranks of new species have been produced; this is evident if we compare our list of amphiploids produced since 1937 with the list made before that date. There is no doubt of a speeded-up tempo, but unless one possesses a broad and deep knowledge of cytogenetics, he will fail to see that the expected "miracles" have been forthcoming. The introduction of a new variety of wheat by ordinary standards requires about 15 years.[66] To produce a new polyploid variety is as difficult, if not more so.

11.4: Classification of Polyploids

The two principal classes of polyploids are (1) autoploids derived from homozygous diploids, e.g., tetraploid maize,[60] and (2) amphiploids, like *Raphanobrassica*,[24] resulting from hybridization. These two types are not difficult to distinguish. They are extremes with the autoploid carrying four sets of homologous chromosomes *AAAA*, and the amphiploid, two diploid sets *AA* and *BB*. The difficulties in classifying polyploids arises when dealing with examples between the different types, that is, polyploids with both autoploid and amphiploid characteristics.[66] There are many cases — and more are being made continuously — that are intergrading types and, as such, are not easily classified into the autoploid or the amphiploid category.

Problems of classification in polyploidy are similar to those in other systematic studies. For example, everyone agrees on which individuals of the species belong to the Mammalia and the Spermatophyta; however, among the microorganisms a classification problem has new difficulties. Since the bacteria are so widely studied in relation to human disease, the medical bacteriologists find it illogical to group them with the fission fungi, or Schizomycetes, of the plant kingdom. As a matter of fact, some bacteria do have plant and animal characteristics, and so present a distinct problem in classification. Likewise in polyploidy, the borderline cases have characteristics that are both autoploid and amphiploid. As colchicine increases the number of polyploids, the intergrading types are increasing at the same time.

The artificially induced hexaploid *Phleum nodosum,* created by colchicine,[55] may be used as an example of the disagreement on classification because the true nature of its autoploidy is in dispute. When all the evidence is carefully reviewed in this case, the complexities of classification become very real. These are problems requiring further study which cannot be resolved entirely in this review. There are other cases. In fact, the group between the autoploid and amphiploid provides the most interest and perhaps the greatest opportunity for practical and theoretical work in polyploidy. Even though one cannot decide definitely on the classification, there is no need for concern, for he may utilize the opportunities presented by these intergrading polyploids without classifying them.

One way to explore this group has been opened by an inquiry into the special kind of polyploid called the "segmental allopolyploid."[66] Good reasons were given to justify the establishment of this special group. Some types of polyploids have segments of chromosomes so closely associated that pairing is between the two parental genomes, and therefore they cannot be considered as strictly amphiploid; but in other segments, there is enough differentiation to prevent pairing of the chromosomes that originate from the different parents. Viewing the chromosomes segment by segment, instead of as whole chromosomes or even whole genomes, gives one a more critical picture of the basis for borderline types between the autoploid and the amphiploid. Theoretical and practical aspects are greatest among the polyploids that fall between the unquestionable autoploid and amphiploid.

Pairing of chromosomes is of limited value in classifying the polyploids even though this cytological method is one way to point out the difference between the autoploid and the amphiploid. Some diploid species hybrids may show pairing at the diploid level, but this does not necessarily happen. On the other hand, complete lack of pairing at the diploid level does not insure total bivalents at the polyploid stage.[42] Less and less reliability is being placed on pairing of chromosomes as a measure of homology and a means of distinguishing the autoploid from the amphiploid. As more examples come into view, the case for pairing is increasingly complicated. Other factors must be considered.

Sterility and fertility characteristics may separate the amphiploid from the autoploid. The latter is invariably less fertile than the diploid, and the amphiploid changes from a sterile condition to a fertile one upon doubling of the chromosomes. In reviewing many cases, one can find wide variation in degree of sterility among the autoploid and the amphiploid cases. Actually, the causes of sterility are so complex that this relationship is of little help in trying to classify the two types. Yet basically, sterility may be closely related to some basic cytogenetic mechanism.

The best solution to the classification problem appears to be the chart developed by Clausen and his colleagues[18] on which they place the amphiploids in a relative position depending upon a series of characteristics that place the type closer or farther from one of the two classes. Table 12 of their work is worth considerable attention for those interested in the classification of polyploids. As would be expected, the known polyploids form an intergrading series from the extreme autoploid to the amphiploid, which is a completely diploid-ized type. Colchicine-induced polyploids cause increasing inter-gradation as more and more examples appear.

For purposes of reviewing the colchicine-induced polyploids, re-sorting to taxonomic authority has served a very useful purpose. If the polyploid has been a product of doubling a species hybrid in-volving accepted species, then the type is considered amphiploid, while the diploids made tetraploid are autoploid. Admittedly the system is artificial and does not delve into the real problem that makes a polyploid what it is. However, with the view of handling large amounts of data and many polyploids, this method of classifica-tion is simpler. At no time has the basic feature of the segmental allopolyploid or its significance been overlooked. Those character-istics that are peculiar to the segmental allopolyploid are important practically and in certain evolutionary aspects.

11.5: Principles of Polyploid Breeding

Within five years, from 1938 to 1942, examples of all the major agriculture species of Sweden were converted into polyploids.[46, 69, 1] In other places throughout the world vast numbers of polyploids were created at about this same time. Colchicine accounted for many of the new polyploids, but few of these could be used in agriculture. [73, 65, 49, 54, 56, 57, 63, 35, 62, 44, 19, 21, 22, 30, 32, 3, 5, 8, 9, 15, 16] This may come as a shock to practical agronomists. A re-examination of the principles basic to polyploid breeding was needed. Since so much material was at hand, polyploids were used to test a number of points about chro-mosome doubling as a method of plant breeding. The principles enu-merated below have been stated directly as such or indirectly through the work of a number of investigators.

The application of colchicine permitted the production of large numbers of polyploids from diploids. One would expect these new polyploids to replace the standard diploid varieties.[60] However, artificially induced polyploids are, at the beginning, "raw" polyploids without exception.[46] Such types are generally unselected, so the task of plant breeding has only begun after the polyploid has been made.[46] Too many investigations disregarded the principle of raw polyploids and tested the tetraploids against the selected diploids. Naturally, the tetraploids failed to measure up to diploids in all-around per-formance. What is even more surprising is the condemnation of colchicine when tetraploids, apparently as raw polyploids, failed to outperform the best diploids. Statements that colchicine causes "harm"[47] to the plants are also difficult to understand.

A second principle well known to practical breeders is the use of large populations. If one starts with a few plants, his project is doomed before a start has been made. Two qualifications should be stated in this respect. The self-fertilized species should be used with more strains and fewer plants from each, while the cross-fertilized types demand many plants, but these can be taken from fewer strains. In both instances, large numbers of tetraploid genotypes must be made as the material for future selection work.[46] Naturally, a few plants cannot serve as a substitute for mass production.

Each successful tetraploid must eventually have genotypical balance. Through selection the relation between plant and its environment must be brought into an adjustment.[18] Practical breeders are acquainted with the need for the all-around performance of more than one characteristic. It is not enough to acquire disease resistance, or some other quality, to the exclusion of those equally as important.[67] The new tetraploids are no exception in this respect. The transfer of a specific gene for disease resistance must not be permitted at the expense of the whole genotype which may be thrown out of balance — that is, if success in a practical way is anticipated. Therefore, the opportunities for selection begin with the polyploid, and the difficulties are also started as we shall learn in subsequent sections.

The genetic traits of the polyploid are an accumulation of those contributed by the diploid. It does not follow that a very good diploid will always give rise to the best polyploids. But there is this rule to be observed that a polyploid, like the diploid, is a plant with genetic traits that segregate and respond in selection according to the same rules as the diploid.

In judging the chromosomal numbers of natural species, there is a law of optimal numbers above or below which the maximum performance or adaptation cannot be expected. The polyploid series of *Phleum* is a good example.[46] Those types with best characteristics as polyploids were found in the numbers 6×7, and 11×7. One cannot expect to achieve success by doubling a tetraploid, so the diploid species are needed for a start. Chromosomal doubling of natural tetraploids in cotton from 52 to 104 chromosomes creates very weak and poor plants; obviously this exceeds the optimum number.[8] There is, however, another point to be remembered: If the number of diverse genotypes can be increased during the process of doubling high numbers with plants having good fertility, vigor and growth are possible. Merely stating that the numbers cannot be above a certain value is too limiting. In nature the natural polyploids are combinations of two or more genomes that can be recognized. For example, the hexaploid wheat combines three genomes, and after this process the optimal number of 42 seems to be attained.

Cross-fertilizing, or allogamous, species are more promising as a group than the self-fertilizing types. This general rule seems to hold for a large number of plants included in the Svalof experiments. Some qualification needs to be made, for the sampling was not as extensive as might be desired. The changes from incompatability to compatibility upon doubling the number of chromosomes is an involved genetic problem, not merely a result of the tetraploid nature, but consisting of a combination of events that create the changes.[46]

The autoploids are almost without exception less fertile than the diploids.[60] Therefore, seed and fruit yields, if dependent upon seed production, will at once suffer in the polyploid stage, at least before selection can be done to rectify the situation. The sterility barrier is by-passed when a hybridization is included with the doubling; then the degree of fertility generally improves, but not always. The principle of reduced fertility after polyploidy from the diploid should always be considered by every one starting a new project. Then the changes that might be induced by selection in the later generations can be considered along with the sterility-fertility relations. Granted that fertility levels can be raised by selection, the danger of introducing other changes constantly attends the selection processes.

The part of the plant to be used for economic production becomes a first consideration, for the root and shoot yields will not be influenced by sterility. Vegetatively propagated plants are a new problem. They need not pass through the reproductive cycle that is so critical to a polyploid at many levels. Perennial plants are favored, and plants that produce propagating shoots like the grasses are immediately more favorable than the strictly seed-producing annuals.

A principle of transfer of characteristics from one species to another has been mentioned frequently in polyploidy work. Among many species the favorable traits are prominent in the wild species. There is at once a desire to introduce this character into the valuable commercial species. A notable case is the mosaic resistance transfer in tobacco.[17] This problem is discussed in greater detail later, but it should be noted that the transfer of such a trait is in effect a problem of polyploidy breeding. On a plan in blueprint stage, the idea appears relatively simple, but now it is well known that accomplishment is quite difficult. One of the greatest obstacles in transfer is the introduction of undesirable traits along with the desirable ones being sought.

Combining the good features of two diploid species into the amphiploid is another aspect of how hybridization and the doubling of chromosomes offer opportunity for future programs of selection. A new species such as the *Cucurbita moschata* $\times$ *C. maxima* amphiploid combines good traits from two diploids. A new species of economic potential is apparent. However, interspecific segregations in the fifth and sixth generations show that a lack of uniformity can be expected (cf. Chapter 12). Such variation is not what the breeder hopes for in a true breeding variety. By transfer of whole genomes into a hybrid the characters of the polyploid can be influenced. If in later generations there is pairing between the two genomes that originated with the two species, the chance for segregation is good. If the segregates are undesirable and if the interchange is so great that the original type is lost, all the transfer is circumvented by the after-breeding effects. Transfer in *Gossypium* has presented a very difficult problem, that of introducing the good characters and maintaining all the original traits of the cultivated varieties. In spite of the problems, the principle of transfer is basic in polyploid breeding.[61]

The advantages balanced against the disadvantages are necessary for a final evaluation.[51] No tetraploid within a certain species may be expected to surpass the diploid in all respects. Therefore, the desirable traits balanced against the unfavorable ones should be calculated to see whether the new result is in favor of the tetraploid or the diploid. Triploid sugar beets are not perfect, but there is the important fact that the triploids can be grown to a larger root size before the percentage of sucrose decreases than is the case for the diploids.[58] In this way the triploid has an advantage over the diploid, while for seed production, germination, and growth problems the triploid is sometimes at considerable disadvantage beside the diploid. Tetraploid rye offers another notable example of balancing two sets of characters.[51]

All plants arising from treated generations may not be totally tetraploid. The diploid cells may be found mixed with the tetraploid, and a mixoploid condition may persist.[37] Or the layers of cells may differ one from the other, so that the shoot apex is stratified with respect to its ploidy.[23] These are called periclinal chimeras discussed in Chapter 14 (The Aneuploids).[13] From the point of view of polyploid breeding the mixoploids and chimeras are very important problems. The reversion of polyploid to diploid is sometimes explainable on the basis of a chimera, or sometimes it may arise from cross-breeding.

Stabilizing the polyploid by selection and by preventing the reversion to the diploid or through segregation, to some inferior type is a problem that confronts the plant breeder after the polyploid has been produced. The first and second generations may be quite uniform, but later generations less so. Or the first generation may have defects that yield to selection in later generations. The effectiveness of selection between diploid and amphiploid is one of degree and speed rather than absolute difference. Genetic types can be isolated more quickly in diploids than in polyploids if one can base his evidence on a specific character and extend the idea to a whole set of characters.* Selection as a result of interspecific segregation creates a good opportunity for making wholly new lines.[66]

Regardless of the plant, whether diploid or tetraploid, the testing methods are important to success in measuring the gains made, in keeping the good qualities, and in raising the standards if possible. In tetraploid rye the testing side by side of diploid and tetraploid is impossible, and consequently an adjustment must be made by a yield factor with another plant.[51] This at once complicates evaluation of the polyploid against the diploid. There are many other problems of testing peculiar to certain plants, and tetraploids are involved because the success of the polyploid may depend upon the mode of testing rather than the qualities of the polyploid itself.

The list of principles is not complete in the above survey, but a start has been made. More information is needed before the additional principles of polyploidy breeding can be described in greater detail.

11.6: The Scope of Research

Colchicine increased the frequency of induced polyploids beyond that possible with any other method known up to 1937. This discovery had two major effects upon research in the plant sciences all over the world. (1) Polyploidy, already a subject of study, was increased immediately. (2) New programs were started because greater reliability could be placed upon this technique and much time could be saved in converting the diploids into polyploids. The net result of these two developments has been an unusually great expansion in research with polyploidy in many nations.[44, 54] In fact, a detailed review of all work with colchicine goes beyond the permissible allotment of space in this review.

One might single out specific cases where certain scientists have had an exceptional influence upon polyploidy and greater than average progress has been made accordingly. For example, the personal interest that Vavilov took in polyploidy led to great activity in cytogenetics in Russia.[70] In Sweden, Nihlsson-Ehle made special efforts to organize laboratories such as the chromosome laboratory at Svalof and other institutes in that country.[46] These and other special institutes[43] throughout the world were at work on problems in polyploidy before colchicine became known as a tool for creating poly-

---

*See Reference No. 103 in Chapter 12.

ploids. When colchicine appeared to be useful, its future possibilities were expressed in several American papers[70] published by Chronica Botanica in 1940. A broad view was taken at this time.

The progress made in Sweden from 1937 to 1947 was rapid. Scientists from every nation observed the scope of this work as a result of demonstrations made before two international congresses, the genetics meeting of 1948 and the botanical meeting of 1950. Obviously, the discovery of colchicine in 1937 appeared at a very favorable time in the history of plant sciences in Sweden. A large amount of work was done in Russia from 1937 to 1947, but less attention has been given to this contribution.[74] Already in 1945, Professor Zebrak reported in a lecture at the University of California that numerous polyploids in the *Triticum* group had been made, perhaps not exceeded elsewhere in the world.[74] The extensive report on the situation in biological sciences in Russia made in 1948 gives a general survey of the status of research with polyploidy before 1947. After 1948 the use of colchicine was apparently not encouraged in Russia.[47] There can be no doubt that Vavilov had an important influence on the use of polyploidy as a research method.

Japanese geneticists have made direct and special contributions to practical and theoretical phases of polyploidy.[54] The triploid watermelon, triploid sugar beet, tetraploid radish, and tetraploid melon have been put into agricultural practice since 1937.[54] Much progress has been made at the Kihara Biological Institute, Kyoto, where a number of workers have been able to make their contributions. Furthermore, the influence of this laboratory was directed to other institutes in Japan. Polyploidy has been a familiar subject, and there has been close integration of theoretical and practical problems under the direction of one group of workers.[43]

Accomplishments in the field of polyploidy by three nations, Sweden, Russia, and Japan, are quite out of proportion to the relative number of scientists, and particularly of geneticists, in each country. In this respect, the progress made in the United States is far behind these others if one compares the total work in plant sciences in relation to the progress made in the area of polyploidy. Therefore, one cannot understand why colchicine and polyploidy are thought to be tools owned solely by America. They are not. In fact, no nation can claim a priority in the use of colchicine and in progress made by its application to polyploidy. The records of the Seventh International Genetics Congress show some unbalance, but by the time the Ninth Congress was held, there was an equalization, so that no single group has dominated the program of colchicine and problems in polyploidy. Historically the situation has been clarified since the early period of work with colchicine.

There is another aspect in the scope of research with colchicine that tends to be overlooked. Scattered throughout the world, special institutes were at work on species whose background was recognized to be polyploid, such as *Gossypium*,[8, 15, 67, 35] *Nicotiana*,[35] *Triticum*,[49, 74] *Solanum*, and others. Theoretical problems and the practical importance of polyploidy were well known before 1937. One outstanding case is the British Empire Cotton Research Station at Trinidad, British West Indies, where diploid and tetraploid *Gossypium* was studied in detail (cf. Chapter 12). Soon after colchicine became known, it was applied to the sterile hybrids on hand.[67] The drug was merely incidental to the whole project, and many polyploids were made as a matter of routine in the larger program. For these reasons research with colchicine did not get prominent notice in their publications.

The application of polyploidy breeding in *Nicotiana* began before colchicine was discovered. After 1937 the number of polyploids for this genus was increased.[17] A transfer of disease-resistant traits from one species to another is an example of polyploid breeding and a contribution of experimental genetics.[17]

Breeding programs with forage species,[4] *Triticum*,[49] fruits, and flowers are under way in many places. The state and federal stations in the United States alone represent a large program.[22] Polyploidy is included in many of these programs. Public and private institutions throughout the world have put colchicine to work.

A complete list of research centers and projects using colchicine would be large. The bibliography and list of polyploids indicate the international character of such research.

REFERENCES

1. AKERMAN, A. Swedish Seed Association, Annual Report. 1950. Sverig. Utsadesf. Tidskr. 61:124–91. 1951.
2. ANDERSON, E. Introgressive hybridization. John Wiley and Sons, New York. 1949.
3. ANDRES, J. Sojas tetraploides obtenidas por tratamienta con colchicina. Univ. Buenos Aires Inst. Genet. 2:95–102. 1944.
4. ATWOOD, S. Cytogenetics and breeding of forage crops. Academic Press, New York. Vol. 1. 1947.
5. ————, AND BREWBAKER, J. Multiple oppositional alleles in autoploid white clover. Genetics. 35:653. 1950.
6. BATES, G. Polyploidy induced by colchicine and its economic possibilities. Nature. 144:315–16. 1939.
7. BEAL, J. Induced chromosomal changes and their significance in growth and development. Amer. Nat. 76:239–52. 1942.
8. BEASLEY, J. The production of polyploids in *Gossypium*. Jour. Hered. 31:39–48. 1940.
9. BELL, G. Investigations in the Triticinae. I. Colchicine techniques for chromosome doubling in interspecific and intergenene hybridization. Jour. Agr. Sci. London. 40:9–18. 1950.
10. BELLING, J. Production of triploid and tetraploid plants. Jour. Hered. 16:463–66. 1925.

11. BLAKESLEE, A. Déboublement du nombre de chromosomes chez les plantes par traitement chimique. C. R. Acad. Sci. Paris. 205:476–79. 1937. The present and potential service of chemistry to plant breeding. Amer. Jour. Bot. 26: 163–72. 1939.

12. ———, AND AVERY, A. Methods of inducing doubling of chromosomes in plants. Jour. Hered. 28:393–411. 1937.

13. ———, et al. Induction of periclinal chimeras in *Datura stramonium* by colchicine treatment. Science. 89:402. 1939.

14. BRAGDO, M. When the chromosomes are doubled. Colchicine and polyploidy. Norsk. Hagetid. 67:27–28. 1951.

15. BROWN, M. Polyploids and aneuploids derived from species hybrids in *Gossypium*. Hereditas Suppl. Vol. Pp. 543–44. 1949.

16. CAPELLETTI. C. La Colchicina ed i poliploidi. Saggiatore. 2:293–306. 1941.

17. CLAUSEN, R. Mosaic resistance ransferred from wild tobacco to cultivated varieties through science of genetics. Calif. Agr. 3 (7) :7, 16. 1949.

18. CLAUSEN, J., et al. Experimental studies on the nature of species. II. Plant evolution through amphiploidy and autoploidy with examples from the *Madiinae*. Carnegie Inst. Wash. Publ. 564. Pp. 174, 1945.

19. CRANE, M., AND LEWIS, D. Genetical studies in pears. Jour. Genet. 43:31–43. 1942.

20. CUA, L. A newly devised colchicine method for inducing polyploidy in rice. Bot. Gaz. 112:327–29. 1951.

21. DARLINGTON, C. The fruit, the seed, and the soil. Oliver and Boyd, Edinburgh. 1949.

22. DARROW, G. Polyploidy in fruit improvement. Sci. Monthly. 70:211–19. 1950. Breeding of small fruits in the United States. Sci. Monthly. 75:288–97. 1952.

23. DERMEN, H. Ontogeny of tissues in stem and leaf of cytochimeral apples. Amer. Jour. Bot. 38:753–60. 1951. Polyploidy in the apple. Jour. Hered. 43:7–8. 1952.

24. DOBZHANSKY, T. Genetics and the origin of species. Columbia Univ. Press, New York. 446 pp. 1941.

25. DORST, J. Neue Wege auf dem Gebiete der Pflanzenzuchtung besonders in Holland. Schweiz. Landiv. Mh. 29:411–27. 1951.

26. DUSSEAU, A., AND FARDY, A. Hybrides amphidiploïdes de *Nicotiana* obtenus par l'action de la colchicine. Rev. Cytol. et Cytophysiol. Vég. 7:24–44. 1944.

27. EIGSTI, O. Research with colchicine in retrospect. The Biologist. 22:143–51. 1941.

28. ———, AND DUSTIN, P., JR. (*see* Ref. No. 16. Chap. 1) .

29. ———, AND TENNEY, B. Colchicine—a report on experiments. Univ. Okla. Press, Norman, Okla. 40 pp. 1942.

30. EMSWELLER, S. Polyploidy in *Lilium longiflorum*. Amer. Jour. Bot. 36:135–44. 1949.

31. ———, AND RUTTLE, M. Induced polyploidy in floriculture. Amer. Nat. 75: 310–26. 1941.

32. FRANDSEN, K. Iakttagelser over polyploidie Former av nogle kulturplanter. Tidsskrift f. Planteavl. 49:445–96. 1945.

33. GAULDEN, M., AND CARLSON, J. Cytological effects of colchicine on the grasshopper neuroblast *in vitro*, with special reference to the origin of the spindle. Exp. Cell Res. 2:416–33. 1951.

34. GOODSPEED, T. El tabaco y otras especies del género *Nicotiana*. Bol. Fac. Agron. Vet. Buenos Aires. No. 22. 1942.

35. ———, AND BRADLEY, M. Amphidiploidy. Bot. Rev. 8:271–316. 1942.

36. HAVAS, L. A colchicine chronology. Jour. Hered. 31:115–17. 1940.

37. HILL, H., AND MEYERS, W. Isolation of diploid and tetraploid clones from mixoploid plants of rye grass (*Lolium perenne* L.) , produced by treatment of germinating seeds with colchicine. Jour. Hered. 35:359–61. 1944.

38. HUDSON, P. Personal communication. Cambridge Univ., England. 1953.

39. HUSKINS, C. Polyploidy and mutations. Amer. Nat. 75:329–44. 1941.

40. JORGENSEN, C. The experimental formation of heteroploid plants in the genus *Solanum*. Jour. Genet. 19:133–210. 1928.

41. KARPECHENKO, G. Tetraploid six-rowed barleys obtained by colchicine treatment. C. R. Dokl. Acad. Sci. URSS. 27 (1) :47–50. 1940.
42. KEHR, A., AND SMITH, H. Multiple genome relationships in *Nicotiana*. Cornell Univ. Memoir 311. Pp. 19. Agr. Exp. Sta., Ithaca, New York. 1951.
43. KIHARA, H. History of polyploidy. Monograph on polyploidy. Baisusei Sogensha. Tokyo. March 25, 1947.
44. KRYTHE, J., AND WELLENSIEK, S. Five years of colchicine research. Bibliog. Genetica. 14:1–132. 1942.
45. KUCKUCK, H., AND LEVAN, A. Vergleichende Untersuchungen an diploiden und tetraploiden leinsippen und tetraploiden Kreuzungsnachkommenschaften nach vieljahriger Selektion. Züchter. 21:195–205. 1951.
46. LEVAN, A. Polyploidiforadlingens Nuvarande Lage. Sver. Utsadesf. Tidskr. Pp. 109–43. 1945.
47. LYSENKO, T. The situation in biological science: Verbatim report of the proceedings of the Lenin Academy of Agricultural Sciences of the U. S. S. R. Foreign Languages Publishing House, Moscow. 631 pp. 1949.
48. MANGELSDORF, P. Evolution under domestication. Amer. Nat. 86:65–77. 1952.
49. McFADDEN, E., AND SEARS, E. The genome approach in radical wheat breeding. Jour. Amer. Soc. Agron. 39:1011–25. 1947.
50. MENDES, A. Observacões citologicas em Coffea. XI. Metodos de tratamento pela colchicina. Bragantia. 7:221–30. 1947.
51. MÜNTZING, A. New material and cross combination in *Galeopsis* after colchicine-induced chromosome doubling. Hereditas. 27:193–201. 1941. Cyto-genetic properties and practical value of tetraploid rye. Hereditas. 37:1–84. 1951.
52. NEBEL, B. Cytological observations on colchicine. Collecting Net. 12:130–31. 1937.
53. ———, AND RUTTLE, M. Action of colchicine on mitosis. Genetics. 23:161–62. 1937. The cytological and genetical significance of colchicine. Jour. Hered. 29:3–9. 1938.
54. NISHIYAMA, I., AND MATSUBAYASHI, G. A list of induced polyploids in the plant (a review). Kihara Inst. Biol. Res. Seiken Ziho. 3:152–71. 1947.
55. NORDENSKIOLD, H. Synthesis of *Phleum pratense*, L. from *P. nodosum*, L. Hereditas. 35:190–214. 1949.
56. PAL, B., AND RAMANUJAN, S. Plant breeding and genetics at the Imperial Agricultural Research Institute, New Delhi. Indian Jour. Genet. and Plant Breeding. 4:43–53. 1944.
57. PARTHASARATHY, N., AND KEDHARNATH, S. The improvement of the *Sesame* crop of India. Indian Jour. Genet. and Plant Breeding. 9:59–71. 1949.
58. PETO, F., AND BOYES, J. Comparison of diploid and triploid sugar beets. Can. Jour. Res. Sec. C. Bot. Sci. 18:273–82. 1940.
59. RAMANUJAM, S., AND DESHMUK, M. Colchicine-induced polyploidy in crop plants. III. Oleiferous Brassicae. Indian Jour. Genet. and Plant Breeding. 5:63–81. 1945.
60. RANDOLPH, L. An evaluation of induced polyploidy as a method of breeding crop plants. Amer. Nat. 75:347–65. 1941.
61. RICHMOND, T. Advances in agronomy. Vol. 2:63–74. Academic Press, Inc., New York. 1950.
62. RUTTLE, M., AND NEBEL, B. Cytogenetic results with colchicine. Biol. Zentralbl. 59:79–87. 1939.
63. SACHAROV, V., et al. Autotetraploidy in different varieties of buckwheat. C. R. Dokl. Acad. Sci. URSS. 46:79–82. 1945.
64. SEARS, E. Amphidiploids in the Triticinae induced by colchicine. Jour. Hered. 30:38–43. 1939. Amphidiploids in the seven-chromosome Triticinae. Mo. Agr. Exp. Sta. Bull. 336:1–46. Columbia, Mo. 1941. Chromosome pairing and fertility in hybrids and amphidiploids in the Triticinae. Mo. Agr. Exp. Sta. Bull. 337. Pp. 1–20. Columbia, Mo., 1941. The cytology and genetics of the wheats and their relatives. *In* Advances in genetics. 2:239–70. Academic Press, Inc., New York. 1948.

65. SIMONET, M. Production d'amphidiploïdes fertiles et stables par intercroisements d'espèces rendues autotetraploïdes après traitements colchiciniques. C. R. Acad. Agr. France. 33:121–23. 1947.
66. STEBBINS, G. Types of polyploids. *In* Advances in genetics. Vol. 1. Acad. Press, Inc., New York. 1947. Variation and evolution in plants. Columbia Univ. Press, New York. 643 pp. 1950.
67. STEPHENS, S. The internal mechanism of speciation in *Gossypium*. Bot. Rev. 16:115–49. 1950.
68. TRAUB, H. Colchicine-induced *Hemerocallis* polyploids and their breeding behaviour. Plant Life. 7:83–116. 1951.
69. TURESSON, G. Kromosomfördobling och växtförädling. Weibulls III. Arbok for Vaxtforadling och Växtodling. 41:16–23. 1946.
70. VAVILOV, N. Genetics in the USSR. Chron. Bot. 5:14–15. 1939.
71. WADA, B. (*see* Ref. No. 43, Chap. 1).
72. WELLENSIEK, S. The newest fad, colchicine and its origin. Chron. Bot. 5:15–17. 1939. Methods for producing Triticales. Jour. Hered. 38:167–73. 1947.
73. WEXELSEN, H. Polyploidiforedling. En Oversikt. Forskning Fors. Landbruk. Oslo. 1:287–310. 1950.
74. ZHEBRAK, A. New amphidiploid species of wheat and their significance for selection and evolution. Amer. Nat. 80:271–79. 1946.

ADDITIONAL REFERENCES FOR LISTS OF POLYPLOIDS INDUCED BY COLCHICINE

DELAY, C. Nombres chromosomiques chez les phanerogames. Rev. Cytol. Biol. Vég. 12:1–368. 1951.
TISCHLER, G. Allgemeine Pflanzenkaryologie. Gebrüder Borntraeger, Berlin-Nikolassee. 1953.

CHAPTER 12

The Amphiploids

12.1: Amphiploidy and Implications

New species can arise suddenly by interspecific hybridization and doubling of the chromosomes. Such an act in nature separates the new amphiploid, a potential species, from its parental progenitors. New amphiploid species are able to invade new habitats, an invasion not possible by either parent. A new ecological range, as well as re-productive isolation from all other species, is acquired. More data are now at hand from amphiploids produced in the laboratory, be-cause colchicine has provided an effective method for making the poly-ploids after the interspecific hybridization has been made. Principles of theoretical and practical value can be developed.

Not all autoploids and amphiploids separate into clear-cut cate-gories since certain of their characteristics tend to overlap.[82] Many amphiploids produced by colchicine show autoploid characteristics.[21] The genetic and cytological changes that take place in later genera-tions of propagation among such amphiploids are difficult to interpret when there is interchange between the two parental genomes. A classification designed by Clausen, Keck, and Heisey sought to visual-ize how a gradual merger between autoploids and amphiploids obtains if a number of cases are compared. Table 12 in their paper places amphiploids in positions from the upper left-hand corner to the lower right, in a gradient from autoploid to amphiploid.[21] The conclusions incorporated in this chart were made after analyzing natural and experimentally produced amphiploids.

While the limits between some autoploids and amphiploids are not clearly defined, the requirements for the success of an amphiploid as a new species are extremely sharp, almost to the point of being restrictive. Limits appear to be set that cannot be violated, that is, if the new plants are to succeed in nature. We should consider whether the requirements for success in agricultural situations are not equally restrictive. The requirements may be somewhat different, but new polyploids must meet exacting demands in order to succeed as new crop species.

The diploid, interspecific hybrid, if it is to become a successful polyploid, must have good vigor, excellent growth of vegetative characters, and an all-around vegetative cycle that is in harmony with its environment.[21] Combined with these characteristics, the two parental genomes should be incompatible in the diploid hybrid to the extent that no interchange can occur between them. There should be no gene exchange between the parental sets of chromosomes, which means no intergenomal pairing. Briefly, the diploid hybrid according to these requirements should be entirely sterile until a doubling of the chromosomes occurs. Working in almost direct opposition to these conditions, describing the source of amphiploid from diploid hybrids between species, are biological laws that tend to prevent achieving the best-suited sterile hybrid. To acquire such genome incompatibility between the parents, one immediately moves the relationships of the two species farther apart. Usually the farther apart they are, the more difficult the hybridization will be. Even after the hybrid has been made, a more distant relationship often results in plants that are weak, poor in vigor, and lacking in good growth generally. A poorly growing diploid hybrid cannot be expected to change into a vigorous, successful amphiploid by merely doubling the number of chromosomes.

If hybrids are made from species too closely related, gene exchanges between the parental sets of chromosomes occur. Then after four or five generations, segregations tend to destroy the individuality of the amphiploid from the parental type.[21] Of course, by gene exchange the transfer of a trait from one species to another at the polyploidy level can occur. The moment gene exchanges take place, the future of the amphiploid as a distinct and isolated individual becomes endangered.[4] Cytological mechanisms may automatically cause the plants of later generations to drift to one or the other parental type.

Experimentally produced amphiploids have been studied for enough generations to demonstrate that genetic exchanges can take place between the two parental sets of chromosomes. From a plant breeder's point of view this would seem to offer opportunity. Otherwise a strict independence between genomes, like those of *Raphanobrassica,* permits a true breeding type distinct from either parent, but further hybridization with either parental species to improve the amphiploid is ineffective.[26] If the amphiploid is not like the *Raphanobrassica* case and intergenomal pairing does occur, gene exchange leads to segregation in F_2 and later generations. Many segregates may be weak, sterile, and poor. Occasionally, new and vigorous combinations may arise. Certainly a series of new lines can be developed when there is exchange between genomes.[75]

Suppose that lines are isolated by selection after interspecific segregation among progenies of amphiploids. One cannot expect these lines to compete in nature as successful independent amphiploids in the same rank as a distinct and differentiated species. From an agricultural standpoint these lines need not be new species, and they may or may not be valuable as new polyploids. If the transfer of genetic traits is made from one parental species to another, and the species of commercial importance is improved, the result is not a new polyploid.[20] For example, mosaic resistance was transferred from *N. glutinosa* to the *N. tabacum* genome.[111] The characteristics of commercial tobacco plants were not changed, but the disease resistant factor was added. Chromosome numbers were finally stabilized by selection after backcrossing at the same number as *N. tabacum* 48, and after specific selection only a few traits were transferred from *N. glutinosa*. All but the resistance to disease were eliminated. As an amphiploid then, the new *N. tabacum* with only the disease-resistance characteristic added can hardly be considered as an independent type.

Stability of a new amphiploid is proportional to the gene exchange between the two parental genomes. Lack of interchange favors relative constancy; conversely, interchange promotes instability. Experimentally produced amphiploids of all gradations from those with much interchange to others with very little, offer excellent opportunity to explore certain basic propositions controlled and observed after selection,[103, 4] either in nature or under guidance.

Doubling of the chromosomes among sterile diploid hybrids may be done either through gametic processes, i.e., production of unreduced gametes, or by somatic doubling. The accidental doubling in nature has occurred largely by the gametic processes. On the other hand, colchicine is most effectively applied to somatic tissues. The differences between these methods of doubling the chromosomes are important and should be compared when such comparisons can be made.

12.2: Amphiploidy in the Gramineae

Economically, the grasses comprise the most important family among all plants. Polyploidy is common in many groups including agricultural species. Generally, their origin has been through hybridization and doubling of the chromosomes. Autoploidy is limited as a method of speciation[53] in grasses compared with amphiploidy.[105] Polyploidy among grasses presents problems[57, 10, 11, 5, 70] that involve both theoretical and practical aspects.[17, 23, 47, 59, 35, 86, 90, 104] The origin of hexaploid wheat[108] has many theoretical phases,[86, 100] and no one can escape the practical importance attached to this one species, *Triticum aestivum* L.[118]

12.2–1: Origin of hexaploid wheat. Bread wheat, *Triticum aestivum* L. (*T. vulgare* Vil.) is mankind's most important single species in cultivation. Millions of people depend on the annual grain production of this plant. As an achievement in agriculture, the accession of this one species alone is man's important contribution as a plant breeder.

Historically, in terms of the long period of agriculture, the 42-chromosome wheats are relatively new. Certainly the tetraploid wheats antedate hexaploids, while diploid species preceded the tetraploids. No hexaploids are known out of cultivation, whereas diploids and tetraploids are represented by wild and cultivated species. Full knowledge of the origin of bread wheat probably will never be obtained, but some phases can be closely inspected by observing the experimentally produced polyploids. Colchicine has been a useful tool in tracking down certain steps in the origin of the hexaploid species, notably *Triticum spelta* and related species.[122]

First, consideration should be given to *Triticum monococcum* L., a 14-chromosome species, to gain some idea of the oldest species of wheat in agriculture today. Another diploid, *Agropyron triticeum* Gaertn., is suspect in the hybridization with *Triticum* which created the tetraploid, or 28-chromosome, species.[70, 100] These two parental types may be called the *A* and *B* genomes, representing *Triticum* and *Agropyron,* respectively.[58]

A large group of cultivated tetraploids, having either free-threshing or invested grains, remain in cultivation as valuable economic species. The *emmer* and *durum* types play an important role in agriculture.[90] One of the most interesting tetraploids is the free-threshing *Triticum persicum.*[58]

Let us return to our hypothesis that *Triticum monococcum* is the genome *A,* and that the diploid genome *B* came from *Agropyron triticeum.*[100] The true contribution made by *Agropyron* may now be so remote that one cannot hope to retrace these steps. Let us assume these diploids combined to make the tetraploid wheats. The evolution from tetraploid to hexaploid may be repeated more easily than that from diploid to tetraploid. By crossing tetraploid *Triticum dicoccoides,* 28-chromosomes, with diploid *Aegilops squarrosa,* a sterile triploid hybrid was obtained.[70, 58] This plant had 21 chromosomes, was sterile, and resembled hexaploid *Triticum spelta,* or spelt wheat. Upon doubling the chromosomes, a 42-chromosome wheat was developed. This synthesized hexaploid hybridized with the natural hexaploid *T. spelta.* The selfed progenies from this hybrid did not throw segregates as one might expect from a wide cross. In fact, no segregation occurred. Pairing at meiosis among the F_1 hybrid did not indicate widely differentiated chromosomes of synthetic *T. spelta*

against natural *T. spelta*.[100, 70] On the contrary, a close homology was
suggested. There was more difference between synthetic *T. spelta*
and natural *T. spelta* when amphiploids were obtained after gametic
doubling[58] than those from somatic doubling.[70]

Crossing with *Aegilops squarrosa* so improved the plant and the
grain that one might expect a naturally occurring fertile plant like
the resulting hybrid to be recognized as a new variant.[70] The geo-
graphic range of *A. squarrosa* should show in general where the
original hybridization took place.[58] This species grows today in the
northwestern Himalayas, the Caucasian region, and over an area
where hexaploid wheats could have originated as a result of the contact of *A. squarrosa* with tetraploid species of *Triticum*. Diploid
Aegilops, known as goat weed, is a very unpromising agricultural
plant;[105] yet its contribution to commercial wheat by a species like
A. squarrosa must be very specific and is apparently necessary. The
genome is called the *D* genome.[57] Therefore, hexaploid wheats are
now identified by genomes *A, B,* and *D,* each representing a genus and
each sharing one-third of the 42-chromosomes.[100, 58, 70] An isolating
mechanism has been discovered in *Triticum* associated with the *D*
genome.[98]

Between the dawn of agriculture and some time not too long ago,
the hexaploid wheat evolved. Exactly when and how many times the
hexaploid species appeared remain unsolved problems. Let us say
at some time between 2000 and 10,000 years ago. Or perhaps the
cross between diploid *Aegilops squarrosa* and tetraploid wheat is
happening today. The amphiploid *Triticum persicum* × *Aegilops
squarrosa,* which is very similar to hexaploid *Triticum,* is a species
obtained from Russia.[58] If more hexaploid cases could be found in
the areas where *Aegilops squarrosa* grows, such additions to our
knowledge would be of great interest.[58]

We know there are parts to the story that must be sketched with
certain reasonable assumptions. It was remarkable that two research
teams,[58, 70] working entirely independent of each other, came so close
to each other in an agreement that *Aegilops squarrosa* is suspected
as one of the diploid species.

Evidence that some other diploid species of *Aegilops* contributed
to wheat now becomes a burden of proof by using a cross involving
other species, or else by other methods to demonstrate how the hexaploid wheats came into existence when they did. For the present at
least, the independent contributions of Japanese and American geneticists that *Aegilops squarrosa* contributed genome *D* still stands.

An important character of *Triticum aestivum* is the free-threshing
feature. The synthetic *T. spelta,* like natural *T. spelta,* was an invested type. How the free-threshing types such as *T. aestivum* L.

evolved remains for further study. Answering the question whether this type arose as a segregate, or directly from a diploid-tetraploid hybridization requires more data.[70, 100] A pattern for research has been established.[108]

Another method for converting the tetraploid species into hexaploids has been reported.[65] Planting the 28-chromosomal species in the autumn instead of spring, a regular procedure for these hard wheat types, after two, three, or four seasons the durum spring wheats, 28-chromosome species, suddenly change into the vulgare or 42-chromosomal soft wheat species. There was no evidence of hybridization, and no intergrading forms. This method obviously differs from the two explanations given by Japanese and American geneticists for the origin of hexaploid species.

12.2–2: Other amphiploids among Triticinae. The amphiploids made from interspecific and intergeneric hybridization among *Aegilops, Triticum,* and *Agropyron* have increased many fold,[5, 9, 11, 57, 67, 74, 88, 100, 101, 118, 66, 68, 86, 90, 98, 110] since the first fertile *Triticum-Agropyron* amphiploid was produced with colchicine in 1939.[94] A wealth of material is at hand to solve the basic problems that determine the progress to be made in using amphiploids.[10, 120] Since all the cases cannot be reviewed, a selection will be made to point out theoretical and practical problems.

Among *Aegilops,* the species have evolved by interspecific hybridization and chromosomal doubling.[57] There are diploid, tetraploid, and hexaploid species represented by haploid numbers, $n = 7$, $n = 14$, $n = 21$, respectively. Since *Aegilops* has contributed to hexaploid wheat, a knowledge of these species is important even though the group has little economic value of its own.

In 1913 Cook discovered a hybrid in Palestine involving the Emmer *Triticum dicoccoides* and some form of *Aegilops.* Later, Percival pointed to *Aegilops cylindrica* as a contributor of the spelt characters in the tetraploid *Triticum.* Evidence accumulated suggesting that *T. aestivum* L. arose as a segregate out of a cross between *T. dicoccoides* and *A. cylindrica.* The amphiploid $(n = 14)$, *Aegilops cylindrica* $(n = 14)$, was synthesized by crossing *Aegilops caudata* $(n = 7) \times A.$ *squarrosa* $(n = 7)$ and doubling the chromosomes with colchicine.[100] Now three sets of data come into focus. First, earlier taxonomic work brought tetraploid *Triticum* and the tetraploid *Aegilops cylindrica* together. Second, the tetraploid *A. cylindrica* evolved from two diploid species, one being *A. squarrosa.* Third, the synthetic amphiploid, *Triticum dicoccoides* var. *spontaneovillosum* $\times$ *Aegilops squarrosa* is similar to natural *Triticum spelta.*[58, 70] In 1931 a speltlike sterile hybrid between tetraploid *Triticum dicoccum* and *Aegilops squarrosa* was made by McFadden, but for want of a ready method to convert this sterile hybrid to a fertile one, the necessary evidence re-mained hidden until fertile hexaploids could be made.[100]

The D genome represented in hexaploid wheat and the genomes of modern diploid *Aegilops squarrosa* are probably very close in their homologies. Also, this genome is not found in any species of wheat tested that had fewer than 21 chromosomes. Tetraploid wheat lacks this genome. Finally, taxonomic characters in *Aegilops squarrosa* correspond to those traits that distinguish the hexaploid wheat from tetraploids.[100] These are: the square-shouldered inflorescence, hollow stem, and articulation of rachis, differentiating *Triticum spelta* from the tetraploid Emmer wheats.[70]

Taxonomic characters were used to trace the probable origin of hexaploid wheat before cytogenetic evidences were at hand. The fact that diploid *Agropyron triticeum* Gaertn. has features distinguish-ing diploid *T. monococcum* from tetraploid wheat arouses interest.[100] Discovering more specifically how genome B was contributed and what its relation to *Agropyron* is, becomes more involved. This genus also has a polyploid series in its evolution. The base is $n = 7$ (Table 12.1).

Some intergeneric hybrids involving *Agropyron* have been made.[5, 11, 9] Hexaploid *T. aestivum* ($n = 21$) and *Agropyron glaucum* ($n = 21$)[88] were combined to make an amphiploid with 84 chromosomes. Strong perennial tendencies arise with these high polyploids. In another case, vigorous plants with 70 chromosomes were derived by adding the hexaploid complements, 42 chromosomes, to the tetra-ploid *Agropyron intermedium,* 28 chromosomes. This particular 70-chromosome fertile hybrid was the first amphiploid to be reported from tests with colchicine.[94]

The genus *Triticum,* represented by three chromosomal levels, $n = 7$, $n = 14$, and $n = 21$, provides much material following inter-specific hybridization. A tetraploid, *T. timopheevi,* has the genome G not common to other well-known species.[26] Another free-threshing tetraploid species, *T. persicum,* produces an interesting series when crossed with *Aegilops squarrosa.*[58] Unquestionably, these amphi-ploids have free-threshing hexaploid bread wheat features.

Within short intervals after colchicine was discovered, more than 80 different amphiploids, involving tetraploid and hexaploid, as well as diploid species of *Triticum* were produced in Russia.[118] Some higher numbers proved to be interesting in their hybridization charac-teristics in subsequent generations. Generally the sterility increased when hybrids above the hexaploid level were created. The ordinary wheat, usually self-pollinated, changed into a cross-fertilizing type as higher-level amphiploids were reached.

The complexity of sterility-fertility relationships appear in the intergeneric and interspecific hybrids among Triticinae.[11, 10, 100, 70, 58]

Chromosomal pairing in the diploid hybrid, or the lack of pairing is not necessarily an index of homology. The intergeneric amphiploid *Aegilops umbellulata* × *Haynaldia villosa* has a reduced fertility.[100] The particular strain made a difference in pairing; environmental and genetic factors, also, influence pairing of chromosomes. Two distantly related species may introduce physiological upsets that cause

TABLE 12.1

DIVERGENT AND CONVERGENT EVOLUTION OF HEXAPLOIDS
(Adapted from McFadden and Sears)

Primary Form Diploid	Divergent Form Diploid	Convergent Form Polyploid

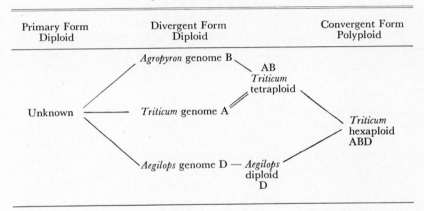

meiotic irregularities.[11] The rule cannot be established that univalency in the F_1 is predictable evidence for obtaining good fertile amphiploids.

Evolution in wheat that finally led to hexaploids may be charted as a divergence in the early period following convergent evolution giving rise to the tetraploid and hexaploid species. Some unknown diploid form evolved into three basic genera: (1) *Agropyron,* (2) *Triticum,* and (3) *Aegilops.* The first two hybridized and gave rise to a series of tetraploid species. A second step in evolution involved the combinations between tetraploid *Triticum* and *Aegilops.* A chart is used to help visualize these evolutionary patterns (Table 12.1).

Since such valuable species have arisen through combinations of genomes, this approach was suggested as a "radical" method of wheat breeding. Desirable characters would be transferred to *T. aestivum* L. by using specific series of synthesized amphiploids. Four were suggested. The first series involves the *D* genome from *Aegilops squarrosa* added to various tetraploids because the hybrids are more fertile than crosses between tetraploids and hexaploids within *Triticum.* A second series involves combinations between tetraploid wheat and

Aegilops other than *A. squarrosa*. Third, the combined genomes *A* and *D* united with various species of *Agropyron* would lead to ways for introducing genes from the latter genes to the present *B* genome of hexaploid wheat. Fourth, the synthesized *B* and *D* genomes added to diploid *Triticum* would allow transfer of einkorn characters to the hexaploid wheat. Such a program is exceedingly involved; however, it merits serious attention. (cf. Chapter 11. Ref. No. 49).

12.2–3: Triticum aestivum L. × *Secale cereale L.– Triticale.* In 1876 the first hybridization between wheat and rye was made. About 4 per cent of hybridizations between wheat and rye give some idea of the success to be expected. Under unusual circumstances a fertile 56-chromosome F_2 can be obtained. An unreduced gamete most likely explains the mode of doubling. Since colchicine became available, new methods[114] have been developed to increase the production of *Triticales*.[18, 35, 77]

There are five well-known strains,[21] (1) Rimpau 1891, (2) Meister 1928, (3) Lebedeff 1934, (4) Taylor 1935, and (5) Müntzing 1936. Since 1936 many more have been made. Actually no accurate record can be given because of the number of unpublished cases.

Biologically the 56-chromosome plant is of interest because the constant number has been maintained in the Rimpau strain after more than fifty generations. Backcrosses to wheat give some index of the stability that *Triticales* can maintain. The 56-chromosome plants survive better, are taller, and maintain a stable genetic mechanism in spite of some meiotic irregularities.[21] At meiosis in the F_1 very little pairing has been observed, 0–3 pairs; and upon doubling, mostly bivalents are seen with as high as 6 unpaired chromosomes in some strains. There is practically no homology between the wheat and rye chromosomes.[21]

Among backcross progenies a pair of rye chromsomes have been substituted for one pair of wheat chromosomes (cf. Chapter 14, Ref. No. 37), so there would appear to be slight possibility for gene exchange under selection. In nature the *Triticale* could evolve as a new species because there is some degree of difference between the strains regarding fertility and segregations in the subsequent generations. However, the *Triticale* would remain at the octoploid level, and consequently, a group of new species could evolve with 56 chromosomes[21] (cf. Chapter 14, Ref. No. 37, 27, 46, 51).

Economically these species bring into one plant two of the world's important bread-producing species, wheat and rye. Since doubling the chromosomes can be done with colchicine, a serious attempt to improve *Triticale* on a large scale should have possibilities.

An all-out attack on this problem was begun in 1939 in Holland; it involved the processing of hundreds and even thousands of combinations.[114] A new method of clonal division and vegetative propagation of the F_1 plant was devised so that several hundred plants could be obtained in one season. These were treated by soaking the roots in colchicine.[114] Fertile spikes indicated 56-chromosome plants. The work was progressing satisfactorily until in 1944 the research plot became the scene for World War II. Because of considerable loss of material and change in personnel, the original plan had to be modified radically.

It is encouraging from the viewpoint of polyploidy that *Triticales* are now regarded as potential breeding material instead of a genetical curiosity, as it was for a good many years.

12.2–4: Artificial and natural polyploids in Gramineae. Large-scale synthesis of polyploids by colchicine can be of use theoretically and practically.[105] Newly created polyploids in grasses were placed for testing on range, pasture, and untended habitats. Following such an introduction, continuing records will show up the potentialities for adaptation of the new species, for the competitive success or failure would become evident after several generations. To a degree, principles governing success apply to polyploidy among intensively culti-vated situations, as well as in pastures or wild habitats.[105]

Among *Triticales* we mentioned the maintenance of constant 56-chromosomal plants after fifty generations of culture. Backcrosses to wheat always favored the more vigorous 56-chromosomal plants. Apparently a stabilizing mechanism operates in the *Triticales* complex. Undoubtedly this is true for many polyploids among grasses where 70 per cent of the species are natural polyploids. Therefore, new polyploids with high numbers and complex genomic additions should bring important facts to our attention.[21]

Such projects involving artificial and natural polyploids carried out by Stebbins and his associates have already added important in-formation.[105, 52] Further research based on long-range objectives will surely advance our knowledge of polyploidy.

In the valleys and foothill regions of California, agricultural prac-tices have created three ecological situations into which natural and artificial polyploids should show differences in adaptation. First, the once native grasslands that have been there are heavily grazed and are now covered with annual species from Europe. Second, ungrazed fields nearby are filled with introduced species. Third, there are pastures suitable for reseeding forage crops or grasses and for con-trolled grazing. Obviously this is a unique situation representing three unstable plant associations. Into these habitats artificial as well as natural polyploids can be introduced by seed and/or vegetative starts.[105]

Large populations of artificial polyploids, both autoploid and amphiploid, were made by colchicine methods.[105] One successful autoploid, *Ehrharta erecta,* will be discussed in the next chapter. Here general outline of the amphiploids will be sketched. Polyploids from 24 interspecific crosses involved six genera: *Bromus, Agropyron, Elymus, Sitanion, Melica,* and *Stipa.* Major emphasis was given to *Bromus* because thirteen combinations were taken from this genus. Considerable cytogenetical information has already accumulated for three out of five recognized sections. Representative species are native to the American continents; perennials and annuals and natural polyploidy series exist.[105]

A polyploid with 112 somatic chromosomes involving *Bromus carinatus* and *B. marginetus* exceeds the 84-chromosome level, highest known for the genus under natural conditions. The artificial polyploid into the C_4 generation was vigorous, apparently more than the F_1 hybrid as shown by considerable vegetative growth that occurred in the garden. A successful allopolyploid with 112 chromosomes was a remarkable new case testifying to an effective use of colchicine when combined with an appropriate hybridization.[105]

Even more notable were the polyploids *B. carinatus-trinii* and *B. maritimus-trinii,* which apparently combine the genomes from seven different ancestral diploid species, thereby being 14-ploid, containing 98 somatic chromosomes. The immediate success demonstrated by these polyploids is of exceptional interest when viewed together with the implications about amphiploidy mentioned in the first section of this chapter. The hybrids were very vigorous and meiotic processes were irregular after doubling; plants in the C_3 and C_4 generation showed seed fertility in the range from 70 to 94 per cent. In all probability this is a successful polyploid.[105]

As shown by this work and an increasing number of other cases, sterility-fertility relationships cannot be predicted in advance. Of all the problems that confront polyploidy breeders, sterility-fertility status among the newly created polyploids may well be the most significant.[52] The lowered fertility in autoploids has been confirmed again and again. A conclusion that amphiploids necessarily have higher fertility can be very misleading. A breeder using artificial polyploidy must face the problems of sterility. Accordingly, two factors stand out as deserving primary consideration: vigor and fertility.

12.3: Gossypium

Special methods were devised for treating interspecific, sterile hybrids of *Gossypium* with colchicine.[3, 7, 27, 34, 54, 69, 106, 119] Since fertile amphiploids would be produced at once upon doubling the number of chromosomes, a theory of the origin of tetraploid species could be tested. Skovsted proposed that the American tetraploids involved genomes from an Asiatic diploid and an American wild diploid species. By hybridization between the Asiatic and American diploids, and doubling of chromosomes, a tetraploid species like *G. hirsutum* arose in nature. Now the test could be repeated experimentally, and those investigators who had been studying species hybrids at the time promptly applied colchicine. The synthesis was announced independently from two laboratories.[7, 43] *G. arboreum* ($n = 13$, Asiatic diploid) $\times$ *G. thurberi* ($n = 13$, American diploid) was changed from a 26-chromosome hybrid to a 52-chromosome amphiploid. The plants were cytologically similar to *G. hirsutum*. The synthetic amphiploid hybridized with natural tetraploids, and surprisingly good pairing at metaphase was obtained. A conclusive experiment had been performed. The hypothesis of Asiatic-American origin of tetraploid cotton was confirmed.[7, 43]

A useful classification[7] was formulated to bring together data about geographical distribution, morphology, chromosomal pairing, numbers, and chromosomal structure differences. The genomes from each region were given letters as follows: (1) Asiatic species, A_1 and A_2; (2) African diploids, B; (3) Australian species, C; (4) American diploid species, D_1 to D_6; and (5) Arabian-India diploids, E. The Asiatic species represent a central position with affinities to American, Australian, and Arabian-Indian species. They are closer in relationship to African species than the other groups. Arabian-Indian species are distant to all and particularly farther from the American diploids. One advantage of this system is the code that can be used for describing amphiploids.[7] If the American tetraploids were derived from an Asiatic and an American source, the amphiploid should read 2 (AD) with an appropriate subscript to indicate the species of tetraploid. Accordingly the *G. hirsutum* would be 2 $(AD)_1$. Table 12.2 illustrates the use of genomes and some of the important species with their geographical distribution.

Experimentally produced amphiploids are potentially new species because the duplications made by hybridization of diploids and doubling the chromosomes do not exactly replicate the natural one.[15] Some kind of differentiation occurred after the first amphiploids arose. A spontaneously occurring amphiploid,[15] *G. davidsonii* $\times$ *G. anomalum,* showed how a new species might have arisen in nature and become isolated from other types. A counterpart of this spontaneously occurring cotton was made by colchicine. The data for these cases were similar.[106]

Problems in polyploidy among species of *Gossypium* were well known before colchicine was discovered.[48] Gene systems were conceived to account for the way in which diploid and tetraploid species became differentiated. By the use of experimentally produced amphiploids, relations between genomes and the problem of speciation could be studied more extensively. Specialists in *Gossypium* began to realize more specifically that problems remained unsolved.[106]

Interspecific hybrids between the two tetraploid species are vigorous and fully fertile in the first generation. These species, G. *hirsutum* and G. *barbadense,* both carry desirable qualities.[15] Attempts to combine the best features of each in a new variety have not been as successful as one might wish.[106] The second generation and subsequent ones give rise to weak, sterile, and undesirable types. Backcrossing to either parent has not led to new levels of improvement. One might well ask if the combining of characters from other species, which are

TABLE 12.2

GENOMES OF *Gossypium*

(After Brown and Beasley, and Menzel)

Natural Species and Tetraploid Tri-species Hybrid	Descriptions	Genome Formula
Gossypium herbaceum L.	Asiatic 13-chromosome	$2A_1$
G. arboreum L.	Asiatic 13-chromosome	$2A_2$
G. anomalum Wawra. and Peyr.	African 13-chromosome	$2B_1$
G. sturtii F. Muell.	Australian 13-chromosome	$2C_1$
G. thurberi Tod.	American 13-chromosome	$2D_1$
G. armourianum Kearney	American 13-chromosome	$2D_{2-1}$
G. harknessii T. S. Brandeg.	American 13-chromosome	$2D_{2-2}$
G. davidsonii Kellogg	American 13-chromosome	$2D_3$
G. klotzchianum Anderss.	American 13-chromosome	$2D_3$
G. aridum (Rose and Standley) Skovsted	American 13-chromosome	$2D_4$
G. raimondii	American 13-chromosome	$2D_5$
G. stocksii M. Mast.	Arabian-Indian 13-chromosome	$2E_1$
G. hirsutum L.	American 26-chromosome	$2(AD)_1$
G. barbadense L.	American 26-chromosome	$2(AD)_2$
Hexaploid G. hirsutum $\times$ herbaceum $\times$ G. harknessii		$2(AD)_1A_1 \times 2D_{2-2}$
Hexaploid G. hirsutum $\times$ arboreum $\times$ G. harknessii		$2(AD)_1A_2 \times 2D_{2-2}$
Hexaploid G. hirsutum $\times$ anomalum $\times$ G. harknessii		$2(AD)_1B_1 \times 2D_{2-2}$
Hexaploid G. hirsutum $\times$ stocksii $\times$ G. armourianum G. harknessii		$2(AD)_1E_1 \times 2D_{2-1} \times 2D_{2-2}$
Hexaploid G. hirsutum $\times$ stocksii $\times$ G. raimondii		$2(AD)_1E_1 \times 2D_5$

possible now that many fertile amphiploids can be produced, will not face the same difficulties confronting a breeder who tries to combine the characters of the already well-known Upland and Sea Island cottons.

If some chromosomal mechanism prevents the recombinations of genes contributed by each parent, then merely growing large progenies and exercising selection can hardly be expected to yield results.[106] The evolution of the tetraploid from diploids can be explained by the hybridization and doubling of chromosomes. This does not explain the differentiation of the tetraploid species after they once originated as an amphiploid. An argument supported by considerable data[106] asserts that a structural differentiation of chromosomes was basic to speciation and this was of the cryptic type, that is, in very small segments, so that a differentiation could not be observed by pairing or irregularly arranged chromosomes at meiotic metaphase. Therefore, a genetic hybridity and a hybridity caused by the differentiation of small chromosomal segments could not be detected by the ordinary genetic and cytological methods. The nature and extent of chromosomal differentiation may be measured by tracing marked genes in subsequent generations and recording the rates at which the genes are lost by successive backcrossing. Such chromosomal differentiation may be important in *Gossypium*.[106] At least, the suggestion has led to reflection on these problems in polyploidy.

Among the second generations of the interspecific hybrid between *G. hirsutum* and *G. barbadense,* asynaptic genes account for the sterility observed, notably when certain parents are used.[7] Genes for asynapsis have been found in both genomes *A* and *D*. By the use of trisomics, additional data about these asynaptic types have been collected. The fully sterile plants eliminate the completely asynaptic types, but partial asynaptic types are carried along.[15] Some of the phenomena attributed to a cryptic structural hybridity might be explained on the basis of asynaptic and partially asynaptic genes.[15]

Sterility resulting from asynaptic genes is a kind of genic[26] sterility and may well be important in such sterility that causes failure in chromosomal pairing. The extreme sterility at the diploid hybrid level can be overcome by doubling the chromosomes. But a sterility due to asynaptic genes is not cured through doubling the number of chromosomes. Later generations introduce new problems in maintaining the fertility level as well as the characters brought together in the hybrid. If by selection some desirable characters contributed into the hybrid are eliminated and undesirable ones retained, polyploid breeding is faced with a difficult task. To incorporate into commercial varieties the desirable characters found in other species can be put down on paper more easily than producing the plants. One step is hybridization and the doubling of chromosomes; the next procedure requires some new approaches.

Certain species are totally incompatible.[15] The tri-species[16] hybrids have overcome these difficulties, for some genomes can be brought together in a tri-species hybrid not possible in a regular hybridization. *Gossypium arboreum* and *G. harknessii* have not been brought together except when the hexaploid *G. hisutum* $\times$ *G. arboreum* was crossed with *G. harknessii*. In this manner a tetraploid brought together genomes $(AD)_1 A_1 D_2$ representing *G. hirsutum, G. arboreum,* and *G. harknessii,* respectively. Six new tetraploid tri-species hybrids were developed by this method[16] (Table 12.2).

From a plant-breeding standpoint, amphiploids incorporating genomes of *G. anomalum, G. raimondii,* and *G. harknessii* with the commercial strains of *hirsutum* are promising and represent a new attack on the problem of cotton improvement.[95] Increases in fiber strength are possible; however, a problem arises when one tries to gain in fiber strength and also maintain the good qualities necessary for commercial varieties of *hirsutum*. Much cytological work is needed; integrating the theoretical knowledge with practical testing appears to be the outstanding problem at the moment. A final practical contribution resulting from the incorporation of characters from other species is promising. Numerous amphiploids have been made in a short time. Much has been done with colchicine as a preliminary to the larger work of sorting out, by polyploid breeding, gains from accumulated knowledge.

Among polygenomic hybrids, mosaics in flower and leaf appeared.[72] Increasing the number of chromosomes shows some increasing tendency toward mosaicism, but number alone does not determine the degree. This is a side problem with no specific explanation except that the polyploids exhibit such characters.[72, 16] Another side problem is the somatic reduction in numbers of chromosomes within a hexaploid species hybrid. An original plant with 78 chromosomes developed sectors that were triploid, having 39 chromosomes. Perhaps the method offers a way to extract useful components from a complex hybrid.[16, 72]

Aneuploids in *Gossypium* are readily developed because the triploids and pentaploids are unbalanced types. Backcrossing and selection for trisomics and tetrasomics are possible among the synthetic polyploids. Resultant aneuploid types have their effects upon leaf texture, color, and structure. New lines with an extra pair of chromosomes, 54 instead of 52, may include Asiatic or American chromosomes placed into the opposite germ plasm.[15] *Intra*specific and *inter*specific trisomics and tetrasomics were obtained. Such lines may be partially stable, fertile, and morphologically distinguishable.[15]

12.4: *Nicotiana*

A theory of evolution was experimentally verified when *N. digluta* was made in 1925. The parental species, *N. tabacum*, a natural tetraploid with 48 chromosomes ($n = 12$), and the diploid *N. glutinosa* were hybridized to make the sterile triploid with 36 chromosomes. A fertile hexaploid was isolated that had 72 chromosomes. This number was a new and high one for the genus. Previous to the development of *N. digluta*, 48 chromosomes was the highest number.[12, 40, 41] Using colchicine, *N. digluta* was resynthesized. Since then numbers higher than hexaploid have been built into polyploids of *Nicotiana*.[56] These polyploids were made by bringing together the proper species in hybridizations and doubling the chromosomes of the hybrids. A combination of three natural tetraploids included 144 chromosomes in one plant.[56] Another report of 176 chromosomes has been made.[60]

The development of plants with high numbers is not the sole objective. Of particular significance is the combining of widely diverse genomes in order to establish higher polyploid-amphiploids that are fertile, vigorous, and relatively stable in later generations of propagation.[56] The changes that take place in subsequent generations of these polyploids show what mechanisms might operate genetically when new species at new levels of chromosomal numbers become established. Furthermore, the effects of selection upon these types are of basic importance.[103, 4]

An important development that resulted from the synthesis of *N. digluta* was the eventual transfer of mosaic resistance to the commercial varieties of tobacco.[111] The necrotic factor from *N. glutinosa* was transferred to the *N. tabacum* genome.[20, 38] An example of polyploid breeding is illustrated by this program. After full review of the work necessary to make the transfer, one becomes convinced that these methods are not short cuts.

Realizing all that was involved in the requirements for transfer and the cytological and genetic data at hand as late as 1943, there was no complete assurance that the factor for resistance in *N. glutinosa* could be incorporated in the genome of *N. tabacum*.[22] Each time the transfer was tried, disadvantageous traits were carried along with the chromosome contributed by *N. glutinosa*. Therefore, the problem was one of maintaining the good features of commercial tobacco varieties and utilizing only the disease resistance of the *glutinosa* type. Fortunately, some chromosomal change occurred during generations of selection, and a true tobacco type with mosaic resistance of the kind noted for *N. glutinosa* appeared in the cultures. The plant had 48 chromosomes and possessed the resistance factor incorporated in the *tabacum* genome.[38] Perhaps one might call the new variety, *N. tabacum* var. *virii* after a type made by Kostoff.[60] No doubt only a small segment of the chromosome from *N. glutinosa* was transferred to a chromosome of *N. tabacum*. If more than a small segment were involved, greater disturbance to the genotypical balance of the *tabacum* genome might be expected.[60]

Evidence that parts of chromosomes were involved was given by the fact that homozygous, low-blooming, mosaic-resistant segregates[111] that were different from the Burley tobacco appeared in backcrossing *N. digluta* to *N. tabacum*. These segregates in one case appeared in the fifth backcrossing generation. Similar segregates were obtained when Gerstel's 50-chromosome "alien additional race," which had a pair of *N. glutinosa* chromosomes, was backcrossed to *N. tabacum*. The number of chromosomes during crossing was reduced to 48. In the process these homozygous, low-blooming, mosaic-resistant plants, that differed from Burley tobacco, appeared much the same as when *N. digluta* was the starting material.[111]

The assumption may be made that an interchange had occurred between the two genomes. In this case a segment was transferred from one chromosome of a genome to another chromosome of the opposite genome. The exchange was small, and transfer was limited to the disease-resistance character. When whole chromosomes of *N. glutinosa* were substituted for a whole chromosome of *N. tabacum*, the differences were such that substitution races differed from regular varieties of tobacco.[111]

Morphologically and genetically distinct populations were isolated among specific amphiploids as well as diploid hybrids. If the selection was directed to a particular character, the progress made toward a certain goal was faster at the diploid level than the amphiploid.[103] Generally, the amphiploid populations were less fertile. The tremendous power of selection that is possible among amphiploids can be demonstrated if the particular type has some intergenomal exchange.[4]

Among species of *Nicotiana* the genetic systems are close enough to permit hybridization, yet removed from each other and sufficiently differentiated to provide sterile hybrids between species. Upon doubling the number of chromosomes, the amphiploids are fertile and partially sterile.[2, 6, 12, 28, 32, 33, 35, 41, 83, 102, 113] There is enough pairing at the diploid level to indicate that in some combinations of species, exchange between genomes can occur. Such exchange leads to interspecific segregation in the F_2 and subsequent generations.

Pairing of chromosomes at the diploid level of interspecific hybrids is not a true picture of pairing when the amphiploid is derived. Five cases with some bivalents at the F_1 stage had no multivalents in the polyploid.[56]

By interspecific hybridizations and doubling of chromosomes, synthetic tetraploids have been made that resemble *N. tabacum,* yet lack the same genotypical balance that exists in the natural species. Even though the diploid species, *N. sylvestris,* and certain diploids of the *tomentosa* group may be combined to make a polyploid that resembles *N. tabacum,* the exact genetic duplication has not been accomplished.[60] Usually the sterile hybrids doubled somatically are female-sterile. Sterility is caused by failure at the embryo-sac stage. When a long procedure of backcrossing was involved, a fairly fertile synthetic *N. tabacum* was obtained.[60] When the synthetic was crossed with a natural species, the segregation in the second generations was like the variability found between varietal crosses.

A list of the amphiploids made with colchicine is necessarily large. There are more objectives involved than have been outlined in this section. *Nicotiana* provides some good material for the study of polyploidy both from a practical and a theoretical point of view.[40, 41, 20, 38, 103, 28, 29, 6, 1, 2, 12, 32, 33, 81, 83, 102]

12.5: Dysploidy Combined With Amphiploidy

Within the Cruciferae a natural group called the *Brassica* comparium by Clausen, Keck, and Heisey, form a dysploid series as follows: $n = 8$, $n = 9$, $n = 10$, $n = 11$, $n = 12$, $n = 17$, $n = 18$. If the artificial amphiploids are added, the series rises to the hexaploid level, i.e., dysploid, $n = 27$ and $n = 28$. At once some fundamental problems can be predicted from what has been said before.

Some notable historical events in cytogenetics occurred with this group. The first cross between radish and cabbage was produced by Sageret in 1826. One century later, Karpechenko demonstrated fertile *Raphanobrassica* plants.[21] After Sageret's time, the cross was repeated by others. With colchicine, autotetraploid *Raphanus* was crossed with autotetraploid *Brassica* thereby repeating the intergeneric hybrid by another method.[37, 59, 73] Previously the sterile diploid hybrid was made, and fertile plants were selected after unreduced gametes united.[44]

Fruit structure in the *Raphanobrassica* polyploids is proportionally radish or cabbage, depending on the genomes present. Accordingly, diploid, triploid, tetraploid, and pentaploid series can be obtained with different doses of whole genomes.[21]

Judging from the total lack of pairing in the F_1 hybrid at diploid levels along with the independence maintained in the amphiploid, gene exchange at diploid level is exceedingly limited. Hybridization and the synthetic amphiploids have raised the level above tetraploidy as illustrated by amphiploids of the *Brassica* comparium.[93, 73, 59, 44, 50, 19, 36, 37, 124, 125]

Three basic genomes are represented by diploid species of *Brassica*; *B. campestris, n* = 10, or *a*; *B. nigra, n* = 8, or *b*; and *B. oleracea, n* = 9, or *c*. There is some evidence of homology between *a* and *c*, but no bivalents are formed between *b* and either *a* or *c*. The tetraploid species *B. carinata* would have genomes *ac cc*; *B. juncea aa bb*; and *B. carinata bb cc*. Accordingly, the hexaploid *B. chinensis* $\times$ *B. carinata* would have *aa bb cc* as genomes, or 27 bivalents.[50]

Economically these genera of the Cruciferae comprise one of the most important groups with world-wide distribution. The number of amphiploids made at the tetraploid level has increased with the use of colchicine. [19, 36, 37, 44, 50, 73, 93, 116, 117, 121]

Synthesized amphiploids, comparable to the natural tetraploid species of *Brassica,* can be hybridized readily and show possibilities for selection in the succeeding generations. A large number of progenies are under study by Gosta Olsson at Svalof, Sweden.

12.6: Other Interspecific Hybrids and Amphiploids

Four species of *Galeopsis,* two diploid and two tetraploid, became subject to colchicine methods as soon as the drug was announced for its polyploidizing action. Since the first Linnean species *Galeopsis tetrahit* L. was produced by hybridizations with the two diploid species, following doubling by gametic non-reduction, one of the first uses for colchicine was a repetition of *Galeopsis tetrahit* L. By first inducing autotetraploid *G. pubescens* and *G. speciosa,* the amphiploid was produced with little difficulty. Within a short time much polyploid material was at hand for this genus.[75]

Cross combinations between diploid and tetraploid *Galeopsis* usually fail, but genomes of diploid species can be hybridized at the tetraploid level, using induced autotetraploids with natural tetraploids.[75] These crosses succeeded. Quantitative conditions control the hybridization. More crosses were made to confirm this point.[75]

The octoploid number, 64, exceeds the optimum number for these genotypes, for octoploid *G. tetrahit* and *G. bifida* are much inferior to the natural tetraploids of these species.[75] Basic cytogenetical data have been increased many fold with the use of colchicine.

Cytogenetical data from certain interspecific hybrids among *Solanum* suggested that there may be small structural differentiations between chromosomes of diploid species.[46] Such changes may have significance in the evolution of species within *Solanum*. At least, considerable data for interspecific hybrids have been accumulated already, and more can be expected.

The case presented for *Gossypium* proposing "cryptic structural differentiation" as a speciation mechanism was recalled as an interpretation for problems in *Solanum*.[46] Certain species of potato carry valuable economic traits, e.g., specific resistance to phytophora, and these would be desirable to incorporate in the present polyploid species, *S. tuberosum.*

A study of meiosis in hybrids between *S. demissum* and *S. rybinii* as well as in haploid *S. demissum* shows pairing and suggests similarities coupled with these observations; the backcrossing of F_1 *S. demissum* $\times$ *S. tuberosum* to *S. tuberosum* showed increased seed set with each backcross.[46] One is led to recall the well-known elimination of donor parent genotypes in certain interspecific backcrosses involving *Gossypium hirsutum* and *G. barbadense*.[106] These species have been studied extensively, and recombintions on a gene-for-gene basis that would permit transfer from one species to another runs into serious difficulty after backcrossing. If a similar situation holds in *Solanum,* then the program of amphiploidy and species hybridization requires further analysis.[46]

Enough similarity exists between genomes of *S. rybinii, S. tuberosum,* and *S. demissum* to produce bivalents. By multiple crosses other species like *S. antipoviczii* can be crossed to *S. tuberosum* through the amphiploid *S. antipoviczii* $\times$ *S. chacoense*.[109] Another case, *S. acaule* and *S. ballsii,* can be introduced through appropriate amphiploids crossed to *S. tuberosum* when the species in question cannot be crossed alone. For practical work such an approach appears promising,[107] of course, dependent upon chromosomal differentiation, which may increase the difficulties considerably.[107, 109, 63, 46]

Three amphiploids can be made within the genus *Cucurbita*.[85] These are: *C. maxima* $\times$ *C. pepo, C. maxima* $\times$ *C. mixta,* and *C. maxima* $\times$ *C. moschata*.[115] The first is self-sterile; the second is slightly self-fertile and segregates noticeably; the third is self-fertile and cross-sterile with parental species. A relatively stable population develops from the third amphiploid with slight segregation. The amphiploid carried insect resistance to squash vine borer (*Melittia satyriniformis* Hubner), contributed by *C. moschata,* plus flavor and fruit characteristics, contributed by *C. maxima.* Diploid varieties, Buttercup, Banana, Golden Hubbard, and Gregory, represent *C maxima;* Butternut, Golden Cushaw, and Kentucky Field, *C. moschata.* According to tests carried out at Cheyenne, Wyoming, Burlington, Vermont, and Feeding Hills, Massachusetts, insect resistance was stabilized. The fruits compared favorably with the comparable varieties. In general, this particular combination may be regarded as a "potential new species" with prospects of becoming valuable economically (cf. Chapter 13).[85]

Theoretical problems must not be disregarded.[115] A variant like *C. pepo* appeared sporadically in the first and later generations of the Eastern material. Taxonomic similarity to *C. pepo* raises the question of interspecific segregations. Some lack of uniformity showed up in the fifth and later generations, where the early stages were uniform and did not segregate for fruit color, shape, and size. Some intergenomal pairing may have occurred. A homology between certain chromosomes was demonstrated with some pairing in the diploid hybrid. Such amphiploids should make excellent material to test the principles basic to amphiploidy and their practical possibilities.[115]

The interspecific hybrid *Trifolium repens* × *T. nigrescens* was made by crossing two colchicine-induced polyploids of the respective species involved.[14] By special culturing methods the hybrid was saved in the seedling stages. The explanation for incompatibility at the tetraploid level can be adapted from the case in diploids.[13] Particularly interesting in the amphiploid *Trifolium* is the fact that the incompatibility applied to diploids and to autoploids holds for the polyploid that brings the two species together. The loci of genes which determine incompatibility must be at the same place in both species; furthermore, intergenomal pairing must occur in order to explain the genetic mechanism of incompatibility through oppositional alleles.

A new species, *Ribes nigrolaria,* was created by the use of colchicine and hybridization. Two Linnean species, *Ribes nigrum,* the black currant, and *R. grossularia,* the gooseberry, were the diploid parents. Thus genomes from two important horticultural species were combined. These were developed and are under observation at the Alnarp Horticultural Station, Sweden, under the direction of Professor Fredrik Nilsson.

Among these and other cases there should come into prominent use new plant breeding materials that combine the genic composition from two or more natural and artificial species. In some instances only a specific trait such as disease resistance may be desired. The key to a new plateau for plant breeders can be found among artificial amphiploids.

REFERENCES

1. ALCARAZ, M. The transmission of resistance to mosaic in tobacco hybrids. 9th Internat. Cong. Genet. Bellagio, Italy. No. 269. 1953.
2. ――――, AND TAMAYO, A. The production of tetraploid plants of *Nicotiana rustica* and *N. tabacum* by use of colchicine. Bol. Inst. Nac. Invest. Agron. Madrid. 11:46–87. 1944.
3. AMIN, K. Application of colchicine to cotton. Indian Farming. 4:257–58. 1943.
4. ANDERSON, E. (*see* Ref. No. 2, Chap. 11) .
5. ARMSTRONG, J., AND McLEMAN, H. Amphiploidy in Triticum-Agropyron hybrids. Sci. Agr. 24:285. 1944.
6. BARTOLUCCI, A. Il fenomeno della poliploidia ed il tabacco. I. L'uso della colchicina e della centrifugazione dei semie per trasformare gl'ibridi sterili in ibridi fertili. Boll. Tech. R. Inst. Sper. Tabacchi Schiafati. 36:141–48. 1939.
7. BEASLEY, J. The production of polyploids in *Gossypium.* Jour. Hered. 31: 39–48. 1940. Meiotic chromosome behavior in species, species hybrids, haploids, and induced polyploids of *Gossypium.* Genetics. 27:25–54. 1942.

8. ———, AND BROWN, M. The production of plants having an extra pair of chromosomes from species hybrids of cotton. Rec. Genet. Soc. Amer. 12:43. 1943.
9. BELL, G. *(see* Ref. No. 9, Chap. 11).
10. ———, AND SACHS, L. Investigations in the *Triticinae*. Jour. Agr. Sci. 43:105–15. 1953.
11. BOYES, J., AND WALKER, G. Causes of sterility in *Triticum-Agropyron* amphiploids. 9th Internat. Cong. Genet. Bellagio, Italy. No. 64. 1953.
12. BRADLEY, M., AND GOODSPEED, T. Colchicine-induced allo and autopolyploidy in *Nicotiana*. Proc. Nat. Acad. Sci. 29:295–301. 1943.
13. BREWBAKER, J. Self incompatibility in diploid and tetraploid *Trifolium hybridum*. 9th Internat. Cong. Genet. Bellagio, Italy. No. 82. 1953.
14. ———, AND KEIM, W. A fertile interspecific hybrid in *Trifolium*. Amer. Nat. Vol. 87, No. 836. P. 323.
15. BROWN, M. Polyploids and aneuploids derived from species hybrids in *Gossypium*. Hereditas. Suppl. Vol. Pp. 15–16. 1949. The spontaneous occurrence of amphiploidy in species hybrids of *Gossypium*. Evolution. 5:25–41. 1951.
16. ———, AND MENZEL, M. New trispecies hybrids in cotton. Jour. Hered. 41:291–95. 1950. Polygenomic hybrids in *Gossypium*. I. Cytology of hexaploids, pentaploids and hexaploid combinations. Genetics. In press.
17. CASADY, A., AND ANDERSON, K. Hybridization, cytological and inheritance studies of a sorghum cross-autotetraploid sudangrass. Agron. Jour. 44:189–94. 1952.
18. CHIN, T. Wheat-rye hybrids. Jour. Hered. 37:195–96. 1946.
19. CHOPINET, R. Sur quelques hybrides expérimentaux interspécifiques et intergénériques chez les Crucifères. C. R. Acad. Sci. Paris. 215:545–47. 1942.
20. CLAUSEN, R. *(see* Ref. No. 17, Chap. 11).
21. CLAUSEN, J., *et al. (see* Ref. No. 18, Chap. 11).
22. CLAYTON, E., AND McKINNEY, H. Resistance to common mosaic disease of tobacco. Phytopath. 31:1140–42. 1941.
23. CUA, L. *(see* Ref. No. 20, Chap. 11).
24. DARROW, G. *(see* Ref. No. 22, Chap. 11).
25. DEODIKAR, G. Cytogenetic studies on crosses of *Gossypium anomalum* with cultivated cottons. I. Indian Jour. Agr. Sci. 19:389–99. 1949.
26. DOBZHANSKY, T. *(see* Ref. No. 24, Chap. 11).
27. DOUWES, H., AND CUANY, R. Progress report from experiment stations 1949–1950. Emp. Cott. Gr. Corp. London. 1951.
28. DUSSEAU, A., *et al. Nicotiana* polyploïdes: espèces tetraploïdes et hybrides interspécifiques amphidiploïdes obtenus par l'action de la colchicine. C. R. Acad. Sci. Paris. 218:124–26. 1944.
29. ———, AND FARDY, A. Comportement cytogenetique de l'hybride interspécifique *Nicotiana rustica* L. var. Zlag (n=24) × *N. paniculata* L. (n=12) hautement stérile transformé en hybride amphidiploïde fertile après traitement à la colchicine. C. R. Soc. Biol. Paris. 137:235–36. 1943. Hybrides amphidiploïdes de *Nicotiana* obtenus par l'action de la colchicine. Rev. Cytol. et Cytophysiol. Vég. 7:24–44. 1944.
30. EIGSTI, O., AND DUSTIN, P., JR. *(see* Ref. No. 28, Chap. 11).
31. EMSWELLER, S., AND LUMSDEN, D. Polyploidy in the Easter lily. Proc. Amer. Soc. Hort. Sci. 42:593–96. 1943.
32. FARDY, A. Espèces tetraploïdes et hybrides interspécifiques amphidiploïdes et triples diploïdes de *Nicotiana*, obtenus par l'action de la colchicine. Publ. Inst. Exp. Tabacs de Bergerac, I Sér. B. 2:121–27. 1945.
33. ———, AND HITIER, H. Hybrides triples obtenus à partir de trois espèces de *Nicotiana* et transformation de ceux-ci en hybrides diploïdes par l'action de la colchicine. C. R. Acad. Sci. Paris. 219:594–96. 1944. Formes amphidiploïdes du genre *Nicotiana* obtenues par l'action de la colchicine. C. R. Acad. Sci. Paris. 220:251–53. 1945. Espèces tetraploïdes et hybrides interspécifiques amphidiploïdes et triples diploïdes de *Nicotiana* obtenus par l'action de la colchicine. C. R. Acad. Agr. France. 33:136–38. 1947.
34. FATALIZADE, F. Acenaphthene-induced polyploidy in *Nicotiana*. C. R. Dokl. Acad. Sci. URSS. 22:180–83. 1939.

35. FORLANI, R. Ibridi Triticum x Secale. Genetica Agraria. Roma. 1:335–43. 1948. Ibridi di Triticinae resi fertili con colchicina. Ann. Sper. Agrar. Roma. 5: 1079–94. 1951.
36. FRANDSEN, K. The experimental formation of Brassica juncea Czern et Coss. Dansk. Bot. Arkiv. 11:1–17. 1943.
37. FUKUSHIMA, E. On the intergeneric F₁ hybrid between Brassica carinata Braun and Raphanus sativus L. Jap. Jour. Genet. 18:202–3. 1942.
38. GERSTEL, D. Inheritance in Nicotiana tabacum. XVII. Genetics. 28:533–36. 1943. XIX. Genetics. 30:448–54. 1945. XX. Jour. Hered. 36:197–206. 1945. XXI. Genetics. 31:421–27. 1946. Transfer of the mosaic-resistance factor between H chromosomes of Nicotiana glutinosa and N. tabacum. Jour. Agr. Res. 76:219–23. 1948.
39. GLOTOV, V. Amphidiploid fertile form of Mentha piperita L. produced by colchicine treatment. C. R. Dokl. Acad. Sci. URSS. 28:450–53. 1940.
40. GOODSPEED, T. (see Ref. No. 34, Chap. 11).
41. ——, AND BRADLEY, M. (see Ref. No. 35, Chap. 11).
42. GYORFFY, B., AND MELCHERS, G. Die Herstellung eines fertilen amphidiploiden Artbastardes Hyoscyamus niger x H. albus durch Behandlung mit Kolchizinlösungen. Naturwiss. 26:547. 1938.
43. HARLAND, S. New polyploids in cotton by the use of colchicine. Trop. Agr. Trinidad. 17:53–54. 1940.
44. HOSODA, T. Fertility of colchicine-induced amphidiploids between Brassica and Raphanus. Agr. and Hort. Japan. 21:515. 1946.
45. HOWARD, H., AND MANTON, I. Autopolyploid and allopolyploid watercress with the description of a new species. Ann. Bot. n.s. 10:1–14. 1946.
46. ——, AND SWAMINATHAN, M. Species differentiation in the section Tuberarium of Solanum with particular reference to the use of interspecific hybridization in breeding. Euphytica. 1:20–28. 1952.
47. HUNZIKER, J. Estudio citogenetico de un hibrido entre Elymus y Agropyron (Gramineae). 9th Internat. Cong. Genet. Bellagio, Italy. No. 304. 1953.
48. HUTCHINSON, J., et al. The evolution of Gossypium. Oxford Univ. Press, England. 160 pp. 1947.
49. INOUE, S. A method for measuring small retardations of structure in living cells. Exp. Cell Res. 2:513–17. 1951.
50. IWASA, S. On the artificially raised abc trigenomic triploid and hexaploid species hybrids in Brassica. Kyushu Univ. Fac. Agr. Sci. B 1390–99. 1951.
51. IYENGAR, N. Cytogenetical investigations on hexaploid cottons. Indian Jour. Agr. Sci. 14:142–51. 1944.
52. JAKOB, K. The cytogenetics of some hybrids and allopolyploid in the genus Bromus (section Bromopsis). 9th Internat. Cong. Genet. Bellagio, Italy. No. 305. 1953.
53. KARPECHENKO, G. (see Ref. No. 41, Chap. 11).
54. KASPARYAN, A. A colchicine-induced amphidiploid-Upland x Egyptian cotton. C. R. Dokl. Acad. Sci. URSS. 26:163–65. 1940.
55. KEHR, A. Monoploidy in Nicotiana. Jour. Hered. 42:107–12. 1951.
56. ——, AND SMITH, H. Multiple genome relationships in Nicotiana. Cornell Univ. Memoir 311. 19 pp. Agr. Exp. Sta., Ithaca, N. Y. 1951.
57. KIHARA, H., AND KONDO, N. Studies on amphidiploids of Aegilops caudata x Ae. umbellata induced by colchicine. Kihara Inst. Biol. Res. Kyoto. Seiken Ziho. 2:24–42. 1943.
58. ——, AND LILIENFELD, F. A new synthesized 6x wheat. Hereditas. Suppl. Vol. Pp. 307–19. 1949.
59. KONDO, N. Chromosome doubling in Secale, Haynaldia and Aegilops. Jap. Jour. Genet. 17:46–53. 1941. A new Raphanobrassica from the cross, 4X-Raphanus sativus L. × 4X-Brassica oleracea L. Jap. Jour. Genet. 18:123–30. 1942.
60. KOSTOFF, D. Nicotine and citric acid content in the progeny of the allopolyploid hybrid N. rustica L. X N. glauca Grah. C. R. Dokl. Acad. Sci. URSS. 22:121–23. 1939. Cytogenetics of the genus Nicotiana. States Printing House, Sofia, Bulgaria. 1073 pp. 1943.

61. KRYTHE, J., AND WELLENSIEK, S. (*see* Ref. No. 44, Chap. 11).
62. LAPIN, V. Production of an amphidiploid basil *Ocimum canum* Sims. X *Ocimum gratissimum* L. by colchicine treatment. C. R. Dokl. Acad. Sci. URSS. 23:84–87. 1939.
63. LIVERMORE, J., AND JOHNSTONE, F. The effect of chromosome doubling on the crossability of *Solanum chacoenese, S. Jamesii* and *S. bulbocastanum* with *S. tuberosum.* Amer. Potato Jour. 17:170–73. 1940.
64. LORZ, A. Personal communication. 1953.
65. LYSENKO, T. (*see* Ref. No. 47, Chap. 11).
66. MALIANI, C. Indagini italiane sui grani perenni. Giorn. Agr. Domen. 61:344. 1951.
67. MATSUMOTO, K., AND KONDO, N. Two new amphidiploids in *Aegilops.* Jap. Jour. Genet. 18:130–33. 1942.
68. MATSUMURA, S. Genetics of some cereals. Ann. Rpt. Nat. Inst. Genet. Japan. 1:22–27. 1951.
69. MAUER, F. On the origin of cultivated species of cotton. A highly fertile triple hybrid. Bull. Acad. Sci. U.S.S.R. Ser. Biol. (*from* Plant Breeding Abst., 1939) 9:318. 1938.
70. McFADDEN, E., AND SEARS, E. The artificial synthesis of *Triticum spelta.* Genetics. 30:14. 1945. The origin of *Triticum spelta* and its free-threshing hexaploid relatives. Jour. Hered. 37:81–89. 1946. 107–16. 1947. *See also* Ref. No. 49, Chap. 11.
71. MENDES, A. Coffee cytology. Hereditas Suppl. Vol. Pp. 628–29. 1949.
72. MENZEL, M., AND BROWN, M. Polygenomic hybrids in *Gossypium.* II. Mosaic formation and somatic reduction. Amer. Jour. Bot. 39:59–69. 1952.
73. MIZUSHIMA, U. On several artificial allopolyploids obtained in the tribe *Brassiceae* of *Cruciferae.* Tohoku Jour. Agr. Res. 1:15–27. 1950.
74. MOTIZUKI, A. Induzierte Amphidiploidie von *Aegilops columnaris* Zhuk. und *Triticum timopheevi* Zhuk. Kihara Inst. Biol. Res. Seiken Ziho. 2:43–54. 1943.
75. MÜNTZING, A. (*see* Ref. No. 51, Chap. 11).
76. MURRAY, M. Colchicine-induced tetraploids in dioecious and monoecious species of the Amaranthaceae. Jour. Hered. 31:477–85. 1940.
77. NAVALIKHINA, N. Restitution of fertility in a wheat-rye hybrid through colchicine treatment. C. R. Dokl. Acad. Sci. URSS. 27:587. 1940.
78. NILSSON, F. Polyploids in *Ribes, Frageria, Raphanus* and *Lactuca.* Hereditas suppl. pp. 34–35. 1949.
79. ———, AND ANDERSSON, E. Polyploidy hos släktet Medicago. Sverig. Utsadesf. Tidskr. LI:363–82. 1941.
80. ———, AND JOHANSSON, E. New types of hybrids within the genus *Fragaria.* Sverig. Pomol. For. Arsskr. 45:146–51. 1944.
81. NOGUTI, Y. Studies on the polyploidy in *Nicotiana* induced by the treatment with colchicine. I. General observations on the autotetraploid of *Nicotiana rustica* and *N. Tabacum.* Jap. Jour. Bot. 10:309–19. 1939.
82. NORDENSKIOLD, H. (*see* Ref. No. 55, Chap. 11).
83. OKA, H. The improvement of *Nicotiana* by means of polyploidy. Agr. and Hort. Japan. 16:2001–2. 1941.
84. PARTHASARATHY, N., AND KEDHARNATH, S. (*see* Ref. No. 57, Chap. 11).
85. PEARSON, O., *et al.* Notes on species crosses in *Cucurbita.* Proc. Amer. Soc. Hort. Sci. 57:310–22. 1951.
86. PERAK, J. *Triticum durum* tetraploide obtenido por colchicina. Ann. Inst. Fitotech. Santa Catalina. 2:7–8. 1940.
87. PESOLA, V. Survey of plant breeding. Dept. Agr. Res. Inst. Finland. Z. Pflanzens. 29:282–87. 1951.
88. PETO, F., AND BOYES, J. Hybridization of *Triticum* and *Agropyron.* VI. Induced fertility in vernal emmer × *A. glaucum.* Can. Jour. Res. Sec. C. Bot. Sci. 18: 230–39. 1940.
89. ———, AND YOUNG, G. Colchicine and the production of new types of forage crops. Nature. 149:641. 1942.
90. POPPE, W. Rpt. 5th Western Wheat Conf. U.S.D.A. Washington. 5:82. 1950.

91. RAMANUJAM, S. An interspecific hybrid in *Sesamums S. orientale* × *S. prostratum* Retz. Curr. Sci. Bangalore. 11:426–28. 1942.

92. ———, AND DESHMUKH, M. Colchicine-induced polyploidy in crop plants. III. Oleiferous *Brassicae*. Indian Jour. Genet. and Plant Breeding. 5:63–81. 1945.

93. ———, AND SRINIVASACHAR, D. Cytogenetic investigations in the genus *Brassica* and the artificial synthesis of *B. juncea*. Indian Jour. Genet. and Plant Breeding. 3:73–88. 1943.

94. RAW, A. Intergeneric hybridization. A preliminary note of investigations on the use of colchicine in inducing fertility. Jour. Dept. Agr. Victoria. 37:50–52. 1939.

95. RICHMOND, T. (*see* Ref. No. 61, Chap. 11).

96. RUDORF, W. Die Bedeutung der Polyploidie für die Evolution und die Pflanzenzüchtung. Angew. Bot. 25:92–101. 1943. Neue Beobachtungen an Bastarden zwischen *Phaseolus vulgaris* L. und *Phaseolus multiflorum* Lam. 9th Internat. Cong. Genet. No. 128. Bellagio, Italy. 1953.

97. RUTTLE, M., AND NEBEL, B. (*see* Ref. No. 62, Chap. 11).

98. SACHS, L. Reproductive isolation in *Triticum*. 9th Internat. Cong. Genet. No. 286. Bellagio, Italy. 1953.

99. SCHROCK, O. Beobachtungen an einem Bastard zwischen Luzerne und Gelbklee und seiner Nachkommenschaft. Zuchter. 15:4–10. 1943. 21:109–10. 1951.

100. SEARS, E. (*see* Ref. No. 64, Chap. 11).

101. SIMONET, M. Production d'amphidiploïdes fertiles et stables par intercroisements d'espèces rendues autotetraploïdes après traitements colchiciniques. C. R. Acad. Agr. France. 33:121–23. 1947. Étude cytogénétique de l'amphidiploïde *Aegilops ventricosa* × *Triticum dicoccoides*. 9th Internat. Cong. Genet. No. 306. Bellagio, Italy, 1953.

102. ———, AND FARDY, A. Comportement cytogénétique d'un hybride amphidiploïde fertile *Nicotiana tabacum* L. var. purpurea Anast. × *N. sylvestris* Speg. et Comes. obtenu après traitements à la colchicine. C. R. Acad. Sci. Paris. 215:378. 1942.

103. SMITH, H. Induction of polyploidy in *Nicotiana* species and species hybrids by treatment with colchicine. Jour. Hered. 30:290–306. 1939. Polyploidy in *Nicotiana*. Amer. Nat. 75:307–9. 1941. The development of morphologically distinct and genetically isolated populations by interspecific hybridization and selection. 9th Internat. Cong. Genet. No. 139. Bellagio, Italy. 1953.

104. SMITH, L. Cytology and genetics of barley. Bot. Rev. 17:1–355. 1951.

105. STEBBINS, G. (*see* Ref. No. 66, Chap. 11). Hereditas Suppl. Pp. 461–85. 1949.

106. STEPHENS, S. I. Colchicine produced polyploids in *Gossypium*. Jour. Genet. 44:272–295. 1942. II. Jour. Genet. 46:303–12. 1945. Meiosis of a triple species hybrid in *Gossypium*. Nature. 153:82–83. 1944. Genome analysis in amphidiploids. Jour. Hered. 40:102–4. 1947. The cytogenetics of speciation in *Gossypium*. I. Selective elimination of the donor parent genotype in interspecific backcrosses. Genetics. 34:627–37. 1949. (*See* Ref. No. 67, Chap. 11).

107. SWAMINATHAN, M. Notes on induced polyploids in the tuber-bearing *Solanum* species and their crossability with *S. tuberosum*. Amer. Potato Jour. 28:472–89. 1951.

108. THOMPSON, W., *et al*. The artificial synthesis of a 42-chromosome species resembling common wheat. Can. Jour. Res. Sec. C. Bot. Sci. 21:134–44. 1943.

109. TOXOPEUS, H. Preliminary account in a new amphidiploid: *Solanum artificiale*. Genetica. 24:93–6. 1947.

110. UNRAU, J. The use of monosomes and nullisomes in cytogenetic studies of common wheat. Sci. Agr. 30:66–89. 1950.

111. VALLEAU, W. The genetics of mosaic resistance in *Nicotiana glutinosa*. Jour. Agr. Res. 78:77–79. 1949. Breeding tobacco for disease resistance. Econ. Bot. 6:69–102. 1952.

112. VAARAMA, A. Inheritance of morphological characters and fertility in the progeny of *Rubus idaeus* × *areticus*. 9th Internat. Cong. Genet. No. 130. Bellagio, Italy. 1953.

113. WARMKE, H., AND BLAKESLEE, A. Induction of simple and multiple polyploidy in *Nicotiana* by colchicine treatment. Jour. Hered. 30:419–32. 1939.

114. WELLENSIEK, S. Methods for producing *Triticales*. Jour. Hered. 38:167–73. 1947.
115. WHITAKER, T., AND BOHN, G. The taxonomy, genetics, production and uses of the cultivated species of *Cucurbita*. Econ. Bot. 4:52–81. 1950.
116. YAKUWA, K. On allopolyploids obtained from 4x *Brassica chinensis* L. × 4x *Brassica napus* L. Jap. Jour. Genet. 19:229–34. 1943.
117. YAMADA, Y. Some field observations on the tetraploid strains of *Brassica pekinensis*. Jap. Jour. Genet. 18:177–78. 1942.
118. ZHEBRAK, A. Production of amphidiploids of *Tr. durum* × *Tr. timopheevi*. C. R. Dokl. Acad. Sci. URSS. 25:56–59. 1939. Production of a *T. timopheevi* × *T. durum* v. *hordeiforme* 010 amphidiploid by colchicine treatment. C. R. Dokl. Acad. Sci. URSS. 29:604–7. 1940. Experimental production of *Triticum polonicum* × *Tr. durum* amphidiploids through colchicine treatment. C. R. Dokl. Acad. Sci. URSS. 29:400–403. 1940. Production of *T. persicum* × *T. timopheevi* amphidiploids. C. R. Dokl. Acad. Sci. URSS. 31:485–87. 1941. Colchicine-induced amphidiploids of *Triticum turgidum* × *Triticum timopheevi*. C. R. Dokl. Acad. Sci. URSS. 31:617–19. 1941. Comparative fertility of amphihaploid and amphidiploid hybrids *T. timopheevi* × *T. durum* v. *hordeiforme* 010. C. R. Dokl. Acad. Sci. URSS. 30:54–56. 1941. Synthesis of new species of wheats. Nature. 153:549–51. 1944. Production of amphidiploids of *Triticum orientale* × *Triticum timopheevi* by colchicine treatment. C. R. Dokl. Acad. Sci. URSS. 42:352–54. 1944.
119. ———, AND RZAEV, M. Mass production of amphidiploids by colchicine treatment in cotton. C. R. Dokl. Acad. Sci. URSS. 26:159–62. 1940.
120. ZHURBIN, A. Comparative study of cell sizes of auto and allopolyploids. C. R. Dokl. Acad. Sci. URSS. 18:467–70. 1938.

ADDITIONAL REFERENCES

121. FRANDSEN, K. The experimental formation of *Brassica napus* L. var. *Oleifera* DC. and *Brassica carinata* Braun. Dansk. Bot. Ark. 12:1–16. 1947.
122. KIHARA, H., *et al.* Morphology and fertility of five new synthesized wheats. Rpt. Kihara Inst. for Biol. Res., Kyoto Seiken Ziho. No. 4:127–40. 1950.
123. LAMM, R. Investigations on some tuber-bearing *Solanum* hybrids. Hereditas. 39:97–112. 1953.
124. NISHIYAMA, I. Polyploid studies in the Brassiceae. Mem. Research Inst. Food Sci., Kyoto Univ. 3:1–14. 1952.
125. NISHIYAMA, I., AND INAMORI, Y. Polyploid studies in the Brassiceae. III. Mem. Research Inst. Food Sci., Kyoto Univ. 5:1–13. 1953.

CHAPTER 13

The Autoploids

13.1: Autotetraploids

Oenothera lamarckiana, var. *gigas,* discovered by Hugo de Vries at the beginning of the twentieth century, proved to have twice the number of chromosomes found in a related species. After colchicine became known, this classic polyploid was repeated.[207] Plants with the doubled number of chromosomes are not considered mutants, even though originally the concept of mutation advanced by de Vries was in part taken from his experiences with *Oenothera.* Increasing the number of chromosomes increases the number of genes, not the kind. No one would consider as mutations the production of diploids from monoploids,[31] or of triploids from hybrids between tetraploids and diploids. Colchicine is not a mutagenic agent in any sense, either for production of chromosomal changes or in its capacity as a polyploidizing agent.[34]

Without exception, the autoploids produce fewer seed than the diploid from which they originated by doubling. Great variations in fertility are found from species to species, from almost total sterility to values as high as 75 per cent.[203] In subsequent generations the fertility level can be raised. Among tetraploid *Melilotus alba* two groups of tetraploids have been isolated, high-fertility and low-fertility lines.[91]

Many comparisons have been made between diploids and the related tetraploids, on a physiological, morphological, chemical, anatomical, ecological, as well as cytogenetic basis. The differences are well known, and the original gigas features have been demonstrated over and over.

Certain problems relating to chromosomal mechanisms and fertility have not yet been solved. Less and less agreement is found on the causes for lowered fertility in the autotetraploids. Autotetraploids from homozygous lines of maize are less fertile than the corresponding types from heterozygous diploids.[171] Comparative studies in *Antirrhinum* showed that between intravarietal and intervarietal tetraploids the problem of fertility involves something more complex than a mere analysis of meiotic disturbances created in the tetraploids.[201]

The ecological requirements of autoploids are not as distinctive from the diploids as are these requirements in amphiploids and their parental diploids.[34] Hybridization does not activate processes in autoploidy, and evolution at the tetraploid level must occur through gene and chromosomal changes which are undoubtedly very slow.

From a practical standpoint, the lowered fertility at once placed the tetraploid at a yield disadvantage. But these facts were well known before colchicine was discovered. The problem in using tetraploids becomes one of balancing the advantages against the disadvantages, and then measuring the net gain, in comparison with the accepted competing diploid varieties. The use of polyploidy is not a quick way to develop new and improved varieties. Some projects were undertaken with high hopes that revolutionary methods were at hand. By now most of those concepts have been revised. For some, polyploidy has been totally dropped as a method for improving varieties. These are instances where the techniques should never have been started; in others, the programs are stopping short of probable success. Revised programs using polyploidy are in progress in many laboratories throughout the world.

13.1—1: The cereals and polyploidy. In the autumn of 1951, large quantities of seed of autotetraploid steel rye were distributed to farmers in Sweden.[132] The first tetraploid rye was made before colchicine was discovered and it proved to be inferior. Therefore, one might suspect other polyploids in rye to be poor. Several more polyploid varieties induced by colchicine have also proved inferior to the best diploid varieties. There were variations in the different tetraploids as well as variation among plants. Finally a superior tetraploid was derived from a diploid variety of steel rye, and this formed the beginning of this valuable series.[132] A report on the cytogenetics and practical value of tetraploid rye is a good guide for steps necessary to develop tetraploid varieties.

Testing the performance of tetraploid rye and diploid varieties was difficult because plots could not be planted side by side. The diploid pollen falling on tetraploid flowers greatly reduced the seed yield of the tetraploid. Therefore, special tests had to be worked out before a demonstration of practical value for the tetraploid rye was possible.

Like all autotetraploids, the cell size was larger than that of the diploid. Pollen measurements were a reliable index for tetraploidy, but even less complex for practical selection was the size of seed, which was larger among tetraploids. When large populations were studied, the diploid and tetraploid spikes could be separated by using the size of seeds for comparison. This was quite as safe as making pollen measurements, so the need for counting chromosomes in the preliminary stages of sorting was not required.[13] Such rules can be adopted for other projects.

In regard to vegetative and floral characters, the tetraploids were taller and of stiffer straws; the degree of tillering was lower; and the number of flowers was reduced. But kernel size and weight exceeded that of the diploid. However, the hectoliter weight values were lower. Tetraploid steel rye had good sprouting ability and was able to stand the winter conditions as well as diploid rye. There were no marked differences in maturity values between the two types. The baking quality of the flour of the tetraploids was superior to the diploid in the preparation of both the soft and the hard breads.[4]

Morphologically, the tetraploid rye, like most autoploids, showed the following differences from the diploid: (1) stems were thicker and stouter; (2) tetraploids were taller; (3) leaves were larger; (4) leaves were thicker; (5) leaves were somewhat shorter and broader; (6) leaves were greener; (7) floral parts were larger; and (8) seeds were larger.[132]

From a practical standpoint, the advantages gained by tetraploid steel rye over the diploid arose from a favorable balance of two positive properties as against the four more or less negative characteristics. The lower seed setting (20–25 per cent), reduced tillering, lower number of flowers per spike, and tendency to shed basal spikelets, were counterbalanced by the superior baking quality of the flour and the improved sprouting ability of the seed.[132]

Artificially produced tetraploids in rice have been made with a number of important varieties.[103] The tetraploids were distinctly larger-grained, heavier-awned, and more robust generally. While the grains were heavier, a reduced fertility counterbalances the gain in weight per grain. Here again tetraploids manifest the usual disadvantage. These raw tetraploids were without immediate practical use for the reasons already well known. Moreover, there was much doubt that by further selection the fertility could be raised high enough to overcome the yield disadvantage from a reduced fertility.

Another approach to polyploidy as a means for improving rice was made. The F_1 hybrids *Oryza sativa* var. *indica* $\times$ *O. sativa* var. *japonica* are very sterile in some combinations. This sterility has blocked the possible utilization of a hybrid between the subspecies. There is no apparent meiotic irregularity in the hybrid, and the causes of sterility remain unknown. Autotetraploids seldom exceeded

60 per cent fertility, while in the parental diploid fertility was over 90 per cent. Yet the hybrid between the subspecies *japonica* and *indica* may even drop to 11 per cent when fertility is measured by seed formation. Sterile F_1's, if doubled, immediately raised the seed formation higher than autotetraploids.[36] As the fertility decreased in a given F_1 hybrid, the fertility increased in the corresponding tetraploid. That is, the more sterile the diploid F_1 hybrid, the higher was its restoration of seed fertility after doubling.[36] Pollen sterility approximated the same rules. Thus the disadvantage met by strict autotetraploidy seems to be overcome in this type of program. Some real obstacles may yet be encountered in trying to stabilize the polyploid that combines *japonica* and *indica* genomes. Further segregation must be studied.

No quick results can be expected in spite of the apparent solution to the fertility problem, for the tetraploids from hybrids are, like all tetraploids, unselected. Judging from the high multivalent formation, segregating progenies in F_2 and later generations can be expected. This fact may offer exceptional plant breeding opportunities along with serious obstacles. Obviously, these plants and such methods will receive attention in the future as another approach toward plant improvement in rice.

An extensive literature is devoted to autotetraploid barley.[200] Some spontaneous $4n$ races have been isolated. Also, colchicine has been used by several investigators. Morphological characters that change with polyploidy are well catalogued along with several excellent physiological studies. The progress has been summarized in a comprehensive review, and little more need be added. The practical uses for barley have not come up to those of autotetraploid rye.

Autotetraploid maize has been followed over a long period, since the earliest strains were made by heat treatment, before colchicine methods were available. Fertility differences cannot be correlated entirely with chromosomal processes at meiosis. The slower growth and reduced fertility are disadvantages of the tetraploid. The doubling of monoploids to autodiploids will be developed in another section.

Other cereals of economic importance, being natural polyploids, require other approaches. The autoploids are inferior to diploids and provide genetic materials only.

13.1—2: Forage, range, and pasture species. Raw polyploids in some species of *Trifolium* showed an immediate advantage over the diploid in forage production.[113] The data were obtained from limited scale testing. When the tetraploids were distributed for larger scale trials, the difficulties not encountered with small tests then appeared.[3]

After revising the methods for making tetraploids and choosing much larger samples, 50 commercial varieties of red clover, new tetraploids superior to the first, were developed.

In Scandinavian countries notable progress has been made with red clover, *T. pratense.* Twenty-eight chromosomes does not appear to exceed the optimal number. The yield of forage is also independent of seed production. The seed setting becomes important for propagation purposes but not yield of forage. At least five major tetraploid varieties have been tested over several areas in Denmark, Norway, and Sweden. The results are encouraging as a method for improving red clover by polyploidy.[113, 63, 92, 220] It is of interest that the new tetraploids in red clover do not necessarily come from the best diploid strains. Only by testing the tetraploids can their true value be judged.

In addition to gigas features valued for forage production, the earlier and more rapid growth in the second year was better than in diploids. Undoubtedly, the tendency toward a perennial habit in polyploids would seem to be correlated with this trait. Susceptibility to insects and diseases are a weakness in most strains, diploids as well as tetraploids, but there were some red clover tetraploids with excellent insect and disease resistance. One red clover strain, Sv. 054, from a diploid variety Merkur had good yielding capacity and resistance to the nematode, clover eel.

Diploid alsike clover, *T. hybridum,* made tetraploid, showed promise at once, giving consistent increases in forage from 15 to 25 per cent. For overwintering capacity the alsike clover was good from the start.[220] Continued successful performance stimulated a change to breeding on the tetraploid level. Without doubt, these two tetraploid clovers have made satisfactory performance.

A third species, *T. repens* (white clover), was not successful, but as this is a natural tetraploid, 32 chromosomes, further increases presumably took the number to 64, a number above the optimum for the species. We must conclude that one cannot draw a general rule for all clover breeding (cf. Chapter 11, Ref. No. 4).

The tetraploid *Melilotus* suffered from a reduced fertility and was not as promising for practical purposes, although there were enough differences in fertility among eight plants of tetraploids to make progress in selecting toward higher fertility.[91] Crosses and selections demonstrated that higher levels of self-fertility could be obtained. If interspecific hybridization could be effected, the combined germplasm would open another avenue for analysis.

Polyploidy has been obtained in *Medicago sativa, M. media, M. lupulina,* and *M. denticulata.*[234] Vigorous strains appeared among these polyploids; however, the usual reductions in seed setting were met. Since there are diploids as well as natural tetraploids within the group, some hybridization would appear possible. The crossing of autotetraploids with natural tetraploids offers a method to be tried.[143]

Phleum pratense was made up in chromosomal series, ranging from diploid to twelve-ploid.[113] Analyses for vigor, forage production, and quality were done to check the optimum number, below or above which poorer performance was noticed. Progenies with 56 to 64 chromosomes were more vigorous than the 42-chromosomal plants or the polyploids with 84 chromosomes. This principle of optimum numbers must be recognized in polyploidy breeding. Hexaploid *Phleum nodosum* was made by first doubling the chromosomes with diploid *P. nodosum*.[152] The tetraploid was treated again and a hexaploid was isolated. Of special interest is the close correspondence between the natural species, *P. pratense* L., and the hexaploid, *P. nodosum*.

Lolium perenne in the tetraploid state was compared to the diploids.[135] Morphological and physiological studies brought to attention characters such as winter injury, sugar content, dry matter, moisture, leaf structure, tillering, and flowers. The autotetraploids of seven species of grasses were compared in regard to both morphological and cytological details. No specific advantages were demonstrated for the tetraploids.

Autotetraploid Sudan grass, *Sorghum vulgare* var. *sudanense,* and Johnson grass, *S. halopense,* were hybridized to make a pasture species.[29] Autotetraploid Sudan grass incorporated better forage characters into the hybrid. One observation confirmed that the autotetraploid would hybridize while the diploid Sudan grass always failed. Later generations followed for this hybrid segregated for the dry and juicy stalk quality. The segregations were closer to 35:1 than 20.8:1, meaning that random chromosome segregation had occurred.[29] These polyploids showed a tremendous possibility for selection.

13.1–3: Polyploidy in fruit, vegetable, flower, and forest species. Polyploidy and fruit improvement in the United States have been summarized in this way. The problem is like that of a "builder surveying the possibilities of his materials and the usefulness of his tools." Materials are enormous and tools are now available. Colchicine is one of those important tools, while the materials include an abundance of plants in nature and under cultivation. "The only limits are his blueprint, his time, and his industry."[39]

The diploid, woodland strawberry, *Fragaria vesca*, $2n = 14$, is found in many parts of the northern hemisphere. Cultivated varieties are octoploids, $8n = 56$. Autotetraploids from *F. vesca*, $4n = 28$, were made and crossed with 56-chromosome cultivated strains. Such hybrids were 42-chromosome hexaploids. These were crossed back to cultivated types and provided material for selection.[190] Further search for natural species useful in polyploidy is underway. Disease resistance, flavor, quality, and size have been incorporated into hexaploids. There were reportedly 24 breeding projects in the U.S.A. engaged in various aspects of strawberry work. There are important cytogenetical strains in polyploid series at hand in the Botany Department at the University of Manchester, England.[73]

Including wild and cultivated varieties, chromosomal series from $2n = 14$ to $12n = 84$ exist among the blackberries and raspberries. Perhaps no other fruit can be correlated any more directly to polyploidy than this one. The Nessberry, Logan, Boysen, along with hundreds of forms of polyploid blackberries are in existence. Since there are polyploids at hand, artificial doubling is not so necessary. Where faster progress may be required, or the changing of sterile hybrids to fertile ones, colchicine serves as a useful tool.[39]

Many cultivated cranberries are diploid, and in nature, tetraploid as well as diploid species exist.[42, 43] Some sterile hexaploids have been reported. By doubling the number of the cultivated diploid, a parental stock was made for crossing with the wild tetraploid. Selections from all the important cultivated diploid varieties were doubled. These types were selfed and hybridized. Such types have been grown on large scale since their origin, and raw polyploids are being converted into genotypically balanced types.

Perhaps polyploidy as a direct mode for improvement in grapes has advanced as far as any fruit crop of the United States. Here naturally occurring sports, often chimeras, proved to be tetraploid. They occurred in sufficient abundance, so that artificial doubling by colchicine has not been necessary. Giant fruited sports from the vinifera and bunch grapes are tetraploid.[155] These studies have progressed to a stage where newly named tetraploid varieties now combine important characters and are distributed as improved types.

Named tetraploid varieties of summer radish were released in Japan and tested widely enough to demonstrate a superiority for the new polyploid. In vigor and growth the tetraploid exceeded the diploid. Outstanding resistance to the common club root disease was obtained with the tetraploid. The usual gigas features accompany these autotetraploid radishes.[144]

Polyploidy in water cress increased the succulence of leaves, which feature made the tetraploid strains more desirable for salads.[81] Increased content of vitamin C in the water cress, which is expected in tetraploids, was an advantage over diploids. One disadvantage was the slower-growing characters of tetraploids. Like the autotetraploid rye, apparently a balance between the positive characters against the negative ones is needed. When an immediate superiority in favor of tetraploids, such as leaf size, succulence, and vitamin content increase can be demonstrated, the promise for future polyploidy breeding offers some hope. Without some initial advantage or promise, the use of polyploidy must be questioned for practical purposes.

Direct autotetraploidy in tomatoes has not brought improvements. There seem to be hybridization possibilities.[24] Similarly, within the large group of *Solanum,* an interspecific hybridization is probably the most useful approach.[209] *S. tuberosum,* the commonly cultivated species, is already polyploid; doubling is therefore of no value. *S. antipoviczii* × *S. chacoense* amphiploid was fertile with *S. tuberosum.* By this procedure the disease resistance to phytophora from one species, *S. antipoviczii,* should be transferable into a polyploid hybrid.[218] The advantages gained from such work can be maintained because vegetative propagation fixed the features once obtained.

The quality of tetraploid muskmelons, *Cucumis melo* L., was definitely superior to the comparable diploid variety.[14] Enough seed can be produced to propagate the tetraploid adequately. These polyploids were made in several laboratories; each reported improvements. In one instance, taste tests were conducted in such a way that identity of ploidy was not revealed. Without exception, the choice fell to the tetraploid. Since ten different varieties were made tetraploid, a larger number of them were used in comparison with the polyploid and diploid.

A new potential economic species of *Cucurbita* was developed by doubling the chromosomes of a hybrid between *C. maxima* and *C. moschata.* One species, *C. moschata,* carried insect resistance to the hybrid while fruit characters were contributed by the other parent. These characters were not entirely stable in the hybrid, but showed more stability in the polyploid. Fruits matured earlier in the amphiploid than in either parent. In the first generation of the amphiploid there was little or no segregation. Later, up to the fifth generation, there appeared segregation for fruit color, shape, and size. Evidently some intergenomal pairing occurred, and occasional bivalents could be observed during meiosis of the diploid interspecific hybrid. A variant that resembled another species, *C. pepo,* appeared. This type was completely sterile to either the 2*n* or 4*n* lines. Since the same variant has reappeared, considerable theoretical interest becomes attached to this segregate. Large-scale tests in several locations showed that a new potential economic species of *Cucurbita* has been made (cf. Chapter 12).

The gigas characters accompanying induced polyploidy became attached to colchicine as soon as the effectiveness of this method was announced. Probably the first plantsmen to give serious attention to colchicine were those interested in developing ornamentals. The reasons for this appeal of larger flowers are easily understood. One hundred and nine varieties chosen by iris fanciers from a total of 12 best selections were studied for chromosome numbers. Not one was diploid, but 108 were tetraploid, and one was triploid. Practically all these were developed and selected without studying chromosomes, but in this case the potential of polyploids was forcefully demonstrated.[54]

It is no surprise to find many persons attracted to the possibilities to be gained from colchicine. Larger flowers were anticipated.

Among the first colchicine-induced tetraploids to be distributed were snapdragon, phlox[52], and marigold. Work with carnation[206], poinsettia[206], day lilies[219], and lilies[54] has yielded tetraploids. There are numerous projects under way with many ornamentals, annuals, perennials, and shrubs. Improved flower size, darker and more compact plants, with greater drought resistance were obtained with tetraploid *Vinca rosea L.*[187] Also the flowering period was extended longer than in the diploid. While seed production was reduced, this disadvantage was balanced with other positive characters in the tetraploid.

13.1–4: Plants yielding special products of economic importance: fibers, oils, latex, drugs, beverages. Autotetraploids increased the size of seed, fruit, leaf, stem, and root, and larger plant organs should yield more substances of economic importance.[236] Oil-bearing seeds such as sesame, *Brassica,* and flax, all have lower seed production as tetraploids. Flax is a notable case where the fertility drops extremely low. Rubber increase in *Koh saghyz* and *Hevea* are objectives. Fiber improvements in *Hibiscus,* cotton, flax, jute, and hemp have been sought via polyploidy. Anabasine in polyploid *Nicotiana* increased with polyploidy.

13.2: Triploidy

Hybrids from a tetraploid seed parent crossed with a diploid pollinator are triploid. As such these are not stable, and both male and female gametes are sterile from unbalanced chromosomal distributions. The vegetative vigor is not lowered, in fact many triploids are extremely vigorous. Among the good varieties of apples, triploids are common. In nature some triploid species are widely distributed. *Polygonatum multiflorum* is an example of a triploid having a range from the northwestern Himalayas throughout Europe.

The two kinds of triploids are the autotriploid and allotriploid. The former arises from an autotetraploid crossed back to the parental diploid, whereas the allotriploids involve two species. In these cases bivalents and univalents are found at meiosis. Triploids offer the opportunity for increasing the frequency of aneuploids since the triploid female gametes are viable with one or two chromosomes above and below the haploid number. Another common practice is doubling the triploid to make hexaploids. Such a bridge is regularly followed in *Gossypium,* where the hybrid between American tetraploid and a species becomes a sterile triploid.

Certain advantages may be gained from triploids that are not possible otherwise. If the optimum chromosomal number is closer to triploid than tetraploid, production may be increased over either diploid or tetraploid. If ripened seeds can be eliminated or reduced, as in the triploid watermelon, a new type fruit is obtained. These features in triploids are limited but seem important.

Finally triploidy raises problems of seed production: an extra propagation of parental stocks to preserve the two types, as well as a specific hybridization to produce the seed for each generation. Success may depend upon solving these problems. Triploid seeds do not germinate as well as those of other polyploids. Furthermore, the cross between tetraploids and diploids cannot be readily made for all autoploids.

13.2–1: Triploids in watermelons. Reasoning from the fact that seedless fruits in nature are due to certain reproductive failures, the idea was conceived that seedless watermelons would result if triploids were made. The female sterility notable among triploids would lead to this achievement. Such work was initiated in Japan in 1939. Ten years later the first triploid watermelon fruits appeared on the market in Japan.[97, 100, 101] This may be regarded by practical breeders as a very short time for the production of a new variety. Triploid watermelons were a new concept involving hybridization and polyploidy breeding procedures.

The tetraploid parents are produced by colchicine applied at the seedling stage. These plants have 44 chromosomes and are easily distinguished from the diploid by seed size, pollen size increase, and other characteristics. After the tetraploids are produced, these varieties become the seed parent with the diploids as pollinators to make the triploid.[97, 100, 235]

Seeds obtained from a tetraploid fruit and pollinated by the diploid are triploid. Upon planting such triploid seed, fruits without seeds may be had. Early in the season, and late, the ovules develop hard coats that resemble seeds. These are empty, but the term *seedless* becomes meaningless when fruits show these cores or empty seeds. Therefore, the term triploid is far more desirable. To avoid these difficulties, the first pistillate flowers are removed to eliminate the fruits with seed shells.[97]

When triploid plants are growing, pollinations must be made by diploids because the pollen of triploids (flowers) is not sufficient to induce fruit development. Thus, interplanting diploids with triploids causes fruit development among triploids. However, the sterility of the female precludes seed setting even though viable diploid pollen is present. This is the general scheme in producing triploid watermelons that under specific circumstances set seedless fruits.

The general procedure of formation of triploid fruits is set forth diagrammatically in Figure 13.1. Only crosses involving the female

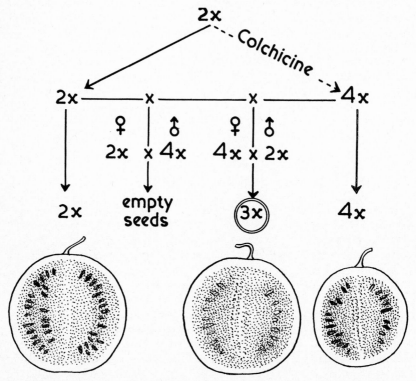

Fig. 13.1—Triploid watermelon. Propagation of triploid seed by crossing diploid and tetraploid lines. Use of colchicine to make tetraploid stocks. Fruits from diploid, triploid, and tetraploid stocks. (Adapted from Kihara)

as tetraploid and the male as diploid pollinator are successful. Reciprocal procedures do not succeed.

As in autotetraploids, the size of flowers increases in proportion to the increase in chromosome number. This relation holds for tetraploid pollen and stomata. Triploid pollen is variable in size and cannot be made to fit the proportional increase as chromosome numbers increase. Many grains are empty while others are full and may be huge.

The 3X seed is a tetraploid seed with triploid embryos obtained from a diploid pollination. The 3X seeds are slightly thinner, averaging 1.7 mm. in thickness as compared with about 2.7 mm. for the 4X seeds. This feature is of practical value in sorting 3X and 4X seeds if the tetraploids are left to open pollination from tetraploid and diploid pollen in the same field. In Figure 13.2 the sizes of diploid and tetraploid seeds are contrasted.

If longitudinal sections are made of mature seed, the diploid, or 2X, seeds show a completely filled cavity, while the 3X and 4X seeds fill the space up to 82.5 and 90.1 per cent, respectively. Accordingly, a weaker germination is a characteristic of the 3X seeds. This becomes a point of considerable practical importance and must be overcome with proper culturing conditions. Such seed cannot be planted in the field with diploid and be expected to produce the same field stand for both varieties.

Genetic markers are helpful to distinguish triploid fruits from tetraploid and diploid. Dark-green, parallel striping is dominant over smooth color, therefore fruits pollinated by diploid with the stripe character show in the triploid if tetraploid fruits are non-striped. Tetraploid fruits may have this mark (Fig. 13.2).

Yielding capacity of triploid plants exceeds the diploid by almost twice. Variations appear depending upon the particular varietal combinations. The increase in number of fruits per unit area is particularly significant both as to number and weight.

Triploid fruits are seedless because chromosome distribution to gametes is irregular. Trivalent associations form among the 33 chromosomes. At reduction division, less than 1 per cent of the gametes obtain a complete set of 11 chromosomes necessary for a balanced gamete. Ninety-nine plus per cent have numbers ranging from 11 to 22 chromosomes. Sterility is induced, and pollination with viable pollen does not produce seed because of female sterility. When pollinations are prevented on triploids, fruits do not set.

Special cultivation procedures are necessary for triploid watermelons: soil should be sterilized, seed planted in beds kept at 30°C., and transplantation procedures carried out to insure a field stand of vigorous plants. Once the triploid is established, its growth exceeds that of the diploid and continues longer during the season. A ratio of 4 or 5 triploid plants to 1 diploid provides adequate pollen to set fruit on triploids; the latter become parthenocarpic.

A summarizing paper by Professor H. Kihara of the Kyoto University, Kyoto, Japan, on triploid watermelons, published in the Proceedings of the American Society for Horticultural Science,[97] was recognized as an outstanding contribution to horticultural science. Accordingly, this publication was chosen to receive the Leonard H. Vaughn Award in vegetable crops. The published works from Volumes 57 and 58 of the Proceedings were considered in the competition for this honor.

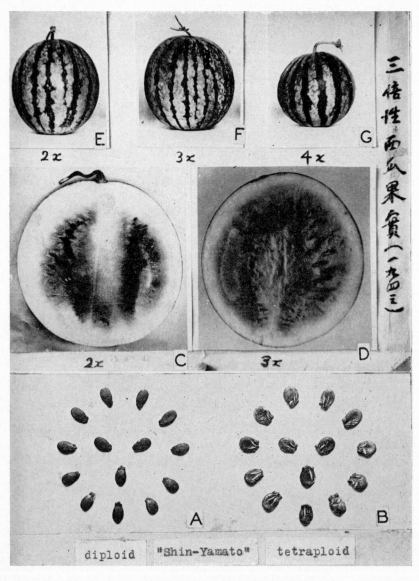

三倍性西瓜果實（一九四三）

Fig. 13.2—Photographs of diploid, triploid, and tetraploid fruit and seed. (Photographs furnished by Professor H. Kihara, Kyoto, Japan)

In Japan, production of triploids as a method for improving watermelon production has been successfully explored. The opinions of American horticulturists on this subject vary with the experiences gained from testing the Japanese varieties. Success is reported in personal communications from Professor E. C. Stevenson, Purdue University, Lafayette, Indiana, and Professor W. S. Barham, North Carolina State College, Raleigh, N. C. Undoubtedly other unpublished reports in America and elsewhere concur in many of the general observations published by Kihara and his associates relative to yield advantages, disease resistance, and improved quality.

Seed production and wide-scale commercial growing will increase as better adapted varieties are made available. Some problems peculiar to cultivating triploids and to seed production need attention in the American system. If watermelons of better quality can be obtained, fruits produced without seeds, or almost so, and if triploid varieties are placed in the hands of commercial growers who can produce melons more profitably than by present methods, the problems of seed production and triploid cultivation will eventually be solved. The time required for this transition in America is difficult to calculate; however, the records of acceptance of hybridization in maize set a standard that might well obtain in watermelon seed production and commercial growing of this fruit.

The application of colchicine to the problems of watermelons represents a most specific and outstanding practical advantage gained from the use of this drug.

13.2–2: Triploid sugar beets. Early in the colchicine era polyploidy breeding was directed at the improvement of sugar beets. Raw tetraploids did not prove to be as good as the parental diploids. This was to be expected for reasons outlined in the section on principles of polyploidy breeding.[8, 63, 113, 114, 122, 172, 185]

A significant report was made that triploid plants yielded more sugar than diploids because the larger roots maintained the same percentage while the diploid tended to reduce the percentage of sugar per hundred grams as the larger-sized beets developed. An additional set of chromosomes raising the number from 18 to 27 did not prove detrimental to volume of sucrose per acre of plants. This represented an important advancement in sugar beet breeding[63] (Fig. 13.3).

If triploids were superior — and this has been shown in several cases — then special procedures were required to produce triploid seed. Tetraploid seed parents are made, and then pollinations are carried out with the diploid. Studies by Japanese workers show practical plans for making triploids.[237]

The increase in sucrose per unit area of cultivated triploids justified the additional work to make triploids which produce more sucrose than either diploid or tetraploid, in this case, the 2X or 4X sugar beets. Intervarietal 3X hybrids between high-yielding tetraploids and disease-resistant diploids will prove better than any of the present triploids.

Large-scale production of 3X seed remains a serious problem. However, the self-incompatibility of the species can be used to ad-

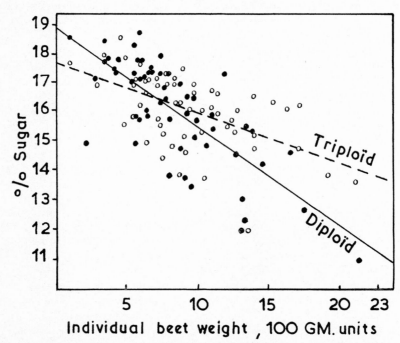

Fig. 13.3—Weight of root and percentage of sucrose production does not decrease at same rate as in diploid when large roots are produced. The addition of another set of chromosomes does not pass the optimum for sugar production per acre. (After Peto and Boyes)

vantage. This alternate planting of 4X and 2X varieties can be used. Seventy per cent of the seeds from the 4X plants are triploid on an open pollination basis. About 30 per cent from diploid are triploid seed. Other factors are involved, such as maturity dates, pollen tube growth, and environment that influences seed production. The optimum number of chromosomes has not been exceeded in the triploid.[121, 122]

Through the cooperative activities of the National Institute of Genetics Laboratory of Plant Breeding, Hokkaido University, the Hokkaido Agricultural Experiment Station, and the Japan Beet Sugar Manufacturing Company, improvement of sugar beet by means of induced polyploidy has progressed very satisfactorily.[237]

The 3X beets are more vigorous; they grow better and always yield more than other beets. Large-scale tests in 1949 and 1950 proved the superiority of the 3X beets.

13.2–3: Triploid fruits. Some of the best varieties of apples, Stayman, Winesap, and Baldwin, are widely known. Since giant sports can be produced by colchicine, in similar fashion to the naturally occurring types, the drug has ready application in apple breeding. Triploids can be made from hybrids between tetraploid and regular diploid varieties. These have possibilities for winter hardiness according to tests by special laboratory equipment.[71] Among 31 tetraploids, two varieties were exceptionally hardy. *Malus baccata,* a diploid species, has been polyploidized and might well be the start for breeding stock.

Triploid guavas have been reported occurring in nature. Such types are seedless. Tetraploids induced by colchicine were promising sources for making crosses between diploid and tetraploid.[86] Assuming that other qualities could be controlled, polyploidy for this economic crop and particularly seedless fruit production should represent an important improvement.[86]

13.3: Monoploids and Autodiploids

The first monoploid plant discovered in 1922 proved that plants existed with one set of chromosomes. More than 30 genera have been added to the list with monoploids reported for one or more species.[95] The improvement of methods for detecting monoploids is an important part of the program. At once geneticists recognized that doubled monoploids became homozygous diploids. The theoretical and practical use for breeding purposes should not be underestimated. Since the first monoploids were reported, the practical value for homozygous breeding stock to produce hybrid maize has been developed extensively.[31]

The frequencies of the appearance of monoploids are low. Their propagation after isolation from diploid cultures depends upon the doubling of chromosomes in tissues that develop the pollen and egg cells. Colchicine serves adequately for increasing the sectors that double to give rise to fertile tissues. The problem that remains is to find ways to increase the frequency of producing monoploids, applicable to a large number of plants.

A prediction was made that the discovery of methods to increase the frequency of monoploids would mark another period in the history of polyploidy breeding (cf. Chapter 11, Ref. No. 43). According to this scheme the *Drosera* research by Rosenberg marked the beginning; a distinction between allopolyploidy and autopolyploidy was the second phase; and colchicine in 1937 was the beginning of the third period. Large-scale production of monoploids is a discovery for the future.

The frequency of increasing monoploids has been improved by special methods adapted for a few species. Twin seedlings proved to have a high incidence of monoploids in flax, cotton, and peppers. The monoploids derived from the twin embryo method were isolated and doubled to make the homozygous diploids.[130, 217] As a basis for improving commercial varieties some application has been made in this direction.[217] Since many seeds can be run over the germinators, more monoploids are discovered than was possible by field selection. *Gossypium* was treated by these methods.[15]

Significant differences in the frequencies of monoploids have been found with certain stocks of maize. Previously selected strains were better than unselected ones. Open-pollinated varieties, generally, were comparatively low for production of parthenogenesis.[31] By appropriate genetic markers, introduced from the pollen parent, the detection of monoploids at seedling stages is improved. Color genes from the pollinator are expressed in the diploid, but not those from the maternal monoploids. Cytological confirmation of the monoploids among the colorless seedlings proved that the marking system was reliable.

Monoploid sugar beet obtained from seed taken from a colchicine-treated shooting plant has been found. Their occurrence is quite rare. In another instance, the monoploids were derived from colchicine-treated populations. An interspecific hybrid of *Nicotiana* produced two monoploid plants. One of the plants was like one parent, *N. glutinosa,* and the other like *N. repanda.* In the original cross the former parent was the female type and latter was used as the pollinator.

An important use for colchicine arises for making autodiploids from monoploids, thereby increasing the number of plants that can be propagated. By spontaneous doubling some sectors regularly produce viable pollen and eggs. Injecting 0.5 ml. colchicine into the scutellar node of the monoploid seedling proved to increase the amount of good pollen produced, an index of doubling.[31] A unique feature and application of the autodiploids of maize arises from the fact that genetic systems are fixed as gametes and testable as such. Thereafter the autodiploid reproduces the fixed system of genes.

13.4: Conclusion

The number of autoploids is larger than that of the amphiploids. Reference numbers in this chapter and other chapters will be useful to check the many kinds of plants already studied. The volume of literature has developed so extensively that every example could not be cited in the space alloted. Only selected examples that pointed out principles and basic features about polyploidy were chosen for the text discussion.

REFERENCES

1. ABEGG, F. The induction of polyploidy in *Beta vulgaris* L. by colchicine treatment. Proc. Amer. Soc. Sugar Beet Techn. 3:118–19. 1940.
2. ABRAHAM, A. Natural and artificial polyploids in tapioca. Proc. 31st Indian Sci. Cong. Assoc. Pt. III. P. 91. 1944.
3. AKERBERG, E., The application of cytology to herbage plant breeding. Imp. Agr. Bur. Joint Publ. 3:52–61. Swedish Seed Assoc. 1940.
4. AKERMAN, A. Swedish Seed Assoc., Ann. Rpt. 1950. Sverig. Utsadesf. Tidskr. 61:124–91. 1951.
5. ANDRES, J. (*see* Ref. No. 3, Chap. 11).
6. ARENKOVA, D. Polyploide Rassen bei der Hirse. C. R. Dokl. Acad. Sci. URSS. 29:332. 1940.
7. ARMSTRONG, J. A tetraploid form of annual rape induced by colchicine. Trans. Roy. Soc. Can. 44:21–38. 1950. Cytological studies in alfalfa polyploids. 9th Internat. Cong. Genet. No. 299. Bellagio, Italy. 1953.
8. ARTSCHWAGER, E. Colchicine-induced tetraploidy in sugar beets: Morphological effects shown in progenies of a number of selections. Proc. Amer. Soc. Sugar Beet Techn. 5:296–303. 1942.
9. ATWOOD, S. The behavior of oppositional alleles in polyploids of *Trifolium repens.* Proc. Nat. Acad. Sci. 30:69–79. 1944.
10. BADENHUIZEN, N. Colchicine-induced tetraploids obtained from plants of economic value. Nature. 147:577. 1941.
11. BAKER, R. Induced polyploid, periclinal chimeras in *Solanum tuberosum.* Amer. Jour. Bot. 30:187–95. 1943.
12. BANNAN, M. Tetraploid *Taraxacum kok-saghyz.* I. Characters of the leaves and inflorescences in the parental colchicine-induced generations. Can. Jour. Res. Sec. C. Bot. Sci. 23:131–43. 1945.
13. BATES, G. Polyploidy induced by colchicine and its economic possibilities. Nature. 144:315–16. 1939.
14. BATRA, S. Induced tetraploidy in muskmelons. Jour. Hered. 43:141–48. 1952.
15. BEASLEY, J. Hybridization, cytology and polyploidy of *Gossypium.* Agr. Exp. Sta., College Station, Texas. Chron. Bot. 6(17/18):394–95. 1941.
16. BELLING, J. (*see* Ref. No. 10, Chap. 11).
17. BERNSTROM, P. Cleisto- and chasmogamic seed setting in di- and tetraploid *Lamium amplexicaule.* Hereditas. 36:492–506. 1950.
18. BHADURI, P. Artificially raised autotetraploid *S. nigrum* and the species problem in the genus *Solanum.* Proc. 32nd Indian Sci. Cong. Pt. III. P. 77. 1945. Artificially induced autotetraploid jute and the problem of making interspecific crosses between *C. olitorius* and *C. capsularis.* Proc. 32nd Indian Sci. Cong. Pt. III. P. 78. 1945.
19. ——, AND CHAKRAVARTY, A. Colchicine-induced autotriploid jutes, *C. capsularis* and *C. olitorius* and the problem of raising improved varieties. Sci. and Culture. 14:5, 212–13. 1948.
20. BLAKESLEE, A. Annual report of director of department of genetics. Carnegie Inst. Wash. Year Book. 40:211–25. 1941.
21. ——, AND AVERY, A. Induction of diploids from haploids by colchicine treatment. Genetics. 24:95. 1939.
22. ——, *et al.* Characteristics of induced polyploids in different species of angiosperms. Genetics. 24:66. 1939. Induction of polyploids in *Datura* and other plants by treatment with colchicine. Genetics. 23:140–41. 1938.
23. BOGYO, T. A. Poliploidia szerepe a fajok kialukulászbán és elter jedésében kulonos figyelemmel a novenynemesitesre, Bethlen Gabor Irodalmi Nyomdai Rt. Budapest. 1941.

24. BOHN, G. Colchicine treatments for use with tomatoes. Jour. Hered. 38:157–60. 1947. Sesquidiploid hybrids of *Lycopersicon esculentum* and *L. peruvianum.* Jour. Agr. Res. 77:33–53. 1948.
25. BRADLEY, M., AND GOODSPEED, T. (*see* Ref. No. 12, Chap. 12).
26. BREMER, G. Personal communication. 1953.
27. CALVINO, E. Esperienze sull'applicazione della colchicina diverse piante da fiore. La Costa Azzura. Sanremo. 23:4–14. 1943.
28. CAMARA, A. Personal communication. 1953.
29. CASADY, A., AND ANDERSON, K. Hybridization, cytological and inheritance studies of a sorghum cross. Agron. Jour. 44:189–94. 1952.
30. CASTRO, D. DE. Two artificial karyological races of *Luzula purpurea.* 9th Internat. Cong. Genet. No. 246. Bellagio, Italy. 1953.
31. CHASE, S. Production of homozygous diploids of maize from monoploids. Agron. Jour. 44:263–67. 1952.
32. CHEN, S. Studies on colchicine-induced autotetraploid barley. I–II. Cytological and morphological observations. Amer. Jour. Bot. 32:103–6. Studies on colchicine-induced autotetraploid barley. III. Physiological studies. Amer. Jour. Bot. 32:177–79. Studies on colchicine-induced autotetraploid barley. IV. Enzyme activities. Amer. Jour. Bot. 32:180–81. 1945.
33. CHOPINET, R. (*see* Ref. No. 19, Chap. 12).
34. CLAUSEN, J., et al. (*see* Ref. No. 18, Chap. 11).
35. CRANE, M. 41st Ann. Rpt. John Innes Hort. Inst. Pomology Dept. Pp. 10–13. 1950.
36. CUA, L. Fertile tetraploids of *Japonica* × *Indica* in rice. Proc. Jap. Acad. 27:43–48. 1951.
37. DALBRO, K. Colchicin-induced chromosome doubling in horticultural plants. Kungl. Vet. Hojsk. Aarsskr. 204–30. 1950.
38. DANIELSSON, B. Polyploida hasseltyper. Sverig. Pomol. For. Arsskv. 46:116–22. 1945.
39. DARROW, G. (*see* Ref. No. 22, Chap. 11).
40. DAWSON, R. Cinchona polyploids. Lloydia. 11:81–85. 1948.
41. DECOUX, L., et al. Résultats préliminaires en vue d'étudier l'action de la colchicine sur le développement de la betterave. Publ. IBAB (Inst. Belge pour l'Amélioration de la Betterave), Tirlemont, Belgium. 10:45. 1942.
42. DERMEN, H. Colchicine, polyploidy and technique. Bot. Rev. 6:599–635. 1940. Inducing polyploidy in peach varieties. Jour. Hered. 38:77–82. Periclinal cytochimeras and histogenesis in cranberry. Amer. Jour. Bot. 34:32–43. 1947. Polyploidy in the apple. Jour. Hered. 43:7–8. 1952.
43. ———, AND BAIN, H. Periclinal and total polyploidy in cranberries induced by colchicine. Proc. Amer. Soc. Hort. Sci. 38:400. 1941. A general cytological study of colchicine polyploidy in cranberry. Amer. Jour. Bot. 31:451–63. 1944.
44. ———, AND DARROW, G. Colchicine-induced tetraploid and 16-ploid strawberries. Proc. Amer. Soc. Hort. Sci. 36:300–301. 1938.
45. ———, AND SCOTT, D. A note on natural and colchicine-induced polyploidy in peaches. Proc. Amer. Soc. Hort. Sci. 36:299. 1938.
46. DOBZHANSKY, T. (*see* Ref. No. 24, Chap. 11).
47. DOIG, J. Experiments with colchicine. Prof. Gard. 1:310. 1949.
48. DORSEY, E. Chromosome doubling in the cereals. Jour. Hered. 30:393–95. 1939.
49. DOUWES, H. Colchicine treatment of young cotton seedlings as a means of inducing polyploidy. Jour. Genet. 51:7–25. 1952.
50. DUSSEAU, A. Effects of tetraploidy in sorghum. C. R. Acad. Sci. Paris. 221:115–16. 1945.
51. EIGSTI, O., AND DUSTIN, P., JR. (*see* Ref. No. 16, Chap. 1).
52. ———, AND TAYLOR, H. The induction of polyploidy in *Phlox* by colchicine. Proc. Okla. Acad. Sci. 22:120–22. 1942.
53. ———, AND TENNEY, B. (*see* Ref. No. 29, Chap. 11).
54. EMSWELLER, S. (*see* Ref. No. 30, Chap. 11). Recent developments in lily breeding techniques. Sci. Monthly. 72:207–16. 1951.
55. ———, AND BRIERLEY, P. Colchicine-induced tetraploidy in *Lilium.* Jour. Hered. 31:223–30. 1940.

56. ———, AND LUMSDEN, D. (*see* Ref. No. 31, Chap. 12) .
57. ———, AND RUTTLE, M. (*see* Ref. No. 31, Chap. 11) .
58. ———, AND STEWART, R. Diploid and tetraploid pollen mother cells in lily chimeras Proc. Amer. Soc. Hort. Sci. 57:414–18. 1951.
59. ERNOULD, L. Le bouturage chez la betterave. Publ. IBAB (Inst. Belge pour l'Amélioration de la Betterave) , Tirlemont, Belgium. 12:55. 1944. L'auto-polyploidie Experimentale chez la betterave. Cellule. 3:363–430. 1946.
60. EVANS, A. Personal communication. 1953.
61. EYSTER, W. The induction of fertility in genetically self-sterile plants. Science. 94:144–45. 1941.
62. FRAHM-LELIVELD, J. Polyploidii bij planten door chemische verbindingen. Chron. Nat. 104:321–34. 1948. Experiments with polyploidogenic and other agents in different types of plants under tropical conditions. Ann. Rev. Bot. Gardens Buitenzorg. 51:231–67. 1949.
63. FRANDSEN, K. Nye iagtagelser over tetraploid og diploid Foderbede. Forelobig Meddelelse fra DLF og FDB's Foredlingsvirksomhed pa Otoftegaard. 1946. Iagtagelser over polyploide Former av nogle Kulturplanter. Tidsskr. f. Plant-eavl. 51:640–65. 1948. Iagtagelser over polyploide Former af Kulturplanter. Beretn. NJF's Kong. Oslo. 508–27. 1948.
64. FUKUSHIMA, E. On the intergeneric F₁ hybrid between *Brassica carinata* Braun and *Raphanus sativus* L. Jap. Jour. Genet. 18:202–3. 1942.
65. FURUSATO, K. Polyploid plants produced by colchicine. Bot. and Zool. 8:1303–11. 1940.
66. FUTUKAITI, S. Tetraploid Asiatic cotton plants induced by the colchicine treatment. Bot. and Zool. 8:597–601. 1940.
67. GABAEV, G. Experiments on colchicine and acenaphthene treatment of the cucumber for the production of polyploids. C. R. Dokl. Acad. Sci. URSS. 28:164–66. 1940.
68. GLOTOV, V. (*see* Ref. No. 39, Chap. 12) .
69. GOLUBINSKIJ, J. A tetraploid form of *Ocinum canum* Sims. experimentally produced. C. R. Dokl. Acad. Sci. URSS. 15:261–62. 1937.
70. GRANER, E. Tratamento de mandioca pela colchicina. I-nota preliminar sôbre polyploida indicada pela diferenca de tamaho dos estômatos. Jour. de Agron. 3:83–98. São Paulo. 1940. Polyploid cassava. (Induced by colchicine treatment.) Jour. Hered. 32 (8) :281–88. 1941.
71. GRANHALL, I., AND OLDEN, E. De tetraploida applenas utny tjande I Vaxt-foradlingarbetet. Balsgard, Sweden. 1952.
72. GYORFFY, B. Tetraploid paprika. Acta Biologica, Pars Bot. (Szeged) . 5:30–38. 1939. Die Colchicinmethode zur Erzeugung polyploider Pflanzen. Zuchter. 12:139–49. 1940.
73. HARLAND, S. Personal communication. 1953.
74. HARTMAIR, V. Eine künstlich erzeugte fertile tetraploide Melone. Bodenkultur. Vienna. 4:142–44. 1950.
75. HECHT, A. Colchicine-induced tetraploidy in *Oenothera*. Proc. Indiana Acad. Sci. 51:87-93. 1942. Induced tetraploids of a self-sterile *Oenothera*. Genetics. 29:69–74. 1944.
76. HELLINGA, G. Colchicine and breeding of forest trees. Tectona. 39:392–94. 1949.
77. HILL, H., AND MEYERS, M. Isolation of diploid and tetraploid clones from mixaploid plants of rye grass, produced by treatment of germinating seeds with colchicine. Jour. Hered. 35:359–61. 1944.
78. HIRAYOSHI, I. Studies on artificial polyploids of forest trees. Bot. and Zool. 10:54–56. 1941. Studies on artificial polyploids in the forest plants. II. Some observations on polyploid *Kiri*. Kihara Inst. Biol. Res. Seiken Ziho. 4:17–21. 1950.
79. HOFMEYER, J. The use of colchicine in horticulture, with special reference to *Carica papaya* L. Farming So. Afr. 16:311–12, 332. 1941. Further studies of tetraploidy in *Carica papaya* L. So. Afr. Jour. Sci. 49:225. 1945.
80. HOSODA, T. (Fertility of amphidiploids between *Brassica* and *Raphanus*) . Agr. and Hort. Tokyo. 21:515. (On the dimension of F₁ seeds in crosses among

Brassica, Sinapis and *Raphanus*). Agr. and Hort. Tokyo. 21:516. 1946. On the fertility of *Raphanus-Brassica* and *Brassica-Raphanus* obtained by colchicine treatment. Jap. Jour. Genet. 22:52–53. On the dimension of F_1 seeds obtained by inter-specific and inter-generic crosses among *Brassica, Sinapis* and *Raphanus*. Jap. Jour. Genet. 22:51–52. 1947.

81. HOWARD, H. The size of seeds in diploid and autotetraploid *Brassica oleracea* L. Jour. Genet. 38:325–40. 1939. The effect of polyploidy and hybridity on seed size in crosses between *Brassica chinensis, B. carinata,* amphidiploid *B. chinensis-carinata,* and autotetraploid *B. chinensis.* Jour. Genet. 43:105–19. 1942. Autotetraploid green watercress. Jour. Hort. Sci. 27:273–77. 1952.

82. HUNTER, A., AND DANIELSSON, B. Induced polyploidy in horticultural crops. Progress Report 1934–1948. Div. Hort., Central Exp. Farm. Ottawa, Canada. Pp. 40–47. 1949.

83. HYDE, B. Forsythia polyploids. Jour. Arnold Arb. 32:155–56. 1951.

84. INOUE, Y. Colchicine-induced tetraploid in Chinese cabbage, *Brassica pekinensis* Rupr. Jap. Jour. Genet. 15:318–19. Tetraploid melons from colchicine treatments. III. Bot. and Zool. 7:1879–82. The results of colchicine treatment on melon. Bot. and Zool. 7:793–94. 1939.

85. ———, AND ABE, S. Tetraploid melons from colchicine treatments. Jour. Hort. Assoc. Japan. 10:109–19. 1939.

86. JANAKI-AMMAL, E. Personal communication. 1953.

87. JARETSKY, R., AND SCHENK, G. Versuche mit Acenaphten und Colchicin an Gramineen und Leguminosenkeimlingen. Jahrb. Wiss. Bot. 99:13–19. 1940.

88. JENSEN, H., AND LEVAN, A. Colchicine-induced tetraploidy in *Sequoia gigantea.* Hereditas. 27:220–24. 1941.

89. JOHNSSON, H. On the C_0 and C_1 generations in *Alnus glutinosa.* Hereditas. 36:205–19. 1950.

90. ———, AND EKLUNDH, C. Colchicinbehandling som method vid Växtförädling av lövträd. Svensk. Papperstid. Medd. 43:355–60. 1940.

91. JOHNSON, I., AND SASS, J. Tetraploidy in *Melilotus alba* induced by colchicine. Proc. Iowa Acad. Sci. 49:254. 1942. Self and cross-fertility relationships and cytology of autotetraploid sweet clover, *Melilotus alba.* Jour. Amer. Soc. Agron. 36:214–27. 1944.

92. JULEN, G. Investigations on diploid, triploid and tetraploid lucerne. Hereditas. 30:567–82. 1944. Clover and timothy breeding; breeding of red and Alsike clover. Hereditas Suppl. Pp. 44–45. 1949.

93. KASPARAYAN, A. (*see* Ref. No. 54, Chap. 12).

94. KEDHARNATH, S., AND PARTHASARATHY, N. Varietal differences in the breeding behaviour of colchicine-induced autotetraploids of chilli, *Capsicum annuum* L. Indian Jour. Genet. and Plant Breeding. 10:14–20. 1950.

95. KEHR, A. (*see* Ref. No. 55, Chap. 12).

96. KIELLANDER, C. Demonstration of the Conifer Department. Hereditas Suppl. Pp. 54–55. 1949.

97. KIHARA, H. Triploid watermelons. Proc. Amer. Soc. Hort. Sci. 58:217–30. 1952.

98. ———, AND KISHIMOTO, E. Erzeugung polyploider Individuen durch Colchicin bei *Celosia cristata.* Agr. and Hort. 13:2623–28. 1938.

99. ———, AND KONDO, N. Studies on amphidiploids of *Aegilops caudata* $\times$ *Ae. umbellata* induced by colchicine. Kihara Inst. Biol. Res. Seiken Ziho. 2:24–42. 1943.

100. ———, AND NISHIYAMA, I. An application of sterility of autotriploids to the breeding of seedless watermelons. Kihara Inst. Biol. Res. Seiken Ziho. 3:92–103. 1947.

101. ———, AND YAMASHITA, K. A preliminary investigation for the formation of tetraploid watermelons. Kihara Inst. Biol. Res. Seiken Ziho. 3:89–92. 1947.

102. KONDO, N. (*see* Ref. No. 59, Chap. 12).

103. KONDO, Y. (An induction of polyploid rice-plants by treatment with colchicine). Agr. and Hort. 17:209–11. 1942.

104. KOSTOFF, D. Irregularity in the mitosis and polyploidy induced by colchicine and acenaphthene. C. R. Dokl. Acad. Sci. URSS. 19 (3) :197–99. 1938.

105. KRISHNASWAMY, N., *et al.* An autotetraploid in the pearl millet. Curr. Sci. 19:252–53. 1950.
106. KRUG, C., AND CARVALHO, A. The genetics of *Coffea.* Vol. 4:127–58. 1951. Academic Press, Inc., New York.
107. KUMAR, L. Induction of polyploidy in crop plants. Curr. Sci. Bangalore. 11: 112–13. 1942. A comparative study of autotetraploid and diploid types in mung. Proc. Indian Acad. Sci. Sect. B 21:266–68. 1945.
108. LAMM, R. Notes on octoploid *Solanum sunae.* Hereditas. 29:193–95. 1943. Self-incompatibility in *Lycopersicon peruvianum* Mill. Hereditas. 36:509–11. 1950.
109. LANGHAM, D. Fertile tetraploids of sesame, *Sesamum indicum* Loew, induced by colchicine. Science. 96:204–5. 1942.
110. LAPIN, V. (*see* Ref. No. 62, Chap. 12) .
111. LARSEN, P. The aspects of polyploidy in the genus Solanum. II. Production of dry matter, rate of photosynthesis and respiration, and development of leaf area in some diploid, autotetraploid and amphidiploid Solanums. K. Danske Vidensk. Selsk. Biol. Medd. 18:1–51. 1943.
112. LATTIN, G. Spontane und induzierte Polyploidie bei Reben. Zuchter. 12:225–31. 1940.
113. LEVAN, A. Tetraploidy and octoploidy induced by colchicine in diploid *Petunia.* Hereditas. 25:109–31. 1939. Framstallning av tetraploid rodklover. Sverig. Utsadesf. Tidskr. 50:115–24. 1940. Plant breeding by the induction of polyploidy and some results in clover. Hereditas. 28:245–46. 1942. The response of some flax strains to tetraploidy. Hereditas. 28:245–46. 1942. Polyploidiforadlingens Nuvarande Lage. Sverig. Utsadesf. Tidskr. Pp. 109–43. 1945. A haploid sugar beet after colchicine treatment. Hereditas. 31:399–410. 1945. Polyploidy in flax, sugar beets and timothy. Hereditas Suppl. Vol. Pp. 46–47. 1949.
114. ——, AND OLSSON, P. On the decreased tendency to bolting in tetraploids of mangels and sugar beets. Hereditas. 30:253–54. 1944
115. LEWIS, D., AND MODLIBOWSKA, I. Genetical studies in pears. IV. Pollen tube growth and incompatibility. Jour. Genet. 43:211–22. 1943.
116. LITTLE, T. Tetraploidy in *Antirrhinum majus* induced by sanguinarine hydrochloride Science 96:188–89 1942.
117. LUTKOV, A. Mass production of tetraploid flax plants by colchicine treatment. C. R. Dokl. Acad. Sci. URSS. 22:175–79. 1939.
118. MALHOTRA, S., AND MEHRA, P. Colchicine-induced autotetraploid *Argemone mexicana.* Proc. 31st Indian Sci. Cong. Assoc. Pt. III. P. 92. 1944.
119. MARTENS, P., *et al.* Obtention par la colchicine, de betteraves sucrières triploïdes et tetraploïdes. Publ. IBAB (Inst. Belge pour l'Amélioration de la Betterave) , Tirlemont, Belgium. 12:251–56. 1944.
120. MASIMA, I. Studies on the tetraploid flax induced by colchicine. Cytologia. 12:460–68. 1942. Chromosome pairing in autotetraploid plants. A review. La Kromosome. 3–4:148–62. 1947.
121. MATSUMURA, S. Induzierte Haploidie und Autotetraploidie bei *Aegilops ovata* L. Bot. Mag. Tokyo. 54:404–13. 1940.
122. ——, *et al.* Genetische und zytologische Untersuchungen bei *Beta*-Arten. II. Colchicininduzierte polyploide Pflanzen und ihre Nachkommen *Beta vulgaris.* Kihara Inst. Biol. Res. Seiken Ziho. 1:16–23. 1942.
123. MEHLQUIST, G. Role of genetics in floriculture. Genetics. 24:75. 1949.
124. MEHRA, P. Colchicine-induced polyploids in *Momordica charantia* and *Hyoscyamus niger.* Proc. 32nd Indian Sci. Cong. Assoc. Pt. III. Pp. 76. 1945.
125. MENDES, A. Polyploid cottons obtained through use of colchicine. I. Cytological observations in octoploid *Gossypium hirsutum.* Bot. Gaz. 102:287–94. 1940. Observacoes citologicas em Coffea. XI. Metodos de tratamento pela colchicina. Bragantia. 7:221–30. 1947. (*see* Ref. No. 71, Chap. 12. 1949) .
126. MENDES, L. Investigacoes preliminares sobre a duplicacao do numero de cromosomios da Seringueira pela acao da colchicina. Inst. Agro. Norte. Bol. Tecn. 7:1–60. 1946.

127. MIZUSHIMA, U. (On the study of allo- and autopolyploids induced in *Brassica, Sinapis* and *Raphanus*). Agr. and Hort. 19:697–700. 1944.

128. MOL, W. DE. Colchicine-Proeven met enige *Scilla*-Soorten ter Verkryging van polyploide Vormen. Naturivet. Tijdschr. Amsterdam. 32 pp. 1950.

129. ———, AND WESTENDORFF, W. Morphologische und cytologische Abweichungen bei *Bellevallia* usw. durch Colchicin, sowie der theoretische und praktische Wert der Colchicin-Behandlung im Vergleich zu dem Werte anderer Mittle. Cellule. 48:261–76. 1940.

130. MORGAN, D., AND RAPPLEYE, R. Twin and triplet pepper seedlings. A study of polyembryony in *Capsicum frutescens*. Jour. Hered. 41:91–95. 1950.

131. MUENDLER, M., AND SCHWANITZ, F. Über einen Ertrags- und Dungungsversuch mit diploiden und autotetraploiden Munchener Bierrettich. Zuchter. 14:137–40. 1942.

132. MÜNTZING, A. Various demonstrations. A. Autotetraploidy in barley and rye, C. Material of ryewheat (Triticale). Hereditas Suppl. Pp. 48–50. 1949. Cytogenetic properties and practical value of tetraploid rye. Hereditas. 37:1–84. 1951.

133. ———, AND RUNQUIST, E. Note on some colchicine-induced polyploids. Hereditas. 25:491–95. 1939.

134. MURRAY, M. Colchicine-induced tetraploids in dioecious and monoecious species of the Amaranthaceae. Jour. Hered. 31:477–85. 1940.

135. MYERS, W. Colchicine-induced tetraploidy in perennial ryegrass (*Lolium perenne*). Jour. Hered. 30:499–504. 1939. Cytology and genetics of forage grasses. Bot. Rev. 13:319–421. 1947.

136. NAKAJIMA, G. The tetraploid plant *Corchorus capsularis* and *Abutilon avicennae* raised by colchicine method. Jap. Jour. Genet. Suppl. Vol. 121–31. 1947. The tetraploid plants in Quamoclit raised by the colchicine method. Jap. Jour. Genet. 25:81–90. 1950.

137. NAKATOMI, S. Induced polyploidy in Asiatic varieties of cotton plant by colchicine treatment. Proc. Crop. Sci. Soc. Japan. 12:16–20. 1940.

138. NAVASHIN, M., AND GERASSIMOVA, H. Production of tetraploid rubber-yielding plant, *Taraxacum koksaghyz* Rodin, and its practical bearing. C. R. Dokl. Acad. Sci. URSS. 31:43–46. 1941.

139. NEGODI, G. Poliploidi da colchicina in *Bellis perennis, B. annua, Antirrhinum orontium, Mimosa pudica, Nigella sativa, Helianthus annuus, Ricinus communis, Cucurbita pepo*. Atti, Mem. Acc. Sci., Modena. 5:15–47. 1941.

140. NEWCOMER, E. A colchicine-induced homozygous tomato obtained through doubling clonal haploids. Proc. Amer. Soc. Hort. Sci. 38:610–12. 1940. A colchicine-induced tetraploid cosmos. Some comparisons with its diploid progenitors. Jour. Hered. 32:161–64. 1941. An F_2 colchicine-induced tetraploid cabbage and some comparisons with its diploid progenitors. J. Elisha Mitchell Sci. Soc. 59:69–72. 1943.

141. NILSSON-EHLE, H. Framstallning af skogsträd med ökat kromosomtal och okat verkesproducsion. Svensk Papperstidning. Nr. 2. 1938.

142. NILSSON, F. Tetraploidi hos päronplantan framkald med hjälp av colchicin. Sverig Pomol. För. Arsskr. 41:103–7. 1940. Polyploids in Ribes, Fragaria, *Raphanus* and *Lactuca*. Hereditas Suppl. Pp. 34–35. 1949. Some experiments with tetraploid tomatoes. Hereditas. 36:181–202. 1950.

143. ———, AND ANDERSSON, E. (*see* Ref. No. 79, Chap. 12).

144. NISHIYAMA, I. Polyploid plants induced by the colchicine method. Jap. Bot. and Zool. 6:74–76. 1938. Studies on artificial polyploid plants. I. Production of tetraploids by treatment with colchicine. Agr. and Hort. Tokyo. 14:1411–22. 1939. Studies on artificial polyploid plants. IV. Comparative studies on 1X-4X plants in *Capsicum annuum* L. Jap. Bot. and Zool. 8:905–13. 1940. Studies on the artificial polyploid plants. VI. On the different growth of the diploid and tetraploid radish in the winter season. Jour. Hort. Assoc. Japan. 13:245–51. 1942. (On the genus cross between autotetraploid plants of *Raphanus* and *Brassica*). Agr. and Hort. Tokyo. 21:11–12. 1947.

145. ———, AND KAWAKAMI, K. Studies on artificial polyploid plants. IX. Yield comparison of diploid and tetraploid radishes in the north of Manchuria. Kihara Inst. Biol. Res. Seiken Ziho. 3:119–22. 1947.

146. ——, AND Matsubayashi, G. *(see* Ref. No. 54, Chap. 11) .
147. ——, AND Meguro, T. Studies on artificial polyploid plants. X. A preliminary cultivation of the tetraploid radish "Minoyonbai-daikon" in Hokkaido. Kihara Inst. Biol. Res. Seiken Ziho. 3:123–24. 1947.
148. ——, *et al.* Studies on artificial polyploid plants. II. The effect of colchicine on germinating seeds. Bot. and Zool. 8:47–52. 1939.
149. Noguti, Y. Studies on the polyploidy in spinach. Jap. Jour. Genet. 19:106–7. 1943.
150. ——, AND Sugawara, T. On the autopolyploids in *Fagopyrum* and *Helianthus.* Jap. Jour. Genet. 18:117–18. 1942.
151. ——, *et al.* Studies on the polyploidy in *Nicotiana* induced by the treatment with colchicine. I. General observations on the autotetraploid of *Nicotiana rustica* and *N. tabacum.* Jap. Jour. Bot. 10:309–19. 1939. Studies on the polyploidy in *Nicotiana* induced by the treatment with colchicine. II. Growth rate and chemical analysis of diploid and its autotetraploid in *Nicotiana rustica* and *N. tabacum.* Jap. Jour. Bot. 10:343–64. 1949.
152. Nordenskiold, H. Synthesis of *Phleum pratense* L. from *P. nodosum* L. Hereditas. 35:190–202. 1949.
153. Nygren, A. The genesis of some Scandinavian species of *Calamagrostis.* Hereditas. 32:131–38. 1946.
154. Okuma, K., AND Oka, H. On the fertility of autotetraploidy. Bot. and Zool. 8:1196–98. 1940.
155. Olmo, H. Breeding new tetraploid grape varieties. Proc. Amer. Soc. Hort. Sci. 41:225–27. 1942.
156. Olsson, G. Auto- and allo-polyploidy in the genus *Brassica.* Hereditas Suppl. Pp. 47–48. 1949.
157. ——, AND Rufelt, B. Spontaneous crossing between diploid and tetraploid *Sinapis alba.* Hereditas. 34:351–65. 1948.
158. Ono, T. Investigations on the production of polyploids of barley and other cereals. Idengaku Zasshi Jap. Jour. Genet. 22:55–56. 1947. Studies on polyploid barley. Jap. Jour. Genet. Suppl. Vol. 1:75–77. 1949.
159 Oomen, H. Polyploidy in canna. Genetics. 24:333–38. 1949.
160. Pal, B., *et al.* Colchicine-induced polyploidy in crop plants. II. Chilli *Capsicum annuum* L. Indian Jour. Genet. and Plant Breeding. 3:115–20. 1941.
161. Parthasarathy, N., AND Kedharnath, S. *(see* Ref. No. 57, Chap. 11) .
162. Perak, J. *Triticum durum* tetraploide obtenido por colchicina. Ann. Inst. Fitotec. Santa Catalina. 2:7–8. 1940.
163. Peto, F., AND Boyes, J. *(see* Ref. No. 58, Chap. 11) .
164. ——, AND Hill, K. Colchicine treatments of sugar beets and the yielding capacity of the resulting polyploids. Proc. Amer. Soc. Sugar Beet Techn. 5:287–95. 1942.
165. ——, AND Young, G. Colchicine and the production of new types of forage crops. Nature. 149:641. 1942.
166. Pienaar, R. Cytogenetic study of the genus *Eragrostis.* Thesis: Library Univ. of Witwatersrand, Johannesburg, South Africa. 1953.
167. Pirschle, K. Wasserkulturversuche mit polyploiden Pflanzen. I, II, Biol. Zentralbl. 62:9, 10, 253–79, 455–82. 1942. Weitere Untersuchungen Über Wachstum und "Ertrag" von Autopolyploiden. 80:126–56, 247–70. Z. Indukt. Abstamm. Vererb. Lehre. 1942.
168. Ramanujam, S., AND Deshmukh, M. Colchicine-induced polyploidy in crop plants. III. Indian Jour. Genet. and Plant Breeding. 5:63–81. 1945.
169. ——, AND Joshi, A. Colchicine-induced polyploidy in crop plants. I. Indian Jour. Agr. Sci. 11:835–49. 1941. Interspecific hybridization in *Nicotiana.* Indian Jour. Genet. and Plant Breeding. 2:80–97. 1942.
170. Randolph, L. An evaluation of induced polyploidy as a method of breeding crop plants. Amer. Nat. 75 (759) :347–65. 1941.
171. Rajan, S., *et al.* Breakdown of tetraploidy in colchicine-induced autotetraploid *Eruca sativa* Lam. Indian Jour. Genet. and Plant Breeding. 10:43–55. 1950.
172. Rasmusson, J., AND Levan, A. Tetraploid sugar beets from colchicine treatments. Hereditas. 25:97–102. 1939.

173. Richharia, R., and Persai, D. Tetraploid til (*Sesamum orientale* L.) from colchicine treatment. Curr. Sci. 9:542. 1940.

174. Ross, H. Die Vererbung der Immunität gegen das Virus X in tetraploidem *Solanum acaule*. 9th Internat. Cong. Genet. No. 273. Bellagio, Italy. 1953.

175. Rudorf, W. (*see* Ref. No. 96, Chap. 12).

176. Ruttle, M., and Nebel, B. (*see* Ref. No. 62, Chap. 11).

177. Rybin, V. Tetraploid *Solanum rybinii* Juz et Buk. produced by colchicine treatment. C. R. Dokl. Acad. Sci. URSS. 27 (2):151–54. 1940.

178. Saharov, V., *et al.* High fertility of buckwheat tetraploids obtained by means of colchicine treatment. Nature. 154:613. 1944.

179. Saito, K. Studies on inducing polyploid flower plants and their utilization. III. Jour. Hort. Assoc. Japan. 19:195–99. 1950.

180. Salomon, E. *Sorghum sudanese* Stapb. tetraploide obtenido por colchicina. Ann. Inst. Fitotec. Santa Catalina. 2:13–16. 1940.

181. Sampayo, T., and Castro, D. Colchicine-induced tetraploidy in *Luzula purpurea* Link. Nature. 166:1114–45. 1950. Observacaoes sobre a autotetraploidia induzia pela colquicina em. Agron. Lusitana. 1951.

182. Sando, W. A colchicine-induced tetraploid in buckwheat. Jour. Hered. 30: 271–72. 1939.

183. Schenk, G. Versuche zur Erzeugung einer polyploiden *Mentha piperita* durch Colchicin und Acanaphten. Die Deutsche Heilflanze, Schriftenreihe. No. 8. 1941.

184. Schildt, R., and Akerberger E. Studier över tetraploid och diploid råg vid Ultunafilialen 1949. Sverig. Utsädesf. Tidskr. 61:254–68. 1951.

185. Schlosser, L. Polyploidie in der Zuckerrübenzüchtung. Deut. Landwirt. Gesell. Mitt. 67:551–52. 1952.

186. Schnack, B. Variaciones producidas en *Salvia splendens* por la accion de la colchicina. Ann. Inst. Fitotec. Santa Catalina. 1:175–80. 1939. Obtencion de polyploides en *Gallardia pulchella* Foug., por la accion de la colchicina. Ann. Inst. Fitotec. Santa Catalina. 2:9–12. 1940.

187. Schnell, L. The induction of polyploidy in *Vinca rosea*. Amer. Jour. Bot. 28:5s. 1941.

188. Schrock, O. (*see* Ref. No. 99, Chap. 12).

189. Schwantz, F. Untersuchungen an polyploiden Pflanzen. VIII. Zuchter. 20: 131–35. 1950.

190. Scott, D. Cytological studies on polyploids derived from tetraploid *Fragaria vesca* and cultivated strawberries. Genetics. 36:311–25. 1951.

191. Sengbusch, R. Polyploider Roggen. Zuchter. 12:185–89. 1940. Polyploide Kulturpflanzen. Zuchter. 13:132–34. 1941.

192. Shalygin, I. Production of tetraploids in *Lolium* by treating germinating seeds with colchicine. C. R. Dokl. Acad. Sci. URSS. 30:527–29. 1941.

193. Shifriss, O. Polyploids in the genus *Cucumis*. Jour. Hered. 33:144–52. 1942.

194. Shimamura, T. Experiments of inducing tetraploid in tomatoes by means of colchicine. Jap. Jour. Genet. 14:304–8. 1938.

195. ———, and Kobayashi, T. Studies on artificial polyploid plants of *Sesamum orientalis* L. Jap. Jour. Genet. 22:29. 1947.

196. Shimotomai, N. The artificially produced polyploids in *Chrysanthemum cinerariaefolium* Visani. Jap. Jour. Genet. 22:30. 1947.

197. Simonet, M. De l'obtention de variétés polyploïdes à grandes fleurs après application de colchicine. Tribune Hort. 23:645–46. De l'obtention d'un *Linum usitatissimum* tetraploïde après application de colchicine. Rev. Hort. 110:159–61. 1938.

198. Sinoto, Y., and Sato, D. Colchicine polyploids in *Fagopyrum*. Bot. and Zool. 7:1398–1402. 1939. Polyploidi de colchicine in *Fagopyrum*. Sci. Genet. 1:354. 1940. Polyploids and aneuploids in *Tricyrtis formosana*. Jap. Jour. Genet. 18:88–90. 1942.

199. Smith, H. Induction of polyploidy in *Nicotiana* species and species hybrids by treatment with colchicine. Jour. Hered. 30:290–306. 1939.

200. Smith, L. Cytology and genetics of barley. Bot. Rev. 17:1–355. 1951.

201. Sparrow, A., *et al.* Comparative cytology of sterile intra- and fertile intervarietal tetraploids of *Antirrhinum majus* L. Amer. Jour. Bot. 29:711–15. 1942

202. STAIR, E., AND SHOWALTER, R. Tetraploidy in tomatoes induced by the use of colchicine. Proc. Amer. Soc. Hort. Sci. 40:383–86. 1942.

203. STEBBINS, G. The significance of polyploidy in plant evolution. Amer. Nat. 74:54–66. Comparative growth rates of diploid and autotetraploid *Stipa lepida*. Amer. Jour. Bot. 28:6s. 1941. The cytological analysis of species hybrids. II. Bot. Rev. 11:463–86. 1945. Types of polyploids. *In* Advances in genetics. Vol. 1. Acad. Press, Inc., New York. 1947. The evolutionary significance of natural and artificial polyploids in the family Gramineae. Hereditas Suppl. Vol. Pp. 461–85. 1949. Variation and evolution in plants. Columbia Univ. Press, New York. 1950.

204. STEINEGGER, E. Polyploidy researches on medicinal plants. Mitt. Natur. Forsch. Ges. Bern. 6. 1949. Der Alkaloidgehalt tetraploider Datura Spezies. Pharm. Acta Helv. 26:188–94. 1951.

205. STEPHENS, S. (*see* Ref. No. 106, Chap. 12).

206. STEWART, R. Colchicine-induced tetraploids in carnations and poinsettias. Proc. Amer. Soc. Hort. Sci. 57:408–10. 1951.

207. STOMPS, T. Über die künstliche Herstellung von *Oenothera lamarckiana* gigas de Vries. Ber. Deutsch. Bot. Ges. 60:125. 1942.

208. STRAUB, J. Chromosomenuntersuchungen an polyploiden Blutenpflanzen. I. Ber. Deutsch. Bot. Ges. 57 (10):531–44. 1939. Die Beseitigung der Selbststerilität durch Polyploidisierung. Ber. Deutsch. Bot. Ges. 59:296–304. 1941.

209. SWAMINATHAN, M. (*see* Ref. No. 107, Chap. 12).

210. TABATA, H., AND KURIYAMA, H. On the chromosome doubling induced by colchicine in rice plant. Jap. Jour. Genet. 24:90–93. 1949.

211. TANG, P., AND LOO, W. Polyploidy in soybean, pea, wheat, and rice, induced by colchicine treatment. Science. 91:222. 1940.

212. TAKENAKA, Y. Notes on cytological observations in *Colchicum* with reference to auto-toxicosis and sterility. Cytologia. 16:95–99. 1950.

213. TANDON, S. Colchicine induced polyploidy in spinach. Curr. Sci. 19:66. 1950. Colchicine-induced polyploidy in *Brassica oleracea* var. botrytis L. Sci. and Culture. 16:483–84. 1951.

214. TATUNO, S., AND TOMINAGA, Y. Über die künstlichen Polyploiden bei *Raphanus sativus* L. Jap. Jour. Genet. 22:31–32. 1947.

215. THOMPSON, R., AND KOSAR, W. Polyploidy in lettuce induced by colchicine. Proc. Amer. Soc. Hort. Sci. 36:641–44. 1939.

216. TOMINAGA, Y. Über die künstlich erzeugten Tetraplonten von *Gossypium*. Jap. Jour. Genet. 21:60–61. 1946. Morphologische und cytologische Untersuchungen über den amphidiploide Gattungsbastard *Heteropappus arenarius* × *Kalimeris incisa*. Jap. Jour. Genet. 21:83. 1946.

217. TOOLE, M., AND BAMFORD, R. The formation of diploid plants from haploid peppers. Jour. Hered. 36:67–70. 1945.

218. TOXOPEUS, H. *Solanum artificiale* and its breeding value. Natuurw. Tijdschr. Nederl. Indie. 102:168–69. 1946. Note on the effect of colchicine treatment of *Hibiscus sabdariffa* and *Hibiscus cannabinus* L. Genetica. 24:330–32. 1948.

219. TRAUB, H. (*see* Ref. No. 68, Chap. 11).

220. TURESSON, G. (*see* Ref. No. 69, Chap. 11).

221. ———, et al. Demonstrations in the experimental garden, Bot. Genet. Inst. Roy. Agr. Coll., Upsala, Sweden. Hereditas Suppl. Vol. Pp. 60–62. 1949.

222. UCHIKAWA, I. Studies on artificial polyploids in vegetable plants. I. Production of tetraploids in *Cucurbita* by treatment with colchicine and acenaphthene. Kihara Inst. Biol. Res. Seiken Ziho. 3:125–44. 1947.

223. VAARAMA, A. Cryptic polyploidy and variation of chromosome number in *Ribes nigrum*. Nature. 162:782. 1948.

224. WARMKE, H. Polyploidy investigations. Annual report of director of department of genetics. Carnegie Inst. Wash. Year Book. 41:186–89. 1942. Experimental polyploidy and rubber content in *Taraxacum kok-saghyz*. Bot. Gaz. 106:316–24. 1945.

225. WEDDLE, C. Two colchicine-induced polyploids of the greenhouse chrysanthemum and their progeny. Proc. Amer. Soc. Hort. Sci. 38:658–60. A species hybrid of Calendula — its F_2 population and its tetraploid. Proc. Amer. Soc. Hort. Sci. 39:393–96. 1941.

226. WEICHSEL, G. Polyploidie, veranlasst durch chemische Mittel, insbesondere Colchicinwirkung bei Leguminosen. Zuchter. 12:25–32. 1940.
227. WEISSENBOCK, K. Studien an colchizinierten Pflanzen. I. Anatomische Unter-suchungen. Phyton. 1:282–300. 1949. Studien an colchizinierten Pflanzen. II. Phyton. 2:134–52. 1950.
228. WEXELSEN, H. Polyploidiforedling. En oversikt. Forskning Fors. Landbruk. Oslo. 1:287–310. 1950.
229. YAMAGUTI, Y. Inheritance of autotetraploid *Portulaca*. Jap. Jour. Genet. Suppl. Vol. 1:119–20. 1949.
230. YAMASAKI, M., *et al*. Polyploid kowliang (*Andropogon sorghum*) induced by colchicine. Agr. and Hort. 15:641–46. 1940.
231. YAMASHITA, K. Cotton plants treated with colchicine. Jap. Jour. Genet. 16: 267–70. 1940.
232. ZHEBRAK, A., AND RZAEV, M. (*see* Ref. No. 119, Chap. 12).
233. ZHURBIN, A. (*see* Ref. No. 120, Chap. 12).

ADDITIONAL REFERENCES

234. ATWOOD, S., AND GRUN, P. Cytogenetics of alfalfa. Bibliog. Genetica. 14:133–88. 1951.
235. FURUSATO, K. The tetraploid watermelon, Kaho, raised by the colchicine method. Rpt. Kihara Inst. for Biol. Res. Kyoto. Seiken Ziho. 5:131–32. 1952.
236. JOSEFSSJN, A. Tetraploida rovor, förädling och Forsök vid Sveriges Utsädes-förening. Sverig. Utsädesf. Tidskr. 3:165–80. 1953.
237. MATSUMURA, S. Improvement of sugar beets by means of triploidy. Science-Sha, 5 Higashi-katamachi, Bunkyo-ku, Tokyo, Japan. 134 pp. 1953.

CHAPTER 14

The Aneuploids

14.1: Aneuploids Among the Treated Generation

The variations in numbers of chromosomes through loss or gain of extras were first appreciated for their possible value in fundamental cytogenetics by Belling and Newton.[26] Since then the aneuploids have been accumulating in large numbers for many genera. A new group of aneuploids was developed when colchicine was used with large populations of treated plants. Certain plants were deficient for a chromosome, and among the diploid species these losses were very rare but significant.[6] All diploid deficient types, including the $2n - 1$ *Datura stramonium* plants, failed to set seed. The origin of such types is an interesting problem, for the action of colchicine must be interpreted somewhat differently from the usual doubling of chromosomes.[4] Apparently a mitotic disturbance, the loss of a chromosome at the time of treatment, is transmitted through mitotic processes until meiosis, when these types are discovered.

That diploid deficient plants are rare is emphasized when we learn that only 55 spontaneously occurring 23-chromosomal types $(2n - 1)$ have been recorded from among more than 2 million *Datura* plants recorded over a period of years.[6] From a standard line *l* of *Datura,* the frequency of a $2n - 1$ plant is 1 out of 20,879 offspring, compared with 7 such types found among 2135 plants growing from treated cultures.[6] The frequencies are increased by colchicine more than 70 times over the naturally occurring rate. Since the records were made from pollen mother cells, only the diploid deficiencies from the subepidermal layer that fell in the germ line were calculated. Therefore, the incidence of $2n - 1$ tissues created by colchicine was higher than these figures show.

Out of 88 plants in the deficient class, 81 were tetraploid deficient kinds, i.e., $4n - 1$ or $4n - 1 - 1$. Similar to the diploid deficient plants, the tetraploid deficient cases arose from the effects of colchicine.[4]

One other fact is striking. There were, in all, 173 chromosomes lost; and the largest type, known as the L chromosome, was missing more often than other types. Previous data for spontaneously occurring *Datura* showed that the 1 + 2, or L chromosome was missing more often than any other type. Special morphological traits are fairly reliable for recording *Datura* progenies.[4]

Before these data were reported, missing chromosomes were known in *Drosophila*. *Nicotiana*[48] heteroploids were obtained by other treatments, and a genetic demonstration proved the loss of chromosomes in a culture of *Hyocyamus niger*. Since the *Datura* work was published, deficient types have been recognized in *Nicotiana*,[48] *Lilium*,[20] and *Eruca*.[39] There must be many that have escaped notice and also records that are not specifically listed here.

If one looks at the recovery stages from colchicine, the explanation for the tetraploid deficient types can be seen easily. One or two chromosomes are left outside the restitution tetraploid nucleus. The causes of a diploid deficient case require additional examination because a c-mitosis leading to a tetraploid restitution nucleus would not have taken place unless a distributed c-mitosis of unequal distribution, 23 and 25 respectively, occurred. The 23-chromosome cell would lead to a deficient cell and the 25 to extra-chromosome types. There is yet another explanation. When grasshopper neuroblasts were treated at certain concentrations that did not completely destroy the spindle, certain chromosomes were lagging. Presumably an incomplete inhibition could cause one chromosome to lag. The fact that the largest chromosome of *Datura* was the one most often missing is of interest.[4] To assume that tetraploid deficient types and the diploid deficiencies arose from a similar action on the spindle appears to be oversimplification of the problem.

Among the progenies of these treated plants there appeared also extra-chromosomal types.[4] The fifteen-year breeding record for *Datura* showed that $0.16 + .019$ per cent of the $2n$ plants recorded were extra-chromosomal types.[6] Among the 2135 plants, $0.52 + .105$ per cent had one or more chromosomes. This value is 3.36 times the probable error, and combining data for two years leads to a value 4.42 times the probable error.[4] An increase caused by colchicine seems a reasonable explanation. Of the extra-chromosomal types induced by colchicine, ten plants had $2n + 1$ chromosomes, one had $2n + 1 + 1$, and three were $4n + 1$. If colchicine increased the frequency, the action had to occur at mitosis during treatment. A specific action on the spindle directed to one chromosome is suggested.

Aneuploids from treatments in *Lilium longiflorum* were analyzed from root tips and not the pollen mother cells.[20] Out of 500 plants treated and analyzed, 303 cases from roots were counted. Eight aneuploids were found; these were either $4n$ deficient or $4n$ plus one chromosome.[20] Among heteroploids in *Nicotiana,* deficient types $(2n - 1)$ like those in *Datura* were found. Similarly, in *Eruca sativa* the plant was lacking two chromosomes, $2n - 2$. No explanation different from that advanced for *Datura* has been made. The deviation originated when colchicine acted on somatic mitosis.

In view of these cases we are prompted to suggest that the subtype of exploded c-metaphase, the distributed c-metaphase, should be studied further with respect to unequal distributions of chromosomes following treatment with colchicine. Activity of this type was often observed in pollen tubes of *Polygonatum,* but the relation to such phenomena has been for the most part overlooked. As a basis for an action of colchicine on mitosis that leads to numbers other than the true polyploids, illustrations are abundant in cultures of pollen tubes which account for a variety of deviating numbers that might occur when colchicine acts on mitosis.

14.2: Mixoploidy From Colchicine

The action of colchicine upon individual cells was emphasized in the first studies with *Allium* roots. A single root tip treated for 72 hours may yield cells with many chromosomes while other cells remain diploid. It has been confirmed many times that within one meristematic group there may remain diploid cells alongside tetraploids. Such tissues are described as mixoploid. These cases should not be confused with sectorial chimeras since the word means *mixed together.*

A cyto-histological study of maize after treatment with colchicine showed that different areas may become tetraploid more readily than others.[41] Treatment of maize plants with colchicine rarely gives rise to a completely tetraploid plant.[41] Certain branches of the tassel show tetraploid, and others, diploid pollen. Whether these are true sectorial chimeras or the result of mixoploid conditions has not been decided.

Another case of mixoploid tissues from treated plants was followed through enough generations to prove that mixoploids were involved rather than sectorial chimeras.[24] *Lolium perenne* L., $2n = 14$, was originally treated by subjecting seed to colchicine.[24] Plants with tetraploid cells, determined by measurements of pollen grains and chromosomal counts in root tips, were isolated. Supposedly tetraploid tillers were being separated and transplanted. Also some clones were separated as progenitors for control diploid clones. Selections were again made for diploid and tetraploid clones.[24] As before, chromosomes were counted. For two generations such propagation was continued, yet mixoploid tissues persisted into the seventh gen-

eration of vegetative propagation in spite of well planned and carefully followed methods of determining numbers of chromosomes.
These seven generations were preceded by four vegetative generations
in which two were selected after chromosomes were determined to
guide the selection.

In some cases individual anthers yielded diploid and tetraploid
microspore mother cells.[20] Clearly a mixoploid tissue gave rise to
these anthers. Remembering that tested plants were removed from
the tetraploid progenitors by several generations of propagation, the
persistence of diploid and tetraploid cells with neither one crowding
out the other is of particular interest. *Lilium* is considered to be
tetraploid on the basis of chromosome counts; yet diploid and tetraploid pollen mother cells have been found in the same anther of
lilies.[20] In one test a generation was grown by scale propagation and
ten plants were selected. One plant from scale propagation and three
plants obtained by dividing the original bulb yielded flowers with
anthers that had both diploid and tetraploid cells. The parent plant
was supposedly a tetraploid.

Both cases mentioned here, *Lilium* and *Lolium,* represent vegetative propagations, and in each instance colchicine created a mixoploid tissue. Projects that involve vegetative increase present complex
problems, the true nature of which remains unsolved.

14.3: Chimeras Induced by Colchicine

In longitudinal section, the apical meristem of *Vinca rosea* L.
shows a distinct layering of cells.[14] These are clearly illustrated with
the photomicrograph in Figure 14.1, *A* and *B.* Using terminology
promoted by plant anatomists, the first layer is called T_1 and the next
T_2. These, then, refer to the first and second layers of a *tunica.* The
third layer and cells deeper in the apex are called the *corpus,* initialed
C_1 and C_2. Lower than C_2 no specific layers can be observed.[14]

From species to species the limits of the tunica and corpus may
vary. For example, *Vinca minor* L., obviously related to *V. rosea,* was
described with three layers of tunica and a fourth as the corpus. If
the older terminology of Hanstein is related to the tunica-corpus
concept using *Vinca minor* as an example, then T_1 is equivalent to
Hanstein's dermatogen, T_2 and T_3 are the same as periblem, and C_1
is the plerome. Another and different labeling has been used in recent cyto-chimeral studies following polyploidy induced by colchicine.
The layers are called *L*-I, *L*-II, and *L*-III, etc. without reference to a
tunica and corpus.[14]

The point to be strongly emphasized here is not the terminology
but the fact that the various layers make a definite and precise contribution to the shoot axis and to such parts of shoot as the flower

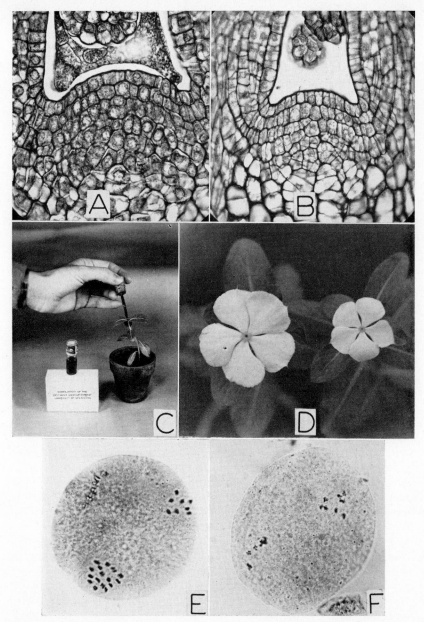

Fig. 14.1—A comparative study of **Vinca rosea** L. diploid and tetraploid strains. **A.** Shoot apex of tetraploid plants showing layers of cells, outermost is the first tunica or T$_1$, second layer T$_2$, third layer C$_1$, and deeper strata become C$_2$, etc. **B.** Shoot apex of diploid plant and foliar primordia. **C.** Brush method for treating young plants with colchicine. **D.** Size differences between the tetraploid and diploid flowers. Larger flower is tetraploid. **E.** Tetraploid pollen mother cell, n—16. **F.** Diploid pollen mother cell, n—8. (Contributions from the Botany Department, University of Oklahoma, Norman, Oklahoma. Adapted from Schnell)

parts and leaf. Since the cells of the first layer at the apex always divide anticlinally and not periclinally, all epidermal cells trace their origin back to the first layer as seen in the shoot apex. Accordingly, the second layer divides anticlinally, and tissues originating from the second layer will be independent in genetic make-up from the first, and in many cases from the third. If colchicine changes the cells of the first layer to tetraploidy while the second layer remains diploid, then the epidermal cells will be tetraploid and the pollen grains diploid, because the sporogenous tissues originate from the second layer. This condition is called a periclinal chimera. Various combinations can be had.

When geneticists realized that the treated plants might look like tetraploids yet reproduce as diploids, the significance of periclinal chimeras began to be truly appreciated.[7, 8] Moreover, developmental problems can be traced with closer attention to the origin of tissues, because specific periclinal chimeras should yield certain results in the mature organs.[42, 43, 44] If the pollen develops from the second layer, T_2, just beneath the epidermis, which is T_1, then diploidy and tetraploidy will be found in pollen and epidermis according to the changes in T_1 and T_2. That is to say, a tetraploid second layer, T_2, should produce tetraploid pollen mother cells while diploid guard cells originate from diploid T_1. The situation has been proved to be just that way. These are periclinal chimeras.

An important series in *Datura* was clearly described showing that the development of petals, sepals, pistil, ovules, and stamen could be traced back to specific layers of the apical meristem. Similar periclinal chimeras were found in the cranberry.[16] Cyto-histological changes were described in detail. One important conclusion was reached. Stem and lateral bud apices were seldom converted into total polyploidy. Therefore, semiwoody and woody plants propagated following treatment with colchicine, required special attention with care given to the nature of polyploidy induced.[16] Periclinal chimeras following treatment with colchicine have been reported many times since the first cases were reported for *Datura*.[42, 45]

By induced polyploidy, specific and discrete layers were demonstrated for *Datura stramonium* L.[42] The leaf and flower were traced back to the shoot apex. One important type useful in detecting origins was a diploid outer layer, an octoploid second layer, and a diploid third layer.[42] Any tissue that originated with an octoploid layer was unquestionably marked by the size of cells. Development of the carpel was traced in *Datura*.[42] The periclinal chimeras were used to discover specifically how the style, stigma, calyx, and corolla differentiated. In questions regarding axial or foliar origin for such parts as the stamen it can be stated more precisely how development takes place.

When numerous periclinal chimeras were demonstrated among well-known varieties of apples, interest was again intensified because the breeding behavior depended upon the specific chromosomal nature of a particular chimera.[15, 16] If the layer that produced pollen was diploid, triploid, or tetraploid, then entirely different results in hybridization could be expected. Periclinal tetraploid giant sports of McIntosh should be of great interest since tetraploids in subepidermal layers breed on the tetraploid level.[16] Some important varieties are triploid, many are diploid, while some sports are chimeras. Two naturally occurring chimeras in apples are: (1) the 2-4-2 type and (2) the 2-2-4.

The pomological curiosity known as "sweet and sour" from the Rhode Island Greening is meaningfully interpreted as a periclinal chimera. The sour portion originates from the outer layer and the third layer, whereas the sweet portion takes its origin from the second layer.[16]

Seven years after colchicine treatment, a McIntosh tree bore fruit that was giant-like, and similar to the diploid-tetraploid periclinal sport which occurs in nature. The induced type proved to be a periclinal chimera. By adventitious buds that originate from deeper layers, a complete tetraploid stock can be obtained. When crossed with diploids, this becomes breeding material for new triploid varieties. With better knowledge of periclinal chimeras, breeding in many fruit trees can be expected to advance.

Another kind of chimera is the sectorial chimera. As the name implies, sectors are either diploid or tetraploid. The changes occur in a mass of cells not limited to layers. This type was studied in *Datura*.[8] One branch becomes tetraploid and another diploid, depending on the origin of a specific branch.[7]

The wide distribution of periclinal chimeras in polyploids derived from colchicine shows that the change is not unusual. While our discussion is limited to only a few species, important work has been done with *Lilium, Solanum,* and many other plants. The principles as outlined with fruits and *Datura* are basic to all chimeras.

14.4: Sex Determination and Polyploidy

As was stated in the introduction to this chapter, polyploidy and special problems in botany did not arise suddenly when colchicine became known for its use in research. At this time, however, there was an immediate increase in papers dealing with such problems. A notable case was the relation between sex and polyploidy in plants.[55] One may erroneously conclude that new ideas were conceived as soon as colchicine was discovered. A proper perspective is needed here to evaluate properly the role played by an improved method such as colchicine proved to be. Whether the colchicine technique had been developed then or not, a proof that dioecious races in plants could be established as polyploids would certainly have been reported when it was, in 1938.[55]

As early as 1925 the similarity in ploidy between animals and dioecious plants was observed.[53] Both cases were generally diploid. Among many plants polyploidy was a mode of species formation. These were not dioecious. Therefore, an explanation for the lack of polyploidy in animals and in dioecious plants seemed to be related to the diploid state. When a polyploid species of *Empetrum hermaphroditum* was found to be hermaphroditic, the fact was particularly interesting because there was a related diploid species, dioecious *Empetrum nigrum*.[55] Conflicting evidence accumulated when a dioecious tetraploid strain of *Vallisneria* was reported. Briefly this was the state of affairs when Westergaard decided to test the hypothesis by making tetraploids from diploid dioecious species of *Melandrium*. He began the project in spite of the fact that no well developed methods for making polyploids were available at that time. Colchicine had not been announced.[10, 55, 53]

In America, polyploidy and sex determination in plants were started because colchicine should quickly lead to the evidence needed to test the question raised by Muller about sex determination as limited to diploidy in animals and dioecious plants.[5] The projects in Denmark and America were started about the same time and first results from each came close together.[55] Yet there was no awareness that either was studying the same problem.

Soon other work began in Japan,[38, 34] and there were additional studies in America.[33] A large volume could be compiled from this problem after only a few years of investigation. Some excellent work was done and colchicine provided enough breeding material to demonstrate conclusively that sex determination was not limited to a diploid state when plants were under consideration. However, male and female plants are not strictly comparable to maleness and femaleness among animals. In plants there are three kinds, with respect to production of flowers: (1) plants producing staminate, or pollen-bearing, flowers, (2) some giving pistillate, or seed-producing, flowers, and (3) plants that have staminate and pistillate structures in the same flower. These are called male, female, and hermaphroditic, respectively.[55]

Adopting the sex-determining code used for animals, notably *Drosophila*, diploids are XX as females and XY for males; in addition there are other chromosomes called autosomes. A tetraploid female carries the chromosomes XXXX and male $XXYY$ with a tetraploid set of autosomes designated $4A$. At once, it can be seen that another combination $XXXY$ may exist at the tetraploid level. If further crossing between tetraploids and diploids and between triploids and diploids were carried out, combinations could be extended to *XYY, XXXY, XXXYY, XXXXY*. Obviously, a great range may be produced. Everyone agrees that the *Y* chromosome is a determiner for maleness because the presence of this chromosome once or twice clearly impresses its influence on the plant. Only when four *X* chromosomes are opposing the one *Y* does the flower change to a hermaphrodite. This tendency begins to show slightly among the *XXXY* type. The *XY* and *XYY* are male without exception.[53]

The Danish[55] and American[53] polyploids differed with regard to the possible influence of autosomes and the role of the *X* chromosome as a female determiner. Some of the differences may be due to sources of diploid plants and some difference to method as well as interpretation. Two critical papers must be studied if one wishes to weigh the evidence: one by Warmke,[53] and another by Westergaard.[55]

Cytologically the *Y* chromosome can be distinguished from the smaller *X*. In turn, the *X* is larger than any autosomes. This feature is highly desirable because certain problems would be difficult to interpret otherwise. The hybrid generation between tetraploid *XXXX* and tetraploid *XXYY* throws 1 female to 12 males. The diploid sex ratios are 1:1. Looking at the chromosomes, it can be seen that most males are *XXXY* (89 per cent) and only a few *XXYY* (4 per cent). The association between *X-Y* and *Y-Y* is more frequent than between *X-Y* and *X-Y*. A high proportion of gametes were *XY* and the *XX* and *YY* classes were low. If a male with chromosomes *XXXY* was crossed with a female *XXXX*, the offspring showed 50-50 male:female ratios. Similar results were obtained with *Acnida tamariscina* (Nutt.) wood,[33] and for *Melandrium dioecum* var. *album* described above.[54]

In nature, the excess 4*n* males that are *XXXY* instead of *XXYY* would fertilize a large majority of the 4*n* females *XXXX;* hence, equal populations of males and females at the tetraploid level could be expected. From an evolutionary standpoint tetraploids differing on the basis of *X* and *Y* determining maleness and femaleness could be established much the same as a diploid species. A tetraploid race of *Rumex acetosa* has not been demonstrated as a stabilized dioecious type.[54]

Autotetraploid hemp gave an excess of females in the second generation following polyploidy.[34] This was a reversal over the diploid male-female proportions. Less cytological attention has been given to this species.

Polyploidy provides a method for deciding whether the male or female is heterogametic, that is, carrying the *XY*. A test was made for *Silene otites* since cytological methods did not give a solution in this case.[53] Polyploid plants would become *XXXX* and *XXYY,* but the designation of male or female remains unknown. Crossing these tetraploids gives three types of offspring, $XXXX, XXXY,$ and $XXYY$. About 5 males to 1 female are obtained. The female is tested by making triploids, mating tetraploids with diploids. A female XXXX, the $3n$ population crossed to male XY, should be 1:1, male, female. If the $3n$ population is 5 males to 1 female the constitution would be $XXYY$. The tests showed 1:1 ratios; thus females were homogametic as in $Melandrium$.

14.5: Aneuploids and Colchicine

Aneuploids can be created by colchicine in two ways. One procedure involves direct action on dividing cells in meristems.[4] The other method is indirect, following specific breeding procedures after polyploids have been made. Until colchicine was discovered, the first types were very rarely seen, particularly the diploid deficient plants, $2n - 1$. These were discussed on page 347. In this section the better-known, indirect method for developing aneuploids is discussed.

The scope has been expanded to more species because colchicine has stimulated the production of tetraploids. It is well known that tetraploids crossed with diploids create triploids. These in turn, when crossed back to diploids, become a rich source for off-type plants, those with extra chromosomes. Among the higher levels, pentaploids are excellent sources for aneuploids. Propagating auto-tetraploids regularly throws plants with somatic numbers deviating from the euploid value.

Distribution being unequal at meiosis, the chromosomes in the megaspore mother cell and the pollen mother cell cause the numerically different types. Sometimes transmission of extra types can be done through the seed parent only. In other cases the transmission of certain aneuploids is known only at high levels of polyploidy. If a particular morphology of the plant can be identified with aneuploidy, spontaneously occurring cases are usually high enough to create a large reservoir of extrachromosomal types.

Aneuploids among $Datura, Zea, Nicotiana, Triticum,$ and other genera have been studied extensively and have been used for specific genetical tests before colchicine methods came into prominence. In other instances, such as $Gossypium$,[3, 11] their isolation in large numbers began when this ready method for producing polyploids was discovered.

14.5–1: Trisomics and tetrasomics. In 1915, A. F. Blakeslee found a mutant in the cultures of *Datura stramonium*. This was called the "Globe mutant" because this plant had a globose capsule distinct from the usual patterns. Five years later, in 1920, John Belling demonstrated cytological evidence that this plant and others found between 1915 and 1920 each contained a single extra chromosome. In 1938, a summary covering 60,000 field-grown offspring from types with extra chromosomes was published.[6] The term *trisomic,* as the extra chromosomal plant was called, is used in cytogenetics.

With the use of colchicine in polyploidy and in *Beta* there arose an opportunity to study the effect of chromosomal variation in sugar beets.[30] It is one of the most intensively studied species as well as one of great practical importance in many countries. The large-scale production of tetraploids in 1938 with subsequent triploids opened opportunity to study variation in regard to chromosomal numbers. Since triploidy was discussed in the chapter on autoploidy, that will not be repeated. Here the influence of separate chromosomes, the trisomics, are of special consideration.[30]

Progenies from triploids intercrossed, and backcrossed to diploids, included plants with chromosomal numbers from diploid to tetraploid and beyond. One or more plants ranged from 18 to 36 chromosomes.[30] Between 37 and 45 several classes were missing. This material arose from colchicine-treated seed of the Hilleshog strain at Svalof, Sweden. When the seed parent was a triploid and the pollen parent diploid, all numbers from $2x$ to $3x$ were recovered. A reciprocal cross yielded an excess of diploids (77 per cent) with classes from 21 to 25 missing. The transmission difference between seed and parent confirms what had been learned long ago. Extensive pollen tube studies by J. T. Buchholz demonstrated the effect of extra chromosomes in *Datura* upon the male gametophyte.

Effects of different chromosomal classes upon a whole series of morphological and physiological characters in sugar beet were compared. Since this study permitted analysis of the entire population, certain advantages were presented that had never been possible before this time. Every chromosomal class from 18 to 36, inclusive, was analyzed as follows: (1) field estimation, (2) weight of tips and roots, (3) refractometer determinations, and (4) leaf development. The trisomics were distinct in plant characteristics, and the particular chromosome stamped its influence on growth habit. An interesting problem that requires more attention is the possible correlation between vigor increase and decrease in the size of the extra chromosome. This point becomes important when transfer of characteristics by single chromosomes is attempted. In addition to single trisomics, two plants with 20 chromosomes were studied. Plants beyond the 36 chromosomes, including a 42-chromosome plant, had good vigor. Finally the optimal numbers as would be predicted have three modes; these are diploid, triploid, and tetraploid. Maximum viability occurs at the euploid number.[30]

Five different chromosomes from *Nicotiana langsdorffii,* a small flowered species, was studied as trisomic in relation to corolla size. The background into which the extra chromosome was introduced was the hybrid between *N. langsdorffii* and *N. sanderaea, a long-*flowered species.[48] Since each trisomic could be detected by plant appearance the influence upon particular structures could be ana-

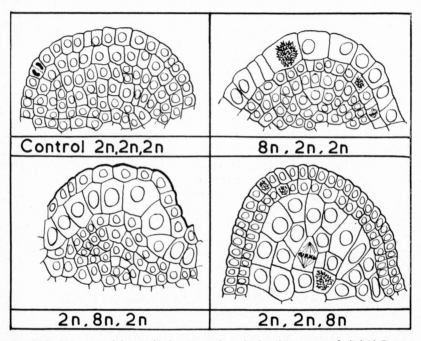

Fig. 14.2—Diagrams of longitudinal sections through the shoot apex of diploid **Datura stramonium** L. and three layers of periclinal chimeras. **Upper left,** diploid layers of tunica and corpus. **Upper Right,** octoploid tunica and diploid layers beneath. **Lower left,** first tunica diploid, second tunica octoploid, corpus diploid. **Lower right,** tunica diploid and corpus octoploid. (After Blakeslee and Satina)

lyzed. Three of the five chromosomes, when in trisomics, reduced the corolla in all regions, but two chromosomes decreased one region and increased another. This method was applied to find the relation between whole chromosomal additions and size effects. The conclusion was reached that size is determined by genes according to a geometric proportion. Eventually, size in *Nicotiana* flowers can be resolved as a "cumulative geometric effect." [48]

Hexaploids combining two species of *Gossypium* crossed back to *G. hirsutum* lead to aneuploids with one or two chromosomes from the diploid species introduced in the hexaploid. The characters influenced are: leaf, floral parts, size and shape of bolls, as well as fiber and seed coat. Cytological study of these trisomics is valuable for determining the nature of chromosomal differentiation among specific chromosomes.[11]

Some fertile, partially stable plants can be derived by selfing inter-species trisomics instead of the tetraploid number or the extra chromosome; morphologically distinguishable 54-chromosome lines were produced. The interest in these types lies in their constitution because the extra pair may be from an Asiatic-American wild or an African species. This pair is added to the naturally occurring *G. hirsutum,* a tetraploid 52-chromosome plant.[11]

Another type, the *intra-species trisomics,* arises from polyploids of *G. hirsutum.* By selfing and appropriate crossing between various trisomics in this class, both double trisomics and tetrasomics were developed.

There are then two types of tetrasomics identifiable by the extra pair, the intra-species tetrasomic and inter-species tetrasomic. As the word suggests, the latter pair is derived from strains from another species, whereas the intraspecific tetrasomics are limited to one species.[11] Morphologically both types may be distinguishable from the species. A remarkable fertility is retained when a pair comes from another species, but the intraspecific tetrasomics are almost completely sterile. A great many cytological problems can be solved with these types. Trisomics and tetrasomics have been obtained in *N. sylvestris.* Among the off-type plants from a progeny of monoploid pollinated by diploid, trisomics were derived in wheat. Further selfing yielded tetrasomics. These added chromosomal types are not easily detected in hexaploid wheat. Some homozygous speltoid wheat proved to be 44-chromosomal plants. Tetrasomics and trisomics may have been involved in the dwarf and subcompactoid types.[31]

14.5—2: Nullisomics and monosomics. Chromosomes lost in diploid plants do not survive. This was reviewed in an earlier section. Tetraploids in *Datura* also lacking a chromosome or two failed to set seed. Additions in diploids have been propagated extensively, but these are often transmitted only through seed parents.

At the polyploid level, missing chromosomes are tolerated.[27] For that reason some important work can be done with two general types: (1) monosomics, those plants lacking one chromosome, and (2) nullisomics in which a pair is missing.[51] The latter are well known among hexaploid wheat.[46] In *Gossypium* and *Nicotiana* a success similar to that for hexaploid wheat has not been achieved with nullisomics.[12]

Monosomic plants have been found in *Gossypium* spontaneously, through nondisjunction in trisomics, and after intergeneric pollination.[11] Since the transmission of haplo-deficient gametes fails in *Gossypium,* the further utilization of monosomics is stopped. In contrast to this situation, monosomic analysis developed for *Nicotiana* has proved most useful in many genetic tests, notably in establishing linkage groups; surveying amphidiploids for specific genetic characters.[12] The technique applied to *Nicotiana* suggests that other groups might profit from these methods.[23] There are limitations to this method among such a group as *Gossypium,* where polyploids are common; yet the use of monosomics is limited. No nullisomics are reported for *Gossypium.*[11]

Quite another situation exists in hexaploid *Triticum aestivum* L., where nullisomics and monosomics can be applied to genetic problems.[51] As we mentioned for trisomics, the number of different types with one whole chromosome extra should equal the haploid number. For *Datura,* 12 primary trisomic types exist. In *Nicotiana* the total monosomics possible is 24. Accordingly, 21 nullisomics would be expected or equal to the 21 pairs representing hexaploid wheat.[46]

For each pair missing, the 20-chromosome plant has specific characteristics. Nullisomics may be numbered from I to XXI.[46] None is completely sterile, and certain are fertile in both male and female. Some are female-fertile only, others male-fertile only. Some nullisomics pollinated by normal plants give more monosomes of a particular type, as well as trisomes. The incidence is more than a random occurrence. For example, nullisomic III produced more monosomic IV and XV than other types of monosomes.

Particular tetrasomics may cancel the effects of certain nullisomics. Such compensating cases are known for wheat and oats. For example, tetrasomic II compensates for nullisomic XX so that the plant is very nearly normal even as the male gametophyte.[46] There does not seem to be a competitive advantage between pollen-deficient for chromosome XX and duplicated for II. Common properties in the segments of these chromosomes would appear to be a cause for the compensation. There seems to be no pairing between tetrasome II and nullisome XX. These are, in very brief sketch, problems related to polyploidy.

Seven chromosomal pairs corresponding to the *D genome* in hexaploid wheat are dwarf nullisomics and differ from each other according to the specific pair missing. These nullisomics were derived from among offspring of *Triticum polomicum,* genomes *AABB,* $\times$ *T. spelta, AABBDD.* These 7 nullisomics are lettered *a, b, c, d, e, f, g,* respectively. Twenty-one nullisomics from a Chinese wheat (*T. aestivum* L.) should throw light on the *D* genome by hybridizing the dwarf nullisomics and those from *T. aestivum,* which had a different origin.[31]

Success has been achieved in transferring mosaic disease resistance from one species to another in *Nicotiana.* The commerical tobacco received a chromosomal pair from *N. glutinosa,* which contributed the necrotic factor for resistance. Alien additional races included a pair from one species and 24 pairs from *N. tabacum.* By another series of crosses, alien substitution races were formed, whereby a pair of chromosomes were substituted in the *N. tabacum* genome.[23] Other species carry factors that can be traced by successive crosses into the interspecific hybrid, then by a backcrossing procedure through a number of generations. The monosomic method of analysis has been worked out with good success in *Nicotiana.*[12]

REFERENCES

1. AKERMAN, A., AND MACKEY, J. A genetical analysis of some speltoid strains. Hereditas. 34:301–20. 1948.
2. BAKER, R. Induced polyploid, periclinal chimeras in *Solanum tuberosum.* Amer. Jour. Bot. 30:187–95. 1943.
3. BEASLEY, J., AND BROWN, M. (*see* Ref. No. 8, Chap. 12).
4. BERGNER, A. Chromosomal deficiencies in *Datura stramonium* induced by colchicine treatment. Amer. Jour. Bot. 27:676–83. 1940.
5. BLAKESLEE, A. Effect of induced polyploidy in plants. Amer. Nat. 75:117–35. 1941.
6. ———, AND AVERY, A. Fifteen-year breeding records of 2n + types in *Datura stramonium.* Cooperation in Research. Carnegie Inst. Wash. 501:315–51. 1938.
7. ———, *et al.* Induction of periclinal chimeras in *Datura stramonium* by colchicine treatment. Science. 89:402. 1939.
8. ———, *et al.* Utilization of induced periclinal chimeras in determining the constitution of organs and their origin from the three germ layers in *Datura.* Science. 91:423. 1940.
9. ———, *et al.* Characteristics of induced polyploids in different species of Angiosperms. Genetics. 24:66. 1939.
10. ———, *et al.* Chromosome investigations. Annual report of director of department of genetics. Carnegie Inst. Wash. Year Book. 37:35–40. 1938.
11. BROWN, M. (*see* Ref. No. 15, Chap. 11).
12. CLAUSEN, R. (*see* Ref. No. 17, Chap. 11).
13. CLAUSEN, J., *et al.* (*see* Ref. No. 18, Chap. 11).
14. CROSS, G., AND JOHNSON, T. Structural features of the shoot apices of diploid and colchicine-induced, tetraploid strains of *Vinca rosea* L. Torrey Bot. Club Bull. 68:618–35. 1941.
15. DARROW, G. (*see* Ref. No. 22, Chap. 11).
16. DERMEN, H. Colchicine, polyploidy and technique. Bot. Rev. 6:599–635. 1940. Simple and complex periclinal tetraploidy in peaches induced by colchicine. Proc. Amer. Soc. Hort. Sci. 38:141. 1941. Periclinal and total polyploidy in peaches induced by colchicine. Genetics. 26:147. 1941. The mechanism of colchicine-induced cytohistological changes in cranberry. Amer. Jour. Bot. 32:387–94. 1945. Inducing polyploidy in peach varieties. Jour. Hered. 38:77–82. 1947. Polyploid pears. Jour. Hered. 38:189–92. Periclinal cytochimeras and histogenesis in cranberry. Amer. Jour. Bot. 34:32–43. 1947.
17. ———, AND BAIN, H. (*see* Ref. No. 43, Chap. 13).
18. ———, AND DARROW, G. (*see* Ref. No. 44, Chap. 13).
19. EINSET, J. Cytological basis for sterility in induced autotetraploid lettuce. Amer. Jour. Bot. 21:336–42. 1944. Aneuploidy in relation to partial sterility in autotetraploid lettuce. Amer. Jour. Bot. 34:99–105. 1947.
20. EMSWELLER, S. Polyploidy in *Lilium longiflorum.* Amer. Jour. Bot. 36:135–44. 1949. (*see* Ref. No. 54, Chap. 11).
21. ———, AND STEWART, R. Diploid and tetraploid pollen mother cells in lily chimeras. Proc. Amer. Hort. Sci. 57:414–18. 1951.

22. FRANZKE, C., AND ROSS, J. Colchicine-induced variants in sorghum. Jour. Hered. 43:107–15. 1952.
23. GERSTEL, D. (*see* Ref. No. 38, Chap. 12).
24. HILL, H., AND MEYERS, M. (*see* Ref. No. 37, Chap. 11).
25. HUNTER, A., AND DANIELSSON, B. (*see* Ref. No. 82, Chap. 13).
26. HUSKINS, C. (*see* Ref. No. 39, Chap. 11).
27. KATTERMAN, G. Über konstante Halm-behaarte Stämme aus Weizenroggen-bastardierung mit 2n=42. Z. Indukt. Abstamm. Vererb. Lehre. 74:354–97. 1938.
28. KERNS, K., AND COLLINS, J. Chimeras in the pineapple; colchicine-induced tetraploids and diploid-tetraploids in the Cayenne variety. Jour. Hered. 38: 323–30. 1947.
29. KIHARA, H. (*see* Ref. No. 43, Chap. 11).
30. LEVAN, A. The effect of chromosomal variation in sugar beets. Hereditas. 28:345–400. 1942.
31. MATSUMURA, S. Genetics of some cereals. Ann. Rpt. Nat. Inst. Genet. Japan. 1:22–27. 1951.
32. MUNTZING, A. New material and cross combinations in *Galeopsis* after colchicine-induced chromosome doubling. Hereditas. 27:193–201. 1941. Aneuploidy and seed shrivelling in tetraploid rye. Hereditas. 29:65–75. 1943.
33. MURRAY, M. (*see* Ref. No. 134, Chap. 13).
34. NISHIYAMA, I., *et al.* Studies on artificial polyploid plants. XI. Changes of the sex ratio in the progeny of the autotetraploid hemp. Kihara Inst. Biol. Res. Seiken Ziho. 3:145–51. 1947.
35. OLMO, H. (*see* Ref. No. 155, Chap. 13).
36. OLSSON, G., AND RUFELT, B. (*see* Ref. No. 157, Chap. 13).
37. O'MARA, J. Cytogenetic studies in *Triticale* I. Genetics. 25:401–8. 1940.
38. ONO, T. Polyploidy and sex determination in *Melandrium*. I. Colchicine-induced polyploids of *Melandrium album*. Bot. Mag. Tokyo. 53:549–56. 1939. Polyploidy and sex determination in *Melandrium*. II. The effect of polyploidy upon sex in *M. album*. Bot. Mag. Tokyo. 54:225–30. 1940. Polyploidy and sex determination in *Melandrium*. III. Intersex in *M. album*. Bot. Mag. Tokyo. 54:348–56. 1940. The effects of polyploidy upon morphological and physiological characters in *Pisum sativum*. Bot. and Zool. 8:1265–74. 1940. Studies on artificial polyploidy in hops. Bot. and Zool. 10:63–68. 1942.
39. RAJAN, S., *et al.* (*see* Ref. No. 171, Chap. 13).
40. RAMANUJAM, S., AND DESHMUKH, M. (*see* Ref. No. 168, Chap. 13).
41. SASS, J., AND GREEN, J. Cytohistology of the reaction of maize seedlings to colchicine. Bot. Gaz. 106:483–88. 1945.
42. SATINA, S. Periclinal chimeras in *Datura* in relation to development and structure (a) of style and stigma (b) of calyx and corolla. Amer. Jour. Bot. 31: 493–502. 1944. Periclinal chimeras in *Datura* in relation to the development and structure of the ovule. Amer. Jour. Bot. 32:72–81. 1945.
43. ――――, *et al.* Demonstration of the three germ layers in the shoot apex of *Datura* by means of induced polyploidy in periclinal chimeras. Amer. Jour. Bot. 27:895–905. 1940.
44. ――――, AND BLAKESLEE, A. Periclinal chimeras in *Datura stramonium* in relation to development of leaf and flower. Amer. Jour. Bot. 28:862–71. 1941.
45. SAWYER, M. A colchicine-induced chimera in a *Datura* hybrid, 2n for one species and 4n for another. Amer. Jour. Bot. 36:802. 1949.
46. SEARS, E. Nullisomics in *Triticum vulgare*. Genetics. 26:167–68. 1941. Cytogenetic studies with polyploid species of wheat. II. Additional chromosomal aberrations in *Triticum vulgare*. Genetics. 29:232–46. 1944. The sphaerococcum gene in wheat. Rec. Genet. Soc. Amer. 15:65–66. 1946. The cytology and genetics of the wheats and their relatives. *In* Advances in genetics. 2:239–70. Academic Press, Inc., New York. 1948.
47. ――――, AND RODENHISTER, H. Nullisomic analysis of stem rust reaction in *Triticum vulgare* var. Timstein. Rec. Genet. Soc. Amer. 16:50–51. 1947.

48. SMITH, H. Effects of genome balance, polyploidy, and single extra chromosomes on size in *Nicotiana*. Genetics. 28:227–36. Studies on induced heteroploids on *Nicotiana*. Amer. Jour. Bot. 30:121–30. 1943.
49. SMITH, L. (*see* Ref. No. 200, Chap. 13).
50. TAKENAKA, Y. Relation between the genome and gigantism and its bearing on plant breeding. Jap. Jour. Genet. 18:155–56. 1942.
51. UNRAU, J. (*see* Ref. No. 110, Chap. 12).
52. VAARAMA, A. (*see* Ref. No. 223, Chap. 13).
53. WARMKE, H. A new method for determining the sex heterozygote in species with morphologically undifferentiated sex chromosomes, and its application to *Silene otites*. Genetics. 27:174. 1942. Sex determination and sex balance in *Melandrium*. Amer. Jour. Bot. 33:648–60. 1946.
54. ————, AND BLAKESLEE, A. Sex mechanism in polyploids of *Melandrium*. Science. 89:391–92. 1939. Effect of polyploidy upon sex mechanism in dioecious plants. Genetics. 24:88–89. 1939. The establishment of a 4n-dioecious race in *Melandrium*. Amer. Jour. Bot. 27:751–62. 1940.
55. WESTERGAARD, M. Studies on cytology and sex determination in polyploid forms of *Melandrium album*. Dansk. Bot. Arkiv. 10:3–131. 1940.

CHAPTER 15

Criteria for Judging Polyploidy

15.1: Sterile Hybrids Made Fertile

In the final analysis, polyploidy is determined by counting the number of chromosomes, and comparing this number with the diploid or untreated plant. Some rapid and accurate methods are available for judging polyploids indirectly.

If a sterile species hybrid begins seed production after treatment with colchicine, the evidence is good that polyploidy has been induced.[41] Geneticists knew that doubling the number of chromosomes in a sterile species hybrid was a critical test for demonstrating the effectiveness of the drug.[3, 31, 41, 44, 47] Species hybrids of *Gossypium* were treated immediately.[4] Plants that flowered, yet failed to set bolls and seed, began seed production in those sections of the plant treated with a proper concentration of colchicine. Therefore, without counting the number of chromosomes, the preliminary efficiency of a treatment could be estimated. The chance doubling that might have occurred through unreduced gametes is of such low frequency that the effects of colchicine were not obscured by natural or spontaneous doubling.

Amphiploids among *Nicotiana* were made in large numbers.[42] The list of artificially induced polyploids increased within a few years.[24] Combining the first data from *Gossypium* and *Nicotiana* proved the value of colchicine beyond doubt.

Many combinations of interspecific and intergeneric hybrids were converted into amphiploids within the Triticinae.[1, 5] From one project, 18 amphiploids involving 10 species were created within two years.[41] The production of good pollen and eventually seed in the sectors of treated plants that showed the effects of doubling was reliable criterion for amphiploidy. Estimates of how effective colchicine was upon these plants could be checked on a percentage basis. Some modifications were necessary because the monocotyledonous species had to be treated differently from the dicotyledonous types.

After the amphiploids in Triticinae were produced in such large numbers, it was demonstrated that both monocotyledons and dicotyledons
were being doubled by the use of colchicine.

A barrier in plant breeding had been removed or considerably
reduced by the discovery of a ready technique for making sterile hybrids fertile and estimating the effectiveness by seed production. In-
compatibilities such as failure to make hybridizations must now be
overcome. Some work on embryo culture has been used to excellent
advantage.

15.2: Appearance of Polyploids

New leaves and stems that grow from treated sectors are usually
wrinkled, thicker, and darker green, and have coarser texture, as
compared with the untreated plants.[4, 7, 14] An increase in thickness of
the tetraploid leaf can be judged by holding the leaves between
thumb and forefinger. By such methods a rough sorting of tetraploids
can be made among large populations of treated cultures. Those
that have not responded can be quite accurately eliminated.

Specific marks on the leaves such as veins, hairs, and glands are
valuable references for the first sorting of possible changed types.
The outline of the leaves changes; they are usually shorter and more
rounded than the diploid leaves.

Flowers of the tetraploid plants are larger (Fig. 15.1*B*) and more
compact than the diploid (Fig. 15.1*A*). These changes were correlated with chromosomal determinations (Fig. 15.1*C, D*). Tetraploid,
triploid, and diploid flowers form a decreasing series in size of flower.
These proportionate changes are illustrated for watermelon strains.
At the tetraploid level, optimum size is reached, and beyond that
point the increase in sets of chromosomes actually reduces the size
of the flower. Among the best varieties of *Iris,* polyploids are favored
over diploids.[40] The increase in size of flower has been a goal for the
improvement of ornamental species.

A tetraploid plant has a more rugged appearance, looks sturdier,
and has certain giant-like features. Usually the rates of growth are
slower, but even the final growth does not produce a plant as tall as
the diploid. Among polyploid watermelons, the vine remains green
over more days than among diploids, disregarding disease factors.
Another difference between the stems of diploids and those of tetraploids is the shape of the apex as viewed in longitudinal section (cf.
Chapter 14).

15.3: Fruit and Seed

The development of larger seeds from tetraploid lines is a consistent macroscopic characteristic that has been confirmed for hun-

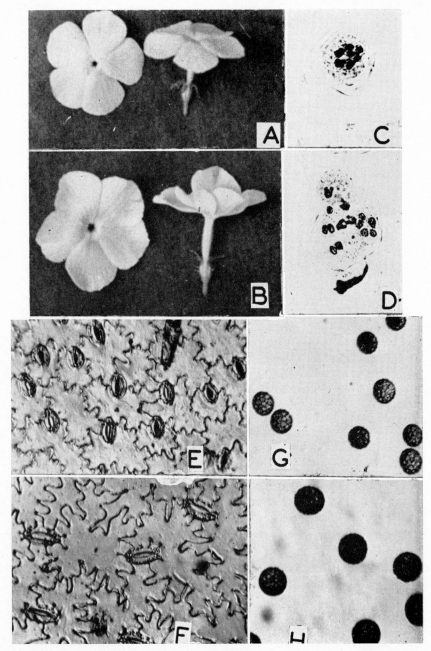

Fig. 15.1—Flower, pollen, stomata, pollen mother cells of diploid and tetraploid strains of **Phlox drummondii. A, B.** Diploid and tetraploid flowers, respectively. **C.** Pollen mother cell with 7 bivalents. **D.** Tetraploid pollen mother cell, n—14. Note quadrivalency. **E, F.** Stomata of diploid and tetraploid respectively. **G, H.** Pollen grains of diploid and tetraploid, respectively. (After Eigsti and Taylor)

dreds of cases.[26] The sizes can be judged by volumetric measurement, weights, or length and width measurements. As a sorting method for choosing the tetraploid rye plants in the treated generation, size of seed is a reliable feature.[32] The grain weights of tetraploid rye were distinctly separated from diploids. Table 15.1 shows the increase based on thousand-grain weights for diploid and tetraploids. A mean weight of 30.34 was obtained for diploid and 46.50 for tetraploid.[32]

Increasing the size of seed has been used as an argument to improve the crop yield of diploids through polyploidy. The fallacy lies in the fact that the seeds of tetraploids may be larger and heavier, but the reduced number of seeds per plant prevents complete use of the increase. Reduced fertility in autoploids is the most common cause of decreased yield in number of seeds. Decreased seed production in watermelon brought out this relation. A comparison of ten fruits, diploid and tetraploid, showed avarages of 290.0 and 92.7 per fruit, respectively.[21] Since cultivation was similar and the varieties were strictly comparable, the reduction was directly correlated with tetraploidy. For reasons discussed in the previous chapter, triploids are without seeds.

Amphiploids do not show the same consistent increase in seed weight or size compared with the parental species. A comparison between amphiploids and parental types was made among species of *Bromus* of the Gramineae. On the basis of weight for 200 seeds, the amphiploid increased as much as 75 per cent, while other increases were not more than 17 per cent[44] (Table 15.2). Genetic factors and the contributions by each parent have a greater influence than merely doubling the number of chromosomes.

A given kind of plant may regularly show specific marks among the tetraploid seeds. Close inspection of the tetraploid seed of watermelon showed that fissures developed in the seed coat upon drying.[21] A rupture of the outer layers of ovules creates this condition. These marks as well as size of seed are good criteria for making preliminary sorting of the tetraploid. Another distinction was the thickness of "triploid" seeds and tetraploid. Seed from tetraploid fruit pollinated by diploids are called "triploid" seed and are thinner than the seed from tetraploid fruits pollinated by tetraploids.[21] Other marks such as coarseness, special spines, ridges, and color differences, once noted can be reliably used as guides in selection among treated plants and the tetraploid generations.[4, 11, 15, 16, 17, 18]

Fruits of tetraploids are not necessarily larger than those of diploids. Nevertheless, distinguishing marks can be found among tetraploid fruits. The external marking, shape, and attachment to plant are some of the features that have been used. Parthenocarpic fruits, such as the triploid, may be somewhat triangular.[21] The fleshy por-

TABLE 15.1

KERNEL WEIGHT IN DIPLOID AND TETRAPLOID RYE VARIETIES

(After A. Müentzing[32])

Variety	Thousand-Grain Weight (grams)																Number of Trials	Mean Weight (grams)
	24	26	28	30	32	34	36	38	40	42	44	46	48	50	52	54		
Steel rye, diploid........	1	2	4	4	2	2											15	30.34
Steel rye, tetraploid........									2	1	2	6	1	3			15	46.60
Wasa II, diploid........	2	....	4	3	2												11	29.55
Wasa II, tetraploid........									2	1	1	3	3	1			11	46.27

tion of tetraploid tomatoes may be coarser, and for that reason the polyploids are less desirable than the diploid. Many fruited plants of horticultural importance show direct correlation between fruit size and polyploidy within certain limits. Valuable tetraploid varieties of grapes are larger and superior to diploids. Tetraploid muskmelon

TABLE 15.2

SEED WEIGHTS OF SPECIES AND ALLOPOLYPLOID DERIVATIVES OF THE HEXAPLOID SPECIES OF *Bromus* (*Ceratochloa*)

Species of Polyploid	Strain	Weight of 200 Seeds (*grams*)	Increase Over Arithmetic Mean Between Parts (*per cent*)
B. catharticus	Waite	3.1	....
B. catharticus	Berkeley	3.3	....
B. catharticus	San Antonio	2.5	....
B. haenkeanus	Carmel	1.5	....
B. haenkeanus	Sparks	1.2	....
B. stamineus	Berkeley	1.9	....
B. catharticus-haenkeanus	Waite-Carmel	3.5	52
B. catharticus-haenkeanus	Berkeley-Sparks	2.7	17
B. catharticus-haenkeanus	San Antonio-Carmel	2.5	25
B. haenkeanus-stamineus	Carmel-Berkeley	2.4	41
B. haenkeanus-stamineus	Sparks-Berkeley	2.8	75
B. haenkeanus-stamineus	San Antonio-Berkeley	3.6	64

fruits were more promising than the diploids according to sampling methods made in one study.

Pistillate flowers of tetraploids pollinated with pollen from diploid strains may reduce the size of grain in such a plant as rye. Normally these species are cross-fertilized, so planting side by side gives the diploid pollinator an advantage over the slower-growing pollen from tetraploid flowers.[17] Yield is at once reduced. The effect of diploid pollen upon fruit development in watermelon is quite the opposite. The triploid plants must be interplanted with diploids to insure pollination, for the diploid pollen stimulates parthenocarpic or seedless fruit formation. The number of fruits produced by triploids may be double the number for a representative diploid. Yield trials showed that this feature favors the polyploid.

15.4: Physiological Differences

Excellent reviews have been made to differentiate the diploid and tetraploid plants.[34] An ever-increasing number of autotetraploids adds more material for such study, including physiology, incompatibility,[2, 48] morphology, and anatomy. Final superiority of the tetraploid depends upon the physiology of the particular strains.[6, 43, 206] Advantages such as protein content,[37] vitamins,[34] yield of sucrose,[38] and other valuable characters[25, 28, 36] are products of the functioning plant.

A superior baking flour was produced by the tetraploid rye varieties. Bread with better texture and color, as well as a larger volume of bread per sample of flour was made from the tetraploid flour. The value for tetraploid was 279 in contrast to the value 260 for a diploid, or an increase of 10 per cent in favor of the tetraploid. Higher protein content was correlated with the improved baking properties and these were in turn correlated with the tetraploid varieties.

Increased sugar content in triploid watermelon and tetraploid muskmelon improved the eating quality. Increases from 8 to 9 per cent for diploids were shown to be raised to 12 per cent in the triploid. The quality and final test of any variety depends upon the genetic nature of the diploid or the hybrid, so that variation exists between tetraploids quite as much as between diploids. The induction of polyploidy does not automatically guarantee improved fruit quality.

In a previous chapter, reference was made to the significant increase in amount of sugar produced in the larger sizes of triploid roots compared with the diploid. Tetraploid sugar beets are generally lower in yield of sucrose per unit weight of root. Other plant products, such as latex produced by *Taraxacum kohsaghyz* and translated into rubber production, gave the tetraploids an increase of three times the diploid. Drug production in *Datura stramonium* showed increased atropin in the tetraploid. Another species, *Cannabis sativa,* showed increased potency of the marihuana content when additional sets of chromosomes are built into a variety. Environment influences potency of drug production as noted in Chapter 5, but the addition of chromosomes also causes changes in production of special plant products.

The superiority of tetraploid red clover and alsike clover may be correlated with an increase in forage production. The amount improves in the second year over the first. Enough tests have been made with these forage crops, and on a sufficiently large scale, that the conclusion of increased leafage is reliable.[1]

15.5: Microscopic Characteristics

Pollen size may be used for preliminary sorting of polyploids before the final chromosomal counts are made for a particular plant. This microscopic classification permits one to handle large numbers of individuals. After the macroscopic identifications are completed, a logical step is to measure the pollen grains.

True autotetraploids have larger grains than the diploid (Fig. 15.1*H, G*). Microscopes are equipped with measuring oculars that make this procedure routine. The correlation between the size of the pollen grain and the number of sets of chromosomes has been so well established that no further discussion need be made on this point. Triploid pollen grains are notable for their irregular dimensions and are useful in separating triploid and tetraploid plants on a field scale basis.

The mean diameters for the diploid and tetraploid watermelon varieties were 57.3 and 67.5, respectively. The smaller grains in triploids averaged 62.1 and the larger sizes, 67.5. Similar size comparisons have been made for the guard cells of epidermal cells. A photomicrograph (Fig. 15.1 *E, F*) gives a visual picture of the differences between the larger tetraploid and smaller diploid. Also the distribution of guard cells varies; the diploid cells are closer together than the tetraploid.

The relation between the size of pollen grains and guard cells of a given plant are important for the reasons discussed in the previous chapter under the subject of periclinal chimeras. If the pollen is tetraploid and the guard cells are diploid, treatment with colchicine has produced a chimera in which the deeper layer that produced the pollen was made tetraploid and the outer layer remained diploid. A reverse situation may occur. In these instances the guard cell would show tetraploid characteristics and the pollen, diploid. The breeding behavior of such a plant would be that of a diploid. Seed from this plant would not lead to the expected tetraploid types, according to information based on the guard cell sizes. Sometimes, a mixture of diploid and tetraploid pollen exists in the same anther, or mixtures of diploid and tetraploid guard cells appear on the same leaf. These cases are a result of mixoploidy, a direct action of colchicine.

In cross section the leaf of the diploid is not as thick as that of the tetraploid. Usually extra layers of cells of the mesophyll are present.

Pollen mother cells undergoing meiosis are universally used for counting chromosomes and determining the associations between chromosomes during pairing. Acetocarmine stains have speeded up such cytological work. Photomicrographs in Figure 15.1 show the differences in numbers of chromosomes and some difference in the association. Section *D* shows the multivalents in contrast to the one in *C* (Fig. 15.1).[10]

Other cells, such as the generative cells in pollen tube cultures, root tips, and leaf cells, may be used for counting the number of chromosomes. At the second meiotic division and the division of the microspore, chromosomal counting may be easier than at the first meiotic metaphase.

Comparisons at meiotic metaphase of diploid sterile hybrids and the amphiploid are important for an understanding of the possible associations that form between chromosomes of opposite genomes. While this evidence is not infallible, correlations may be obtained between pollen fertility, possible intergenomal exchange between chromosomes, and reasons for the failure in seed setting of the polyploid.

15.6: Ecological Considerations

The success of a polyploid in nature or in agriculture depends upon how closely the new variety meets the requirements for each situation. Productivity or adaptation are measured in terms of the responses such as yield, disease resistance, drought resistance, and cold tolerance. The elimination in nature occurs through competition and in agriculture at the hands of the agronomist. Wide differences exist between diploid varieties, and considerable improvement can be done at the diploid level without stepping up to the tetraploid. Adaptation problems increase, rather than decrease, with the use of tetraploids. Autotetraploid rye clearly showed that the kind of plant used to make the diploid may be as important as any other feature.

Trying to measure the rates at which artificial polyploids become established under natural conditions strikes at some basic problems in polyploidy. Already differences have been recorded for the success of the tetraploid over the diploid, or vice versa. An unusually high seed production, about 75 per cent, in autoploid *Ehrahata erecta* played some part in the establishment of the new type under natural conditions. This situation held for ungrazed conditions, but where grazing occurred, the low-growing habit of the diploid assured survival better since the flowers, being closer to the soil level, were not destroyed as readily. This is one example of the critical differences that determine success or failure of the tetraploid.[44]

Wilt diseases are devastating to watermelons in Japan. Appreciable resistance to *Fusarium niveum* was exhibited by the triploid and tetraploid varieties. By selection, notable progress can be made for insect and disease resistance if an initial advantage is provided through the production of tetraploids. Autotetraploid radishes were more resistant to the common club root disease, yielded more, and had greater vigor than diploids.

The succulence of water cress leaves was improved by increasing the number of chromosomes, but the growth rates being slower among the tetraploid reduced the yield. Fewer cuttings can be made per season with tetraploids. The slower growth and prolonged flowering period for ornamental species is advantageous. No single trait can be established as a rule that will hold for all polyploids. In the above cases a few instances are cited which indicate that each problem must be dealt with independently according to the requirements.

15.7: Fertility

Two general methods are used to judge the fertility level of a specific polyploid: (1) percentage of good pollen as demonstrated by microscopic test, and (2) the amount of seed set. Fertility differences and chromosomal phenomena at meiosis have been correlated, but no general rule that explains the total possibility has been established.[33] Unequal distributions of chromosomes in the meiotic stages from first metaphase do cause unbalance in chromosomes in the pollen, and ultimately in the gamete. Triploids are notoriously bad with respect to chromosomal balance.[21] When the percentage of pollen that appears to be good is used to express the fertility ultimately judged by seed production, some reservations must be made.[8]

Female sterility in the ovule arises at meiosis and may or may not be the same as for pollen. Some polyploids are female-sterile and pollen-fertile, and vice versa. The embryo-sac stages are difficult to study because an involved cytological technique is required.[8]

Among progenies of amphiploids the first generation may be quite fertile, while later generations may segregate due to weak and low fertility. By successive selection the fertility level may be raised, or there may be mechanisms for improving fertility by elimination of those genotypes that are deficient or have no survival value.

Perhaps no other aspect of polyploidy is more controversial than this subject of fertility in the immediate product of doubling and in the subsequent generations. Practically and theoretically the problems are unsolved at this point.

REFERENCES

1. AKERMAN, A. (*see* Ref. No. 1, Chap. 11).
2. ATWOOD, S. (*see* Ref. No. 9, Chap. 13).
3. BLAKESLEE, A. (*see* Ref. No. 11, Chap. 11).
4. BROWN, M. Polyploids and aneuploids derived from species hybrids in *Gossypium*. Hereditas Suppl. Vol. Pp. 15–16. 1949.
5. CHIN, T. (*see* Ref. No. 18, Chap. 12).
6. CLAUSEN, J., *et al.* (*see* Ref. No. 18, Chap. 11).
7. CUA, L. (*see* Ref. No. 20, Chap. 11).
8. DAS, B. Cytological and embryological basis for sterility in autotetraploid sweet clover *Melilotus alba* Desr. Iowa State College Jour. Sci. 27:537–61. 1953.
9. DERMEN, H. Detection of polyploidy by pollen-grain size. (I) Investigation with peaches and apricots. Proc. Amer. Soc. Hort. Sci. 39:96–103. 1938.
10. EIGSTI, O. The effects of colchicine upon the division of the generative cell in *Polygonatum, Tradescantia,* and *Lilium.* Amer. Jour. Bot. 27:512–24. 1940.
11. ———, AND TAYLOR, H. (*see* Ref. No. 52, Chap. 13).
12. EINSET, J. (*see* Ref. No. 19, Chap. 14).

13. EKDAHL, I. Gigas properties and acreage yield in autotetraploid *Galeopsis pubescens.* Hereditas. 35:397–421. 1949.
14. EMSWELLER, S. (*see* Ref. No. 30, Chap. 11).
15. ERNOULD, L. (*see* Ref. No. 59, Chap. 13).
16. FRANDSEN, K. (*see* Ref. No. 63, Chap. 13).
17. HAKANSSON, A., AND ELLERSTROM, S. Seed development after reciprocal crosses between diploid and tetraploid rye. Hereditas. 36:256–96. 1950.
18. HOFMEYER, J. (*see* Ref. No. 79, Chap. 13).
19. JULEN, G. (*see* Ref. No. 92, Chap. 13).
20. KEHR, A., AND SMITH, H. (*see* Ref. No. 56, Chap. 12).
21. KIHARA, H. (*see* Ref. No. 97, Chap. 13).
22. ———, AND NISHIYAMA, I. (*see* Ref. No. 100, Chap. 13).
23. ———, AND YAMASHITA, K. (*see* Ref. No. 101, Chap. 13).
24. KOSTOFF, D. Cytogenetics of the genus *Nicotiana.* States Printing House. Sofia, Bulgaria. 1073 pp. 1943.
25. KRYTHE, J., AND WELLENSIEK, S. (*see* Ref. No. 44, Chap. 11).
26. KUCKUCK, H., AND LEVAN, A. (*see* Ref. No. 45, Chap. 11).
27. LANG, A. Beiträge zur Genetik des Photoperiodismus. II. Photoperiodismus und Autopolyploidies. Z. Naturforsch. 2b:36–44. 1951.
28. LEVAN, A. (*see* Ref. No. 113, Chap. 13).
29. MANN, L. Fruit shape of watermelon as affected by placement of pollen on stigma. Bot. Gaz. 105:257–62. 1943.
30. MRKOS, H. Über Erfahrungen bei der Herstellung von Tetraploiden mit Hilfe von Colchicin und Schnellmethoden zur Untersuchung der Chromosomenanzahl. Bodenkultur, Vienna. 4:138–41. 1950.
31. MUENDLER, M., AND SCHWANITZ, F. (*see* Ref. No. 131, Chap. 13).
32. MÜNTZING, A. (*see* Ref. No. 51, Chap. 11).
33. MYER, W. Meiosis in autotetraploid *Lolium perenne* in relation to chromosomal behaviour in autopolyploids. Bot. Gaz. 106:304–16. 1945.
34. NOGGLE, G. The physiology of polyploidy in plants. I. Review of the literature. Lloydia. 9:155–73. 1946.
35. NORDENSKJÖLD, H. Genetical study in the mode of segregation in hexaploid *Phleum pratense.* 9th Internat. Cong. Genet. No. 54. Bellagio, Italy. 1953.
36. OLSSON, G., AND RUFELT, B. (*see* Ref. No. 157, Chap. 13).
37. O'MARA, J. (*see* Ref. No. 37, Chap. 14).
38. PETO, F., AND BOYES, J. (*see* Ref. No. 58, Chap. 11).
39. RAJAN, S., *et al.* (*see* Ref. No. 171, Chap. 13).
40. RANDOLPH, L. Personal communication. 1951.
41. SEARS, E. (*see* Ref. No. 64, Chap. 11).
42. SMITH, H. (*see* Ref. No. 199, Chap. 13).
43. SMITH, L. (*see* Ref. No. 200, Chap. 13).
44. STEBBINS, G. (*see* Ref. No. 66, Chap. 11).
45. STEINEGGAR, E. (*see* Ref. No. 204, Chap. 13).
46. STEWART, R. (*see* Ref. No. 206, Chap. 13).
47. STEPHENS, S. (*see* Ref. No. 106, Chap. 12).
48. STOUT, A., AND CHANDLER, C. Hereditary transmission of induced tetraploidy and compatibility in fertilization. Science. 96:257–58. 1942.
49. UNRAU, J. (*see* Ref. No. 51, Chap. 14).
50. WEXELSEN, H. (*see* Ref. No. 73, Chap. 11).

CHAPTER 16

Techniques of Colchicine Treatment

A. In Animals

16A.1: Solutions

It has been explained in Chapter 5 that the substance which has been repeatedly called *colchicine* in this book may have differed from author to author. One reason for this discrepancy is the factor of crystallization. Whereas pure, amorphous colchicine is very soluble in water, crystallization from aqueous or chloroformic solutions yields complex crytals which are less soluble and may have other biological properties.[55] Colchicine may crystallize with $\frac{1}{2}$ molecule of water, with $\frac{1}{2}$ molecule or 1 molecule of chloroform. This last form of crystalline colchicine is only soluble in water in the proportion of 4 per cent.[55] It has often been used in experimental research. In botanical work, results may be modified by the presence of chloroform, which is itself a mitotic poison.[55] In experiments on animals, where the amounts of colchicine used are far smaller and the solutions much more dilute, the presence of chloroform does not appear to have any importance. But, for any quantitative estimation of the activity of the drug, it must not be forgotten that crystalline colchicine with 1 molecule of chloroform contains 25 per cent by weight of the solvent.[55] On the other hand, chemical work has demonstrated that the plant *Colchicum* contains many alkaloids closely related to colchicine, but with different pharmacological properties.[51, 52] One of these, desmethylcolchicine, is found in the colchicine preparations of the U.S. Pharmacopeia.[36] In the most recent work on colchicine, care has been taken to purify the alkaloid before testing it.[26, 9] This applies only to a very small number of the papers, and some results may differ because the injected drug differed in its mode of preparation from the plant.[1] While the above-mentioned differences are only of importance for quantitative work, the changes that colchicine may undergo in solution are far more important, especially for work with warm-blooded animals or tissue cultures. Colchicine solutions should always be freshly prepared, or kept protected from the action of oxygen and light. For work on plants, where rather concentrated solutions are used and where no problems of general toxicity arise, this is not so important. In animal work, and especially for all work on birds or mammals, it is most important to use freshly prepared solutions.[43] Standing in the presence of air, colchicine appears to undergo a slow oxidation about which little is known (cf. Chapter 7). This decreases the spindle-inhibiting action, but may not affect similarly the general toxicity, which is increased in cold-blooded animals such as frogs.[37] These remarks apply to solutions, whether in water or fatty solvents. The latter have been mainly used for local applications in cancer chemotherapeutic tests.[10, 8]

The important point is that each paper should mention clearly the origin of the colchicine, whether crystalline or not, whether purified and how, the method of preparing the solutions before the experiments, and the temperature at which these are conducted. It is only in this way that a valid comparison of results is possible.

16A.2: Temperature

In Chapter 7, several instances have been given of the effect of temperature on the action of colchicine. This has long been known, but has often been overlooked.[29] Most workers mention that the alkaloid does not influence cell division in unicellular organisms (cf. Chapter 4). However, while *Paramecium* is unaffected by colchicine solutions at a one per cent concentration at 15°C., the same solutions kill the paramecia in less than 4 hours at 33°C. Exposure to this temperature is in itself not harmful to the organisms.[35]

These temperature effects are not yet understood properly. They explain the considerable differences between colchicine pharmacology in cold-blooded animals and in birds and mammals (cf. Chapter 7). For instance, colchicine-arrested metaphases remain intact for hours and even days (Fig. 2.2) in amphibia; in mammals, on the contrary, the nucleus of a cell arrested at metaphase by a spindle poison undergoes rapid destruction. In all *in vitro* work, the temperature should be constant and checked carefully.

16A.3: The Study of Mitosis

Colchicine may be utilized for many different purposes when analyzing mitotic growth, and techniques may considerably differ. For instance, in studies on the morphology of chromosomes or pseudospindle in arrested metaphases, quantitative data, except those about effective colchicine concentration, may not be of paramount importance. The same may apply to some work where colchicine is mainly a tool for increasing the "visibility" of cellular division. When the topography of mitotic growth is the main purpose, several instances of which have been given in Chapter 9, precise data about the mitotic rate may not be important. On the contrary, when using colchicine to assess the importance of cellular proliferation, either in complex tissues or in tissue cultures, it is indispensable to understand the complex action on the mitotic count. This point will be considered further.

Special techniques for the production by colchicine of abnormal growth in embryos have been mentioned in Chapter 8. The experimental creation of polyploid animals has been one aim of colchicine research. The methods used and the results obtained merit some discussion, which will be found in the last paragraph of this chapter.

16A.3–1: In vivo studies. Many methods have been utilized in the study of c-mitosis in animal cells; they are all variants of two: viz., placing cells in contact with colchicine solutions, or injecting these by various routes into the cell or into the animal.

The intracellular injection is of great interest, for it was possible to demonstrate by this procedure that some cells were resistant to colchicine since the alkaloid did not penetrate into the cytoplasm. Such experiments have been performed only on one unicellular, *Amoeba sphaeronucleus.* Mitotic division of this species is not affected when it is grown in colchicine solutions. Very minute quantities of a one per cent solution of the akaloid were introduced in the cytoplasm with a micropipette. Typical mitotic arrest, together with formation of polyploid nuclei, resulted when the timing of the injection was properly related to the mitotic cycle.[22]

Many cold-blooded animals, invertebrates, fish, amphibians, have been studied after immersion in colchicine solutions. One important pathway of absorption is through the branchiae. In such experiments, care should be taken to avoid sunlight and to replace the colchicine solution which may lose its activity through chemical changes.

Injection is often the easiest way to administer colchicine to pluricellular animals. In the study of hematopoiesis in the chick, colchicine was simply injected into the egg yolk through the shell.[3] In adult animals, subcutaneous or intraperitoneal injections are the most frequently used. One most important point, if a quantitative study of the number of mitoses is needed, is to inject all animals at the same hour of the day, so as not to be disturbed by the diurnal variations of mitotic rate.[13] This is also influenced by feeding the animals, more precisely by the blood glucose level, and experimental animals should be kept under standard and specified dietetic conditions.[14]

In mammals, and especially the small rodents, which have been widely used for colchicine work, some tissues are most favorable for the study of mitosis and the influence of colchicine and similar poisons. The skin lends itself to repeated biopsies, for instance the ear of the mouse, from which small fragments may be punched out at hourly intervals.[13, 14] However, the mitotic activity of the skin is low, and counting is long and tedious, even after colchicine. The number of mitoses is increased little by mitotic arrest, probably because under normal conditions they are of long duration, up to three hours. The influence of the sexual cycle is considerable (Chapter 9, Fig. 9.6) and must not be overlooked.[13] The cornea may be studied by staining whole mounts and counting the number of mitoses per thousand cells; this method has only been utilized in mammals by one group of workers,[18] though it appears to offer many advantages over the skin. Bone marrow and intestinal crypts are zones of maximal mitotic growth in mammals. They both provide excellent material for studying the action of colchicine. In bone marrow, comparative studies may be made between the white-cell- and the red-cell-forming tissues. In the intestine, quantitative estimation of mitotic growth is possible,[41] though the counting of mitoses may be difficult because of their rapid destruction of pycnosis. The intestinal mitoses have been one of the best tools for the study of mitotic poisons at Brussels. Contrary to the mitoses of lymphoid tissue, which are strongly affected by hormonal influences such as those of the "alarm-reaction" or pituitary-adrenal stimulation,[41] the intestine provides a tissue with uniform growth,[57] not affected by the adrenal cortical hormones.[28] Intestinal fragments should always be taken from the same location, for the mitotic activity is greater in the duodenum, and decreases gradually towards the large intestine, where few mitoses are seen. The gastric mucosa of the mouse has also been proposed;[9, 56] it offers an interesting comparison between squamous-celled and glandular epithelium in a single organ. The regenerating liver is a favorable material in rats, and quantitative estimations of mitotic growth are possible.[11] However, it has been shown that the repartition of mitoses was not uniform throughout the remaining liver.[45]

Local applications of colchicine have been most useful in the study of c-mitosis and regeneration in amphibians.[17] The study of recovery after a prolonged colchicine impregnation (five days) has been discussed in Chapter 2 (cf. Fig. 2.7).[49] The inhibition of regeneration of the tail of *Xenopus* larvae has been illustrated in Chapter 9; the technique involved a local application of an aqueous solution of colchicine to the amputated tail.[44] Local application has also been found useful in studies on the mitotic activity of genital tissues in rodents[58] and of the human vagina before removal of a fragment by biopsy;[54, 50] this is one of the methods for treating human tumors with the alkaloid, prepared in a vaseline-lanoline paste (Chapter 10) .[10, 8] Local applications of colchicine-impregnated agar cut into small fragments have also proved useful in studying the origin of colchicine malformations in eggs;[30] this technique does not seem to have received the attention it deserves.

Another method by which colchicine is brought into direct contact with the cells is the use of the so-called "ascites-tumors" in mice. These are neoplasms freely growing in fluid gathered in the abdominal cavity. Colchicine is injected intraperitoneally, and repeated observations of the cells are possible by removing a small amount of the ascites fluid.[42]

16A.3–2: In vitro techniques. For many studies, it is preferable to keep precise amounts of colchicine in contact with the cells which are studied. This enables the results not to be disturbed by general toxicity reactions and other pharmacological side-effects of colchicine (Chapter 7). More concentrated solutions may be tested, which, injected to whole animals, would have brought death through nervous and respiratory paralysis. These techniques apply especially to warm-blooded animals.

In invertebrates, however, some remarkable results, discussed in Chapters 2 and 3, have been obtained by the study at 38°C. of the isolated nervous system of the grasshopper, *Chortophaga viridifasciata* De Geer. Embryos, at an age equivalent to 14 days' development at 26°C., are removed from the egg in artificial culture medium. The maxillary and thoracic appendages, the head, and the posterior half of the abdomen are discarded, and the embryo is mounted with the ventral nervous system close to a cover slip, which is sealed. These hanging-drop preparations may be observed for several hours under oil-immersion objectives[19, 31] (cf. Chapter 3, and Fig. 3.1). This has proved to be one of the most interesting techniques for the study of the spindle destruction by colchicine and of the mitotic cycle.[19] Isolated eggs of invertebrates, for instance *Arbacia,*[4] should also be mentioned here, although the techniques do not differ from those used in experimental embryology (cf. Fig. 3.3 and Chapter 8).

In mammals, two tissues have provided excellent material for the study of mitosis *in vitro*. Fragments of the ear of mice may be incubated in Warburg flasks, and the action of various chemicals on mitotic growth studied on the epithelium, the mitoses of which persist for several hours, provided that glucose is added to the medium.[15] Bone marrow is readily available in many mammals, including man, and its mitoses may most simply be observed in cover-slip preparations at 37°C. Glucose does not appear to be as necessary as for epidermal cells.[2] This technique has provided most useful data on the physiology of cellular division in bone marrow and on the actions of various substances on rate of cell multiplication (Chapter 9). The cells, which are suspended in homologous serum, are able to divide regularly for more than 24 hours after explantation.[2]

A method for *in vitro* cultivation of immature rat ovaries has been described[7] and should be of great interest for endocrinological research.

Colchicine has been used with the main techniques of tissue culture, especially with hanging-drop preparations, which enable a continuous observation of growth.[12] Some estimation of the quantitative amount of newly formed cells may be made by planimetric measurement of the whole culture, but the influence of cell migration must not be neglected.[12] Tissue cultures are especially favorable for cinemicrographic methods.[12] A very thorough study of the action of colchicine on the rate of mitotic growth and on the repartition of the various types of abnormal or arrested mitoses has been made possible by this technique[12, 42] (Chapter 9, Fig. 9.1). Tissue cultures are also most useful for comparing normal and neoplastic cells,[21] for the study of synergists or antagonists of colchicine, and for testing other mitotic poisons[42] (cf. Chapter 17). It should, however, be mentioned that cultures of chick fibroblasts will not always behave like fibroblasts from mammals.[48] For the study of colchicine derivatives or other spindle poisons, cultures of various types of cells from different animals should be compared.

16A.3–3: Mitotic counts. When colchicine is used as a tool for studying growth (Chapters 9 and 10), when the problem of mitotic stimulation by colchicine is considered (Chapter 9), or when substances acting synergically or as antagonists to the alkaloid are studied (Chapter 17), a precise estimation of the number of mitoses in controls and at various intervals after mitotic arrest is indispensable. Some of the methods outlined in the preceding subsection provide excellent material for counting cell divisions, but even with tissue cultures, the problem may be complicated because only the periphery of the explanted fragment grows rapidly. Precise counts of the total number of cells in mitosis are possible both with the ear-clip technique[13, 14] and the methods of bone-marrow explantation.[2] In more complex tissues a reliable standard may be difficult to find. For instance, many authors define the "mitotic index" as the number of mitoses found in a given area, i.e., so many microscopic fields, of tissue. This is a good method when dealing with uniform and fairly simple tissues, for example, the regenerating liver,[11] but not when complex tissues are considered. In the small intestine of mammals, for instance, it is preferable to count the number of mitoses per hundred glandular crypts. This method has been widely used by the junior author in studies of mitotic poisoning.[24]

Many data obscuring the problem of possible mitotic stimulation by colchicine result from the difficulty of comparing tissues before and after the action of the alkaloid. To cite one instance, the great increase in mitotic activity in the crop-sac of pigeons injected with prolactine and colchicine has been mentioned (Chapter 9). Is it possible to compare quantitatively the mitotic counts in this tissue? From the figures which have been published one may conclude that it is not, for after prolactine and colchicine, there is not the same number of cells in a given area of tissue as in the same area of normal epithelium or of prolactine-thickened crop-sac.[40] A quantitative result could only be correct if it were possible to count a very large number of cells, and not only the mitoses in a given area. Such counts are not often reported in this type of work (Chapter 9). Another error is that of injecting a hormone at a too short interval before colchicine. Theoretically, the mitotic index should remain constant; that is to say, the numbers of cells entering prophase should not vary during the period of action of colchicine. It has been pointed out that this is not often so with hormone-stimulated growth.[16, 23] Considerable errors may result from hasty interpretations of the significance of mitotic increases.

Any quantitative work supposes also that the exact number of cells arrested at metaphase by colchicine is known. In warm-blooded animals, and apparently also in amphibia,[44] this is never so, even with large doses. Increasing the dosage of alkaloid is never a good solution either, for it increases secondary, nonspecific toxic reactions and the percentage of destroyed arrested mitoses, and may also depress the number of prophases. It is often very difficult, especially in mammals, to know exactly how many metaphases with clumped chromosomes undergo degeneration, for this is rapid, and the nucleus breaks down to many small fragments. The data about the duration of c-mitosis in animals are scarce and widely divergent, as pointed out in Chapter 2.[53] It is also necessary, when planning an experiment with colchicine acting as a tool, to know how long after an injection of the alkaloid the animal should be killed. Many factors complicate this estimation: There may be a period of latency like that observed in tissue cultures (Fig. 9.1);[12] some anaphases may persist even with large doses. Recovery starts after an interval which is not always known. In some tissues this may be rather short, and in the study of epidermal mitosis it is recommended to kill the animals six hours after colchicine. This duration appears favorable for many experiments on mammals, but it is obviously too short in cold-blooded animals. Here again, temperature may play a great part, but no quantitative work relating temperature to the duration of action of colchicine exists. In tissue cultures, colchicine may be left to act much longer, and 24 hours is often mentioned in work with bone marrow.[2]

This brings in another problem which we have not yet dealt with: the duration of interphase. It is evident that, if colchicine were acting longer than a normal interphase, no more new prophases would be available and the mitotic index would cease to rise. While most data on grasshoppers,[19] tissue cultures,[12] and complex tissues indicate that interphase is far longer than mitosis, precise information is often lacking. It has been suggested that colchicine itself may provide a means for measuring the duration of interphase.[39] If new prophases were indefinitely provided by the tissues, i.e., if interphase duration did not interfere with mitotic counts, the number of arrested mitoses would increase until all the cells would be in a condition of c-mitosis. This is never observed, and even in the fastest growing tissues never many more than 50 per cent of the cells show c-mitoses. This is because after a certain time no more interphasic cells are ready for prophase. On the curve of the numbers of mitoses in function of time, the time which elapses between the beginning of mitotic arrest and the leveling of the number of mitoses is related to the duration of interphase. Theoretically, under ideal conditions, it is equal to interphase.[39] This is of interest for workers handling colchicine and certainly deserves further study. In the preceding chapters, enough has been said about the complexities of c-mitosis to prevent conclusions to be drawn hastily. One fact remains true: In colchicine experiments, the duration of the action of the alkaloid should be much shorter than the interphasic duration of the cells which are studied.

Considering the great variations in mitotic duration which are mentioned in the literature (from about 30 minutes to three hours in the mouse), our ignorance about the duration of interphase, the difficulties of accurately counting mitoses, and the complexities of colchicine's pharmacology, it is evident that quantitative conclusions are only possible in a few instances. The advantages of tissue cultures are obvious.

16A.4: Polyploidy

Polyploid animals have been produced experimentally,[25, 27, 6] but colchicine has not yet proved very effective in doubling the chromosome number. This is probably only a question of technique, though cellular destruction, nondivision of the centromeres, and restitution during early development (Chapter 8) may be factors which prevent colchicine from acting on animal cells as in plants. Under the heading of polyploidy should be considered only doubling or multiplying by 2, 3, 4, . . . the numbers of chromosomes (cf. Chapter 11). Most results obtained with colchicine are related to triploidy.

Any experimental change in the numbers of chromosomes should be checked by chromosome counts. This point may seem quite obvious, but in early reports of "polyploidy" in mammals, changes in cell volume alone were mentioned. It is known from previous experimental data, mainly on amphibians,[25] that the size of the polyploid animals remains the same, or is even smaller, than the diploid size, though individual cells become larger and larger with increasing numbers of chromosomes. However, to deduce from measurement of cell size alone the degree of -ploidy cannot be accepted as a valid scientific method.[5] Considerable error may be involved; for instance, making smears of red blood cells and comparing the diameters is incorrect and cannot bring evidence of triploidy, as has been claimed.[32, 33] The red blood cell volumes would be a better choice, but these were not measured, either by indirect calculation from the diameter, or by measuring the packed red blood cell volume in a hematocrit tube. Some "polyploid" mammals have been claimed to be larger and to grow faster than the euploid ones.[32, 33] This is in contradiction with all data on amphibia, and as the numbers of colchicine-polyploid animals which have been studied is very small, and as they were not of pure breed, the data lack the necessary statistical significance.[6]

In the work on the unicellular *Amoeba sphaeronucleus*, polyploidy was assessed without counting the chromosomes, which are very numerous and small. Here, the action of the alkaloid injected intracellularly at metaphase could be followed under the microscope. A single nucleus resulted from the arrested metaphase, and its volume was roughly double that of normal amoebae. Checks were made possible by grafting these abnormal nuclei into normal amoebae, and vice versa.[22] The cellular volume became proportional to the size of the nucleus. However, even in these experiments, mitotic abnormalities were observed in the "polyploid" species, and it is not possible to assert with certainty that a true doubling of the chromosome number and not aneuploidy had resulted from the injections of colchicine. Claims of colchicine-induced polyploidy in frogs, rabbits, and pigs have been repeatedly published.[32, 33, 38] The females were artificially fertilized by sperm mixed with colchicine. The alkaloid is supposed to reach the egg at the time of the second maturation division, which would be arrested. The egg would thus remain diploid, and after fertilization with haploid sperm, triploid animals would be expected. Monstrous development in frogs treated similarly had pre-

viously been reported in a short note.[20] A frog sperm suspension with
$2.6 \times 10^{-4} M$ colchicine was most toxic to eggs, and only 8 per cent
of these developed normally. It has been claimed that this did not
result from a direct action of the alkaloid on the eggs at fertilization.[34]

The production of triploidy deserves close attention.[32, 33, 6] A surprising fact is that the rabbits and pigs were considered to have an
abnormal growth with increased weight and size. In the first papers,
triploidy was deduced from the increased size of red blood cells and
spermatocyte heads. The accuracy and significance of these measures
have been severely criticized.[6] However, chromosome counts were
later published. In frogs, tetraploid, but also diploid, triploid, and
pentaploid cells were found.[46] In rabbits, a considerable variation of
chromosome number was found. While the diploid one was the most
frequent, it is clear from the results published that the animals were
heteroploid.[46] The same applies to the single triploid pig. While in
a preliminary note about this animal it was claimed that the mitotic
count in the testicle was "certainly over 45 and not more than 48,"
and that the animal resulted from the fusion of a spermatozoon with
15 chromosomes ("Old Swedish" race) and an egg with a doubled
chromosome complement of 32 (mixed race), the results of a later
publication are by no means so clear.[46, 33]

It is already evident that in producing artificial "polyploids" one
should deal with animals with a well-known number of chromosomes
and should not cross two varieties with different and imperfectly
known numbers.[5] The detailed study of the testicular mitoses of the
abnormal pig shows chromosome numbers varying between 19 and 51,
with an "average" of 49. It was assumed that the probable number of
49 was correct.[33] This should result from the fecundation of a diploid
egg with 2×15 chromosomes by a spermatozoon with 19 chromosomes. Evidence for this is given from the chromosome count of a
normal brother of this pig, which had 34 (19+15) chromosomes.
However, one of the authors mentions as an interesting point that
aneuploid cells could be observed in the so-called triploid.[46]

From these descriptions it is apparent. (1) that colchicine may
have altered the second meiotic division of the egg, but that only indirect evidence is produced, and that the concentration present when
the sperm reached the eggs is unknown; (2) that no polyploid animals have been produced by colchicine, while other methods have
proved quite efficient in amphibia; (3) that triploidy is not proven,
and that aneuploidy is possible.

It remains possible that colchicine may prove as useful in polyploidy breeding in animals as in plants, but the premature claims of
the Swedish authors do not rest on firm ground. The technique of
insemination with colchicine is open to criticism, and even more, the

absence of repeated chromosome counts in various organs. It appears surprising that the bone marrow, the skin, or the cornea was not chosen for chromosome counts and that so many publications and claims rest on such meager technical data.

B. Techniques in Plants

16B.1: Solutions Used

Compared with warm-blooded animals, cells of plants tolerate relatively strong concentrations of colchicine. The substance diffuses rapidly through plant tissues and may be translocated in the plant through the vascular system. Active concentrations remain in contact with the cells for a longer time than is recorded by the total exposure to the drug. Apparently the effects of colchicine are retained for a long time. Penetrability, its low toxicity, and retention in the cell, along with the complete recovery through reversibility by the cell, are unique qualities of colchicine for doubling the number of chromosomes in plants.

Successful procedures have favored stronger solutions applied for shorter periods over the dilute ones applied during long exposure.[3, 4, 9, 11, 13, 15, 18, 21, 22, 24, 25, 26, 27, 30, 17, 33] Schedules with specific concentrations advocated and exposure recommendations are given in the papers. If a universal concentration were selected for treating plants, the strength would be 0.2 per cent aqueous solution. This concentration, or one close to it, has been used more frequently than any other. Wide ranges are effective, but there is an optimum which produces the highest percentages of changed cells. Generally, one gram of colchicine is dissolved in 500 ml. water. The length of time for keeping cells in contact with the drug varies from 24 to 96 hours. In addition to concentration and exposure, the growing conditions of a particular tissue are important. Cells must be in a high state of cell division for maximum effective use of colchicine.[12]

A study of the action of colchicine upon mitosis requires the use of wide ranges in concentration in order to obtain minimum, optimum, and maximum effects. The objectives are somewhat different from using the drug as a tool for making polyploids.

The carrier used for colchicine in treating seed plants may be water, emulsions, agar, or lanolin. Wetting agents have been used effectively. Sometimes the addition of glycerine has been recommended.[9] The emulsions are sprayed on to the plants or lanolin pastes applied, as suitable. Aqueous solutions are applied by dropping, brushing, or total immersion of the plant in the solution. The latter method has been used effectively for root systems and seedlings.

16B.2: Seed and Seedlings

One of the most convenient ways to treat plants uses the germinating seed placed in solution. The seed may be presoaked or placed directly into the colchicine. Different lots may be removed after given intervals. Then some exposures will not cause doubling; others will prove lethal; and other lots will be at the optimum exposure. In this way the most effective concentration and time of exposure can be determined by the survival of treated seeds transplanted after treatment. Overexposures kill the seedlings, and underexposure does not lead to new polyploids.

Plants, when young, are well adapted to treatment. If only the plumule is treated, the roots remain unharmed, and plant growth is not so totally harmed. The growing point may be immersed in colchicine, or the solution applied to the plant by brush treatment. By sowing seeds in rows, and treating each row with different exposures, the differences between too much treatment and too little will show at the time seedlings are ready for transplanting. Selections for probable polyploids can be made at this time.

Seedlings of monocotyledonous plants are difficult to treat with colchicine. Special methods[7, 18, 13, 5] had to be devised for these cases. Admitting the drug to the growing tissues that lie beneath a coleoptile sheath has been the chief problem.

16B.3: Root Systems and Special Structures

Soaking entire root systems has been effective for many species of the Gramineae.[19, 18, 29] An alternate period of soaking in colchicine 12 hours and in water 12 hours has worked out with good success. The number of exposures depends upon the particular experiment, material, and concentration. Reference to specific schedules in the literature shows what directions have been most successful. The technique was developed for sterile species hybrids of grasses and specifically for wheat-rye sterile hybrids to make fertile amphiploids.[33]

Scales of liliaceous plants,[15] bulbs, corms, and rhizomes represent structures that call for modifications in method. Usually a large mass of meristematic tissues are present, and unless the whole group of cells responds, the production of mixoploids and chimeras becomes an inevitable result.

Expanding buds of woody stems require proper timing in order to introduce colchicine when the cells are in their peak of division. In this way mature woody plants can be treated when dormancy is being broken. By grafting the changed sectors, the new polyploids can be propagated.[9] Periclinal and sectorial chimeras are frequently produced in treating woody species. These chimeras may be propagated for generations through grafting. Their role in horticulture is being more fully appreciated from a breeding point of view.

16B.4: Special Techniques for Studying the Action of Colchicine

Pollen grains that can be used for artificial culturing work serve well for testing the action of colchicine upon mitosis and growth processes. The specific morphology of somatic chromosomes were studied in *Polygonatum*, and discovery of natural polyploidy was made directly from these observations. Another valuable feature is the small amount of chemical that can be tested. Other mitotic poisons soluble in water can be adapted for testing with the pollen tube methods.

Several modifications have been made in pollen tube studies since the original paper was published in 1931 by Trankowsky. The particular conditions for an experiment must be worked out and followed thereafter. In pollen tube studies the detail is not as important as a routine which, once successful for an operation, is always done in that way.[6]

Mitosis in the cells of staminal hairs of *Tradescantia* can be studied *in vivo*. Single cells may be followed through the stages of mitosis. When such cells are growing in agar containing colchicine, the total time required for a c-mitosis can be measured. Special chambers for keeping the cells alive for long periods were designed for these studies. While the general technique for observing mitosis in the living cell of *Tradescantia* has been known for many years, the adaptations for experimental cytology are new.[33]

Colchicine was used so effectively with root tips of *Allium cepa* that the test has become known as a method for experimental work, the *Allium cepa* test. Threshold concentrations in relation to solubility are some of the contributions from this method. Standardization of procedures have been devised so that a variety of chemicals can be measured for properties of mitotic inhibition or chromosomal breakage. The time for exposure, for recovery, and for fixation after treatment are important parts of the routine method.

Allowing roots to germinate when suspended over a test solution is a modification of the *Allium cepa* method, and more specifically known as the onion root germination test.

Tissue cultures for excised roots, virus tumor tissue, proliferating cells, and regenerative tissues generally may be adapted for the use of colchicine. *In vitro* and *in vivo* studies are made by these methods.

16B.5: Chromosome Studies

The pollen mother cells stained by acetocarmine are universally a most important source for studying chromosomes in plants. The procedure for determining the number of chromosomes is rapid. More important than deciding what the number might be, are the pairing characteristics at meiotic metaphase, chiasmatal frequencies, lagging of chromosomes at meiotic anaphase, configurations due to translocations, and the irregularities of meiotic processes generally. These are the problems associated with polyploidy that must be studied at the pollen mother cell stage.

Root tips are used for a check of the somatic numbers of chromosomes. Pretreatment of roots before fixation with chemicals that arrest mitosis at metaphase facilitates the study.[2] Distributions of chromosomes in an arrested metaphase are easier to count and compare for size and morphology.[16, 8, 14, 2]

Leaf cells in division combined with acetocarmine and Feulgen technics are another source for counting chromosomes in polyploids and related diploids. The longer period of time during which leaf cells provide material and the abundance and availability of material are favored in this test.

Pollen tube cells that undergo mitosis in the tube rather than inside the pollen grain can be treated with colchicine in sucrose-agar media. Scattered chromosomes are easily counted, and the morphology of somatic chromosomes in haploid sets can be measured.[10]

Causes of sterility in pollen and pollen mother cells may not be the same when viewed in the embryo-sac stages, or among megaspore mother cells. Frequently the polyploid may be pollen-sterile and female-fertile, or vice versa. Transmission of certain extra chromosomes occurs only through the female and not through the male gametophyte. Cytological methods to measure chromosomal variations in the female gametophyte are long and difficult procedures, but they are important to a full knowledge of why some strains are lower in fertility than others.

REFERENCES — SECTION A

1. ASHLEY, J. N., AND HARRIS, J. O. Purification of colchicine by chromatography. Jour. Chem. Soc. P. 677. 1944.
2. ASTALDI, G., AND MAURI, C. La valutazione dell'attivita proliferativa delle cellule miodlari. Studio di un "test stathmocinetico." Haematologica. 33:1–46. 1949. New criteria for the evaluation of the bone-marrow cells mitotic activity. Le Sang. 21:378–82. 1950.
3. ———, BERNARDELLI, E., AND RONDANELLI, E. La colchicine dans l'étude de la prolifération des cellules hémopoïétiques de l'embryon. Rev. Belge Path. 21:406–13. 1952.
4. BEAMS, H. W., AND EVANS, T. C. Some effects of colchicine upon the first cleavage in *Arbacia punctulata*. Biol. Bull. 79:188–98. 1940.

5. BEATTY, R. A. Heteroploidy in mammals. Animal Breeding Abst. 19:283–92. 1951.
6. ———, AND FISHBERG, M. Spontaneous and induced triploidy in pre-implantation mouse eggs. Nature. 163:807. 1949. "Polyploidy in rabbits." Nature. 166:238. 1950. Heteroploidy in mammals. III. Induction of tetraploidy in pre-implantation mouse eggs. Jour. Genet. 50:47–79. 1952.
7. BERRIAN, J. H., AND DORNFELD, E. J. Cellular proliferation in the germinal epithelium of immature rat ovaries. An *in vitro* method for the study of mitotic rate. Jour. Exp. Zool. 115:493–512. 1950. The effects of ribonucleotides on mitosis in the germinal epithelium of immature rat ovaries cultured *in vitro*. Jour. Exp. Zool. 115:513–20. 1950.
8. BOURG, R., AND DUSTIN, P., JR. Le traitement des papillomes vilvaries par l'application locale de colchicine. Presse Méd. 43:578. 1945.
9. BRANCH, C. F., FOGG, L. C., AND ULLYOT, G. E. Colchicine and colchicine-like compounds as chemotherapeutic agents. Acta Unio Internat. Cancrum. 6:439–47. 1949.
10. BRODERSON, H. Mitosegifte und ionisierende Strahlung. Strahlenther. 75:196–254. 1943.
11. BRUES, A. M. The effect of colchicine on regenerating liver. Jour. Physiol. 86:63–64. 1936.
12. BUCHER, O. Zur Kenntnis der Mitose. VI. Der Einfluss von Colchicin und Trypaflavin auf den Wachstumrythmus und auf die Zellteilung in Fibrocytenkulturen. Z. Zellforsch. 29:283–322. 1939. Le rôle de la culture des tissus *in vitro* dans l'étude des poisons de la mitose. Mém. Soc. Vaudoise Sci. Nat. 10:245–70. 1951.
13. BULLOUGH, W. S. Mitotic activity in the adult female mouse, *Mus musculus* L. A study of its relation to the oestrus cycle in normal and abnormal conditions. Phil. Trans. Roy. Soc. B: 231–435. 1946. The diurnal cycles and their relation to waking and sleeping. *Ibid*. 135:212–33. 1948. The effects of experimentally induced rest and exercise on the epidermal mitotic activity of the adult male mouse, *Mus musculus* L. *Ibid*. 135:233–42. 1948.
14. ———, AND EISA, E. A. The effect of a graded series of restricted diets on epidermal mitotic activity in the mouse. Brit. Jour. Cancer. 4:321–28. 1950.
15. ———, AND JOHNSON, M. A. simple technique for maintaining mammalian epidermal mitoses *in vitro*. Exp. Cell Res. 2:445–53. 1951.
16. BURCKHART, E. Z. A study of the effects of androgenic substances in the rat with the aid of colchicine. Doctoral Dissertation. The University of Chicago Library. Chicago, Ill. 1940. A study of the early effect of androgenous substances in the rat by the aid of colchicine. Jour. Exp. Zool. 89:135–66. 1942.
17. BUREAU, V., AND VILTER, V. Action de la colchicine étudiée sur les cellules épithéliales de l'Axolotl. C. R. Soc. Biol. Paris. 132–553–58. 1939.
18. BUSCHKE, W., FRIEDENWALD, J. S., AND FLEISCHMANN, W. Studies on the mitotic activity of the corneal epithelium. Methods. The effects of colchicine, ether, cocaine, and ephedrine. Bull. Johns Hopkins Hosp. 73:143–68. 1943.
19. CARLSON, J. G. Effects of X-radiation on grasshopper chromosomes. Cold Spring Harbor Symp. Quant. Biol. 9:104–12. 1941.
20. CHANG, M. C. Artificial production of monstrosities in the rabbit. Nature. 154:150. 1944.
21. CLEARKIN, P. A. The effect of colchicine on normal and neoplastic tissues in mice. Jour. Path. Bact. 44:469. 1937.
22. COMANDON, J., AND DE FONBRUNE, P. Action de la colchicine sur *Amoeba sphaeronucleus*. Obtention de variétés géantes. C. R. Soc. Biol. Paris. 136: 410–11. 1942. Étude volymétrique comparative d'*Amoeba sphaeronucleus* et de deux variétés obtenues par l'action de la colchicine. *Ibid*. 136:423. 1942. Anomalies de la division observées à partir de noyaux atypiques, chez *Amoeba sphaeronucleus* et ses variétés colchiciniques. *Ibid*. 136:460–61. 1942. Greffes nucléaires croisées entre *Amoeba sphaeronucleus* et l'une de ses variétés colchiciniques. *Ibid*. 136:746–47. 1942. Modifications héréditaires de volume provoquées par l'échange du noyau entre *Amoeba sphaeronucleus* et ses variétés colchiciniques. *Ibid*. 136:747–48. 1942.

23. DUSTIN, A. P. Recherches sur le mode d'action des poisons stathmocinétiques. Action de la colchicine sur l'uterus de lapine impubère sensibilisée par injection préalable d'urine de femme enceinte. Arch. Biol. 54:111–87. 1943.
24. DUSTIN, P., JR. The action of mitotic poisons on normal and pathological blood cell formation. Le Sang. 21:297–330. 1950.
25. FANKHAUSER, G. Induction of polyploidy in animals by extremes of temperature. Biol. Symp. 6:21–35. 1942. The effect of changes in chromosome number on amphibian development. Quart. Rev. Biol. 20:20–78. 1945.
26. FERGUSON, F. C. Colchicine. I. General Pharmacology. Jour. Pharmacol. Exp. Ther. 106:261–70. 1952.
27. FISHBERG, M., AND BEATTY, R. A. Heteroploidy in Mammals. II. Induction of triploidy in pre-implantation mouse eggs. Jour. Genet. 50:455–70. 1952.
28. FREUD, J., AND UYLDERT, I. E. The influence of colchicine upon mitoses in the intestine in normal and adrenalectomized rats. Acta Brev. Neerl. Physiol. 8:16–18. 1938.
29. FÜHNER, H. Die Colchicingruppe. *In* Heffters Handbuch Exp. Pharmakologie. 2:493–507. 1920.
30. GABRIEL, M. L. The effect of local applications of colchicine on Leghorn and polydactylous chick embryos. Jour. Exp. Zool. 101:339–50. 1946. Production of strophosomy in the chick embryo by local applications of colchicine. Jour. Exp. Zool. 101:351–54. 1946.
31. GAULDEN, M., AND CARLSON, J. Cytological effects of colchicine on the grasshopper neuroblast *in vitro*, with special reference to the origin of the spindle. Exp. Cell Res. 2:416–33. 1951.
32. HÄGGQVIST, G. Polyploidy in frogs, induced by colchicine. Proc. Kon. Nederl. Akad. Wetensch. 51:3–12. 1948. Induktion triploider Schweine durch Kolchizin. Verh. Anat. Ges. 49:62–65. 1951. Über polyploide Säugetiere. Verh. Anat. Ges. 48:39–42. 1951.
33. ———, AND BANE, A. Polyploidy in rabbits, induced by colchicine. Nature. 165:841–43. 1950. Chemical induction of polyploid breeds of mammals. Kungl. Svenska Vetenskapakad. Handl. IV Ser. 1:1–11. 1950. Kolchizininduzierte Heterploidie beim Schwein. Kungl. Svenska Vetenskapakad. Handl. IV Ser. 3. Pp. 14. 1951.
34. HALL, T. S. Abnormalities of amphibian development following exposure of sperm to colchicine. Proc. Soc. Exp. Biol. and Med. 62:193–95. 1946.
35. HAUSEMANN, W., AND KOLMER, W. Über die Einwirkung kolloidaler Gifte auf Paramäcien. Biochem. Z. 3:503–7. 1907.
36. HOROWITZ, R. M., AND ULLYOT, G. E. Desmethylcolchicine, a constituent of U.S.P. colchicine. Science. 115:216. 1952.
37. JACOBJ, C. Pharmakologische Untersuching über das Colchicumgift. Arch. Exp. Path. 27:119–57. 1890.
38. JAHN, U. Induktion verschiedener Polyploidie-grade bei *Rana temporaria* mit Hilfe von Kolchizin und Sulfanilamid. Z. Mikr.-anat. Forsch. 58:36–99. 1952.
39. JOURNOUD, R. Recherches sur un élément peu connu de l'hématopoïèse: la durée des mitoses des cellules myéloïdes. Le Sang. 24:355–63. 1953.
40. LEBLOND, C. P., AND ALLEN, E. Emphasis of the growth effect of prolactin on the crop gland of the pigeon by arrest of mitoses with colchicine. Endocrinology. 21:455–60. 1937.
41. ———, AND SEGAL, G. Action de la colchicine sur la surrénale et les organes lymphatiques. C. R. Soc. Biol. Paris. 128:995–97. 1938.
42. LETTRÈ, H. Über Mitosegifte. Ergebn. Physiol. 46:379–452. 1950.
43. LITS, F. Recherches sur les réactions et lésions cellulaires provoquées par la colchicine. Arch. Int. Méd. Exp. 11:811–901. 1936.
44. LÜSCHER, M. Die Hemmung der Regeneration durch Colchicin beim Schwanz der *Xenopus*-larve und ihre entwicklungsphysiologische Wirkungsanalyse. Helv. Physiol. et Pharm. Acta. 4:465–94. 1946.
45. MALINSKY, J., AND LANG, B. Hyperplasie du foie de rat après hépatectomie partielle et influence des corps colchicinés sur celle-ci. C. R. Soc. Biol. Paris. 145:609–12. 1951.

46. MELANDER, Y. Chromosome behaviour of a triploid adult rabbit, as produced by Häggqvist and Bane after colchicine treatment. Hereditas. 36:335–41. 1950. Polyploidy after colchicine treatment of pigs. Hereditas. 37:288–89. 1951.
47. OSGOOD, E. E. The culture of human marrow as an aid in the evaluation of therapeutic agents. Jour. Lab. and Clin. Med. 24:954–62. 1939.
48. PARMENTIER, R. Personal communication.
49. PETERS, J. J. A cytological study of mitosis in the cornea of *Triturus viridescens* during recovery after colchicine treatment. Jour. Exp. Zool. 103:33–60. 1946.
50. PUNDEL, M. P. Étude des réactions vaginales hormonales chez la femme par la méthode colchicinique. Ann. Endocrin. 2:659–64. 1950.
51. SANTAVY, F., AND REICHSTEIN, T. Isolierung neuer Stoffe aus den Samen der Herbstzeitlose, *Colchicum autumnale* L. Helv. Chim. Acta. 33:1606–27. 1950.
52. ———, LANG, B., AND MALINSKY, J. L'action mitotique et la toxicité des nouvelles substances isolées du colchique. Arch. Int. Pharmacodyn. 84:257–68. 1950.
53. SENTEIN, P. La dégénérésence nucléaire après stathmocinèse. C. R. Soc. Biol. Paris. 139:585–87. 1945.
54. SHORR, E., AND COHEN, E. J. Use of colchicine in detecting hormonal effects on vaginal epithelium of menstruating and castrate women. Proc. Soc. Exp. Biol. and Med. 46:330–35. 1941.
55. STEINEGGER, E., AND LEVAN, A. The cytological effect of chloroform and colchicine on *Allium*. Hereditas. 33:515–25. 1947.
56. TIER, H., SCHAUMAN, A., AND SUNDELL, B. Mitotic ratio and colchicine sensitivity of the stomach epithelium of the white rat. Acta Anat. 16:233–44. 1952.
57. VILTER, V. Inibition of colchicinique de la mitose chez les mammifères C. R. Soc. Biol. Paris. 138:605–6. 1944.
58. WILLIAMS, W. L., STEIN, K. F., AND ALLEN, E. Reaction of genital tissues of the female mouse to the local application of colchicine. Yale Jour. Biol. and Med. 13:841–46.

REFERENCES — SECTION B

1. BELLING, J. The iron-aceto carmine method of fixing and staining chromosomes. Biol. Bull. 50:160–62. 1926.
2. BHADURI, P. Improved smear methods for rapid double staining. Jour. Roy. Micr. Soc. 60:3–7. 1940.
3. BREWBAKER, L. Personal communications. 1951.
4. BROWN, M. Personal communications. 1951.
5. CHASE, S. Production of homozygous diploids of maize from monoploids. Agron. Jour. 44:263–67. 1952.
6. CONGER, A. Personal communications. 1953.
7. CUA, L. A newly devised colchicine method for inducing polyploidy in rice. Bot. Gaz. 112:327–29. 1951.
8. DARLINGTON, C., AND LACOUR, L. The handling of chromosomes. The Macmillan Co. New York. 165 pp. 1942.
9. DERMEN, H. Personal communications. 1948.
10. EIGSTI, O. Methods for growing pollen tubes for physiological and cytological studies. Proc. Okla. Acad. Sci. 20:45–47. 1940.
11. EMSWELLER, S. Personal communications. 1950.
12. FYFE, J. The action and use of colchicine in the production of polyploid plants. Imp. Bur. Plant Breeding and Genet. Publ. No. 576. 1939.
13. KIHARA, H. Personal communications. 1948.
14. LACOUR, L . Improvements in plant cytological technique. II. Bot. Rev. 13: 216–40. 1947.
15. MANLEY, T. Colchicine techniques. Hemerocallis Soc. Ybk. 1950:46–49. 1950.
16. MEYER, J. Modification of mitosis by chemicals. Science. 108:2799. 1948.
17. MORGAN, D., AND RAPPLETE, R. Twin and triplet pepper seedlings. A study of polyembryony in *Capsicum frutescens*. Jour. Hered. 41:91–95. 1950.
18. MÜNTZING, A. Personal communications. 1949.
19. NAVASHIN, M., AND GERASSIMOVA, H. Production of polyploids by administering colchicine solution via roots. C. R. Dokl. Acad. Sci. URSS. 26:681–83. 1940.

20. NEBEL, B., AND RUTTLE, M. The cytological and genetical significance of colchicine. Jour. Hered. 29:3–9. 1938.
21. PEARSON, O., *et al.* Notes on species crosses in *Cucurbita*. Proc. Amer. Soc. Hort. Sci. 57:310–22. 1951.
22. RANDOLPH, L. Personal communication. 1948.
23. RASMUSSON, J., AND LEVAN, A. Tetraploid sugar beets from colchicine treatments. Hereditas. 25:97–102. 1939.
24. ROSEN, G. Problems and methods in the production of tetraploids within the genus *Beta*. Socker. Handl. 5. Hafte 10:197–217. Landskrona, Sweden. 1949.
25. SCHNELL, L. The induction of polyploidy in *Vinca rosea*. Amer. Jour. Bot. 28:5s. 1941.
26. SEARS, E. Personal communication. 1948.
27. SMITH, H. Personal communication. 1951.
28. SMITH, L. The aceto-carmine smear technique. Stain Tech. 22:17–31. 1947.
29. STEBBINS, G. Personal communication. 1951.
30. STEWART, R. Personal communication. 1949.
31. TJIO, J., AND LEVAN, A. The use of oxiquinoline in chromosome analysis. Anales Estación Exp. Aula Dei. Zaragoza, Spain. 2:21–64. 1950.
32. WELLENSIEK, S. Method for producing Triticales. Jour. Hered. 38:167–73. 1947.
33. WADA, B. Eine neue Methode zur Lebendbeobachtung der Mitose bei den *Tradescantia*-Haarzellen. Cytologia. 13:139–145. 1943.

CHAPTER 17

Mechanism of Colchicine-Mitosis

17.1: Introduction

While many activities of colchicine have been discussed in the previous chapters, it is evident that this alkaloid would be known merely as an effective treatment for gouty patients (Chapter 7) had it not been for its remarkable property of destroying the spindles of mitotic cells. The consequences of this, both in animal and botanical work, have been described. As a polyploidizing agent alone, colchicine has become of world-wide importance and has opened new vistas in experimental agriculture. The scope of the work which has been published since 1934 is so great that all its aspects cannot be covered in this book. More detailed information on some aspects of the colchicine problems may be found in several review papers to which the attention of the reader is directed.[14, 19, 25, 32, 43, 50, 57, 58, 69, 77, 81, 97, 102, 18, 111]

Many still unsolved problems have been mentioned in the text, and it would be useless to discuss again their various aspects. However, the main action of colchicine, as evidenced by microscopy and by the production of polyploids, is in changing the properties of the spindle. Other chemical or physical agents are also capable of destroying the spindle and preventing mitosis from proceeding. The uniqueness of colchicine appears with greater clarity when it is compared with the other "spindle poisons." While no attempt will be made to cover spindle poisoning, this great field of cellular pharmacology, it appears evident that the mechanisms of c-mitosis may be better understood from the study of other agents altering mitosis like colchicine. Many chemicals closely related to colchicine have been studied, and relations between their chemical structure and their spindle activity throw light on the possible action of colchicine.

17.1–1: Historical. Spindle poisons were known long before colchicine, and the fact that none of them was so successful is in itself a demonstration of the singularity of colchicine. The action of narcotics on divisions of sea-urchin eggs was studied by Hertwig in 1887,[48] two years before the discovery of c-mitosis by Pernice;[95] inactivation of the spindle was conspicuous. Phenylurethane in "narcotic" doses was later used in experimental work to study the influence of mitosis on the respiration;[125] the latter was not modified when the spindle was inactivated. In plants, Nemec[86] studied another narcotic, chloral hydrate. Figure 17.1, which is from a later paper,[98] demonstrates how similar the arrested mitoses after chloral hydrate are to c-mitosis. The induction of polyploid plants was, however, never recorded, probably because of the too great toxicity of this narcotic. This points to one of the principal qualities of colchicine and explains most of its success in practical botanical work: its low toxicity and high efficiency.[92]

A classical monograph dealing with animal cells was written by Politzer,[97] who had done important work in the years 1920–1930. Several basic dyes appear to influence the spindle, but Politzer's work is mainly concerned with chromosome poisons, which act somewhat similarly to the ionizing radiations (so-called "radiomimetic" drugs), and he mentions only occasionally metaphase poisoning and spindle destruction.

In 1929, in A. P. Dustin's laboratory, Piton[96] demonstrated the action of various arsenical derivatives on mitoses in mice. These experiments were later extended to grafted tumors.[29] However, the concept of c-mitosis did not yet exist, and observing the gradual increase in the numbers of mitoses, it was thought that a mitotic stimulation was taking place. Actually, it was only after the study of colchicine that it was clearly realized that arsenicals were also spindle poisons, and much later, that they also influenced plant mitosis. Another curious observation is that of Rosenfeld,[99] who noted arrested metaphases in cells treated with ammonia.

On the other hand, it was demonstrated by Lewis[72] that heat alone could inactivate the spindle. Sax observed a similar behavior of plant mitoses in *Tradescantia*.[104] This research opened a way for the successful production of polyploid plants (cf. Chapter 11) and polyploid vertebrates (cf. Chapter 16A), but it was not linked to the other observations of what came to be called c-mitosis.[70] After the discovery of colchicine, and mainly after the observation of its action on plant cells, a host of new spindle poisons was described, and other chemical and physical means of arresting metaphases were found. None was more efficient than colchicine, with the exception of some derivatives closely related to colchicine.

17.1–2: Colchicine and the spindle. Before discussing further other mitotic poisons, it is important to stress the peculiar properties of colchicine. These have been analyzed at length in Chapters 2, 3, and 4, and only a short summary is necessary at this point. Colchicine is a mitotic poison; that is to say, it belongs to the vast and rapidly increasing group of substances which act specifically on dividing cells. In Chapter 7 many other actions of the alkaloid on "resting" (intermitotic) cells were mentioned, but these are limited to

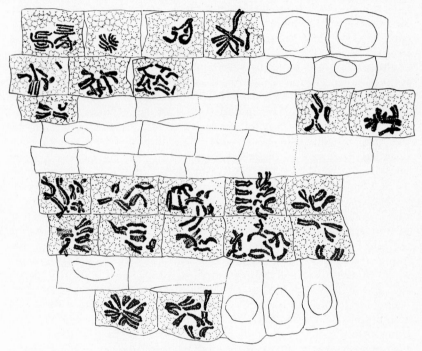

Fig. 17.1—Root tips of **Vicia faba** treated for three hours by a 1 per cent solution of chloral hydrate and replaced for 24 hours in water. Pseudo-metaphases and pseudo-anaphases. (After van Regemoorter,[98] Fig. 1)

some specialized tissues and to some groups of animals. Effects on cell-shape, apart from mitosis, have also been recorded in Chapter 4. These are most interesting for a proper understanding of the c-mitotic effect, but are mainly side-effects, usually brought about with strong concentrations of the alkaloid.

On the contrary, the spindle action is remarkably specific, and solutions of colchicine diluted to one part in one billion, may still exhibit spindle poisoning: colchicine has *high activity*. This is expressed as the inverse of the activity threshold. Colchicine is also of *great efficiency;* that is to say, it acts over a wide range of concentration. This is especially visible in plant cells, where the general toxic reactions of strong doses described in animals (Chapter 7) are avoided. No other spindle poison is at the same time so active and so efficient, though some of the colchicine derivatives may poison animal spindles at concentrations lower than colchicine.[71, 41, 43, 92, 66]

The changes of the mitotic spindles under the action of colchicine have been described at length in Chapter 3. Suffice it to recall here that the fibrous and polarized spindle is very rapidly changed into an amorphous "pseudo-spindle" or "hyaline globule," which is incapable of moving the chromosomes.[40, 51] Much evidence is at hand to demonstrate that the action of the alkaloid is proportional to its concentration and is totally *reversible,* two facts of great importance in the interpretation at a molecular level of spindle inactivation. Chromosome changes are usually only a consequence of the arrest of mitosis, especially in warm-blooded animals. In plants, the continuation of the normal chromosome-cycle in cells devoid of spindles is the basis of colchicine polyploidy. Cytoplasmic changes have been recorded in plants and animals, especially a decrease in the general viscosity, or rigidity, as evidenced by centrifugation.[88] This may be a consequence, and not the cause, of spindle inactivation.

Most of the other cellular changes are indirect consequences of the spindle inhibition. Short and thick chromosomes are frequently met in arrested metaphases. In plant cells, the cycle of chromosome reduplication is not disturbed by the alkaloid, while in animals, only a few instances of polyploid cells resulting from the multiplication of chromosomes in colchicine-treated cells have been recorded. Here, the prolongation of metaphase leads often to degenerative nuclear changes. Modifications in the shape of cells and in the growth of cell membranes have been recorded (cf. Chapter 4). These involve fibrous proteins, and may be of a similar nature to the spindle changes.

Considering the many data that have been gathered, it can be stated here that colchicine appears to be one of the most specific and least toxic of all the spindle poisons. Hence, any work which helps to solve the problem of spindle inactivation by this complex molecule may throw more light on the mechanism of cell division and on the physiology of the peculiar fibrous protein which constitutes the spindle. The importance of this cannot be underestimated, for all cellular growth in nucleated cells involves the separation of the two groups of chromosomes by the fibrous strands of the spindle.*

---

* Whether similar mechanisms exist in bacteria is still open to discussion, though nuclei have been recognized by many authors, and at least one group has tentatively identified a mitotic spindle.[24] It may be that the plurinucleated bacterial forms which arise under the influence of some antibiotics, e.g. penicillin, are true polyploid cells. Some antibiotics have been shown to be spindle poisons in warm-blooded animals,[1] and future work may lead to the extension of the concept of mitotic poisoning to microorganisms.

17.1–3: Materials and methods. While the problems of colchicine technique have been reviewed in Chapter 16, it is necessary to say something more about this subject in introducing a chapter on spindle poisons. The fundamental processes of mitosis are very similar in all nucleated cells, but it would be an error to think about cell division as an identical phenomenon in all nature from the unicellulars to higher plants and animals. Though the changes brought about by exposure to colchicine are nearly identical, it has been pointed out in previous chapters that *Amoeba* reacts only when the alkaloid is injected with a micropipette into the cytoplasm, that in plant cells, chromosome division proceeds for a long time in the absence of any spindle, and that in animals the hormones and other influences regulating cellular multiplication interfere with the action of colchicine (cf. Chapters 7, 8, and 9).

Spindle poisons have been studied by a small group of research workers, and each laboratory has used the cellular material which appeared the most convenient. It would be unwise to compare uncritically results obtained on *Allium* root tips or on sea-urchin eggs with those observed in fibroblast cultures or in mammals injected with colchicine, or to compare colchicine and spindle-poison effects in normal and neoplastic cells, in embryos or in adults, in slow-growing cells or in tissues stimulated to cellular multiplication by the action of hormones — both in plants and animals. These facts may seem evident from previous chapters. The great mass of data that has accumulated for twenty years about spindle poisons can only be discussed with caution. It is clear that the time is not yet ripe for a single theory covering all types of cells. This important point should be kept in mind when, in the next pages, different and apparently conflicting theories are considered. The only firm ground is that of the experimental facts, and this alone provides a varied and interesting insight into the action of spindle poisons.

17.1–4: The problem. The purpose of this chapter can now be defined more clearly. The fundamental problem is that of spindle inactivation by colchicine, a highly specific property of a complex molecule. Other spindle poisons will be considered as far as they help to understand colchicine, and also the modifications of the fibrous properties of the spindle, as evidenced by its structure and by submicroscopic evidence (polarized light) [105, 51] (Chapter 3).

The following points will be considered:

(1) Like most biological activities, spindle formation and modifications during mitosis may be under the control of enzymes. Most work on the effects of colchicine on enzyme systems does not bring much useful evidence, but should be pursued. Some of the latest theories, discussed in Subsections 17.5–2 and –4, point to enzymes as the targets inhibited by colchicine.

(2) A great amount of work on plant cells with a large series of chemicals has indicated that the destruction of the spindle was most closely related to physical properties such as solubility. In short, c-mitosis appeared as a "narcotized" mitosis, and the theories of narcosis explain many findings. It will be seen further whether colchicine fits into such a theory (Subsection 17.3–5).

(3) Work with a molecule as complex as colchicine benefits from experiments with related chemicals having simpler structures. These have clearly indicated which, in the molecule of colchicine, are the groups necessary for the production of c-mitosis. Other substances that inactivate spindles and have definite chemical properties which may explain their action, are of varied structure and range from the simple inorganic arsenic salts to complex molecules, alkaloids, or antibiotics. Though no chemical explanation of spindle destruction by all these substances can be given, the comparison of their structures and activities with that of colchicine throws some light on the singular properties of this alkaloid.

(4) Another approach to the problem of colchicine and the spindle is through the study of antagonists and synergists. Some of the work done in this field has given rise to controversies, but it cannot be ignored. It is evident that the discovery of a substance capable of preventing colchicine from destroying mitotic spindles might at least throw some more light on the biochemistry of the alkaloid and the spindle and on the complex reaction which apparently takes place between them.

From all these studies, however scattered and incomplete they may yet be, emerges an outline of a new cellular pharmacology which should ultimately not only explain why colchicine is a mitotic poison but help, by what can properly be named a "biochemical dissection of mitosis," to explain the mechanics of cell multiplication and of growth.

17.2: Metabolic Actions of Colchicine

We will consider under this heading only the facts which help to explain c-mitosis. Other properties of the alkaloid have been described in Chapters 4 and 7. The resistance of some plants and animals to colchicine will be mentioned. While the mechanism of resistance is very imperfectly understood, it may be related to the influence of the drug on cellular physiology.

17.2–1: Enzymes. The work done in this field has been conducted with quite different purposes, some authors being interested in mitosis, others in possible mechanisms of colchicine treatment of gout, the origin of hemorrhages observed in malignant growths (Chapter 10), or the formation of c-tumors in plants.

An over-all decrease in tumor respiration was one of the first bio-chemical observations on colchicine. Its relation with the inhibition of mitosis is not evident.[10, 106]

It has been demonstrated that a $1.2 \times 10^{-2} M$ solution of colchi-cine inhibits dephosphorylation and the deamination of desoxyribonu-cleotides. Desoxyribonuclease is also inhibited; however, the relation of these facts to mitosis is by no means clear, and the concentrations of colchicine are far greater than those effective in spindle poisoning.[60] In rats injected 0.2 mg. of the drug, a decrease of the alkaline phos-phatase activity was recorded in liver tissue; there was no increased disintegration of ribonucleic acid (RNA).[31] The RNA content of fibroblasts growing *in vitro* was decreased by colchicine.[23] Pyrophos-phatase, an enzyme which was found in great quantities in a benzo-pyrene-induced sarcoma in a rat, was inhibited after a colchicine in-jection, though no action on the enzyme could be detected *in vitro*.[9]

Other work on changes in purine metabolism, possibly linked with the curative effect of colchicine in gout, demonstrates that, while the nucleotidase of the intestine of calves was not affected, that of human serum was inhibited. Xanthine-dehydrase was also inhibited in guinea pigs, but the concentrations of colchicine (50 per cent and more) were far larger than those effective both in spindle poisoning and in therapeutics.[53]

Inhibition of dehydrogenase activity by colchicine and sodium cacodylate, another spindle poison, was reported in 1938,[38] but no further data on this subject have been published since. A strong de-crease of liver dioxyphenylalanine-decarboxylase in rats, and of the pressor amines of the adrenals,[47] may be related to the general toxicity reactions of the alkaloid (Chapter 7). *In vitro* studies of rat liver slices demonstrated an inhibition of creatine synthesis, and blocking of the formation of *p*-aminohippuric acid from *p*-aminobenzoic acid. The methylation of nicotinamide was also inhibited. There appeared to be a relation between amount of drug and degree of inhibition. The formation of creatine from guanidoacetic acid and L-methionine was inhibited by 65 per cent by a $10^{-3} M$ solution of colchicine.[83]

In plant material, enzymatic reactions, *in vitro,* of malt diastase were accelerated by the addition of colchicine; however, the rates of conversion of sucrose by invertase were not influenced.[115] In the ger-minating grains of *Triticum aestivum* L., the activity of amylase was increased by $10^{-6} M$ colchicine. No significant changes of photosyn-thesis have been detected.[42]

Some further results will be considered in the paragraphs on the action of *meso*-inositol (17.5–2) and adenosinetriphosphoric acid (17.5–4). It is evident at this point that no significant relation be-tween enzyme inactivation and spindle poisoning has been detected.

17.2–2: Resistance in plants and animals. Cells of *Colchicum autumnale* L. yield as much as four parts per thousand of alkaloid. Thus, some of the mitoses of the plant may be in close relation to large doses of colchicine, and the questions arose by what mechanism these mitoses are protected, and whether c-mitosis is possible in *Colchicum*. The first experimenters used as a test the bulbous enlargements of the root tips of *Colchicum* and concluded that large doses of colchicine were active. However, as mentioned in Chapter 4, this is only presumptive evidence, and c-tumors may arise without any mitoses taking place (Chapter 4). Cytological work was carried further on several species of *Colchicum* and with various concentrations of the alkaloid.[20] The results were compared to those of the spindle poison, *acenaphthene* (cf. Subsection 17.3–2). No true resistance in excised root tips grown on agar with strong concentrations of colchicine[20] was observed, though the concentration of alkaloid necessary to induce full c-mitosis was considerable (5 per cent in water). The possible influence of the chloroform present in crystalline colchicine has been ruled out; chloroform is only a weak spindle poison.[117] It is clear that mitoses in *Colchicum* are considerably more resistant than any other plant mitoses towards the alkaloid. This type of resistance appears somewhat similar to that of venomous animals towards their own venom, but in the case of the plant, the basic mechanism is not understood and further research would be useful. Evidently, this is linked with the other unsolved problems of the role and metabolism of colchicine in *Colchicum* sp. The glucoside found in the plant, *colchicoside*,[82] may be of some significance (cf. Subsection 17.4–1).

During routine laboratory tests the discovery was made that golden hamsters resist very large doses of colchicine,[90] considerably greater than the lethal doses for rabbits, guinea pigs, mice, and rats. The tests yielded no c-mitotic values, but only toxicity values which proved beyond doubt that natural resistance exists with the hamsters. Another similar case is the resistance of rabbits to aconite.

Hamsters are native to the region where species of *Colchicum* are abundant (cf. Chapter 1). Through a long period of evolution the hamsters may, by the processes of survival of those animals that lived after eating the *Colchicum,* have passed this resistance on to succeeding generations. Any part of the *Colchicum,* leaf, flower, seed, fruit, corm, would contribute generous portions of colchicine that would be lethal to an animal without resistance.

Such resistance displayed by the hamsters is of interest in connection with the evolutionary problems involved. Further work should be done with the mitotic processes to make comparison of the action of colchicine upon these features.

17.3: Physical Action

An inhibition of spindle function and the destruction of its fibrillar structure can be the consequence of physical agents acting on the cells during division. On the other hand, it appears most probable that many of the spindle poisons which have been described do not act by combining in the chemical sense of the word with the spindle proteins, but by altering some of the physical conditions necessary for the proper development of mitosis.

17.3–1: Inhibition of the spindle by physical agents. That modifications of the physical environment of the cell, without any mitotic poison being present, may induce c-mitosis is evidenced from the action of heat, cold, and high hydrostatic pressures.

The reversible changes of the mitotic spindle under the influence of an increased temperature were described in 1933.[72] Before colchicine, heat-shock was perhaps the most reliable method for producing polyploid plants (cf. Chapter 11).[104] It is also one of the most efficient methods of inducing polyploidy in mammals, as mentioned in Chapter 16A. In *Triton vulgaris,* on the contrary, larvae kept in water at 3°C. show a typical metaphase arrest, with chromosomes grouped in a single star. The only difference with colchicine is that the alkaloid does not depress prophases, and that ball metaphases (cf. Chapter 2) are more frequent.[4] The hypothesis that cold should mainly affect the centrosomes and centromeres and prevent the orientation of spindle fibers at their contact[4] is interesting and deserving of further study. Cold may have played a significant part in the evolution of polyploid species, especially during the periods of glaciation.

The action of high hydrostatic pressures, about 200 atmospheres, is similar to that of temperature changes in that it brings reversible changes of the spindle, which loses its fibrous appearance.[94] This has been demonstrated both in animal cells (*Urechis*) and in plants (pollen mother cells of *Tradescantia*). The exact significance of these results is far from being understood and need not be discussed here.

Evidently, the proper functioning of the spindle is only possible within a limited range of physico-chemical conditions. It is thus not surprising that changes induced by chemicals of various and unrelated structures may also arrest mitosis by inhibiting the spindle. Research in this field will now be discussed, and the "narcosis theory" of c-mitosis explained. Most of this work, for obvious experimental reasons, has been conducted on plant cells, mainly the *Allium* root tip, and on eggs of invertebrates or vertebrates. A few observations have been made on tissue cultures.

17.3–2: Simple aromatic and aliphatic mitotic poisons. A very extensive study on plant cells has been conducted by several groups of workers, that happened to be widely separated by the events of the second World War. The similar conclusions which were reached have thus an added significance. The names of Gavaudan (Marseille, France), [41, 43] Schmuck (U.S.S.R.), [107, 108, 109] and Levan and Öster-gren (Lund, Sweden) [70, 71, 91, 92,] should be mentioned at this point. This work began with the search for some polyploidizing agent more effective than colchicine and led to an intensive study of chemicals and of the relation between their structure and their activity. One of the first substances demonstrated to be effective for the induction of polyploidy in plants was *acenapthene* (I). This was discovered in 1938, [107, 85, 119, 34] and the simplicity of its chemical structure, apparently without any relation to that of colchicine, quite naturally led other authors to investigate various aromatic derivatives.

In the following years, haloid derivatives of acenaphthene were also found to be effective c-mitotic poisons, as well as later haloid derivatives of other aromatic compounds, [71, 41, 113, 114] and various derivatives of benzene and naphthalene. All of these were soluble in lipids and, contrary to colchicine, had low water solubility. In France, many mono-substituted derivatives of benzene and naphthalene were tested by the Gavaudans on *Triticum*. This extensive work can only be briefly reviewed here. It appeared that, while benzene was only weakly active, it was necessary only to add some side-chains to obtain effective c-mitotic poisons. One exception was *hexamethylbenzene,* the inactivity of which was linked with its high degree of symmetry. Nitro- and halo-derivatives of benzene and naphthalene were studied, and many found to be mitotic poisons. However, total inactivation of the spindle was not always observed, and partial c-mitosis (mero-stathmokinesis) or abnormalities of spindle orientation (tropokinesis) were often the only cellular changes. C-mitosis was also observed under the influence of anesthetic drugs, such as phenyl-urethane, acetophenone, or anesthesine. [41, 43]

It soon became evident that no definite chemical structure was necessary, but that nearly all aromatic derivatives were c-mitotic poisons under proper experimental conditions, except those with a carboxyl, for instance, benzoic acid, or an amino-group. It was evident that an increased solubility in water was unfavorable for spindle poisoning. More recently, however, *amino-acenaphthene* was demonstrated to be a spindle poison for fibroblasts in tissue culture. [66, 69]

In 1944, the French authors linked their observations with Ferguson's notion of *thermodynamic activity,* which expressed the tendency of a given substance to escape from the phase in which it is dissolved. It can be measured by the relation between the lowest active concentrations of a substance and its highest solubility in water. The conclusion was reached that with only a few exceptions, all the chemicals which had proved to arrest spindle activity acted like chemically indifferent poisons, and that their influence on mitosis was quite similar to the changes brought about in the nervous system by the so-called indifferent narcotics. Physical changes appeared prominent, and c-mitosis was called a "narcotized" mitosis. The substances listed as not following the rule included *aniline, phenol, hexanitrodiphenylamine,* and *colchicine.* The activity of phenol and aniline, two

(I) Acenaphthene

simple derivatives of benzene, demonstrated that in the series of benzene derivatives, the hypothesis that the substances with high thermodynamic potential and high solubility in lipids were the most active spindle poisons, could not be accepted without some corrections.[41, 43]

The Swedish authors,[70, 71, 91, 92] studying the *Allium* root tips, came to nearly identical conclusions, linking lipoid solubility with the mechanism of c-mitosis. They studied a large number of compounds, listed in the papers of Östergren, (cf. also [69]) who proposed a theoretical explanation of "narcotized mitosis" which will be discussed in Subsection 17.3–4. It should be pointed out here that all these experiments could easily be carried out on root tips, but that the conclusions cannot be too rapidly extended to animal cells, which would not resist treatments with strong concentrations of lipoid-soluble substances, often of high toxicity. It is however evident that some drugs known as narcotics in animals, do possess c-mitotic properties.

17.3–3: Narcotics and indifferent inorganic substances. Among the chemicals capable of inducing narcosis in animals, we have already mentioned chloral hydrate,[126, 98, 39] which is a spindle poison, as shown in Figure 17.1. Ethylcarbamate (ethylurethane) is a narcotic in animals and a spindle poison in the egg of *Paracentratus lividus* LK.,[93] in amphibians and in plant cells.[25] In other animal cells, e.g., the intestinal mucosa and the bone marrow of mammals, ethylcarbamate acts like a chromosome poison.[30] Chloroform[76] and ether are known to arrest cell division in plants and in some eggs of animals.[48, 97] In the corneal cells of *Salamandra,* ethyl alcohol, ether, and chlorethone also prevent the proper activity of the spindle.[97]

None of these substances, however, has an activity comparable to that of colchicine, and their mitotic effects are only visible in relatively concentrated solutions.

These facts, demonstrating that no evident relation exists between the chemical constitution and the c-mitotic action, and that lipoid solubility is always present, confirm the theory of c-mitosis as a narcotized mitosis. Lipoid solubility is one of the foundations of Overton's well-known theory of narcosis in animals. The wide use of gaseous narcosis in medical practice prompted some workers to study this group of narcotics on the root tips of *Allium cepa*. These were kept humid in a mixture of atmospheric air and the gases, which were under pressure. Propane, nitrogen, nitrous oxide, methane, argon (under a pressure of 75 atmospheres), and hydrogen (200 atmospheres) induced c-mitosis and typical c-tumors. However, only propane, nitrogen, and nitrous oxide induced polyploid cells, for the other gases depressed too much the number of new mitoses.[35] This observation of c-mitosis under the influence of an inert gas like argon definitely demonstrates that the chemical structure may be quite indifferent to the production of inactive spindles, and that physical changes play a great part. C-mitosis appears at this point to be a general reaction of the spindle under the most varied conditions. Work discussed further will show how far these results may explain the action of colchicine.

17.3–4: Narcosis and colchicine. The facts gathered so far point towards a close relation between metaphasic (spindle) poisoning and lipoid solubility or thermodynamic activity. The precise relation between lipoids and the function of the spindle is by no means clear, and narcotics appears to modify mitosis somewhat like cold[4] or high hydrostatic pressure.[94] It is not surprising that the problem appears complex, for very little is known about the main target of all these poisons, namely, the spindle. That it is fibrous and anisotropic is evident and is no longer discussed.[110, 50] How it functions is the subject of much controversy, for it is not yet demonstrated whether the fibers "pull" the chromosomes towards the poles (after gathering them at the equator of the cell), or if the chromosomes are "pushed" polewards by a "Stemmkörper" lying at anaphase in the center of the cell. The results of colchicine research indicate (Chapter 2) that traction must play an important role in the movements of the anaphase plates, but how this traction takes place and on what support the fibers are anchored are still unsolved problems. The shortening of the fibers involves most probably changes from fibrous to globular proteins, as evidenced by the polarized light data.[51] These changes probably take place first between the two anaphasic plates, where all fibrous structures disappear and later between the poles and the centromeres, where they bring about a shortening of the fibers. The biochemical basis of this complex mechanism is unknown. The chemical constitution of the fibers themselves has not been determined, with the exception of some histochemical work indicating that their proteins are rich in sulfhydryl groups (cf. Subsection 17.4–2).

Any theory linking "narcosis" to spindle changes requires additional investigations with a wider use of specimens from both animals and plants. The Swedish author Östergren[71, 92] has presented evidence for the "narcosis theory" using *Allium* root tip cells as a major testing material. The relationship demonstrated to exist between lipo-solubility and the c-mitotic activity for many substances fits the hypothesis quite well, but there are unanswered questions that do not give us as much supporting evidence as everyone would desire. Therefore, the hypothesis put forward by Östergren at this time requires additional testing. Repeating from the preceding paragraph, it is to be stressed that the lack of specific biochemical evidence drastically limits our understanding, particularly when trying to formulate basic mechanisms for reactions such as the c-mitosis.

Colchicine is a spindle poison with a low thermodynamic activity and extremely high solubility in water. Therefore, this chemical is an exception to the general rule that applies to simpler aromatic derivatives.[91] These relationships are clearly illustrated in Figure 17.2, as drawn from experiments with cells of *Allium* and/or *Triticum*. The proposed theory of a narcosis, while interesting from the standpoint of the biochemistry of the spindle, cannot at the same time apply to colchicine, which appears to act on a *chemical* basis rather than *physically*. This conclusion was reached independently by the French authors.[43] Certain results will now be considered to show that ideas of a chemical relation between alkaloid and spindle appear promising for the ultimate explanation as to how a c-mitosis is accomplished.

17.4: Chemical Action

Two lines of research indicate that spindle poisoning may be related to definite chemical structures, and probably to chemical interference between poisons and spindle fibers. The first is the study of derivatives of colchicine and related molecules. This indicates that minor changes in this complex atomic structure may considerably affect the cytological activity. The second is the study of other mitotic poisons; while those which have been considered so far acted more physically than chemically, there is a small but important group of substances which inactivate the spindle and which possess specific chemical reactivity. After studying these simple spindle poisons, some other substances acting like colchicine, or those with complex molecular structure will be examined briefly. The properties of colchicine will then be compared to those of other poisons.

17.4–1: Colchicine derivatives. These have been studied from three main points of view: their toxicity, their antimitotic activity,

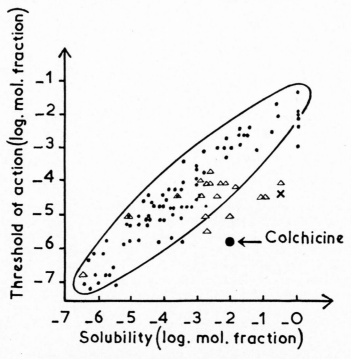

Fig. 17.2—Relation between c-mitotic activity in the **Allium** test and solubility in water. Each dot or triangle corresponds to a different substance. The singular behavior of colchicine is evident. (After Ostergren, 1951[92])

and their inhibition of tumor growth.[27] The spindle poisoning will mainly interest us here, and it should be made clear that this is not necessarily paralleled by other properties of these molecules. For instance, it has long been known that *colchiceine* (II) is less toxic, and also a weaker mitotic poison than colchicine. But desacetylcolchiceine, *trimethylcolchicinic acid* (III),[63] does not interfere at all with cell division in animals, while it may, like colchicine, kill frogs by central nervous paralysis. The opposite is also true; and results to be discussed further point to the possibility of synthesizing derivatives with lower toxicity and greater mitotic-poisoning effects than colchicine.

In the *Allium* test, *trimethylcolchicinic acid* (III) has been shown to induce c-mitosis, but it is thought that the mechanism is quite different from that of colchicine, and related to the amino group of ring B.[117] This derivative has a marked toxicity, while even 20 per cent solutions of colchicine are only slightly toxic for these plant cells.

Before considering in some detail artificial colchicine derivatives, it is important to remember that other closely related alkaloids exist in

(II) Colchiceine   (III) Trimethylcolchicinic Acid

Colchicum, and also that colchicine is probably present in chemical combination with a glucoside. *Desmethylcolchicine* has been found in preparations of colchicine;[49] it differs from colchicine only by one methyl group missing in ring A. It has been proved that it poisons mitosis like colchicine, and demonstrates that two methyl groups are sufficient for this. It is probable that at least one is indispensable. Work by Lettré is interesting in this connection.[66] This author, searching for mitotic poisons with a simpler chemical structure, and basing his researches at the time on the old formula of Windaus in which rings B and C are 6-membered, showed that on fibroblasts in tissue culture, *mescaline* (IV) was without action, while α-*phenyl-β-* (*3, 4, 5-trimethoxyphenyl*) -*ethylamine* (V) is active. Further simplification demonstrated that spindle poisoning was retained in α-phenyl-β (*p*-metholxyphenyl) -ethylamine (VI), which was the simplest possible poison of this group.

The exact chemical structure of several other substances from *Colchicum* and closely related to colchicine is not known yet; they probably differ from the parent molecule by relatively minor changes, [100, 101, 65] and are all more or less active against mitosis.

In *Colchicum,* a substance named *colchicoside,* resulting from a glucosidic linkage of colchicine, the exact chemical nature of which has not been established, has been isolated.[82] It is of interest to note that this poisons spindles, but is 40 times less active than colchicine towards plant mitoses. With diluted solutions, it is observed

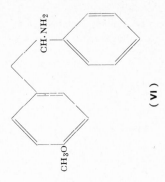

(VI)

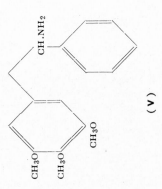

(V)

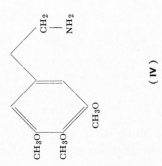

(IV)

that c-tumors (root-tip swellings) occur with solutions which are devoid of any mitotic action. The hypothesis has been put forward that colchicoside may be some kind of detoxication product of colchicine, a fact which may help to explain the resistance of *Colchicum* towards colchicine (cf. Subsection 17.2–2).

The principal changes affecting the action of colchicine are those affecting the *N*-substituted radicals in ring B and the esters of ring

(VII) Colchicine
Isocolchicine

C. Before considering some of these derivatives, it is important to study the results obtained with an isomer of colchicine, iso*colchicine,* (VII) in which the positions of the O and O-CH₃ radicals of ring C are reversed.[116, 117, 65]

The activity of iso*colchicine* has been studied on *Allium* root tips[117] and on fibroblast cultures.[66] Solubility and thermodynamic activity differ considerably from those of colchicine. While the latter is soluble in approximately all proportions in water, iso*colchicine* has a solubility of $50,000 \times 10^{-6} M/1$. The activity thresholds stand at 150 for colchicine and $14,000 \times 10^{-6} M/1$ for the *iso-*compound, the thermodynamic activity of which is 0.28, that is to say, about a thousand times higher than that of colchicine. As a conclusion of this work, it appears "that colchicine, with its low thermodynamic activity is a typical representative of the chemically acting substances, while iso*colchicine* with its 900 times higher thermodynamic activity belongs to the type of unspecifically acting substances." [117] *Isocolchicine* interferes thus with mitosis like the many substances mentioned in the previous paragraph of this chapter. In fibroblast cultures, the difference is not quite so great, for iso*colchicine* is only 50 times less active than colchicine. Two other similar molecules, *ethyl-colchiceine* and iso*ethylcolchiceine,* were compared on the same material: the second was about 200 times less active than the first. These substances have been isolated from *Colchicum.* Other *iso-* derivatives of colchicine have also proved to be without action against neoplasms.[66]

It is premature to discuss the reasons for the weak activity of the *iso-* compounds. One reason which has been put forward is the formation of hydrogen bonds between the side-chains of ring C and ring B, because of the closeness of the methyl groups of these chains in the *iso-* forms. (VII) It has been suggested that the weak antimitotic activity of *colchiceine* may be the consequence of the *iso-* form of this molecule.[65] Other data prove that the activity of colchicine on mitosis is related to both these side-chains.

The substances to be studied now can all be considered as derivatives of *trimethylcolchicinic acid* (III). This compound was demonstrated in some of the first work on colchicine derivatives and mitotic cells in mammals, to be inactive. In cultures of fibroblasts and of neoplastic cells also, no activity could be detected (Table 17.1).[44]

Substitution on ring B *alone* does not yield effective mitotic poisons. On tissue cultures, N-*acetyl-colchicol* and its methyl ether (VIII) have only slight activity. Tables 17.1 and 17.2 give further evidence

TABLE 17.1
LD 50's OF COLCHICINE DERIVATIVES IN MG/KG
(After Goldberg *et al.*[44])

Substance	Mice	Rats	Cats
N-Benzoyl-TMCA *	>700	. . . .	. . . .
TMCA.	200	200	>10
Colchiceine	84	30	>12.5
N-Acetyl-colchicol	56	200	10
TMCA-methyl-ether	46	. . . .	5
N-Benzoyl-TMCA-methyl-ether. . .	32	. . . .	<25
N-Acetyl-TMCA-methyl-ether. . . .	3.5	5.0	0.5

* TMCA = trimethylcolchicinic acid.

of this. The activity of this derivative is comparable to that of *colchiceine*.

However, when ring C remains as in colchicine, it is evident that *N*-substitution in ring B is not of great importance for activity. In tissue cultures, desacetylcolchicine, *trimethylcolchicinic acid methyl ether* (IX), is an effective spindle poison, while the parent substance, desacetylcolchiceine (=TMCA), is almost inactive. N-*benzoyl-tri-*

CH$_3$O NH·COCH$_3$ CH$_3$O NH$_2$

CH$_3$O   CH$_3$O

CH$_3$O   CH$_3$O $= 0$

OCH$_3$ OCH$_3$

(VIII)   (IX)

methylcolchicinic methyl ether has been demonstrated to be one of the most effective derivatives in arresting mitoses in the stomach epithelium of mice.[11, 12, 36]

Substitutions in ring C are the most important, for they yield substances with a greater antimitotic activity than colchicine.[64, 78] These are derivatives of *colchicamide* (X). (This abbreviated spelling is to be preferred to *colchicineamide* or *colchiceinamide,* which are to be found in the literature.) Thirty-five derivatives of this type have been studied by Lettré,[66] who found *N*-methyl-, *N*-ethyl-, and *N*-dimethyl-colchicamide to be most effective in tissue-culture work, the activity decreasing when longer side-chains were added to the amino-group (Table 17.3).

Other derivatives with more extensive changes in ring C, for instance with a six-carbon aromatic ring C, *colchinol* series (XI), or

TABLE 17.2

Minimal Effective Antimitotic Dose of TMCA Derivatives on Corneal Mitoses of Mice, Six Hours After Injection, Expressed as the Fraction of the LD 50 Increasing the Mitotic Index Above That of Controls and Minimal Effective Antimitotic Doses in Various Tissues of Mice

(After Goldberg *et al.*[44])

Substance	Minimal Antimitotic Dose/ LD 50	Minimal Effective Dose		
		Cornea (*mg/kg*)	Regenerating Liver (*mg/kg*)	Tissue Cultures (*μg/kg*)
Colchicine.............	1/10	0.01	0.21	0.35
N-acetylcolchicol.........	1/2	1.0	9.01	28.0
Colchiceine..............	1	4.0	8.01	84.0
TMCA (trimethyl-colchicinic acid)........	>1	inactive	inactive	inactive

N-*benzoyl-colchicinic anhydride* (XII) , have been tested on tumors.[63] None has shown an activity comparable to colchicine, and the reader should refer to the papers of the National Cancer Institute group for detailed data on this subject.[11, 12, 63, 64, 65]

Although colchicine derivatives have been tested on few materials, the main purpose of the work having been a search for substances of

(X)

(XI) N-Acetylcolchinol

(XII)

interest in cancer chemotherapy, the following conclusions can be drawn for the papers published:

1. The *iso*colchicine derivatives, and *iso*colchicine itself, are considerably less active. It appears important that the esterified side-chains of rings B and C are at a proper distance one from another.
2. At least one methoxy group appears indispensable in ring A.
3. The amino group of ring B does not need to be esterified, though this increases the activity.
4. Ring C must be seven-membered, and the hydroxyl group esterified, or better, replaced by an amino group itself esterified (colchicamide derivatives) .

These facts help to reveal which are the active groups of the colchicine molecule. However, they are yet of no help in explaining how these react with the spindle. Results obtained with spindle poisons of very different chemical structure, and indicating relations between this structure and their action, throw further light on the subject of spindle inactivation.

17.4–2: Sulfhydryl poisons. With a few exceptions, most of the work in this field has been done on tissue cultures[50] or in intact warm-blooded animals.[44a] This method has an advantage in that, be-

TABLE 17.3

SMALLEST ANTIMITOTIC DOSES (μg/ml) EFFECTIVE IN ARRESTING
MITOSES IN CULTURES OF CHICK FIBROBLASTS
(After Lettré [66])

Derivative	Dose
Colchiceine	5.0
Colchicine	0.01
Colchicamide	0.01
N-methylcolchicamide	0.0025
N-ethylcolchicamide	0.003
N-propylcolchicamide	0.08
N-butylcolchicamide	0.9
N-methyl-propyl-colchicamide	0.5

cause of the necessity for avoiding toxic side-effects, only small doses may be used. Hence, substances acting as narcotics or producing a "physical" change of the spindle will not be found to have mitotic-poisoning properties.

The most extensively studied in mammals,[96, 29, 73, 30] in invertebrates,[45] on tissue cultures,[74, 13, 55] and in plant cells[79, 22] are simple derivatives of arsenic. *Arsenious oxide* and *sodium arsenite* arrest metaphase by destroying the spindle, and these star metaphases are very similar to those described in Chapter 2. The most effective of the organic arsenicals appears to be sodium cacodylate, or dimethylarsinate (XIII).

In mice, it has been demonstrated that this action was reversible, that is to say, that arrested metaphases could be detoxicated and proceed to a normal telophase.[30] The inactivation of the spindle is thus the consequence of a labile combination of its proteins with arsenic. The detoxicating agent was *dimercaptopropanol* (BAL, British Anti-Lewisite) (XIV), a substance which combines rapidly and strongly with arsenic and other metals. This action of a chemical with two -SH functions suggested that arsenic may have combined with similar

SH groups in the spindle.[30] This hypothesis was in agreement with a theory of spindle activity in which reversible changes of SH to S-S functions were supposed to play a prominent part in the "contractile" properties of the spindle. The further discovery that -SH substances themselves were also spindle poisons, for instance, *dimercaptopropanol* and *sodium diethyldithiocarbamate,* was in agreement with this

```
                /CH3
               /
    O=As————CH3
               \
                \
                 O—Na

        ( XIII )
```

```
    CH—SH
    |
    CH—SH
    |
    CHOH

        ( XIV )
```

hypothesis, if it was considered that a proper equilibrium between reduced and oxydized sulfhydryl functions was indispensable for spindle activity.[30]

This theory of chemical action on the spindle received further support from the discovery that many metals, known to combine with -SH groups, are mitotic poisons.[80] *Ethylmercurychloride* is an example of an organic poison of this type, active on plant cells,[56, 75] while *cadmium* salts are most effective in arresting mitosis in mammals.[122, 30, 2] The inhibition of metaphase by *beryllium* salts, which has been considered to be the result of nuclear phosphatase inhibition,[17] may possibly be explained by the combination of this metal with sulfhydryl groups.

It has been further demonstrated by work on tissue cultures and in injected mice, that the typical -SH poisons, *chloracetophenone, iodoacetic acid,* and *iodoacetamide,* arrested mitoses at metaphase.[44a, 50] However, these substances are very toxic, and have strong inhibitory actions on glycolysis, which may be important in explaining their action on cell division. Some of the complex molecules considered in the next Subsection may also act as -SH poisons.

This does not close the list of mitotic poisons which appear to act chemically on the cells. The most remarkable is *ethylcarbylamine* (C_2H_5CN), which has been demonstrated to modify the course of mitosis in tissue cultures exactly like colchicine.[120] Total inactivation of the spindle with exploded metaphase and, later, formation of numerous micronuclei were conspicuous. Ethylcarbylamine reacts chemically with metals; this chelating property is shared by *diethyldithiocarbamate,* another spindle poison.[30] These results point to some further complexities of the problem; the action of other organic spindle poisons will show how far we are from understanding the basic changes involved.

17.4–3: Complex organic molecules. The mechanism of action of most of the substances mentioned in this subsection is unknown; molecular structures are widely different. However, these drugs are all very active, and it is felt that they modify the spindle more by a chemical than by a physical change. The resin of *Podophyllum* sp. (mandrake) contains several toxic substances, the principal ones being *podophyllotoxin,* α- and β-*peltatins,* and *quercetin.* The crude resin was a popular remedy against warts in the United States, and this observation led to a scientific study of the active substances[54, 21] (XV). These proved to be efficient spindle poisons, and to act most similarly to colchicine, both in skin tumors of man, and in various animal materials.[118] From a chemical point of view, they are complex lactones.[69] Another instance of a lactone acting as a mitotic poison is the antibiotic *patulin* (Bacitracin, clavacin) (XVI). This inhibits remarkably the spindles of erythroblasts in the chick and in many tissues of mice.[1]

It is interesting to compare the formula of patulin with that of *coumarin* (XVII), which has been described as a weak metaphase poison in *Allium* and *Lilium.* Its action may be of the "physical" type, though combination with -SH groups is also possible.[121]

Other substances of plant origin have been found to inhibit mitosis, mainly in tissue cultures of fibroblasts. *Chelidonine*[69] is of interest because of its use in cancer chemotherapy (Chapter 10). In an extensive study of alkaloids, it has been shown that the only active ones were found in the group which is chemically related to *stilbylamine,* and thus to α-*phenyl-*β *(p-methoxyphenyl)-ethylamine* (cf. 17.4–1). These are *narcotin, gnoscopin, chelidonine, homochelidonine, methoxychelidonine,* and *protopin.*[69] Many other substances may yet be discovered when further systematic studies are conduced. This is already underway, and has demonstrated c-mitotic activity in extracts of *Chimaphila maculata* and *Sassafras albidum.*[7]

Other complex substances extracted from plants are *anethol*[62] and *apiol,*[41] which may induce polyploidy. This has also been observed in *Allium* root tips treated with *veratrine.*[128] *Sanguinarine* and *cryptopleurine* are also spindle poisons, and the second, extracted from *Cryptocaria pleurospora,* has been considered as effective as colchicine.[5] Positive effects on mitosis have also been found with extracts of the following plants: *Ervatamia angustifolia, Aristolochia elegans, Euphorbia peplus, Bulbina bulbosa,* and *Strychnos arborea.* *Protoanemomin* is an interesting poison,[33, 121] for its action on the spindle may be prevented by *dimercaptopropanol* (BAL); this is evidence of a chemical reaction.

The list of c-mitotic active substances is much longer, and among chemicals of animal origin or related to the growth of animal cells, *adrenalin*[66, 69] has been found to arrest metaphases in fibroblast cul-

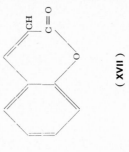

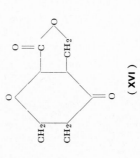

(XV)

(XVI)

(XVII)

tures at a concentration of 0.1 mg/ml, and the antifolic drug, *amino-pterin (4-aminopteroylglutamic acid)* arrests mitoses in tissue culture.[52] This is a remarkable fact, for this antimetabolite when injected into mice, behaves as a strong and typical poison of the "radiomimetic" type, inducing chromosome breakages.[30]

17.4–4: Colchicine compared with other spindle poisons. The spindle structure, which can be destroyed by purely physical means, is evidently adversely influenced by a series of substances which appear to act through their chemical reactivity. Arsenic, the heavy metals (mercury and cadmium), and the sulfhydryl poisons of the iodoacetamide type indicate that -SH groups may play an important role in metaphase dynamics. Some more complex substances, such as the antibiotic patulin, and protoanemonin, may owe their antimitotic properties to the lactone structure, and perhaps also to interference with sulfhydryl. Podophyllotoxin may possibly belong to the same group, but the difficulties of understanding clearly the action of such complex molecules are formidable. There is no indication that colchicine may fit in this type of chemical theory, though the facts gathered by the protagonists of the "narcosis" hypothesis, as well as the study of colchicine derivatives, point towards a chemical combination of the alkaloid with some intracellular receptor.

The comparison of colchicine with other spindle poisons makes clear two facts: the great amount of work which is still necessary to understand the action of this drug, and the notable specificity of colchicine. For, if several chemicals have been quoted as acting similarly, few have been capable of inducing polyploidy, and still none has proved comparable in the practical work on polyploidy in plants. The extraordinary fact is the great efficiency and activity of colchicine, which will remain active when highly diluted, but concentrated solutions of which will not kill the cells. This points to some singular relation between the alkaloid and the spindle.

Further research about the biological activity of the tropolone compounds should help to understand better the chemical action of colchicine in the cell. Thus far, it has not been possible to "simplify" the molecule and obtain spindle poisoning. The few reports on tropolone derivatives indicate some action on mitosis, in *Tradescantia* staminal hair cells, far weaker than colchicine.[124] The necessity for such a complex molecule to achieve with the utmost efficiency what can be done by such simple agents as cold, arsenic, and ethylcarbylamine, is most puzzling. The solution of this problem should bring some important new insight on the submicroscopic and chemical mechanics of mitosis.

Often the mechanism of drug activity has been solved when a proper antagonist could be found, for instance *p*-aminobenzoic acid and the sulfonamides. Some work in this direction has been carried along and will be summarized now.

17.5: Synergists and Antagonists

A possible synergism between animal growth hormones and colchicine has been considered in Chapter 9. In plants, some changes visible after colchicine have been interpreted as evidence[8, 28, 46, 70, 79, 87] of hormonal action of the alkaloid. This has not been proved (cf. Chapter 4). In animal and plant cells, the antagonism of *meso*-inositol and colchicine is still a subject under discussion which merits to be reviewed here. Mention will also be made of a long series of experiments on fibroblasts in tissue cultures. These have led to a novel theory about c-mitosis which will be properly considered in the light of all the facts already gathered in this chapter.

17.5–1: Meso-inositol. γ-Hexachlorocyclohexane ("Gammexane"), a widely used insecticide, has been reported by several authors to induce c-mitosis in *Allium* and other plant cells.[22, 56, 88] Both the γ and the δ isomers have been found to be active,[15] while the first only is of use as an insecticide. Polyploidy and chromosome fragmentation have also been recorded. Gammexane is probably an antagonist of a naturally occurring substance, meso-*inositol*, having the same stereoisomeric structure as this sugar, the biological significance of which appears from its presence in many types of cells.

It was thus not surprising that in 1948 it was announced that *meso*-inositol, (but neither *d*-inositol nor D-sorbitol) prevented, in proper concentrations, the c-mitotic activity of Gammexane in *Allium cepa*.[16] It was, however, more surprising and most interesting that *meso*-inositol was claimed to prevent also the spindle effect of colchicine. The results were given as percentages of the different stages of mitosis, and it is to be regretted that no counts of the total number of cell divisions were recorded. Inositol alone did not interfere with mitosis. The formation of c-tumors, both by Gammexane and colchicine, was also prevented.[16] These results were checked over a wider range of concentrations and times by another author, who found that *meso*-inositol merely delayed the c-mitotic effect of colchicine, which was visible, as in the controls, after 24 hours.[22] Similar delays were observed with other sugars, a solution of saccharose (0.95 mg/ml) suppressing all colchicine mitoses in root tips observed after four hours of treatment, while after 24 hours the c-mitotic effect was normal.[22] Modified cell permeability was thought to explain the results obtained with *meso*-inositol. A confirmation of these findings was found in the observation that colchicine and podophyllotoxine effects were antagonized in the egg of the sea urchin *Lytechinus variegatus* by glucose.[20] The antagonism was never total; it was suggested that inositol may become changed into glucose in the cells. However, in *Allium*, it was demonstrated that the isomer of *hexacyclochlorohexane*, which could not act as an antagonist to *meso*-inositol, was also a spindle poison, and that no true protection was offered by *meso*-inositol against the effects of Gammexane.[15] The different tem-

(XVIII) γ-Hexachlorocyclohexane
("Gammexane")

(XIX) Meso-Inositol

peratures at which the experiments were conducted may explain the conflicting results.

Two papers published in 1951 renewed interest in this problem. In the first, the authors who discovered the action of *meso*-inositol first in plants, brought forward evidence that a similar antagonism existed in rat fibroblast cultures.[84] Here, for the first 12 hours, no difference was observed between colchicine alone and colchicine + inositol, but in the following hours, while the colchicine mitoses remained arrested, the cultures treated with inositol recovered almost completely. This period of 12 hours during which, quite contrary to the plant experiments, inositol does not prove to have any effect, except that of lowering the total numbers of mitoses, is considered to correspond to the duration of interkinesis. The authors suggest that *meso*-inositol may "allow the cell to prepare for a new mitosis," which is surprising, for this would lead one to think that there is no true detoxication of c-mitoses, similar to that of arsenite by BAL, and that these degenerate, and are no longer counted, while other cells enter mitosis. However difficult the interpretation of these results may seem to be, it is significant that neither sucrose, glucose, ribose, sorbitol, nor even *d*-inositol, *meso*-inosose or *epi*-inosose are capable of altering the action of colchicine.[84]

This result is also in contradiction with the facts observed in plant cells, and no conclusion can be drawn at this time. One interesting report, given only in a short note, is that some enzymes of bacterial origin capable of oxidizing inositol are inhibited by colchicine and the parent substances, tropolone and 4, 5-tetramethylene-tropolone.[37,124] Further results on this aspect of the colchicine problem are eagerly awaited; they may help to understand better the biochemistry of the spindle and the physiological functions of *meso*-inositol.[26] As for the action of γ-hexachlorocyclopropane, it may of course be of a "physical" type, similar to that of the numerous other c-mitotic and polyploidizing substances studied in plants.[103]

17.5–2: Other antagonists and synergists. In tissue cultures of rabbit heart fibroblasts, l-ascorbic acid was found to prevent, to a certain extent, the action of colchicine.[13] The numbers of arrested mitoses were smaller, and a careful study of the different types of mitotic abnormalities indicated that the vitamin decreased the amount of spindle inactivation. This was not the result of an action as a vitamin, for d-*araboascorbic acid,* whose properties as a vitamin are 20 times weaker, had the same effect. The two substances are equally reducing, and the interpretation of these results is difficult, for p-*quinone,* an oxydant, also depressed colchicine inhibition of mitoses.[13] An antagonism between colchicine and "soluble prontosil" (sulfanilamide) has been reported in plants,[6] but the effective concentrations of the sulfa drug were about a hundred times those of colchicine, and solubility effects were unavoidable. In animals, sulfanilamide has been claimed to influence colchicine-leukocytosis, but this was only remotely related to mitosis[127] (cf. Chapter 7).

An extract from hearts of embryonic warm-blooded animals has been reported to delay the cytotoxicity of colchicine in fibroblast and myoblast cultures. A colchicine concentration of $2 \times 10^{-5} M$ was without effect after 10 hours in cultures previously treated with the extract. If this was added after the alkaloid, no antagonism was visible.[123] Another more recent observation is that glycosidic substances endowed with cardiotonic activity decrease the action of colchicine in tissue cultures of chick heart fibroblasts.[59]

It appears evident from these data that no true antagonism has yet been found between any substance and colchicine, on a molar basis, and that the only effects observed depend on the presence of substances either of unknown chemical nature or in concentrated solutions.

On the contrary, the search for synergists of c-mitotic activity has yielded important results.[67, 25] Some synergists act mainly by increasing cellular permeability to the alkaloid, and the reader is referred to the paper of Deysson[25] for a detailed study of this type of false synergism. It has been observed only in plant cells. In fibroblast cultures, Lettré has conducted a very large series of experiments, and has discovered that many substances increased the action of colchicine, though having no c-mitotic activity of their own. These synergists belong to the most dissimilar groups of chemicals: alkaloids, steroid hormones, and carcinogenic agents (benzopyrene). The amount of the synergist is always far greater, on a molar basis, than that of colchicine. For instance, while 5.5 mitoses per hundred were found after 0.01 mg/ml of colchicine, the addition of 5 mg/ml of bulbocapnin increased this figure to 23.8. Forty times this dose of bulbocapnin had no action on control cultures. With phlorizin the results are very striking also.

More than 8 times more mitoses are arrested when a solution of phlorizin, which has no antimitotic action, is added to a concentration of colchicine, which is only weakly antimitotic. This is truly a synergistic effect. [67] Its study may most probably increase our knowledge of the physiological action of colchicine, and further work along similar lines with different types of cells is to be expected.

Another interesting colchicine synergist has been reported by P. Rondini and A. Necco (Tumori, 39:161–63, 1953). *Italchine,* an acridine derivative, is itself a mitotic poison, affecting spindle and chromosomes. Small doses, which do not affect mitosis, increase markedly the action of colchicine on chick fibroblasts cultivated *in vitro*. The principal results are apparent from Table 17.4.

17.5–3: The role of adenosine-triphosphoric acid (ATP). That the spindle functions, partly at least, as a fibrous contractile structure has been affirmed repeatedly. The contraction which takes place has

TABLE 17.4
SYNERGIC ACTION OF ITALCHINE AND COLCHICINE ON TISSUE CULTURES OF
CHICK FIBROBLASTS
(Mitoses counted after 48 hours' incubation with the drugs)
(After Rondoni and Necco)

Substances and Concentrations	Pro-phases	Meta-phases	Ana-phases	Telo-phases	Total
Italchine (1/300,000)...........	2.5	18.8	5.03	7.7	34.03
Colchicine (0.0033 µg/ml)...	4.9	42.3	8.86	5.06	61.12
Italchine + colchicine (same concentrations)......	0.5	79.4	2.15	1.07	83.12
Controls.................	4.9	13.8	8.00	10.5	37.2

also been compared to that of muscle. While biochemical data about the nature of the spindle proteins are lacking entirely, it could be imagined that colchicine acted on the contraction mechanism. Most cytological data (cf. Chapter 2) point to an action on the fibers themselves, which can be observed to "dissolve" into a "pseudospindle" or "hyaline globule" under the influence of the alkaloid. In muscular contraction, the role of ATP is well known. Observations of colchicine synergists and theoretical considerations led Lettré to suppose that ATP may also be indispensable for spindle contraction and mitosis, and that colchicine acted on the cell by modifying this mechanism.[69]

Experiments *in vitro* demonstrated that strong concentrations of colchicine inhibited the viscosity fall of complexes of actomyosin and ATP.[3] It was further observed that ATP-ase was inhibited by colchicine at concentrations of 10^{-3} and $10^{-4}\,M$. However, more dilute solutions $(10^{-8}\,M)$, which arrested mitosis, did not affect the enzyme.[61]

A direct antagonist action of ATP and colchicine was difficult to prove, because of the rapid destruction of ATP in fibroblast cultures. Only with very small doses of colchicine was such an antagonism visible. Cultures were grown for 24 hours, and then colchicine, at a concentration of 0.04 mg/ml was added.[68] This arrested, after 24 hours, 55 per cent of the cells in mitosis. When 1 mg/ml of ATP was added at the same time, mitotic inhibition did not start until four hours later. The results are given in Table 17.5. It is concluded that the higher the amount of ATP in a cell, the smaller the action of colchicine, and vice versa.[69]

ATP may play an important part in the conservation of cell form in cultured fibroblasts. The "resting" cells have been considered to be in a condition of permanent contraction, while cells intoxicated with various drugs, such as Victoria blue, have a lower content in ATP, and display a rounded form with rapidly moving surface blebs. If ATP is added to a fibroblast culture, the cells assume a spindle shape, even when dividing. In this condition, ATP would provide the energy necessary for this contraction, and would also protect the spindle against mitotic poisons.[69]

This hypothesis is only a tentative one, and it is not yet proven that colchicine acts by depressing ATP in the cells. Further experiments will be needed to explain the relation between cellular respiration and the formation of the spindle fibers, and also between ATP and the physiology of the spindle. It is apparent that more fundamental knowledge about the dynamics of mitosis is needed before the effect of colchicine and its various synergists may become clear. While these effects are still difficult to understand, there is no doubt that the discovery of the colchicine-mitosis has provided a considerable impetus to such fundamental studies.

17.6: Conclusion: the Singularity of Colchicine

From this chapter it has been made evident that destruction of the fibrillar properties of the spindle, and mitosis arrest at metaphase or pro-metaphase, is by no means limited to colchicine or even to chemical agents. From some angles, it appears as an entirely non-specific reaction of metaphase to agents as different as cold, nitrogen, hydrostatic pressure, lipid-soluble hydrocarbons, or heavy metals. However, that it is in most cases more than a "narcotized" mitosis is evident from the data about sulfhydryl groups, colchicine deriva-

TABLE 17.5

PERCENTAGE OF MITOSES AFTER COLCHICINE AND
ADENOSINE-TRIPHOSPHORIC ACID (ATP) IN
CULTURES OF FIBROBLASTS
(After Lettré and Albrecht[68])

Hours	Colchicine	*id.* $+$ ATP
1......	2.0	2.0
2......	7.7	3.0
3......	11.2	3.3
4......	13.0	5.0
5......	16.4	8.3
9......	27.4	9.4
14......	38.4	23.2

tives, and synergic activities. It is also evident at this point that further progress will only be possible when the biochemical and physiological properties of the spindle are better known. Mitotic poisons are useful tools for this purpose, and it may well be that the solution of this problem will lead rapidly to an understanding of the properties of colchicine. The difficulties of this task are great, and resemble in many aspects those of the study of muscle contraction. The spindle structure is however relatively simple, as far as can be known at this time, and its contractility and reversion to a nonfibrous "hyaline globule" are problems of which a solution appears possible in the not-too-distant future.

Colchicine, from all that has been said in this chapter, must be considered a singular substance. Not only does it possess remarkable side-effects, such as its action on gout, the colchicine-leukocytosis, its action on the nervous system and on muscular contraction, its induction of specific malformations in embryos; it is also the most efficient and active of all mitotic poisons known — with the exception of derivatives of the colchicamide series. It is also the mitotic poison to which the largest amount of work has been devoted. While some substances like podophyllotoxin have received great attention, others, such as the arsenical derivatives, have hardly been studied from the angle of mitosis. It is not because colchicine was one of the first-discovered spindle poisons that it received such attention. Chloral hydrate, acenaphthene, and arsenic may have deserved more detailed studies. Colchicine was investigated from such diverse standpoints because it was not only a mitotic poison like others, but also an ideal tool for the study of growth, and, last but not least, the best poly-ploidogenic agent in plants. As the creation of new polyploid species was taken up with enthusiasm, chemists and morphologists studied more and more the structure and the properties of the alkaloid. It is probably more than mere chance that the unique structure of this tropolone derivative is associated with so many physiological activities. It is reasonable to prophesy that colchicine will long retain its prominent place in the vast chapter of mitotic poisons. Many observations point towards a high degree of specificity in the reactions between the alkaloid and the spindle; if these reactions could be properly understood, that fundamental process of all growth and evolution, mitosis, would appear in a new light.

REFERENCES

1. ASTALDI, G., RONDANELLI, E. G., AND STROSSELLI, E. Effetto mitoclasico della patulina sull'eritroblasto embrionario. Bull. Soc. Ital. Ematol 1 (n°34). 1953.
2. AVANZI, M. G. Osservazioni sull'attività citologica di alcuni composti chimici. Caryologia. 3:234–48. 1950.
3. BARANY, E., AND PALIS, A. Hemmung des Viskositätabfalles in ATP-Actomyosin Mischungen durch Colchicin. Naturwiss. 38:547. 1951.
4. BARBER, H. N., AND CALLAN, H. G. The effects of cold and colchicine on mitosis in the newt. Proc. Roy. Soc. London. B 131:258–71. 1943.
5. BARNARD, C. The c-mitotic activity of cryptopleurine. Austral. Jour. Sci. 12: 30–31. 1949.
6. BAUCH, R. Sulfonamide als Antagonisten der polyploidisierenden Wirkung des Colchicins. Naturwiss.33:25–26. 1946. Sulfonamide und Colchicin. Ein botanischer Beitrag zum Sulfonamid-problem. Die Pharmazie. 4:1–7. 1949.
7. BELKIN, M., FITZGERALD, D. B., AND FELIX, M. D. Tumor damaging capacity of plant materials. II. Plants used as diuretics. Jour. Nat. Cancer Inst. 13: 741–44. 1952.
8. BERGER, C. A., AND WITKUS, E. R. Further studies of the cytological effects of combined treatments with colchicine and naphthaleneacetic acid. Amer. Jour. Bot. 36:794–95. 1949.
9. BLOCH-FRANKENTHAL, L., AND BACK, A. Effect of colchicine on tumor growth and tumor pyrophosphatase. Proc. Soc. Exp. Biol. and Med. 76:105–9. 1951.
10. BOYLAND, E., AND BOYLAND, M. Studies in tissue metabolism. Biochem. Jour. 31:454–60. 1937.
11. BRANCH, C. The mitotic activity of a group of colchicine-like compounds. Fed. Proc. Pt. II. 1:175. 1942.
12. BRANCH, C. F., FOGG, L. C., AND ULLYOT, G. E. Colchicine and colchicine-like compounds as chemotherapeutic agents. Acta Unio Internat. Cancrum. 6:439–47. 1949.
13. BUCHER, O. Zur Kenntnis der mitose. IX. Die Wirkung von Arsenik auf Fibrocytenkulturen. Z. Zellforsch. 30:438–62. 1940. Der Einfluss von Ascorbinsäure, Araboascorbinsäure und p-chinon auf die Colchicinwirkung. Schweiz. Z. Path. Bakter. 2:643. 1947.
14. BULLOUGH, W. S. The energy relations of mitotic activity. Biol. Rev. 27: 133–68. 1952.

15. CARPENTIER, S., AND FROMAGEOT, C. Activité c-mitotique des isomères γ et δ de l'hexachlorocyclohexane, avec des observations sur l'influence du mésoinositol et du mésoinositophosphate de sodium. Biochem. Biophys. Acta. 5:290–96. 1950.

16. CHARGAFF, E., STEWART, R. N., AND MAGASANIK, B. Inhibition of mitotic poisoning by meso-inositol. Science. 108:556–58. 1948.

17 CHÈVREMONT, M., AND FIRKET, H. Action du beryllium en culture de tissus. I. Effets sur la croissance et la mitose. Arch. Biol. 63:411–28. 1952.

18. CHODKOWSKI, K. Die karyoklastischen Gifte, ihr Einfluss auf den Organismus und ihre Bedeutung für die Pathologie. Protoplasma. 28:597–619. 1937.

19. COOK, J. W., AND LOUDON, J. D. Colchicine. *In* The alkaloids. Chemistry and physiology. Vol. II. Edited by Manske, R. H. F., and Holmes, H. L. Academic Press Inc., New York. 1952.

20. CORNMAN, I. Disruption of mitosis in *Colchicum* by means of colchicine. Biol. Bull. 81:297–98. 1941. Susceptibility of *Colchicum* and *Chlamydomonas* to colchicine. Bot. Gaz. 104:50–61. 1942. Alleviation of mitotic poisoning by glucose. Jour. Cell and Comp. Physiol. 35:301–2. 1950.

21. ———, AND CORNMAN, M. E. The action of podophyllin and its fractions on marine eggs. Ann. N. Y. Acad. Sci. 51:1443–87. 1951.

22. D'AMATO, F. Early influence of m-inositol and sugars on gammexane induced c-mitosis. Caryologia. 1:223–28. 1949. The effect of m-inositol on c-mitosis and c-tumor reaction. Caryologia. 1:358–61. 1949. Attività citologica del dimercaptopropanolo (BAL) e del metilarsinato di sodio (arrhenal) e loro azioni combinate. Caryologia. 2:13–22. 1949. Sulla possibilità di impiego del gammesano per la produzione di poliploidi nei vegetali. Atti Convegno Genet. Agraria. Rieti. Pp. 427–31. 1951. Does meso-inositol inhibit the colchicine effect in the roots of *Allium cepa*? Arch. Int. Pharmacodyn. 89:409–14. 1952.

23. DAVIDSON, J. N., LESLIE, I., AND WAYMOUTH, C. The nucleo-protein content of fibroblasts growing *in vitro*. Biochem. Jour. 44:5–17. 1949.

24. DE LAMATER, E. D. A new cytological basis for bacterial genetics. Symp. Quant. Biol. 16:381–412. 1951.

25. DEYSSON, G. Action simultanée du phényluréthane et de la colchicine sur les méristèmes radiculaires d'*Allium cepa*. C. R. Acad. Sci. Paris. 220:367–69. 1945. Contribution à l'étude du "Syndrome mitoclasique." Centre de Documentation Universitaire. Paris. 158 pp. 1948. Recherches sur la perméabilité des cellules végétales. Rev. Cytol. Biol. Vég. 13:153–313. 1952.

26. ———, AND DEYSSON, M. Action du méso-inositol sur la croissance et la mitose des Plantes. Bull. Soc. Chim. Biol. Paris. 32:268–75. 1950.

27. DOWNING, V., HARTWELL, J. L., LEITER, J., AND SHEAR, M. J. Effect of a single injection of colchicine, colchicine derivatives and related compounds on mouse tumors. Cancer Res. 9:598. 1949.

28. DUHAMET, L. Recherches sur l'action de l'hétéro-auxine et de la colchicine sur la croissance de racines isolées de *Lupinus albus*. Rev. Cytol. et Cytophysiol. Vég. 8:35–75. 1945.

29. DUSTIN, A. P., AND GRÉGOIRE, C. Contribution à l'étude de l'action des poisons caryoclasiques sur les tumeurs animales. I. Action du cacodylate de Na et de la trypaflavine sur le sarcome greffé, type Crocker, de la souris. Bull. Acad. Roy. Méd. Belg. 13:585–92. 1933.

30. DUSTIN, P., JR. Some new aspects of mitotic poisoning. Nature. 159:794–97. 1947. Mitotic poisoning at metaphase and -SH proteins. Exp. Cell Res. Suppl. I. Pp. 153–55. 1949. The cytological action of ethyl carbamate (urethane) and other carbamic esters in normal and leukaemic mice, and in rabbits. Brit. Jour. Cancer. 1:48–59. 1947. Sur les lésions nucléaires et chromosomiques provoquées chez la souris par les acides diaminoptéroyl-glutamiques. C. R. Soc. Biol. Paris. 144:1297. 1950.

31. EBNER, H., AND STRECKER, H. 1950. Über die Wirkung des Colchicins *in vivo* auf die alkalische Phosphatase der Rattenleber. Experientia. 6:388–89. 1950.

32. Eigsti, O. J., and Dustin, P., Jr. Colchicine bibliography. Lloydia. 10:65–114. 1947. *Ibid.* 12:185:207. 1949.

33. Erickson, R. O., and Rosen, G. M. Cytological effect of protoanemonin on the root-tip of *Zea mays.* Amer. Jour. Bot. 36:317–22. 1949.

34. Fatalizade, F. A. Acenaphthene-induced polyploidy in Nicotiana. C. R. Dokl. Acad. Sci. URSS. 22:180–83. 1939.

35. Ferguson, J., Hawkins, S. W., and Doxey, D. C-mitotic activity of some simple gases. Nature. 165:1021. 1950.

36. Fleischman, W., and Ullyot, G. Colchicine derivatives. II. Effect on mitotic activity of corneal epithelium. Cancer. 3:130–33. 1950.

37. Franzl, R. E., and Chargaff, E. Bacterial enzyme preparations oxidizing inositol and their inhibition by colchicine. Nature. 168:955–57. 1951.

38. Gal, E. Étude de l'action du cacodylate de soude et de la colchicine sur différentes déshydrogénases. Bull. Soc. Chim. Biol. Paris. 20:1188–1205. 1938.

39. Garrigues, M. R. Action de la colchicine et du chloral sur les racines de *Vicia faba.* C. R. Acad. Sci. Paris. 208:461–63. 1939. Rev. Cytophysiol. Veg. Paris. 4:261–301. 1940.

40. Gaulden, M. E., and Carlson, J. G. Cytological effects of colchicine on the grasshopper neuroblast *in vitro* with special reference to the origin of the spindle. Exp. Cell Res. 2:416–33. 1951.

41. Gavaudan, P., *et al.* Sur la similitude d'action de l'acénaphtène et de la colchicine dans l'inhibition de la caryocinèse. C. R. Soc. Biol. Paris. 129:559–62. 1938. Action sur la caryocinèse et la cytodiérèse des végétaux des isomères de l'apiol du persil. C. R. Acad. Sci. Paris. 210:576–78. 1940. Action sur la caryocinèse, la cytodiérèse, et la morphogénèse des végétaux de quelques dérivés d'hydrocarbures cycliques. Rôle de la constitution chimique et des propriétés physiques. C. R. Soc. Biol. Paris. 133:348–52. 1940. La pathologie expérimentale de la caryocinèse et de la cytodiérèse. Bull. Musée Hist. Nat. Marseille. 1:13–40. 1941. Action du benzène et de ses homologues. C. R. Soc. Biol. Paris. 137:50. 1943. Étude quantitative de l'action mito-inhibitrice des substances aromatiques: définition et terminologie des effets cytologiques utilisés comme tests. *Ibid.* 137:281. 1943. Action mito-inhibitrice de la plupart des fonctions dans la série aromatique opposée à l'activité pratiquement nulle ou réduite de la fonction carboxyle. *Ibid.* 137:570. 1943. Comparaison du pouvoir mitoinhibiteur des substances de la série aromatique en fonction de l'activité thermodynamique de leurs solutions. *Ibid.* 138:267. 1944. Sur la théorie narcotique de la mitoinhibition. *Ibid.* 138:246. 1944. La toxicologie générale et la notion d'activité thermodynamique. Mem. Services Chim. Etat. Paris. 31:384–423. 1944.

42. ———, and Brebion, G. Action sur la photosynthèse de quelques substances inhibitrices de la caryocinèse. Rec. Trav. Toxicol. Pharm. Cell. 2:37–46. 1946.

43. ———. Pharmacodynamie de l'inhibition de la caryocinèse. Librairie Le Francois, Paris. 1947.

44. Goldberg, B., *et al.* Studies on colchicine derivatives. I. Toxicity in mice and effects on mouse sarcoma 180. Cancer. 3:124–29. 1950.

44a. Gompel, C. Sur l'inactivation du fuseau chez la souris par les substances thioloprives. Rev. Belge Path. 22:85–92. 1952.

45. Grégoire, C., and Lison, L. Action des cacodylates sur la glande lymphatique d'*Astacus fluviatilis.* C. R. Soc. Biol. Paris. 117:1217. 1934.

46. Havas, L. Is colchicine a "phytohormone"? Growth. 2:257–60. 1938.

47. Hawkins, J., and Walker, J. M. The effect of colchicine on the enzyme content of regenerating rat liver and on the pressor amine content of the adrenal. Brit. Jour. Pharmacol. 7:152–60. 1952.

48. Hertwig, O., and Hertwig, R. Über den Befruchtungs-und Teilungsvorgang des tierischen Eies unter dem Einfluss äusserer Agentien. Jena Z. Naturwiss. 20:120. 1887.

49. Horowitz, R. M., and Ullyot, G. E. Desmethylcolchicine, a constituent of U.S.P. colchicine. Science. 115:216. 1952.

50. HUGHES, A. F. The effect of iodoacetamide on cell division in chick tissue cultures. Jour. Roy. Micr. Soc. 69:215. 1949. Inhibitors in chick tissue cultures. Symp. Soc. Exp. Biol. 6:256. Cambridge University Press. 1952. The mitotic cycle. The cytoplasm and nucleus during interphase and mitosis. Butterworths Scientific Publications, London. 1952.

51. INOUE, S. The effect of colchicine on the microscopic and submicroscopic structure of the mitotic spindle. Exp. Cell Res. Suppl. 2:305–18. 1952.

52. JACOBSON, W., AND WEBB, M. The two types of nucleic acid during mitosis. Jour. Physiol. 112 (Proc. Physiol. Soc.) 1950. Exp. Cell Res. 3:163–83. 1952. Nucleoproteins and cell-division. Endeavour. 11:200–207. 1952.

53. KEESER, E. Untersuchungen über die Beeinflussbarkheit des Purinstoffwechsels. Arch. Exp. Path. Pharm. 197:187–92. 1941.

54. KING, L. S., AND SULLIVAN, M. Similarity of the effect of podophyllin and colchicine and their use in the treatment of condylomata acuminata. Science. 104:244–45. 1946.

55. KING, H., AND LUDFORD, R. J. The relation between the constitution of arsenicals and their action on cell division. Jour. Chem. Soc. 2086. 1950.

56. KOSTOFF, D. Irregular mitosis and meiosis induced by acenaphthene. Nature. 141:1144–45. 1938. Atypical growth, abnormal mitosis and polyploidy induced by ethylmercury chloride. Phytopathology. 13:91–96. 1940. Atypical growth, abnormal mitosis, polyploidy and chromosome fragmentation induced by hexachlorocyclohexane. Nature. 162:845. 1948.

57. KRYTHE, J. M., AND WELLENSIEK, S. J. Five years of colchicine research. Bibliog. Genetica. 14:1–132. 1942.

58. LABORDE, J. V., AND HOUDÉ, A. Le colchique et la colchicine. Paris. 1887.

59. LANDSCHÜTZ, C. Aufhebung der Mitosegiftwirkung des Colchicins durch herzwirksame Glykoside an Hühnerherzfibroblasten *in vitro*. Naturwiss. 36:379. 1949.

60. LANG, K., SIEBERT, G., AND OSWALD, H. Über die Hemmung von Desoxyribonucleotide spaltenden Fermenten durch Colchicin. Experientia. 5:449. 1949.

61. ———, ———, AND ESTELMANN, W. Hemmung der Adenosintriphosphatase durch Colchicin. Experientia. 7:379. 1951.

62. LEFÈVRE, J. Actions similaires sur les mitoses végétales de l'anéthol et des substances du groupe de la colchicine. C. R. Soc. Biol. Paris. 133:616–18. 1940.

63. LEITER, J., DOWNING, V., HARTWELL, J. L., AND SHEAR, M. J. Damage induced in sarcoma 37 with chemical agents. III. Colchicine derivatives related to trimethylcolchicinic acid and to colchinol. Jour. Nat. Cancer Inst. 13:379–92. 1952.

64. ———, HARTWELL, J. L., KLINE, I., NADKARNI, M. V., AND SHEAR, M. J. Damage induced in sarcoma 37 with chemical agents. IV. Derivatives of colchiceinamide. Jour. Nat. Cancer Inst. 13:731–39. 1952.

65. ———, ———, ULLYOT, G. E., AND SHEAR, M. J. Damage induced in sarcoma 37 with chemical agents. V. Derivatives of colchicine and isocolchicine. Jour. Nat. Cancer Inst. 13:1201–11. 1953.

66. LETTRÉ, H., *et al.* Beitrag zur Beziehung der Mitosegiftwirkung und der Konstitution von Colchicinderivaten. Z. Physiol. Chem. 278:175–200. 1943. Wirkung des Colchicins und N-methylcolchicamids auf die Mitose der Zellen des Mäuse-Ascites Tumors. Z. Krebsforsch. 57:142–50. 1951. Über weitere enifache Mitosegifte. I-amino-acenaphten und Derivative. Z. Physiol. Chem. 288:25–30. 1951. Weitere Untersuchungen über eine Mitosegiftwirkung von Alkaloiden. Z. Physiol. Chem. 287:58–65. 1951. Vergleich von Colchicin, Isocolchicin und Homologen auf ihre Zellteilungshemmende Wirkung. Z. Physiol. Chem. 289:123–27. 1952. Vergleich ringgeschlossener und ringoffener Verbindungen vom Colchicintyp auf ihre antimitotische Wirkung. Z. Physiol. Chem. 291:164–67. 1952. Vergleich homologer 4'-alkoxy-stilbylamine und optischer Antipoden auf ihre Zellteilungshemmende Wirkung. Z. Physiol.

Chem. 289:119–23. 1952. Zur Mitosegiftwirkung substituierter α-phenyl-zimtsaürenitrile. Z. Physiol. Chem. 289:298–308. 1952.

67. ——, *et al.* Über Synergisten des Colchicins. I. Arzneim. Forsch. 1:3–5. 1951. II. Z. Physiol. Chem. 286:138–44. 1950. III. *Ibid.* 286:212–15. 1950. IV. Naturwiss. 37:563. 1950. V. *Ibid.* 38:13. 1951. VI. Z. Physiol. Chem. 287: 53–58. 1951. VII. *Ibid.* 1951. VIII. Naturwiss. 38:70. 1951. X. Klin. Wschr. 29:555. 1951. XI. Naturwiss. 38:214. 1951.

68. ——, AND ALBRECHT, M. Über die Abhängigkeit der Colchicine-wirkung von der Adenosintriphosphorsäure. Naturwiss. 38:547. 1951.

69. ——. Hemmstoffe des Wachstums, insbesondere Mitosegifte. Forsch. u. Fortschr. 18:309–10. 1942. Über Zellteilungsgifte. Scientia. Milan. 45:291–97. 1951. Über Mitosegifte. Ergebn. Physiol. 45:379–452. 1950. Zur Chemie und Biologie der Mitosegifte. Angew. Chem. 63:421–30. 1951. Chemische und biologische Untersuchungen über Mitosegifte. Scientia Pharmaceutica. 20: 75–100. 1952. Zellstoffwechsel und Zellteilung. Z. Krebsforsch. 58:621–31. 1952. Some investigations on cell behaviour under various conditions: a review. Cancer Res. 12:847–60. 1952.

70. LEVAN, A. The effect of acenaphthene and colchicine on mitoses of *Allium* and *Colchicum.* Hereditas. 26:262–76. 1940. The effect of colchicine on root mitoses in *Allium.* Hereditas. 24:471–86. 1938. Cytological reactions induced by inorganic salt solutions. Nature. 156:751–52. 1945. The influence on chromosomes and mitosis of chemicals as studied by the *Allium* test. Hereditas. Suppl. 325–37. 1949.

71. ——, AND ÖSTERGREN, G. The mechanism of c-mitotic action. Observations on the naphthalene series. Hereditas. 29:381–443. 1943.

71a. ——, AND STEINEGGER, E. The *resistance of Colchicum* and *Bulbocodium* to the c-mitotic action of colchicine. Hereditas. 33:552–66. 1947.

72. LEWIS, M. R. Reversible changes in the nature of the mitotic spindle brought in living cells by means of heat. Arch. Exp. Zellforsch. 14:464. 1933.

73. LIMARZI, L. R. The effects of arsenic (Fowlers solution) on erythropoiesis. Amer. Jour. Med. Sci. 206:339–47. 1943.

74. LUDFORD, R. J. The action of toxic substances upon the division of normal and malignant cells *in vitro* and *in vivo.* Arch. Exp. Zellforsch. 18:411–41. 1936.

74a. ——. Chemically induced derangements of cell division. Jour. Royal Microscopical Soc. 73:1–23. 1953.

75. MACFARLANE, E. W. E., AND SCHMOCK, N. G. The colchicine and colchicine-like reaction as a possible response to enzyme poisoning. Science. 108:712–13. 1948.

76. MAINX, F. Versuche über die Beeinflussung der Mitose durch Giftstoffe. Zool. Jahrb. Abt. Allg. Zool. 41:553–90. 1924.

77. MAIROLD, F. Studien an colchicinierten Pflanzen. Protoplasma. 27:445–521. 1943.

78. MALINSKY, J., AND LANG, B. Effets de la colchicine, de l'isocolchicine et de l'amide de colchicine sur la mitose. C. R. Soc. Biol. Paris. 145:613–16. 1951.

79. MANGENOT, G. Effets cytotoxiques de l'arsenic pentavalent. C. R. Acad. Sci. Paris. 210:412–15. 1940. Colchicine et phytohormones. Science. Paris. 69: 25–43. 1942.

80. ——, AND CARPENTIER, S. Le syndrome mitoclasique. C. R. Soc. Biol. Paris. 138:105–6. 1943. Le plomb et le mercure, poisons mitoclasiques. C. R. Soc. Biol. Paris. 139:268–70. 1945.

81. MASCRÉ, M., AND DEYSSON, G. Les poisons mitotiques. Biol. Méd. 40:323–76. 1951.

82. ——, AND ——. Action mitoclasique due colchicoside, comparée à celle de la colchicine. C. R. Acad. Sci. Paris. 234:1901–3. 1952. Action mitoclosique de la desméthylcolchicine, comparée à celles du colchicoside et de la colchicine. C. R. Acad. Sci. Paris. 234:2480–82. 1952.

83. McKINNEY, G. The action of various drugs on certain phases of *in vitro* anabolism. Jour. Pharmacol. Exp. Ther. 100:45–50. 1950.

84. MURRAY, M. R., DE LAM, H. H., AND CHARGAFF, E. Inhibition of the colchicine effect on rat fibroblasts by mesoinositol. Anat. Rec. 106:227. 1950.

Specific inhibition by mesoinositol of the colchicine effect on rat fibroblasts. Exp. Cell Res. 2:165–77. 1951.

85. NAVASHIN, M. Influence of acenaphthene on the division of cells and nuclei. C. R. Dokl. Acad. Sci. URSS. 19:193–96. 1938.

86. NEMEC, B. Über die Einwirkung des Chloralhydrates auf die Kern- und Zellteilung. Jahrb. Wiss. Bot. 35. 1904.

87. NICKELL, L. G. Effect of certain plant hormones and colchicine on the growth and respiration of virus tumor tissue from *Rumex acetosa*. Amer. Jour. Bot. 37:829–35. 1950.

88. NORTHEN, H. Alterations in the structural viscosity of protoplasm by colchicine and their relationship to c-mitosis and c-tumor formation. Amer. Jour. Bot. 37:705–11. 1950.

89. NYBOM, N., AND KNUTSSON, B. Investigations on c-mitosis in *Allium cepa*. Hereditas. 33:220–34. 1947.

90. ORSINI, M. W., AND PANSKY, B. The natural resistance of the golden hamster to colchicine. Science. 115:88–89. 1952.

91. ÖSTERGREN, G., AND LEVAN, A. The connection between c-mitotic activity and water solubility in some monocyclic compounds. Hereditas. 29:496–98. 1943.

92. ———. Cytological standards for the quantitative estimation of spindle disturbances. Hereditas. 36:371–82. 1950. Narcotized mitosis and the precipitation hypothesis of narcosis. Coll. Int. Centre Nat. Rech. Sci. 26:77–88. 1951.

93. PANSINI, R. Contributo sperimentali sui velini antimitotici. II. L'influenza dell'etiluretano sulla morfogenesi delle uova di *Paracentrotus lividus* Lk. Arch. Sci. Biol. Bologna. 35:339–59. 1951.

94. PEASE, D. C. Hydrostatic pressure effects upon the spindle figure and chromosome movement. Jour. Morph. 69:405–42. 1941. Biol. Bull. 91:145. 1946.

95. PERNICE, B. (*See* Ref. No. 78, Chap. 2).

96. PITON, R. Recherches sur les actions caryoclasiques et caryocinétiques des composés arsenicaux. Arch. Int. Méd. Exp. 5:355–411. 1929.

97. POLITZER, G. Die Zellteilung während und nach der Narkose. Ein Beitrag zur Kenntniss der Störungen der Kernteilungsrythmus. Z. Zellforsch. 13:334–63. 1931. Pathologie der Mitose. Protoplasma-Monographien, 7. Gebr. Bornträger, Berlin. 1934.

98. REGEMORTER, D. VAN. Les troubles cinétiques dans les racines chloralosées et leur portée pour l'interprétation des phénomènes normaux. Cellule. 37:43–73. 1926–1927.

99. ROSENFELD, M. Experimental modification of mitosis by ammonia. Arch. Exp. Zellforsch. 14:1–13. 1933.

100. SANTAVY, F., AND REICHSTEIN, T. Isolierung neuer Stoffe aus den Samen der Herbstzeitlose, *Colchicum autumnale* L. Helv. Chim. Acta. 33:1606–27. 1950.

101. ———, LANG, B., AND MALINSKY, J. L'action mitotique et la toxicité des nouvelles substances isolées du colchique (*Colchicum autumnale* L.). Arch. Int. Pharmacodyn. 84:257–68. 1950.

102. SARGENT, L. J., AND SMALL, L. F. The alkaloids. Ann. Rev. Biochem. 52:493–520. 1952.

103. SASS, J. E. Response of meristems of seedlings to benzene hexachloride used as a seed protectant. Science. 114:466. 1951.

104. SAX, K. Effect of variations in temperature on nuclear and cell division in *Tradescantia*. Amer. Jour. Bot. 24:218–25. 1937.

105. SCHMIDT, W. J. Die Doppelbrechung von Karyoplasma, Zytoplasma und Metaplasma. Protoplasma-Monographien. 11. Gebr. Bornträger, Berlin. 1937.

106. SCHMITZ, H. Zur Beeinflussung des Zellstoffwechsels durch Alkaloid. Z. Krebsforsch. 57:405–22. 1951.

107. SCHMUCK, A. The chemical nature of substances inducing polyploidy in plants. C. R. Dokl. Acad. Sci. URSS. 19:189–92. 1938.

108. ———, AND GUSSEVA, A. Active concentrations of acenaphthene inducing alterations in the processes of cell-division in plants. C. R. Dokl. Acad. Sci. URSS. 22:441–43. 1939. Chemical structure of substances inducing polyploidy in plants. *Ibid.* 24:441–46. 1939. The biological activity of isomeric compounds. I. The action of isomeric naphthalene derivatives upon plants. Bio-

chimija. 5:129–32. 1940. Haloid derivatives of aromatic hydrocarbons and their polyploidogenic activity. C. R. Dokl. Acad. Sci. URSS. 26:674–77. 1940. Methoxyl derivatives of benzene and naphthalene studied with regard to their polyploidogenic action on plants. *Ibid.* 30:639–41. Activity of polyploidogenic compounds as influenced by hydrogenation. *Ibid.* 642–43. 1941.

109. SCHMUCK, A. AND KOSTOFF, D. Brome-acenaphthene and brome-naphthaline as agents inducing chromosome doubling in rye and wheat. C. R. Dokl. Acad. Sci. URSS. 23:263–66. 1939.

110. SCHRADER, F. Data contributing to an analysis of metaphase mechanics. Chromosoma. 3:22–47. 1947. Mitosis. Columbia University Press, New York. 1944.

111. SCHULER, H. M. Le problème de la colchicine, substance stathmocinétique, en relation avec ses propriétés physico-chimiques et spectrales. Thèse. Universitè de Strasbourg. Imprimerie Mont-Louis, Clermont-Ferrand. 1942.

112. SENTEIN, P. Arrêt de la segmentation, blocage de la mitose et polyploidie par l'action de l'éthyluréthane sur l'oeuf de Batracien. C. R. Acad. Sci. Paris. 228:706–7. 1949.

113. SIMONET, M. AND GUINOCHET, M. Obtention, par les α-monochloronaphtalène et α-monobromonaphtalène d'effets comparables à ceux exercés sur les caryocinèses végétales par la colchicine. C. R. Acad. Sci. Paris. 130:1057–59. 1939. Sur l'apparition dans les tissus végétaux de cellules polyploides sous l'influence des vapeurs de paradichlorobenzene. C. R. Soc. Biol. Paris. 208:1427–28. 1939. Anomalies morphologiques et caryologiques provoquées, sur les jeunes plantules, par les dérivés halogénés des carbures cycliques. *Ibid.* 131:222–24. 1939.

114. ———. Anomalies de la caryocinèse végétale des types colchiciniques et paradichlorobenzéniques par un dérivé nitré des carbures cycliques: le m-nitro-xylène -1, 3, 5. C. R. Soc. Biol. Paris. 133:561–63. 1940.

115. SMITH, P. (*See* Ref. No. 127, Chap. 4).

116. SORKIN, M. v. *iso*-Colchicin. Helv. Chim. Acta. 29:246–48. 1946.

117. STEINEGGER, E., AND LEVAN, A. Constitution and c-mitotic activity of iso-colchicine. Hereditas. 33:385–96. 1947. The c-mitotic qualities of colchicine, trimethylcolchicinic acid and two phenanthrene derivatives. Hereditas. 34: 193–203. 1948.

118. SULLIVAN, B. J., AND WECHSLER, H. I. The cytological effect of podophyllin. Science. 105:433. 1947.

119. SWANSON, C. P. The use of acenaphthene in pollen tube technic. Stain. Tech. 15:49–52. 1940.

120. TENNANT, R., AND LIEBOW, A. A. The actions of colchicine and ethylcarbyl-amine on tissue cultures. Yale Jour. Biol. and Med. 13:39–49. 1940.

121. THIMANN, K. V., AND BONNER, W. D., JR. Inhibition of plant growth by pro-toanemonin and coumarin, and its prevention by BAL. Proc. Nat. Acad. Sci. 35:272–76. 1949.

122. TOBIAS, J. M., *et al.* The pathology and therapy with 2,3-dimercaptopropanol (BAL) of experimental cadmium poisoning. Jour. Pharmacol. Exp. Ther. 87 (Suppl.):102–18. 1946.

123. TÖRÖ, E., AND VADASZ, J. Untersuchungen über die Wirkung von Colchicin und Corhormon in Gewebekulturen mit Hilfe von Filmaufnahmen. Arch. Exp. Zellforsch. 23:277–98. 1939.

124. WADA, B. The mechanism of mitosis based on studies of the submicroscopic structure and of the living state of the *Tradescantia* cell. Cytologia. Tokyo. 16:1–26. 1950.

125. WARBURG, O. (Oxidation in living cells according to experiments on the eggs of Sea-Urchins). Z. Physiol. Chem. 66:305. 1910.

126. WASEILEWSKI, W. v. Theoretische und experimentelle Beiträge zur Kenntniss der Amitose. Jahrb. Wiss. Bot. 38:377–420. 1902–1903.

127. WIDMANN, H. Die Leukocytenbewegungen des Meerschweinchens und der Weissen Maus in Prontosil-Colchicin Doppelversuch. Untersuchungen zur Frage eines Prontosil-Colchicin Antagonismus. Z. Ges. Inner. Med. 5:90. 1950.

128. WITKUS, E. R., AND BERGER, C. A. Veratrine, a new polyploidy inducing agent. Jour. Hered. 35:130–33. 1944.

Author Index

Subject Index

Abrine, 206
Acenaphthene, 398, 400
  c-mitotic potential, 104
  c-tumor, 104
  compared to colchicine, 82
Acetocarmine methods, 19, 27, 37, 45, 369
Acetophenone, 400
Acetyl chloride, 171
N-Acetylderivative, 163
Acetylamido-group, 160
N-Acetyl-colchicol, 408, 409
N-Acetylcolchinol, 161, 167, 169
N-Acetylcolchinol methyl ether, 161
N-Acetyliodocolchinol, 161, 164, 167
N-Acetyl-TMCA-methyl-ether, 408
P-Acetamidotropolone, 171, 275
P-Aminobenzoic acid, 397
P-Aminohippuric acid, 397
Achromatic sphere, 25, 27, 79, 80, 84
Acnida tamariscina, 353
Acriflavine, 193
ACTH; see adrenocorticotropic hormone
Action of temperature, 374
  in birds, 374
  in mammals, 374
Actomyosin, 420
Addison-Biermer anemia, 210–11, 224
Adenosine-triphosphoric acid (ATP),
  419; *see also* ATP
Adrenal cortex, 177, 193, 226, 230, 232,
  regeneration of, 241
Adrenal medulla, 230
Adrenal mitosis, 193
Adrenals, 226
Adrenocorticotropic hormone (ACTH),
  197, 226, 229
Adrenalin, 181, 413
Adventitious buds, 351
Aegilops, 295–99
  species of: *caudata,* 297; *cylindrica,* 297;
    squarrosa, 295–98; *umbellulata* ×
    Haynaldia villosa, 299
  sterile triploid hybrid, 295
Agranulocytosis, 264
Agrobacterium, 121, 122
Agropyron, 295, 299
  species of: *glaucum,* 298; *intermedium,*
    298; *triticeum,* 295, 298
Alarm-reaction, 177, 178, 190, 197, 376
Alexander of Tralles, 12
Alkaline hydrogen peroxide, 167
  phosphatase, 397

Alkaloid, 7, 160, 167, 179, 418
  classification of, 160
  reagents, 160
Allergy, 197
Allium, 19, 69, 80, 403, 413, 416; *see also*
  C-mitosis
  achromatic sphere, 91
  c-mitotic threshold, 104
  c-tumors, 102, 103, 110
  cepa photomicrographs, 25–27, 79
  cernuum, 112
  colchicine and X-ray, 267, 268
  mitochondria in root tip, 26–27, 91
  root tips, 51, 78, 81, 83, 84, 90, 94, 102,
    104, 395, 399, 407
*Allo*colchiceine, 167
*Allo*colchicine, 167
  structure of, 169
Allomyces javanicus, 123
Allopolyploid species, 367
Allo-syndesis, 276
Alloxan, 241, 244
Alnarp Horticultural Station, 312
Amblystoma
  development, 203
  opacum, regeneration in, 242
  punctatum, regeneration in, 242
American Society for Horticultural
  Science, 329
  Leonard H. Vaughn award, 329
Amino-acenaphthene, 400
Aminocolchicine, 169
Aminopterin, 265, 415
Ammonia, 392
Amoeba, 395
  species of: *proteus,* 126; *sphaeronu-*
    cleus, 35, 58, 126, 381
Amphiasters, disintegration of, 74
Amphibia, 54, 68, 375
  temperature and colchicine poisoning
    in, 194
Amphiploidy
  Aegilops, 294–301
  Aegilops squarrosa, role of, 296
  Agropyron, 297–99
  Brassica, 309–10
  Bromus, 302
  cataclysmic evolution among, 277
  classification of, 288
  convergent evolution, 299
  Cruciferae, 309–10
  defined, 276

Raspberry, 324
Rat, 42, 378
Recovery from colchicine, 379
  in *Allium*, 29, 96
  in animals, 56–58, 96–98
  in corneal tissues, 97
  in liver, 44
  in plants, 56, 94–96
  polyploidy resulting after, 94–95
  principle of reversibility, 91–94
  processes of, 81
  reduction in number of nuclei, 41
  in sarcoma, 27
  after single injection, 57
  stages of, in *Triticum*, 95
  stages of, in *Triturus*, 43
  transfer to water, 94
Rectum, 226
Red blood cells, 188
  diameter of, 188, 189
  forming tissues, 376
  volumes, 381
Red clover, tetraploids, 322
Regeneration, 93, 236–42; *see also*
    Kidney, Liver
  in amphibians, 376
  for c-mitosis study, 376
  in developing animals, 242–46
  and hypertrophy, 236–42
  inhibition of, 245
  of limbs, 242
  liver of rat, 44, 57, 216
  of nerve, 246
  tail of *Xenopus*, 242–45
  of thymus, 241
Regenerative tissues, 385
Renal artery, ligature of, 40, 238
Reproductive isolation, 292
Resins, 140
Resistance, in plants and animals, 398
  by *Colchicum* to colchicine, 107, 398
  of golden hamsters, 107, 398
  to phytohormone tests, 107
Respiration, 103
  cellular, 204
  in tumors, 261
Respiratory paralysis, 377
Retention of colchicine in cell, 383
Reticulocytes, 184, 185
Reversible effects of colchicine, 89;
    see also Reversibility
Reversibility, 31
  capacity to, 93–94
  characteristic important, 91–94
  demonstrated, 94
  necessary for induction of polyploidy,
    92–93
  regeneration of spindle, 94
Reversion to diploidy, 285
Rheumatism, 1, 2, 3
Rhizomes, 384
Rhizotomi, 2, 3

Rhodeus amarus, 226, 227
  nuptial colors, 191
Rhoeo discolor, 109
Ribes
  currant and gooseberry combined, 312
  meiotic irregularities carried over, 116
  new species, *R. nigrolaria,* 312
  species of: *grossularia,* 312; *nigrum,*
    312
Ribonucleic acid, 89, 397
Ribose, 417
Ribose nucleic acid, 121
Ricine, 206; *see also* Abrine
  induces strophosomy, 206
Ricinus, tumors in, 266
Ring A, 161
  presence of benzenoid ring, 161
Ring B, 161–67; *see also* Colchicine
    structure
  recognized as 7-membered, 166
  research on, 161–67
  revision of Windaus concept, 166
Ring C, 167, 168, 409
  of colchiceine tropolonoid, 168
  comparison with tropolones, 168–69
  Dewar's suggestion, 168
  enolone properties derived from, 167
Rodents, 376
Root gatherers; *see* Rhizotomi
Root hairs, 109
  c-tumor, 109
  not polyploid, 109
Root systems, treated with colchicine,
    384–85
Root tip, 369, 386
  Allium, 19, 25, 27, 35, 41, 49, 55, 78, 79,
    83, 84, 85, 96
  c-pairs in, 49, 85
  c-tumors on, 25, 102–7
  colchicine penetrates, 36
  correlation region of, and c-mitoses, 55
  description of c-mitosis in, 28
  distribution of cells in, 55, 79, 95
  of onion seedlings, 34
  pairs of "skis" in, 51
  polyploidy in, 25, 79, 95
  tests with, 19, 34
  wheat, 90
  X-ray on, 105
Root tumor, 25, 103
Roots, encised, 132, 385
Rudimentary cell plates, 89, 90
Rumex acetosa, 132
Russia, 286, 287, 296

S

Saccharomyces cerevisiae, 123
Saccharose, 416
Saffron, 1
Salamandra, corneal cells of, 401
Salivary glands, 269